Hergert

The University of Chicago School Mathematics Project

Geometry

Authors

Arthur Coxford
Zalman Usiskin
Daniel Hirschhorn

About the Cover

A bicycle wheel exhibits segments, angles, parallel lines, concentric circles,
chords, tangents, congruence, circumference, translations, rotations, and curves of the cycloid family.
Each UCSMP secondary text discusses some of these ideas, and all but the cycloid are
brought together in this text.

ScottForesman

Editorial Offices: Glenview, Illinois   Regional Offices: Sunnyvale, California •
Tucker, Georgia • Glenview, Illinois • Oakland, New Jersey • Dallas, Texas

Acknowledgments

Authors

Arthur Coxford
Professor of Education, The University of Michigan

Zalman Usiskin
Professor of Education, The University of Chicago

Daniel Hirschhorn
UCSMP

UCSMP Production and Evaluation

Series Editors: Zalman Usiskin, Sharon Senk

Technical Coordinator: Susan Chang

Director of the Field Trial Evaluation: Sandra Mathison

Director of the Nationwide Evaluation: Penelope Flores

Teacher's Edition Additional Author: Jerry Smith
Niles Township High School West, Skokie, Illinois

Editorial Development and Design

ScottForesman staff, Rusty Kane

We wish to acknowledge the generous support of the **Amoco Foundation** in helping to make it possible for these materials to be developed and tested, and the additional support of the **Carnegie Corporation of New York** in the nationwide field-testing of these materials.

ISBN: 0-673-45269-7

Printing Key 1112131415-RRW-0099989796

It takes many people to put together a project of this kind and we cannot thank them all by name. We wish particularly to acknowledge Carol Siegel, who coordinated the use of these materials in schools; Peter Bryant, Dan Caplinger, Kurt Hackemer, Maryann Kannapan, Mary Lappan and Therese Manst of our technical staff; Sharon Mallo, who wrote some of the ancillary materials; and editorial assistants Matt Ashley, Laura Gerbec, Eric Kolaczyk, Thomas McDougal, and Teri Proske (at Chicago) and Peter Appelbaum (at Michigan).

We wish to acknowledge and give thanks to the following teachers who taught preliminary versions of UCSMP *Geometry*, participated in the pilot and formative research, and contributed many ideas to help improve this book.

Betty Foxx
Collins High School
Chicago Public Schools

Paula Murphy
Corliss High School
Chicago Public Schools

Adrienne Roth Hanus
Taft High School
Chicago Public Schools

Kenneth Kerr
Glenbrook South High School
Glenview, Illinois

Rita Belluomini
Jan Moore
Wayne Wirta
Rich South High School
Richton Park, Illinois

Sharon Mallo
Lake Park East High School
Roselle, Illinois

We also wish to acknowledge the following schools which used earlier versions of UCSMP *Geometry* in nationwide studies. Their comments, suggestions, and performance guided the changes made for this version.

Chaparral High School
Scottsdale, Arizona

Irvine High School
Irvine, California

Mendocino High School
Mendocino, California

Marietta High School
Marietta, Georgia

Hyde Park Career Academy
Taft High School
Chicago, Illinois

Lyons Township High School
La Grange, Illinois

Rich South High School
Richton Park, Illinois

Niles Township High School West
Skokie, Illinois

Fruitport High School
Fruitport, Michigan

North Hunterdon High School
Annandale, New Jersey

Aiken High School
Cincinnati Academy of Mathematics
 and Science
Walnut Hills High School
Cincinnati, Ohio

Carrick High School
Allderdice High School
Pittsburgh, Pennsylvania

We wish to express our thanks and appreciation to the many other schools and students who have used earlier versions of these materials.

UCSMP Geometry

The University of Chicago School Mathematics Project (UCSMP) is a long-term project designed to improve school mathematics in grades K–12. UCSMP began in 1983 with a six-year grant from the Amoco Foundation, whose support continued in 1989 with a grant through 1994. Additional funding has come from the Ford Motor Company, the Carnegie Corporation of New York, the National Science Foundation, the General Electric Foundation, GTE, Citibank/Citicorp, and the Exxon Education Foundation.

The project is centered in the Departments of Education and Mathematics of the University of Chicago, and has the following components and directors:

Resources	Izaak Wirszup, Professor Emeritus of Mathematics
Primary Materials	Max Bell, Professor of Education
Elementary Teacher Development	Sheila Sconiers, Research Associate in Education
Secondary	Sharon L. Senk, Associate Professor of Mathematics, Michigan State University
	Zalman Usiskin, Professor of Education
Evaluation	Larry Hedges, Professor of Education

From 1983–1987, the director of UCSMP was Paul Sally, Professor of Mathematics. Since 1987, the director has been Zalman Usiskin.

The text *Geometry* was developed by the Secondary Component (grades 7–12) of the project, and constitutes the third year in a six-year mathematics curriculum devised by that component. As texts in this curriculum completed their multi-stage testing cycle, they were published by ScottForesman. A list of the six texts follows:

Transition Mathematics
Algebra
Geometry
Advanced Algebra
Functions, Statistics, and Trigonometry
Precalculus and Discrete Mathematics

A first draft of *Geometry* was written, and then piloted in six schools during the 1986–87 school year. After incorporating changes based on these pilots and comments from many students and teachers, the 1987–88 field trial of *Geometry* was tested in 16 schools with students who had not had previous UCSMP courses. Further changes were made and a summative evaluation was conducted in 1988–89 both with students who had and students who had not had previous UCSMP courses. Results are available by writing UCSMP. This ScottForesman edition is based on improvements suggested by that testing, by the authors and editors, and by some of the many teacher and student users of earlier editions.

Comments about these materials are welcomed. Address queries to Secondary Mathematics Product Manager, ScottForesman, 1900 East Lake Avenue, Glenview, Illinois 60025, or to UCSMP, The University of Chicago, 5835 S. Kimbark, Chicago, IL 60637.

UCSMP *Geometry* differs from other geometry books in six major ways. First, it has **wider scope** in content. It integrates algebra with the geometry. It uses coordinates and transformations throughout and in both two and three dimensions. It discusses networks and history and famous problems. These topics are not isolated as separate units of study or as enrichment. Instead they are employed to motivate, justify, extend, and help students with important geometry concepts.

Second, this book has a **different sequence.** Coordinates and transformations, which are critical to building and maintenance of algebra skills and concepts, are studied early. Measurement, area, and volume, topics of importance to all students, are studied earlier than most textbooks. Proof, which requires geometry knowledge and experience, is built up slowly.

Third, this book emphasizes **reading and problem solving** throughout. Students can and should be expected to read this book. The explanations were written for students and tested with them. The first set of questions in each lesson is called "Covering the Reading." These exercises guide the student through the reading and check his or her coverage of critical words, rules, explanations, and examples. The second set of questions is called "Applying the Mathematics." These questions extend the student's understanding of the principles and applications of the lesson. Reading is necessary for the problem solving which pervades this book.

Fourth, there is a **reality orientation** towards both the selection of content and the approaches allowed the student in working out problems. Knowing geometry is of little ultimate use to an individual unless he or she can apply that content. Geometry is rich in applications and problem solving. Real life situations motivate geometric ideas and provide the settings for practice of geometry skills. Calculators are assumed throughout this book (and should be allowed on tests) because virtually all individuals who use mathematics today find it helpful to have them. Scientific calculators are recommended because they use an order of operations closer to that found in algebra and have numerous keys that are needed in certain lessons. Computer exercises show how the computer can be used to develop, verify, and apply geometric concepts. To further widen the student's horizons, "Exploration" questions are found in every lesson.

Fifth, **four dimensions of understanding** are emphasized: skill in drawing, visualizing, and following algorithms; understanding of properties, mathematical relationships, and proofs; using geometric ideas in real situations; and representing geometric concepts with coordinates, networks or other diagrams. We call this the SPUR approach: **S**kills, **P**roperties, **U**ses, **R**epresentations. With the SPUR approach, concepts are discussed in a rich environment which enables more students to be reached.

Sixth, the **instructional format** is designed to maximize the acquisition of geometry skills and concepts. Lessons are intended to be covered in one day. The lessons have been sequenced into carefully constructed chapters which combine gradual practice with a mastery learning approach. Concepts introduced in a lesson are reinforced through "Review" questions in the immediately succeeding lessons. This gives students several nights to learn and practice important concepts. At the end of the chapter, a modified mastery learning scheme is used to solidify acquisition of concepts from the chapter so that they may be applied later with confidence. It is critical that the end-of-chapter content be covered. To maintain skills, important ideas are reviewed in later chapters. Algebra skills are also reviewed throughout the text.

CONTENTS

Chapter 1   Points and Lines   2

Chapter 2   Definitions and If-then Statements   58

Chapter 3   Angles and Lines   104

Geometry is the study of visual patterns. Learning geometry is greatly helped by being able to see these patterns. Poor drawings hide patterns in geometry just as poor computation can hide patterns in arithmetic. Thus for this course you should have good drawing equipment, both for your homework and in class.

In addition to the notebook paper, sharpened pencil, and erasers you should always have, you need to have some drawing equipment.

> Ruler (marked in both centimeters and inches)
> Protractor (to measure angles)
> Compass
> Graph paper

It is best if the ruler and protractor are made of transparent plastic. A good compass is harder to find. We recommend compasses that tighten by using a screw in the middle and can still take regular pencils.

You will need a scientific calculator in many places in this book. We recommend a *solar-powered* calculator so that you do not have to worry about batteries. A good calculator will last for many years. It also helps to have access to a dictionary.

There is another important goal of this book: to assist you to become able to learn mathematics on your own, so that you will be able to deal with the mathematics you see in newspapers, magazines, on television, on any job, and in school. The authors, who are all experienced teachers, offer the following advice.

1. You cannot learn much mathematics just by watching other people do it. You must participate. Some teachers have a slogan:

   Mathematics is not a spectator sport.

2. You are expected to read each lesson. Read slowly, and keep a pencil with you as you check the mathematics that is done in the book. Use the Glossary or a dictionary to find the meaning of a word you do not understand.

3. You are expected to do homework every day while studying from this book, so put aside time for it. Do not wait until the day before a test if you do not understand something. Try to resolve the difficulty right away and ask questions of your classmates or teacher. You are expected to learn many things by reading, but school is designed so that you do not have to learn everything by yourself.

4. If you cannot answer a question immediately, don't give up! Read the lesson again; read the question again. Look for examples. If you can, go away from the problem and come back to it a little later.

We hope you join the many thousands of students who have enjoyed this book. We wish you much success.

CHAPTER 1

Points and Lines

From 1884 to 1886, Georges Seurat, a French artist, worked on the painting reproduced at the left, entitled *Sunday Afternoon on Grande Jatte Island*. This painting is entirely made up of small dots of about equal size. In it Seurat showed that a painting could be made without long brushstrokes. Even delicate figures and shadows could be formed from dots. The original painting, worth millions of dollars today, hangs in the Art Institute of Chicago.

The geometry that you will study in this book involves many different ideas, but almost all these ideas concern visual patterns of forms or shapes. As in Seurat's painting, any form in geometry may be thought of as being made up of many different points. Geometry is the study of such sets of points.

A surprising thing is that points themselves are not always the same. Nor are lines. In this chapter, you will learn about different ways of describing points and lines.

1-1

Dots as Points

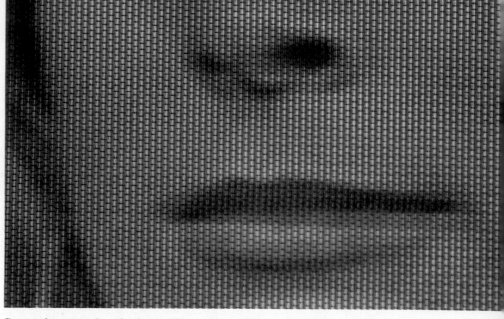

Seurat's actual painting, pictured on the previous page, is over 6 feet high and about 10 feet wide. If you could look at the actual painting from a few feet away, you would see the individual dots that make it up. But if you are far away, or if the picture is reduced in size, you do not see the individual dots.

This also happens with television pictures and computer images. A television screen or computer monitor is made up of tiny dots. Combinations of the dots make up the picture you see. The dots are so numerous and so close together that what you see appears connected. Television and computer people call these dots **pixels.** The pixels are arranged in a rectangular array of rows and columns, called a **matrix.** An IBM PC computer is designed to show its output on a screen having 320 rows and 192 columns of pixels. An Apple Macintosh outputs to a screen with 512 rows and 342 columns. If the screens are the same size, the Macintosh screen will have more pixels per square inch. It would have sharper pictures. We say the Macintosh allows better **resolution.**

Some printers for computers are *dot-matrix printers*. The more rows and columns in the matrix, the better the resolution of the printer, and the better the letters and figures look. For example, a printer might use a matrix with 9 rows and 8 columns. That matrix has $9 \cdot 8 = 72$ cells. To print a letter, the printer puts dots in particular cell centers. One way of making a capital (or upper-case) "A" and a small (or lower-case) "j" is shown below.

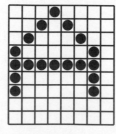
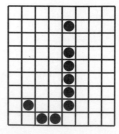

Not all dots are small. Signs can be formed by light bulbs arranged in a large matrix. By turning light bulbs on and off quickly, the letters can look like they are moving. In this way, a long message can be put in a little space. Part of a message is shown below.

You have seen marching bands form letters and simple pictures. When creating a new band formation, the drillmaster (designer) treats each band member like a dot. The more people in a band, the more complicated the pictures that can be created. The starburst pictured at the left is formed by a large number of performers at the opening ceremonies of the Summer Olympics in Seoul, Korea.

These are all examples of dots as *points*. This is the first of four descriptions of points you will study in this chapter.

First description of a point:

A point is a dot.

Lines are made up of points. When a point is a dot, a line is made up of points with space between their centers. The line is called **discrete.** Every line is either **horizontal, vertical,** or **oblique.** Parallel lines are lines which go in the same direction. Think of lines as going on forever. Drawn below are parts of discrete lines.

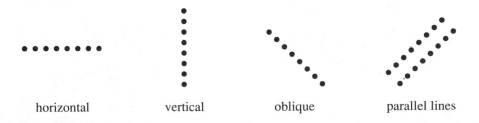

horizontal   vertical   oblique   parallel lines

Points that are part of one line are called **collinear.** When a point is thought of as a dot, then lines have some thickness, and between two points on a line there may or may not be other points. There may be more than one line through two dots depending on whether you require that the line go through their centers. It is possible for two of these lines to cross without having any points in common. Not all lines are like this. As you will later read, when points are not dots, the properties of lines are different.

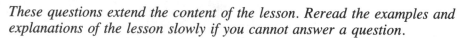

Questions

Covering the Reading

These questions check your comprehension of the reading. If you cannot answer a question, you should go back in the lesson to find the answer.

1. Who painted *Sunday Afternoon on Grande Jatte Island?*

2. What is a pixel?

3. *True* or *false?*   If a screen has more pixels than another screen of the same size, it has better resolution.

4. Why are some printers called "dot-matrix" printers?

5. *True* or *false?*   Two given points can be on several discrete lines.

6. A dot is one description of a(n) _?_ .

7. What is a discrete line?

8. A discrete line may be _?_ , _?_ , or oblique.

9. Points that are on the same line are called _?_ .

Applying the Mathematics

These questions extend the content of the lesson. Reread the examples and explanations of the lesson slowly if you cannot answer a question.

10. How many total pixels are there on:
    a. an IBM PC screen; **b.** an Apple Macintosh screen?

11. Draw two parallel horizontal discrete lines.

12. Draw two discrete lines which cross, but have no points in common.

13. If two screens have the same dimensions, which has the better resolution, one with 200 rows and 300 columns of pixels, or one with 150 rows and 310 columns of pixels?

14. The Mayfield Precision Marching Band wishes to form a block M of the type pictured here. Draw a block M using 60 band members.

15. Pictured at the left is a horse's head as drawn with the help of a computer. The pixels are square.
    a. Which are used to form this picture, black squares or white squares?
    b. How are some parts made to look darker than others?

In 16 and 17, use a 9 row by 8 column dot matrix like the one drawn here.

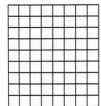

16. Create a dot matrix for the upper-case letters O and R.

17. In most typing, the numeral zero is different from the letter O. Create a zero different from your O in Question 16.

Review

Review questions practice ideas presented in earlier lessons or previous courses. Review questions which cover ideas from previous courses are marked (Previous course).

18. What is the area in square feet of the Seurat painting? *(Previous course)*

19. Suppose $4x - 3y = 12$. What is the value of x if $y = 6$? *(Previous course)*

20. Graph on a coordinate plane: $(6, 5)$, $(6, -4)$, $(2.5, 0.9)$, and $(-\frac{1}{2}, -\frac{1}{2})$. *(Previous course)*

21. Evaluate each expression. *(Previous course)*
    a. $|-23|$ b. $|4 - 19|$ c. $|19.3 - 11|$ d. $|7 - -5|$

Exploration

Exploration questions often require that you use dictionaries or other sources. Frequently they have many possible answers.

22. Find an example of a picture made up of dots in a newspaper or other reading matter.

23. In the "light bulb" sign pictured in this lesson, part of a message is given. What might be the complete message?

24. Use a dictionary to find the meaning of the term "pointillism."

1-2

Locations as Points

A great period of mathematical discovery was during the Greek empire and lasted from about 550 B.C. to 150 A.D. Greek mathematicians of that period made significant advances in number theory and geometry. They considered points not as actual physical dots, but as idealized dots with no size. For them, a point represented an exact location of this idealized dot. A point was considered to be **zero-dimensional,** which means it had no dimensions.

Second Description of a Point:

A point is an exact location.

When two points are locations, it is natural to consider the distance between them. In atlases, maps, and almanacs you can find tables of distances from cities to other cities. For instance, the *1991 World Almanac* gives the road mileage from New York to Los Angeles as 2786 miles. But New York and Los Angeles are both large cities, each many miles across. Some location from which to calculate distances has to be chosen in each city. It may be the city hall, the control tower of an airport, or where two main streets meet.

The road distance from New York to Los Angeles is not the same as the air distance, which the *1991 Information Please Almanac* lists as 2451 miles. Distance between two points depends on the route or path you take.

The shortest path between two locations is along the *line* which contains them. Recall from earlier courses that any line can be made into a **number line.** You can choose any point you want for a zero point and either side of the zero can be the positive side. Every number identifies a point on the line and every point is identified with exactly one number called the **coordinate** of the point. Such a line is said to be **coordinatized.** Drawn below are two views of the same number line ℓ.

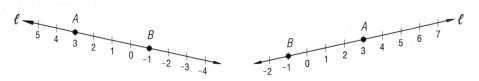

Recall from algebra that the absolute value of a number n is written $|n|$. When n is positive, it equals its absolute value. For instance, $|6.2| = 6.2$. The absolute value of a negative number is the opposite of that number: $|-2500| = 2500$. The absolute value of 0 is 0: $|0| = 0$.

Using the ideas of a coordinatized line and absolute value, *distance* is defined as follows.

Definition:

The **distance** between two points on a coordinatized line is the absolute value of the difference of their coordinates.

In symbols, the distance between two points with coordinates x and y is $|x - y|$. The distance between points A and B is written **AB**.

Example Find AB on the coordinatized line above.

Solution The coordinate of A is 3. The coordinate of B is -1. $AB = |3 - (-1)| = |4| = 4$.

Check Count the units to verify that there are 4 units between A and B.

Caution: When A and B are points, AB is not their product. You cannot multiply points.

Because of properties of absolute value, if you switch the order of the points, the distance will be the same:
$$BA = |1 - 3| = |-4| = 4.$$
For any two points A and B, $AB = BA$. The distance from New York to Los Angeles is the same as the distance from Los Angeles to New York.

Tape measures (when stretched) and rulers resemble coordinatized lines. For example, if you wish to buy draperies or blinds for a window, you need the dimensions of the window. Suppose a tape measure crosses the top of a window at the 6 inch mark and the

bottom at the 81 in. mark. Then the window is $|6 - 81|$ or $|-75|$ or 75 inches tall. When you connect two locations with a ruler, the edge of the ruler lies on a line. Whenever you use a ruler to find distance, you are applying the definition of distance.

When two points are exact locations, there is exactly one line containing them. This line contains the shortest path connecting them. These lines are **dense.** That is, between two points you can always find another point, and there are points as close together as you wish on the line. Lines have length but no thickness and are **one-dimensional.** A good model for part of this kind of line is a laser beam or other light ray.

A **plane** is a set of points thought of as something flat, like a tabletop. (A carpenter's plane is a tool for making things flat and smooth.) In small spaces, like a classroom, the floor can be considered as a plane. An unbent sheet of paper is part of a plane. The surface of the Earth is *not* a plane because it is curved.

tabletop

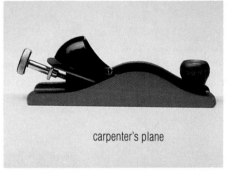

carpenter's plane

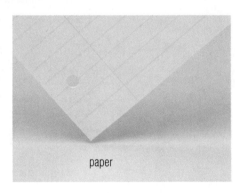

paper

two-dimensional

A **plane figure** is a set of points that are all in a plane. Two or more figures that lie in the same plane are **coplanar.** (So all the points of a plane figure are coplanar.) Points, lines, rays, and segments are plane figures.

With other plane figures, such as squares, circles, and triangles, all the points of the figure do not lie on a single line. Those plane figures are **two-dimensional.**

Spheres, boxes, cubes, and other real objects do not all lie in a single plane. They are **three-dimensional** or **space figures.**

sphere

cube

Covering the Reading

1. Among ancient Greek mathematicians, what was a point considered to be?

2. According to the *1989 World Almanac,* what is the road mileage from New York to Los Angeles?

3. According to the *1989 Information Please Almanac,* what is the air distance from New York to Los Angeles?

4. Define: distance between two points on a coordinatized line.

5. The distance between two points *A* and *B* is written as __?__ .

6. Give the distance between two points with the given coordinates.
 a. 5 and 14 **b.** 14 and 5
 c. -14 and -5

In 7-9, give the distance between two points with the given coordinates.

7. -321 and 32 **8.** 3 and -4

9. *x* and *y*

10. Give the number of dimensions for each figure.
 a. point **b.** plane
 c. line **d.** space

11. What is meant by lines being *dense?*

12. A person stretches a tape measure over a table. At one side of the table the tape measure reads 1″. At the other side the tape measure reads 45″. How long is the table from side to side?

Applying the Mathematics

13. The *1989 Information Please Almanac* gives 2825 miles as the road mileage from New York to Los Angeles. How is it possible that this distance differs from that in Question 2?

14. Why is the road distance from New York to Los Angeles greater than the air distance?

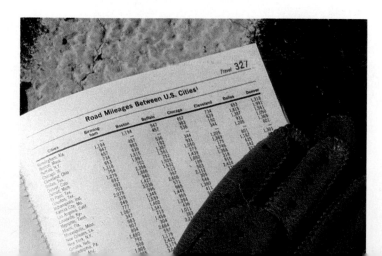

15. Use the following road mileage chart for four cities in Ohio.

	Cincinnati	Cleveland	Columbus	Toledo
Cincinnati		244	108	200
Cleveland	244		139	111
Columbus	108	139		133
Toledo	200	111	133	

How much further is the drive from Cincinnati to Cleveland if you stop in Toledo?

16. a. On a drive to Denver, Colorado, you pass a road marker that reads Denver, 88 miles. Along the same road you pass a later marker that reads Denver, 52 miles. How far have you traveled between markers?

   b. If the first road marker reads x km to Denver and the second reads y km to Denver, how far have you traveled?

Tabor Center Shopping Mall in Denver, Colorado

17. Use the number line below.

   a. Calculate *AB, BC,* and *AC.*
   b. *True* or *false?* $AB + BC = AC.$

18. Fill in the table with T if the statement is *always* true, F otherwise.

	Description of point	
Statement	Dot	Location
A point has some size.		
If two coplanar lines are not parallel, then they have a point in common.		
Between two points on a line there is always a third point.		

12

Every lesson from here on contains review questions which give practice on ideas presented in earlier lessons. Numbers in parentheses after the questions indicate where the idea was first presented. For example, (Lesson 2-1) indicates the question was based on Chapter 2, Lesson 1. If you can't remember how to do a review question, look back at the indicated lesson. Some skills in review exercises provide practice on ideas you learned in earlier courses. They are marked (Previous course).

19. How many dots are on a computer screen whose dimensions are 380 pixels by 192 pixels? *(Lesson 1-1)*

20. If two screens have the same dimensions, which screen has a better resolution, one whose pixels are 380 by 192 or one that is 330 by 154? *(Lesson 1-1)*

21. What is meant by a *discrete* line? *(Lesson 1-1)*

22. Graph the line containing (-2, 1) and (5, -6) on a coordinate plane. *(Previous course)*

23. For the equation $x - 3y = 5$, find the value of y for each given value of x. *(Previous course)*

x	3	-2	5
y			

24. Physicists sometimes speak of space-time. How many dimensions does space-time have?

25. To the nearest 100 miles, how far do you live from each of the following cities?
   a. New York   **b.** Los Angeles
   c. Honolulu   **d.** Moscow

A blend of old and new architecture in Moscow

Ordered Pairs as Points

Portrait of René Descartes (1596-1650) by Jan Lievens

Around the year 1630, the French mathematicians Pierre de Fermat and René Descartes realized that a location in a plane can be identified by an **ordered pair** of real numbers. This is the idea behind coordinate graphing. Below, the three points (0, 0), (3, 2), and (-5.3, 4.8) are graphed. The plane containing these points is called the **Cartesian plane** (named after Descartes' Latin name, Cartesius) or, more simply, the **coordinate plane.** This leads to a third description of a point.

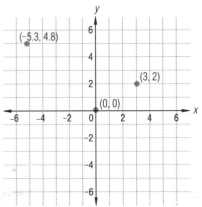

Third description of a point:

> A point is an ordered pair of numbers.

When a point is an ordered pair, a line is the set of ordered pairs (x, y) satisfying the equation
$$Ax + By = C$$
where A, B, and C are specific numbers.

Example   Graph the set of ordered pairs satisfying $3x - y = 5$.

Solution   Find two points on the line. Many people like to make a table. You can choose *any* values for x. In this example, 0 and 3 have been selected.

$$\text{When } x = 0,$$
$$3 \cdot \mathbf{0} - y = 5$$
$$-y = 5$$
$$y = -5.$$
Graph $(0, -5)$.

$$\text{When } x = 3,$$
$$3 \cdot \mathbf{3} - y = 5$$
$$9 - y = 5$$
$$y = 4.$$
Graph $(3, 4)$.

Draw the line through $(0, -5)$ and $(3, 4)$. Put arrows at both ends to indicate that the line goes on forever in each direction.

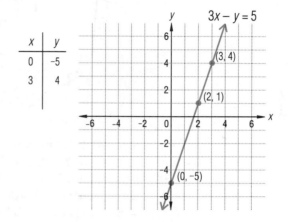

x	y
0	-5
3	4

Check   Find a third point whose coordinates satisfy the equation.
$$\text{When } x = 2,$$
$$3 \cdot \mathbf{2} - y = 5$$
$$6 - y = 5.$$
So $y = 1$. Is the point $(2, 1)$ on the line graphed? Yes, so it checks.

Four important characteristics help to distinguish the various descriptions of points and lines.

1. *Unique line*. Do two points determine a line?

2. *Dimension*. Are points without size? Are lines without thickness? Does the plane have more than one line?

3. *Number line*. Can the points of a line be put into one-to-one correspondence with the real numbers?

4. *Distance*. Is there a unique distance between two points?

Points as dots do not possess the dimension or number line characteristic, and may or may not have the other two characteristics. However, points as locations have all these characteristics. And, since an ordered pair exactly locates a point, points in the coordinate plane have the same characteristics as points as locations.

In the general equation for a line, $Ax + By = C$, the values of A, B, and C determine the tilt and location of the line. When neither A nor B is zero, as in the Example, the line is oblique. When $A = 0$, the equation of the line is of the form $y = k$, where k is the specific number $\frac{C}{B}$, and the line is horizontal. When $B = 0$, the equation of the line is of the form $x = h$, where h is the specific number $\frac{C}{A}$, and the line is vertical.

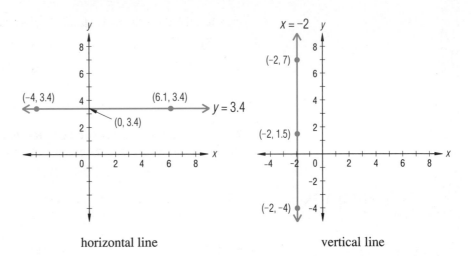

horizontal line   vertical line

Describing points as ordered pairs is very important in mathematics. Sets of ordered pairs may be a curve, and equations can describe that curve. Below are graphed a parabola and an exponential growth curve, two curves that you may have studied or will learn about in other courses. Each curve is described with an equation.

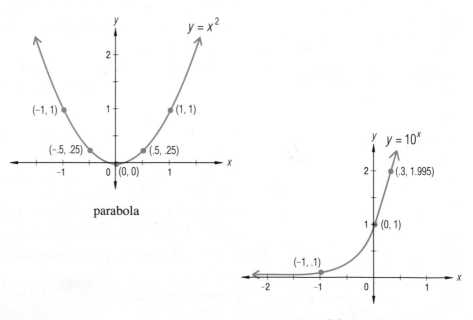

parabola

exponential growth curve

Questions

Covering the Reading

1. Give three descriptions of a point.

2. **a.** Which two mathematicians developed the idea of using ordered pairs of numbers to represent points?
   b. About how many years ago was this done?

In 3-6, classify the line as vertical, horizontal, or oblique.
3. $x - 3y = 5$ 4. $y = -1.234$

5. $x = 8$ 6. $14 - 9y = 32x$

7. **a.** Name the four characteristics of points and lines mentioned in this lesson.
   b. Which are never satisfied by points as dots?
   c. Which are satisfied by points as ordered pairs?

Applying the Mathematics

In 8-11, graph the set of ordered pairs satisfying each equation.
8. $x + y = 0$ 9. $x + 2y = 4$

10. $4x - y = 2$ 11. $4x - 3y = 12$

12. Elaine has $12 in quarters and dimes.
    a. Name five ordered pairs (q, d) of quarters and dimes she might have.
    b. Graph these points.
    c. Are these points collinear?

13. Give an equation for the horizontal line that passes through $(0, -5)$.

14. Give an equation for the vertical line that passes through $(7, -10)$.

15. **a.** Graph the line $x = 3$.
    b. Graph the line $4x + 3y = 6$ on the same coordinate plane.
    c. At what point(s) do the lines intersect?

Review

16. Give the distance between two points on a number line with coordinates 1 and 10. *(Lesson 1-2)*

17. In April of 1989, Hitachi Ltd. advertised a TV screen with approximately 115,200 pixels. If this screen has the same dimensions as the computer screens mentioned on page 4, how does its resolution compare with those? *(Lesson 1-1)*

18. Draw two discrete parallel vertical lines. *(Lesson 1-1)*

19. If the ruler at the left is marked in centimeters, about how long is the segment *AB*? *(Lesson 1-2)*

20. Suppose *C* has coordinate -7 and *D* has coordinate -211. Find:
    a. *CD*;   **b.** *DC*. *(Lesson 1-2)*

21. Use the road mileage chart below for the four largest cities in Georgia. Suppose you want to travel from Columbus to Savannah.
  a. How much further is the drive if you stop in Atlanta?
  b. At 55 mph, about how much longer would it take you?
  (Lesson 1-2, Previous course)

	Atlanta	Columbus	Macon	Savannah
Atlanta		108	82	255
Columbus	108		96	269
Macon	82	96		173
Savannah	255	269	173	

Exploration

22. Points in the coordinate plane with integer coordinates are called **lattice points** (integers are $\{\ldots, -3, -2, -1, 0, 1, 2, 3, \ldots\}$). For example, $(-4, 11)$ is a lattice point, but $(-2.5, 6)$ is not.
  a. Name a lattice point on the line $3x + 2y = 5$.
  b. Name a point on the line $4x - y = 8$ that is not a lattice point.

23. The latitude and longitude of a location on Earth are like coordinates of a point. Look on a map to find the latitude and longitude of the place where you live.

1-4

Points in Networks

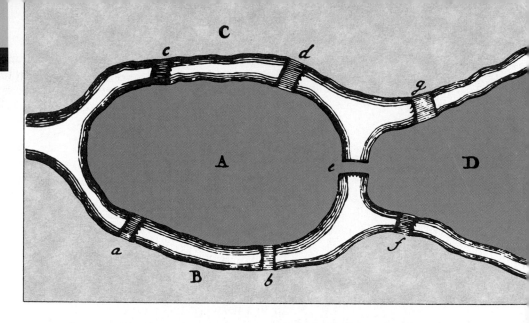

Through the city of Kaliningrad, in the Soviet Union, flows the Pregol'a River. There are two islands in this river, and seven bridges connect the islands to each other and to the shores. In the drawing above, which first appeared in an article by the great mathematician Leonhard Euler (pronounced "Oiler"), the islands are A and D. The bridges are *a, b, c, d, e, f,* and *g.* The shores of the river are B and C.

In the 1700s this city was part of East Prussia and was known as Königsberg. It was common on Sunday for people to take walks over the bridges. These walks and bridges led to a problem.

> Is there a way to walk across all the bridges so that each bridge is crossed exactly once?

You might try to find such a way before reading on.

This question has become known as the **Königsberg Bridge Problem.** Euler solved it in 1736. First he named the islands, shores, and bridges as shown above. He then redrew the map with the islands A and D as very small, and lengthened the bridges. This doesn't change the problem.

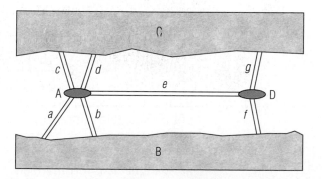

Then he realized that the shores B and C could be small. That again distorts the picture but it doesn't change the problem.

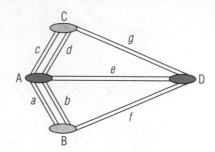

Finally—and this was the big step—he thought of the land areas A, B, C, and D as points and the bridges *a* through *g* as **arcs** connecting them. The result, shown below, is a **network** of points and arcs. In this network there is a path (though not necessarily direct) from any point to any other point. Euler was able to rephrase the original question to become: *Without lifting a pencil off the paper, can the pencil trace over **all** the arcs exactly once?* If the answer is yes, this kind of network is called **traversable.**

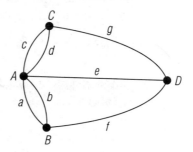

In a network, the *only* points are the endpoints of arcs. These endpoints have no size and are called **nodes** or **vertices.** (The singular of vertices is **vertex**.) Euler noticed that the number of arcs at each node provided a clue as to whether a network was traversable. In the Königsberg Bridge Problem, there are 5 arcs at vertex *A (c, d, e, b,* and *a)* and 3 arcs at each of vertices *B, C,* and *D.*

Networks illustrate a fourth way to describe a point.

Fourth description of a point:

    A point is a node of a network.

Points and lines in networks have different properties than when points and lines are dots, locations, or ordered pairs. For example, a line in a network is an arc or segment connecting either two nodes or one node to itself. There are no points between the nodes. So an arc cannot be coordinatized. Also, two nodes do not determine exactly one arc.

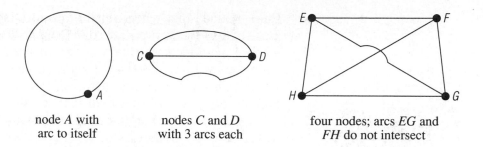

| node A with arc to itself | nodes C and D with 3 arcs each | four nodes; arcs EG and FH do not intersect |

Before we tell you Euler's answer to the Königsberg Bridge Problem, here are three more networks to consider. In these networks, we draw the arcs as segments.

Example 1

How many arcs are at each node of networks I, II, and III?

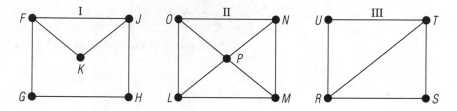

Solution   Network I: There are 2 arcs at vertices G, H, and K, and 3 at F and J.

Network II: There are 3 arcs at vertices L, M, N, and O, and 4 arcs at vertex P.

Network III: There are 2 arcs at S and U, 3 arcs at R and T.

Example 2

Which of the networks in Example 1 are traversable?

Solution   Network I is traversable. One path begins at F and goes to K and then to J to H to G to F to J.

Network II is not traversable. (Try it.)

Network III is traversable. One path is from R to S to T to R to U to T.

If the number of arcs at a node is even, the node is called an **even node.** Otherwise it is an **odd node.** In the Examples, nodes G, H, K, P, U, and S are even nodes while nodes F, J, L, M, N, O, R, and T are odd nodes. These are sometimes called odd or even **vertices.**

Euler noticed that when a path goes through a vertex, it uses two arcs, one to the vertex, and one from it. This led him to realize that when a network has an odd vertex, it *must* be the starting or finishing point for a traversable path. (Look back at Example 2 and verify that the traversable paths of Networks I and III begin and end at odd nodes.) Euler then realized that all four vertices in the Königsberg network are odd. So the Königsberg network is not traversable. In general, whenever a network has more than two odd nodes, it is *not* traversable.

Problems like the Königsberg Bridge Problem may seem frivolous or silly, but there are important real situations that are similar.

Can a telephone company repair crew inspect all the lines without going over any section twice?

Can a school bus route be set up so that the bus drives on each street only once?

Questions

Covering the Reading

1. How many bridges were there in Königsberg?

2. What is the Königsberg Bridge Problem?

3. Who solved the Königsberg Bridge Problem and when?

In 4 and 5, use the Königsberg network.

4. What do the nodes in this network represent?

5. What do the arcs in this network represent?

6. What does it mean for a network to be traversable?

7. What is the description of a point in this lesson?

8. What is the description of a line in this lesson?

9. What did Euler notice about networks?

10. a. Draw a traversable network.
   b. Draw a network that is not traversable.

11. Describe a traversable path for Network III of this lesson different from the one in this lesson.

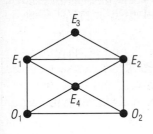

12. The network at the left has 6 nodes.
    a. Copy it. Draw a path that shows that this network is traversable.
    b. At what node does your path begin?
    c. At what node does your path end?
    d. Why are the vertices called *E*s and *O*s?

In 13 and 14, the network is traversable. **a.** Describe a traversable path.
b. At what vertices can a traversable path begin?

13. 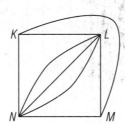   **14.**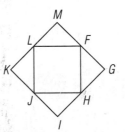

In 15 and 16, **a.** give the number of even and odd nodes; **b.** tell whether the network is traversable.

15.   **16.**

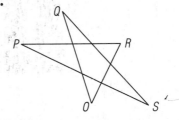

17. a. Draw a network with more arcs than nodes.
    b. Draw a network with more nodes than arcs.

18. An architect is planning a museum. Her sketch is shown. Can a security guard completely walk each part of his route once without going through any part of his route twice? (Hint: Represent the intersection of hallways with nodes, and the hallways themselves with arcs.)

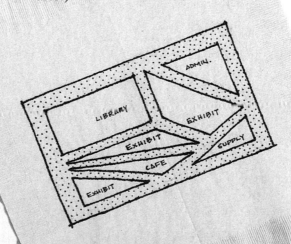

19. Below at the left are statements about points and lines. Fill in each part of the table with A if the statement is always true, S if the statement is sometimes true, or N if the statement is never true.

Statement	Dots	Ordered Pairs	Locations	Node
Between two points on a line there is a third point.				
A line contains infinitely many points.				
Through two points there is exactly one line.				

Review

In 20 and 21, graph the set of ordered pairs satisfying each equation.

20. $4x - 3y = 6$ *(Lesson 1-3)*   **21.** $x = -3$ *(Lesson 1-3)*

22. Give an equation for the horizontal line containing (-2, 5). *(Lesson 1-3)*

23. Suppose *A, B,* and *C* are collinear with coordinates -6, 1, and 14, respectively. Calculate $AB + BC$. *(Lesson 1-2)*

24. Ignoring small thicknesses, give the number of dimensions for a laser beam. *(Lesson 1-2)*

25. Using the number line at the right, find *CD*. *(Lesson 1-2)*

Exploration

26. There are many puzzles using networks. Here is one. Start with a network that has *n* arcs. (The networks below have 4 nodes and 6 arcs.) Name each *node* with a different number from 0 to *n*. Then number each *arc* by the positive difference of the nodes it connects. For example, in the network below at the right, the arc connecting nodes 5 and 3 is named 2 because $5 - 3 = 2$. The goal is to name the nodes in such a way that the *n* arcs are numbered with all the integers from 1 to *n*. Such a network is called a *graceful* network.

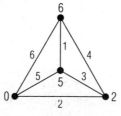

graceful
(arcs are numbered from 1 to 6)

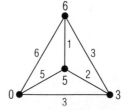

not graceful
(two arcs are numbered 3)

Number the nodes in these three networks so as to make them graceful.

a.   **b.**   **c.**

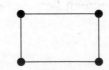

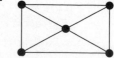

1-5

Drawing in Perspective

The drawings in this book are one- and two-dimensional, but the world is three-dimensional. This presents problems. We know that railroad tracks are parallel and thus do not intersect, but in life and in many drawings and photographs they look as if they will meet if extended. The point where they would meet is called a **vanishing point.**

In the painting above, *Overseas Highway,* the artist, Ralston Crawford, has created a feeling of depth, or **perspective,** by the use of a vanishing point. You can see that the sides of the floor of the bridge meet at the vanishing point. Likewise, the railings on both sides of the bridge are drawn to the same vanishing point.

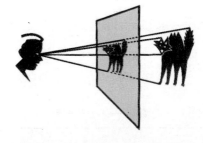

The idea of a vanishing point comes from Renaissance artists. They imagined a clear screen between the viewer and the object they wanted to draw. They connected points on the object to the eye with lines called **lines of sight,** as shown at the left. The points where the lines of sight intersected the screen showed how to draw the object.

These drawings are called **perspective drawings.** In perspective drawings, horizontal (or vertical) lines remain horizontal (or vertical) and parallel. But oblique parallel lines will intersect if extended. The box below has two vanishing points, P and Q. Vertical lines on the box remain vertical and parallel, but the box has been tilted to have no horizontal edges.

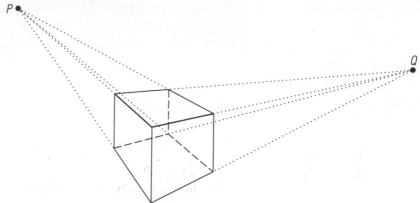

The box drawn below is tilted to have neither horizontal nor vertical edges. It has three collinear vanishing points, R, S, and T. They lie on the **vanishing line** for this drawing. In realistic drawings, the vanishing line is both the horizon and the height of the viewer's eye.

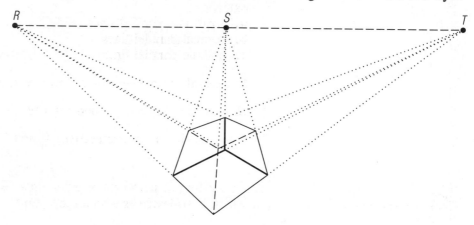

Drawing in perspective can be difficult, so mathematicians often avoid perspective in their drawings. Below, a cube is drawn as most mathematicians would draw it. Notice that the back of the cube, *BCEH,* is the same size as the front, *ADFG.* In the real world, the back of the cube is farther away than the front and it would look smaller. Realist artists would not like this drawing.

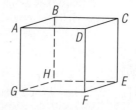

nonperspective drawing
of a cube

Geometers (mathematicians who study geometry) use another technique that preserves a feeling of depth. **Hidden lines,** such as the three back edges of the cube, are shown as dashed lines instead of solid to indicate that they would not normally be seen.

In this book, you will often be asked to draw three-dimensional figures. You are not expected to use perspective unless asked. But you should follow the rules that geometers follow, and dot or dash hidden lines to show depth.

Questions

Covering the Reading

1. **a.** In a perspective drawing, do railroad tracks meet in the distance?
   b. In the real world, do railroad tracks meet in the distance?

2. What is a vanishing point?

3. What are lines of sight?

4. In perspective drawings, tell whether these lines would intersect if extended:
   a. horizontal parallel lines
   b. vertical parallel lines
   c. oblique parallel lines.

5. In general, do mathematicians use perspective in drawings?

6. How are hidden lines in non-perspective drawings drawn?

7. Draw a cube: **a.** in perspective; **b.** not in perspective.

Applying the Mathematics

8. Of the four descriptions of points mentioned in previous lessons, which best describes a vanishing point?

9. Consider these four drawings.

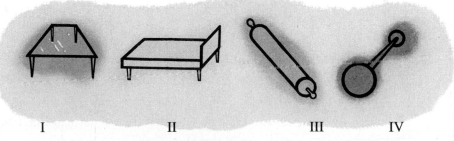

I   II   III   IV

   a. Which are drawn in perspective?
   b. Trace each perspective drawing and find its vanishing point.

10. Make a perspective drawing of a square floor tiled with square tiles.

11. Sally's baby brother has a block with 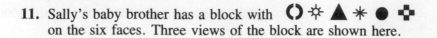 on the six faces. Three views of the block are shown here.

Which pictures are on opposites sides of the block?

12. Opposite sides of a die add to seven. Here a die is seen from a little above one face.

a. What is the sum of the numbers that cannot be seen?
b. Where are these numbers? (Call the faces of the die top, bottom, front, back, right, and left.)

Review

In 13 and 14, is the network traversable? If so, give a route; if not, tell why not. *(Lesson 1-4)*

13.

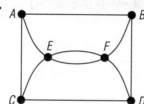

14.

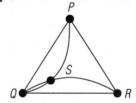

15. a. Represent the floor plan below with a network.
b. Is it traversable? *(Lesson 1-4)*

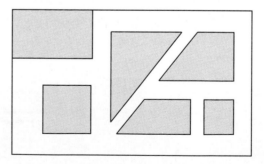

16. Give an equation for the vertical line containing (-1, -6). *(Lesson 1-3)*

17. a. Graph the lines $y = 3x - 2$ and $x + 2y = 5$ on the same coordinate plane.
b. From the graph, estimate the coordinates of the point of intersection. *(Lesson 1-3)*

18. If A has coordinate 461 and B has coordinate -35, find AB. *(Lesson 1-2)*

19. A tape measure was placed against a door. The left side was aligned to the 17 cm mark, and the right side to the 73 cm mark. How wide is the door? *(Lesson 1-2)*

Exploration

20. Below is an example of anamorphic art (*Napoleon III with His Children,* artist anonymous), a perspective drawing where the vanishing point is about 1 meter to the left of the page in the same plane as the page.
   a. Look at the drawing from the vanishing point. Briefly describe the picture.
   b. Why do you think an artist would use such a device?

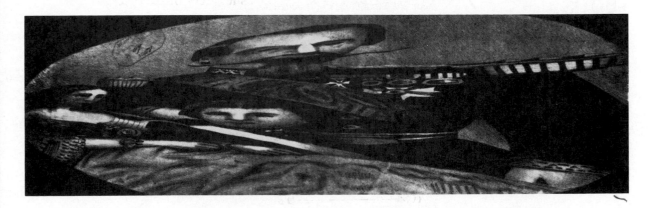

LESSON

1-6

The Need for Undefined Terms

The famous "freedom march" on Washington in 1963. Does the word "freedom" mean the same thing to all people?

A *set* is a collection of objects called *elements*. If the elements are points, then the set is a *figure*. The set of all points from which points of a figure are selected is called *space*. The study of figures in the two-dimensional space of a plane, such as polygons and circles, is called **plane geometry.** The study of figures in three-dimensional space, such as spheres and pyramids, is called **solid geometry.** In this book you will study both plane and solid geometry.

In the previous paragraph, there are many terms. Here two of them are formally defined.

> **Definitions:**
>
> **Space** is the set of all possible points.
> A **figure** is a set of points.

These definitions are useful because they state precisely what these words mean in this book.

Careful definitions are not always needed. However, in some fields, defining terms is not just useful, but necessary. Law, economics, philosophy, science, and labor relations, in addition to mathematics, are some of the fields where precise definitions are necessary. For example, disputes may occur because individuals have no definitions or have different definitions for "overtime" or "freedom" or "force" or "obscene."

Mathematicians try to define terms carefully. However, notice that the meanings of the words "space" and "figure" depend on what a point means. Trying to define "point" presents two problems. First, as you have seen in the previous lessons, there are many possible meanings for "point." A point may be a dot, or a location, or an ordered pair, or a node in a network.

Second, you get into trouble when you try to select a meaning for "point." For instance, suppose you defined a point to be a *spot*. What about the word "spot"? Well, a spot is a *place*. But a place is an *exact location*. Trying to define this term, you might find that the best description of an exact location is "point"!

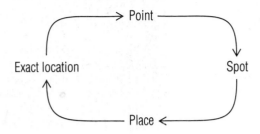

Thus you have returned to the original word which you were trying to define. You have circled back to where you started. When this "circling back" occurs, it usually means you are trying to define basic terms. It is called **circularity.** (Circularity means that you have circled back to any word previously defined, not necessarily the original one.) To avoid circularity, certain basic geometric terms are forced to be *undefined*.

In this book, we choose *point, line,* and *plane* as **undefined terms.** One strength of this is that it allows geometry to be applied to different kinds of points and lines. For instance, we can talk about the distance between (4, 5) and (4, 2), because we can think of (4, 5) and (4, 2) as representing points, and not just pairs of numbers.

Also, very common English words—the articles, prepositions, and conjunctions—are not defined. We assume that you are familiar with many words used in algebra or arithmetic, such as "equation," "number," "equals," "is less than," and so on. So terms like these are left undefined.

Undefined terms (in this book):

Geometric terms: point, line, plane.
Algebraic and arithmetic terms: number, equals, addition,
                                            and so on.
Common English words: the, a, of, into, and, and so on.

If something is not defined, it could mean anything. Point might mean "elephant"! So, to clarify that we are talking about a particular kind of point or line, we will assume points and lines have certain properties. For instance, if we assume that points have no dimensions, you know we are not talking about dots. If we assume that between two points, there is always another point, you know we are not talking about lines in networks. The assumptions about points and lines for this book are given in the next lesson.

Questions

Covering the Reading

1. In geometry, space is the __?__ .

2. In this book, a figure is a(n) __?__ .

3. What is the difference between plane geometry and solid geometry?

4. Name five fields where precise definitions are needed.

5. In an attempt to define a simple word, such as "point," you may find the original word is used in the definition. This is called __?__ .

6. Name three geometry terms undefined in this book.

7. Name two undefined words or phrases from algebra.

8. What assumption about points and lines would indicate that the points and lines are not in networks?

Applying the Mathematics

9. Look up the word "concord" in a dictionary. Try to find a one-word synonym. Look up this synonym. Find a one-word synonym for this second word. Continue this process. How many words did you look up before circularity happened?

In 10 and 11, follow the directions for Question 9 but begin with the following words.

10. inundate

11. satire

In 12 and 13, define the word on your own without a dictionary.

12. freedom

13. number

Review

14. Do mathematicians generally draw in perspective? *(Lesson 1-5)*

15. Draw railroad tracks: **a.** in perspective; **b.** not in perspective. *(Lesson 1-5)*

16. Graph the line with equation $5x + 3y = 15$. *(Lesson 1-3)*

17. Trace the figure below and find the vanishing point. *(Lesson 1-5)*

18. *The New York City Bridge Problem.* Below is a drawing of the five boroughs of New York City, Randall's Island, and New Jersey. (No water separates Brooklyn and Queens.) Bridges and tunnels connect the regions. Draw a network (like the Königsberg bridge network) to represent New York and determine if you could take a driving tour of New York going over each bridge and through each tunnel exactly once. *(Lesson 1-4)*

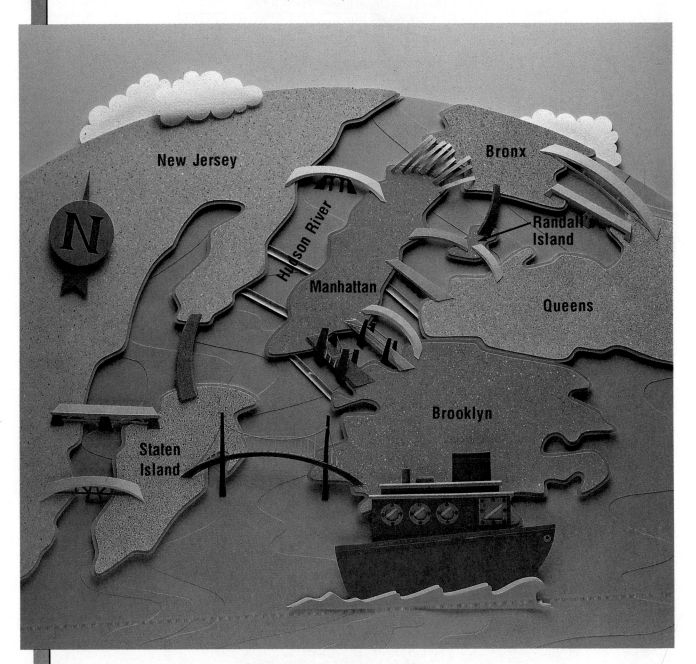

19. Calculate *AB*. *(Lesson 1-2)*

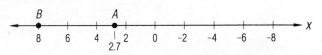

20. Fill in the table with A if the statement is always true, S if sometimes true, or N if never true. *(Lessons 1-4, 1-3, 1-2, 1-1)*

		Description of a point		
Statement	Location	Ordered Pair	Node	Dot
Through two points, there is exactly one line.				
A line is an infinite set of points.				
A point has no size.				

21. Give the number of dimensions in each figure. Assume points are locations. *(Lesson 1-2)*
   a. line   **b.** plane
   c. point   **d.** space

22. Find the distance between (4, 5) and (4, 2). (Hint: graph them.) *(Lessons 1-3, 1-2)*

23. On a number line, graph all solutions to the inequality $x \geq -10$. *(Previous course)*

24. On a number line, graph all numbers t with $\frac{1}{2} \leq t \leq \frac{5}{2}$. *(Previous course).*

25. Some words have many definitions.
   a. Look in a dictionary. How many different definitions are given for the word "point"?
   b. Find another word with as many definitions.

34

Postulates

You have now seen four descriptions of points. Others are possible but are not discussed in this book.

Description	Example
dot	computer screens
location	geography
ordered pair	graphs
node of network	airplane routes

These examples show that points and lines do not have the same properties when different descriptions are used. This is one reason why *point* and *line* are undefined. To make clear which description of *point* and *line* is being followed, assumptions or **postulates** are made about them.

Below we state four assumptions about points and lines. These are grouped together and called the *Point-Line-Plane Postulate*. These assumptions were picked to fit the descriptions of point as location and as ordered pair, since these descriptions are the most used in mathematics and its applications. The assumptions may not fit other descriptions of *point* and *line*.

Point-Line-Plane Postulate:

(a) Unique line assumption Through any two points, there is exactly one line.

Sometimes this is read, "Two points determine a line." This assumption does not apply to the node description of point, where there can be more than one line (arc) connecting two points (nodes).

(b) Dimension assumption Given a line in a plane, there exists a point in the plane not on the line. Given a plane in space, there exists a point in space not on the plane.

Thus, a line has more dimensions than a point, a plane has more dimensions than a line, and space has more dimensions than a plane.

(c) Number line assumption Every line is a set of points that can be put into a one-to-one correspondence with the real numbers, with any point on it corresponding to 0 and any other point corresponding to 1.

This part means that any line can be made into a real number line. Any point on the line can be the origin, either direction can be the positive direction, and any length can be the unit length. It also allows points in the plane to be ordered pairs. This part does not apply to the dot or node description of point.

(d) Distance assumption On a number line, there is a unique distance between two points.

If the points have coordinates x and y, we define this distance to be $|x - y|$.

To repeat: The Point-Line-Plane Postulate limits the points in this book to be locations or ordered pairs. A different postulate would have been needed if we wanted the results to be applicable to the dot or node description of point.

The first purpose served by postulates is to explain undefined terms. A second purpose, just as important, is to serve as a starting point for logically deducing or proving other statements about figures.

For instance, in the figure below, if P and Q are points, m and n cannot *both* be lines. If they were, there would be two lines through P and Q, yet from part (a) of the Point-Line-Plane Postulate, there can only be one. We denote the unique line through P and Q by $\overleftrightarrow{PQ}$ or $\overleftrightarrow{QP}$. $\overleftrightarrow{PQ}$ is read "line PQ."

P and Q are points; m and n are different lines.
Impossible.

Theorems are geometric statements that are deduced from postulates, definitions, or previously deduced theorems. The argument above proves the following theorem.

Line Intersection Theorem:

Two different lines intersect in at most one point.

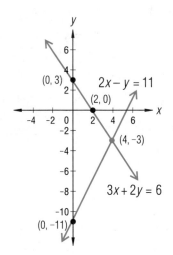

This theorem holds when points are ordered pairs. For instance, in algebra, when you solved the system $\begin{cases} 3x + 2y = 6 \\ 2x - y = 11 \end{cases}$ you found (4, -3) as the point of intersection of the two lines. You also know that sometimes lines do not intersect, and sometimes two equations can describe the same line. When coplanar lines do not intersect in exactly one point, they are called *parallel*. The idea behind parallel is "going in the same direction."

Definition:

Two coplanar lines m and n are **parallel lines**, written **$m \parallel n$**, if and only if they have no points in common, or they are identical.

The most famous organization of postulates, definitions, and theorems (and perhaps the earliest) was by the Greek mathematician Euclid around 300 B.C. In a set of books called *Elements*, Euclid used five geometric postulates and five arithmetic postulates.

The original Elements *were written by Euclid in 300 B.C. No copy of the original exists. Pictured here is a translation by H. Billingsley in the year 1570.*

Postulates from arithmetic and algebra are still used in geometry. Here are the most important postulates for this course. All of these hold for *any* real numbers *a, b,* and *c.* These properties also hold for all algebraic expressions and anything that stands for real numbers. You will review other properties and theorems from algebra in later lessons as they are needed.

Some Postulates from Arithmetic and Algebra

Postulates of Equality

Reflexive Property of Equality: $a = a$

Symmetric Property of Equality: *If $a = b$, then $b = a$.*

Transitive Property of Equality: *If $a = b$ and $b = c$, then $a = c$.*

Postulates of Equality and Operations

Addition Property of Equality: *If $a = b$, then $a + c = b + c$.*

Multiplication Property of Equality: *If $a = b$, then $ac = bc$.*

Substitution Property of Equality: *If $a = b$, then a may be substituted for b in any expression.*

Postulates of Inequality and Operations

Addition Property of Inequality: *If $a < b$, then $a + c < b + c$.*

Multiplication Property of Inequality: *If $a < b$ and $c > 0$, then $ac < bc$.*
If $a < b$ and $c < 0$, then $ac > bc$.

Equation to Inequality Property: *If a and b are positive numbers and $a + b = c$, then $c > a$ and $c > b$.*

Transitive Property of Inequality: *If $a < b$ and $b < c$, then $a < c$.*

Postulates of Operations

Commutative Property of Addition: $a + b = b + a$

Commutative Property of Multiplication: $ab = ba$

Distributive Property: $a(b + c) = ab + ac$

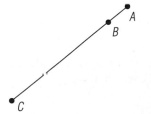

The above postulates should be familiar to you except for the Equation to Inequality Property. This property was worded by Euclid (in Greek) as "the whole is greater than any of its parts." For example, in the figure at the left, suppose $AB + BC = AC$. Then $AC > AB$ and $AC > BC$. The length of the whole segment is greater than the length of any part of it.

Example   In solving an equation, a student changes $3 = 4x + 2$ into
$4x + 2 = 3$. What property justifies the change?

Solution   The right and left sides of the equation have been switched.
Thus the Symmetric Property of Equality has been applied:
If $3 = 4x + 2$, then $4x + 2 = 3$.

Questions

Covering the Reading

1. What is a postulate?

2. What are the two purposes of postulates?

In 3-6, does the named part of the Point-Line-Plane Postulate hold for the
given description of point?

3. part (a) for node

4. part (d) for location

5. part (b) for ordered pair

6. part (c) for dot

7. *True or false?*   Every part of the Point-Line-Plane Postulate holds for
points as locations.

8. What part of the Point-Line-Plane Postulate is violated by this figure?

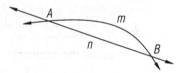

m and *n* are different lines.
m intersects *n* at two points, *A* and *B*.

9. The line through points *X* and *A* is written __?__ or __?__ .

10. *True* or *false?*   According to the definition in this lesson, every line
is parallel to itself.

11. What was Euclid's *Elements?*

12. How did Euclid word the Equation to Inequality Property?

Applying the Mathematics

In 13–19, a postulate from arithmetic or algebra is applied. Name the
postulate.

13. Since $\frac{1}{4} = .25$ and $.25 = 25\%$, $\frac{1}{4} = 25\%$.

14. $4\sqrt{3} = \sqrt{3} \cdot 4$

15. When $2x + 46 = 30$, $2x = -16$.

16. When $2x + 46 < 30$, $2x < -16$.

17. In the figure below, since $PQ + QR = PR$, then $PR > PQ$.

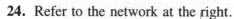

18. If $m = 2x + 5$ and $x = 4$, then $m = 2 \cdot 4 + 5$.

19. $3(x - 2y) = 3x - 3 \cdot 2y$

20. Give the property that justifies each indicated step.
  a. $3x + 4x \quad = x \cdot 3 + x \cdot 4$
  b. $\qquad\qquad = x(3 + 4)$
  $\qquad\qquad\quad\ = x \cdot 7$
  c. $\qquad\qquad = 7x$

21. One of Euclid's assumptions was (in English translation) "If equals are added to equals, the sums are equal." What is the name we give to this property of real numbers?

22. If points are dots on a number line, and a dot is .001 unit in diameter, how many dots can there be between 0 and 1? (Do not include dots at 0 and 1.)

Review

23. Look up the word "proboscis" in a dictionary. Try to find a one-word synonym. Look up this synonym. Find a one-word synonym for this second word. Continue this process. How many words did you look up before circularity occurred? *(Lesson 1-6)*

24. Refer to the network at the right.
  a. How many nodes does it have?
  b. How many arcs does it have?
  c. Is the network traversable? If so, give a route; if not, explain why not. *(Lesson 1-4)*

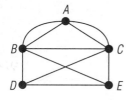

25. a. Represent the floor plan at the left with a network.
  b. Is it traversable? *(Lesson 1-4)*

26. a. Graph $y = x$ and $y = x + 1$ on the same set of axes.
  b. Are they parallel? *(Lesson 1-3)*

27. Classify the line as vertical, horizontal, or oblique. *(Lesson 1-3)*
  a. $y = 7$ \qquad\qquad\qquad **b.** $2x - y = 9$

Exploration

28. Equality satisfies the Transitive Property:
  If $a = b$ and $b = c$, then $a = c$.
  So does $<$:
  If $a < b$ and $b < c$, then $a < c$.
  So does *is an ancestor of*:
  If a is an ancestor of b and b is an ancestor of c, then a is an ancestor of c.
  Find two other things that satisfy the Transitive Property.

1-8

One-Dimensional Figures

The light rays of fiber optics are one-dimensional.

The location of a point on a line can be described with one number. (This is part (c) of the Point-Line-Plane Postulate.) This is why we say that a line is one-dimensional. Parts or subsets of lines are also one-dimensional figures. The most common subsets of lines are *line segments* and *rays. Line* is an undefined term, but the other terms can be defined combining line and a simple idea, betweenness.

A *number* is **between** two others if it is greater than one of them and less than the other. For example, 5 is between -1 and 6.5 since $5 > -1$ and $5 < 6.5$. The number -1 is *not* considered to be between itself and 6.5.

A *point* is **between** two other points on the same line if its coordinate is between their coordinates. Point U above, with coordinate 5, is between the other two points A and B. If you graph -1, 6.5, and *all* points having coordinates between -1 and 6.5, the graph is a *segment*. The points for -1 and 6.5 are the *endpoints* of the segment.

Definition:

The **segment** (or **line segment**) with **endpoints** A and B, denoted $\overline{AB}$, is the set consisting of the distinct points A and B and all points between A and B.

The segment pictured above consists of -1, 6.5, and all points on the line whose coordinates satisfy the inequality $-1 < x < 6.5$.

Recall that AB (with no bar above the A or B) is the distance between A and B, called the **length** of $\overline{AB}$. By the definition of distance, the length is $|-1 - 6.5|$, which is 7.5.

In the example below, point B is between points A and C. Notice the relationship between the three lengths AB, BC, and AC.

Example   Suppose A, B, and C are three points on a number line with coordinates -53, 212, and 670. By calculating distances, show that $AB + BC = AC$.

Solution   First draw a picture.

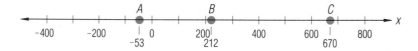

$AB = |-53 - 212| = |-265| = 265$
$BC = |212 - 670| = |-458| = 458$
$AC = |-53 - 670| = |-723| = 723$
So $AB + BC = 265 + 458 = 723$, which equals AC.

The idea shown in the Example can be proved (using algebra) for any three points on a line. It is an important property of betweenness.

Betweenness Theorem:

   If B is between A and C, then $AB + BC = AC$.

Player no. 5 is not between players 32 and 26.

Another way to state the Betweenness Theorem is: If B is on $\overline{AC}$, then $AB + BC = AC$. Using the Betweenness Theorem and the Equation to Inequality Property, you can immediately conclude that if B is between A and C, then $AC > AB$ and $AC > BC$.

A geometric *ray* is like a laser beam. A laser beam starts at a point and, if not blocked, goes forever in a particular direction. In geometry, a ray consists of an endpoint and all points of a line on one side of that endpoint.

Definition:

> The **ray** with endpoint *A* and containing a second point *B*, denoted $\overrightarrow{AB}$, consists of the points on $\overline{AB}$ and all points for which *B* is between each of them and *A*.

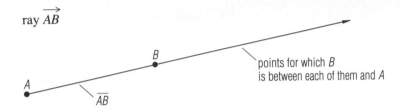

ray $\overrightarrow{AB}$

points for which *B* is between each of them and *A*

$\overline{AB}$

You have drawn rays on a number line when solving inequalities. For example, if *A* has coordinate 5 and *B* has coordinate 7, then $\overrightarrow{AB}$ consists of all points with coordinates $x \geq 5$. If *C* has coordinate 4, then $\overrightarrow{AC}$ points in the opposite direction of $\overrightarrow{AB}$. $\overrightarrow{AC}$ consists of all points with coordinates $x \leq 5$. $\overrightarrow{AB}$ and $\overrightarrow{AC}$ are called *opposite rays*.

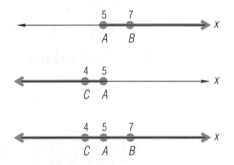

Definition:

> $\overrightarrow{AB}$ and $\overrightarrow{AC}$ are **opposite rays** if and only if *A* is between *B* and *C*.

Notice that, for any two points *A* and *B*, $\overrightarrow{BA}$ and $\overrightarrow{AB}$ are *not* opposite rays. They have many points in common. $\overrightarrow{BA}$ has endpoint *B*, while $\overrightarrow{AB}$ has endpoint *A*.

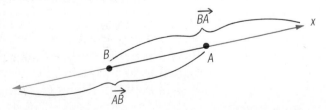

$\overrightarrow{BA}$

$\overrightarrow{AB}$

Caution: Be careful to distinguish among the following symbols. They may look similar, but their meanings are quite different.

$\overleftrightarrow{AB}$ is the *line* determined by points A and B.

$\overrightarrow{AB}$ is the *ray* with endpoint A and containing B.

$\overline{AB}$ is the *segment* with endpoints A and B.

AB is the *distance* between A and B, or the length of $\overline{AB}$.

AB is a single number, while $\overline{AB}$ is a set of points.

Questions

Covering the Reading

1. On a number line, point A has coordinate 2, point B has coordinate -2, and point C has coordinate $\sqrt{2}$. Which point is between the other two, and why?

2. $\overline{AB}$ is the set whose elements are __?__ .

3. A laser beam is like the geometric figure called a(n) __?__ .

4. Match each symbol with the correct description.
   a. $\overline{AB}$ (i) line
   b. $\overleftrightarrow{AB}$ (ii) length
   c. AB (iii) ray
   d. $\overrightarrow{AB}$ (iv) segment

5. $\overrightarrow{MN}$ has endpoint __?__ and contains a second point __?__ .

6. *Multiple choice.* If X is between Y and Z, then
   (a) $XY + YZ = XZ$ (b) $XZ + YX = YZ$
   (c) $XY = XZ$ (d) $XZ + YZ = XY$.

7. *Multiple choice.* If X is between Y and Z, then
   (a) $XZ > XY$ (b) $XY > YZ$
   (c) $XY > XZ$ (d) $YZ > XZ$.

8. *Multiple choice.* Which is not true?
   (a) $\overline{AB} = \overline{BA}$ (b) $AB = BA$
   (c) $\overleftrightarrow{AB} = \overleftrightarrow{BA}$ (d) $\overrightarrow{AB} = \overrightarrow{BA}$

9. A, B, and C are three points on a number line with coordinates 3, 14, and 82. Verify that $AB + BC = AC$.

10. a. On a number line, graph the set of numbers satisfying $y \le 1$.

    b. What one-dimensional figure best describes the graph?

11. a. On a number line, graph the set of numbers satisfying $7 \le x \le 8.3$.
    b. What one-dimensional figure best describes the graph?

In 12 and 13, use the figure below. B is between A and C.

12. If $AC = 100$, find x.

13. If $AB = BC$, find x.

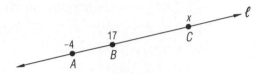

14. Two points are 7 units apart on a number line. The coordinate of one point is -8. What are the possible coordinates of the other?

15. Point Q on a number line has coordinate -5. Find all possibilities for the coordinate of R so that $QR = 21$.

In 16 and 17, use the figure below. K is between A and E. E is between K and F.

16. If $AE = 10$, $KF = 12$, and $AF = 19.6$, find KE.

17. If $AE = 15x$, $KF = 19x$, and $AF = 30x$, find KE.

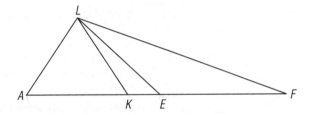

In 18–20, name the postulate from arithmetic or algebra that is being applied. *(Lesson 1-7)*

18. $4(3x - 5) = 12x - 20$

19. If $5x = \frac{1}{5}$, $x = \frac{1}{25}$.

20. When $7 = 2 - x$, then $2 - x = 7$.

21. m and n are coplanar lines. *True* or *false*?
   a. If $m = n$, then $m \,/\!/\, n$.
   b. If m does not intersect n, then $m \,/\!/\, n$.
   c. If m intersects n in exactly one point, then $m \,/\!/\, n$. *(Lesson 1-7)*

22. Three views of the same cube are given below. Which symbols are on opposite faces of the cube? *(Lesson 1-5)*

23. Graph $3x - y = 4$ and $7x + 2y = 5$ on the same axes. *(Lesson 1-3)*

24. Give an equation for the vertical line containing $(7, 3)$. *(Lesson 1-3)*

25. Lines on the surface of the earth do not behave like lines in the plane. Suppose only perfectly north-south lines are considered as lines. (These are lines of longitude.) What part or parts of the Point-Line-Plane Postulate would these lines violate? *(Lesson 1-7)*

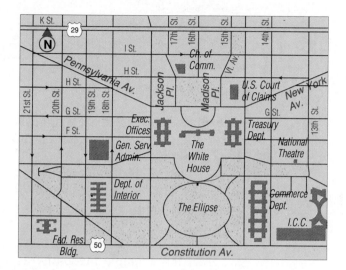

Exploration

26. Two points can be the endpoints of 1 segment. Three points A, B, and C can be endpoints of 3 segments ($\overline{AB}$, $\overline{BC}$, and $\overline{AC}$).
   a. How many segments are determined by 4 points?
   b. How many segments are determined by 8 points?
   c. How many segments are determined by n points?

The Triangle Inequality

The bridge and wires form many triangles.

The Betweenness Theorem states that if B is between A and C, then $AB + BC = AC$. A natural question to ask is what happens when B is not between A and C.

If B does not lie on $\overleftrightarrow{AC}$, then A, B, and C form the vertices of a triangle. It seems from this situation that $AB + BC > AC$. That is, it takes longer to travel from A to B to C than to go from A to C directly. This result is called the *Triangle Inequality*. In this book we treat the Triangle Inequality as a postulate. That is, we do not prove it from other postulates.

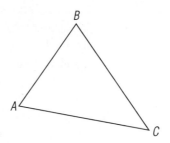

Triangle Inequality Postulate:

The sum of the lengths of two sides of any triangle is greater than the length of the third side.

In $\triangle ABC$ drawn above, this relationship means three inequalities are true:
$$AB + BC > AC \quad \text{and} \quad BC + AC > AB \quad \text{and} \quad AB + AC > BC.$$

Example 1   Can a triangle have sides of length 3″, 5″, and 10″?

Solution   Is the sum of the lengths of the smaller two sides greater than the length of the third side? Is 3″ + 5″ > 10″? No, so there is no triangle with sides of these lengths.

Check If you try to draw such a triangle, you can see that the segments will not meet.

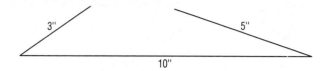

Given two sides of a triangle, the Triangle Inequality Postulate makes it possible to determine the possible lengths of the third side.

Example 2 Suppose two sides of a triangle have lengths 19 cm and 31 cm. What are the possible lengths of the third side?

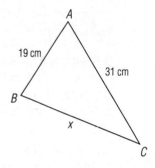

Solution Let x = the length of the third side of the triangle. Substitute into the Triangle Inequality to find the possible values of x.

$$19 + 31 > x \quad \text{and} \quad 19 + x > 31 \quad \text{and} \quad 31 + x > 19.$$

Solve each inequality.

$$50 > x \quad \text{and} \quad x > 12 \quad \text{and} \quad x > \text{-}12.$$

The first two inequalities show that $\overline{BC}$ must be shorter than 50 cm but longer than 12 cm. This can be written as $12 < x < 50$. (The third inequality shows that $\overline{BC}$ must also be longer than -12. But since length is positive, this was already known.)

In this and the last lesson, you have studied two possible locations of B with respect to A and C.

B is between A and C.

$AB + BC = AC$

B is not on $\overleftrightarrow{AC}$.

$AB + BC > AC$

There are two other possibilities for three distinct points A, B, and C.

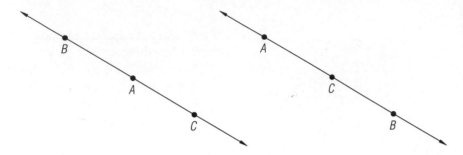

B is on $\overleftrightarrow{AC}$; A is between B and C. B is on $\overleftrightarrow{AC}$; C is between A and B.

It seems obvious from both pictures that $AB + BC > AC$. This can be shown using the algebraic postulates.

Suppose A is between B and C (as on the line drawn above at the left). From the Betweenness Theorem,
$$BC = BA + AC.$$
Adding AB to both sides,
$$AB + BC = AB + BA + AC.$$
Applying the Equation to Inequality Property,
$$AB + BC > AC.$$

In Question 8, you are asked to show that the other possibility also leads to $AB + BC > AC$. (The steps are almost the same.)

When A, B, and C are distinct points, the relationship between AB, BC, and AC can be summarized.

In words	Algebraically
B is between A and C	exactly when $AB + BC = AC$.
B is not between A and C	exactly when $AB + BC > AC$.

Two consequences are important enough to be stated as theorems.

Theorem:

If A, B, and C are distinct points and $AB + BC = AC$, then B is on $\overline{AC}$.

Theorem:

For any three points A, B, and C,
$$AB + BC \geq AC.$$

Example 3   Rosalita lives at *R*, 12 miles from the airport *A* and 3.5 miles from her office *O*. What are the possible distances from her office to the airport?

Solution   Draw a possible picture.
Using the last theorem with points *R*, *O*, and *A*,

$$RO + RA \geq OA \text{ and } RO + OA \geq RA \text{ and } RA + OA \geq RO.$$
$$3.5 + 12 \geq OA \text{ and } 3.5 + OA \geq 12 \text{ and } 12 + OA \geq 3.5.$$
$$15.5 \geq OA \text{ and } \qquad OA \geq 8.5 \text{ and } \qquad OA \geq -8.5.$$

Combining these statements:

$$15.5 \geq OA \geq 8.5.$$

The distance from Rosalita's office to the airport is at least 8.5 miles but no more than 15.5 miles.

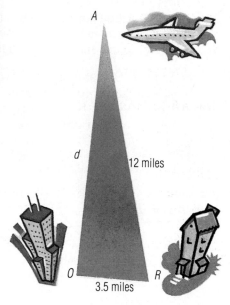

Questions

Covering the Reading

1. State the Triangle Inequality Postulate.

2. Give three inequalities satisfied by the lengths of the sides of △*ABC*.

In 3–5, tell whether the numbers can be lengths of the three sides in a triangle.

3. **a.** 2, 2, 2   **b.** 2, 2, 3   **c.** 2, 2, 4   **d.** 2, 2, 5

4. **a.** 12, 15, 28   **b.** 12, 15, 10   **c.** 12, 15, 2

5. **a.** 1, 2, 3   **b.** 2, 3, 4   **c.** 101, 102, 103

6. Suppose two sides of a triangle have lengths 16 inches and 11 inches. What are the possible lengths of the third side?

7. Suppose A is between B and C. What can you conclude using the Betweenness Theorem?

8. Explain why, if C is between A and B, then $AB + BC > AC$.

9. For any three points A, B, and C, how are the distances related?

10. In Example 3, suppose Rosalita lives 6.5 miles from the airport and 15.5 miles from her office. What then are the possible distances from her office to the airport?

11. *True* or *false*? If $PQ = 17$, $QR = 81$, and $PR = 98$, then Q must be between P and R.

Applying the Mathematics

12. Can the numbers be lengths of the three sides in a triangle?
    a. $\frac{1}{2}, \frac{1}{3}, \frac{1}{4}$ **b.** $\frac{1}{2}, \frac{1}{3}, \frac{1}{5}$ **c.** $\frac{1}{2}, \frac{1}{2}, \frac{1}{4}$

13. Two sides of a triangle have lengths 9 cm and 20 cm.
    a. Must the 9 cm side be the shortest side?
    b. Must the 20 cm side be the longest side?

14. According to a Sheraton hotel directory, there is a Sheraton in the Houston area that is 40 miles from the Houston Intercontinental Airport and 10 miles from Hobby Airport. With this information, you know that the airports are between __?__ and __?__ miles apart.

15. In the triangle below, $x > y$. Then __?__ $< z <$ __?__.
    (Hint: Consider examples and look for a pattern.)

Houston, Texas, skyline

Review

16. **a.** On a number line, graph the set of numbers satisfying $x \leq -5$.
    b. What one-dimensional figure best describes the graph? *(Lesson 1-8)*

17. On the number line below, if $WY = 17$, $WZ = 23$, and $XZ = 21$, find XY. *(Lesson 1-8)*

18. Two points are 13 units apart on a number line. The coordinate of one point is 81. What are the possible coordinates of the other? *(Lesson 1-8)*

19. What postulate of algebra guarantees that $PQ + QR = QR + PQ$? *(Lesson 1-7)*

20. What is a postulate? *(Lesson 1-7)*

21. **a.** Represent the bridges and land pictured below with a network.
b. Is it traversable? *(Lesson 1-4)*

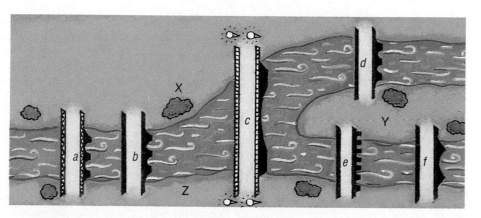

22. Graph $y = 8$ on coordinate axes. *(Lesson 1-3)*

23. If $x = 42$, what is $|14 - x|$? *(Lesson 1-3)*

Exploration

24. The lengths 2″, 2″, 2″, and 2″ can be sides of a quadrilateral, but 2″, 4″, 8″, and 16″ cannot. Is there a "quadrilateral inequality"? That is, is there some general way you can tell when four positive numbers a, b, c, and d can be the lengths of the sides of a quadrilateral?

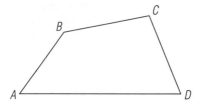

Summary

Geometry is the study of visual patterns. In two-dimensional geometry, the basic building blocks of these patterns are points and lines. Four conceptions or descriptions of points and lines are studied in this chapter. (1) When points are dots, lines are collections of dots in a row. It is possible that between two dots, there might be no other dots. (2) When points are locations, lines are shortest paths between the locations. (3) When points are ordered pairs, lines are sets of ordered pairs (x, y) satisfying $Ax + By = C$. (4) When points are nodes in networks, lines are arcs joining the nodes. Then lines have only two points on them and there may be many lines connecting two points.

In three-dimensional geometry, planes join points and lines as basic building blocks. It is impossible to show a three-dimensional figure on a page exactly as it is. A person can choose to draw the figure in perspective or not. Mathematicians usually do not use perspective.

It is impossible to define all terms in any system because of circularity. The terms left undefined in geometry are *point, line,* and *plane.* So any of the above conceptions of point might be possible. However, the assumptions in the Point-Line-Plane Postulate apply only to points either as locations or as ordered pairs. This postulate indicates which properties points and lines satisfy. It also forms a starting point for deducing other properties.

The properties of points and lines as ordered pairs and locations are the same, so what you learned in algebra about points and lines can be used in geometry. For instance, if point B is between points A and C, then $AB + BC = AC$. However, if B is not between A and C, then by the Triangle Inequality, $AB + BC > AC$. Thus, the shortest distance between two points is along the line containing them.

Vocabulary

Below are the most important terms and phrases for this chapter.
For the starred (*) terms you should be able to give a definition of the term.
For the other terms you should be able to give a general description and a specific example of each.

Lesson 1-1
pixel, matrix, resolution
discrete line, oblique, *collinear

Lesson 1-2
coordinate, coordinatized
number line, *distance, AB
zero-dimensional
dense line, one-dimensional
two-dimensional, plane figure
*coplanar
three-dimensional, space figure

Lesson 1-3
coordinate plane
Cartesian plane
ordered pair, lattice point

Lesson 1-4
Königsberg Bridge Problem
network, arc
traversable network
node, vertex (vertices)
odd node, odd vertex
even node, even vertex

Lesson 1-5
vanishing point, perspective
perspective drawings
line of sight, vanishing line
hidden lines

Lesson 1-6
plane geometry
solid geometry, *space
*figure, circularity
undefined terms

Lesson 1-7
*postulate, $\overleftrightarrow{AB}$, *theorem
*parallel lines
Point-Line-Plane Postulate
Line Intersection Theorem
Reflexive Property of Equality
Symmetric Property of Equality
Transitive Property of Equality
Addition Property of Equality
Multiplication Property of Equality
Substitution Property of Equality

Addition Property of Inequality
Multiplication Property of
  Inequality
Equation to Inequality Property
Transitive Property of Inequality
Commutative Property of Addition
Commutative Property of
  Multiplication
Distributive Property

Lesson 1-8
betweenness of numbers
betweenness of points
*line segment, segment, $\overline{AB}$
length of a line segment
*ray, $\overrightarrow{AB}$, *opposite rays
Betweenness Theorem

Lesson 1-9
Triangle Inequality Postulate

Progress Self-Test

Directions: Take this test as you would take a test in class. Then check your work with the solutions in the Selected Answers section in the back of the book. You will need graph paper and a ruler. Calculators are allowed.

1. Using the number line below, find AB.

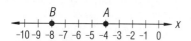

2. Draw a carton:
  a. in perspective; **b.** not in perspective.

3. Graph the line with equation $3x - 2y = 10$.

4. Can 4.8, 9.2, and 3.7 be the lengths of three sides of a triangle?

5. It is 1115 km from Hong Kong to Manila and 1229 km from Hong Kong to Shanghai. From only this information, what can you say about the distance d (in km) from Manila to Shanghai?

In 6 and 7, fill in the table with A if the statement is always true, S if sometimes true, or N if never true.

Statement	Dot	Location	Ordered Pair	Node
Description of Point				
6. A line contains infinitely many points.				
7. A point has size.				

8. How many dimensions does space have?

9. Ignoring its small thickness, how many dimensions does a flat sheet of paper have?

10. If in defining a word, you return to the original word, what has occurred?

11. If two computer screens are the same size,
  a. which screen has better resolution, one whose pixels are 180 by 310 or one that is 215 by 350?
  b. How many pixels are on the screen with the better resolution?

12. A tape measure is stretched across a shelf. If one end reads 4″ and the other 32″, how long is the shelf?

13. The air distance from Chicago to Duluth is 450 miles, but the road distance is 464 miles. Why are the distances different?

14. Graph $y = 4x$ and $x + y = 5$ on the same set of axes.

In 15 and 16, given is an equation of a line. Classify the line as vertical, horizontal, or oblique.

15. $x = \frac{3}{2}$ **16.** $11x + y = 3$

17. **a.** Is the network drawn at the left below traversable?
  b. If so, give a route. If not, explain why not.

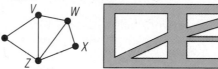

18. **a.** Represent the floor plan above with a network. **b.** Is it traversable?

19. It is 8 minutes by subway from Harvard Square to Park Street. It is 6 minutes by subway from Central Square to Park Street. From only this information, how long would it take by subway to get from Harvard Square to Central Square?

In 20 and 21, a postulate from arithmetic or algebra is applied. Name the postulate.

20. When $3x > 11$, $3x + 6 > 17$.

21. If $AB + BC = 10$ and $AB = 7$, then $7 + BC = 10$.

22. Two points are 19 units apart on a number line. The coordinate of one point is -42. What are the possible coordinates of the other?

23. The graph on a number line of the set of points satisfying $x \geq 40$ is the geometric figure called a(n) __?__ .

24. *Multiple choice.* If E and F are points, which is a number?
  (a) EF (b) $\overline{EF}$ (c) $\overrightarrow{EF}$ (d) $\overleftrightarrow{EF}$

Chapter Review

Questions on **SPUR** Objectives

SPUR stands for **S**kills, **P**roperties, **U**ses, and **R**epresentations.
The Chapter Review questions are grouped according to the
SPUR Objectives for this chapter.

SKILLS deal with the procedures used to get answers.

■ **Objective A:** *Analyze networks. (Lesson 1-4)*

In 1 and 2, refer to the network below.

1. a. How many even nodes are there?
  b. How many odd nodes are there?

2. Is the network traversable?

3. a. Is the network below traversable?
  b. If so, give a path. If not, explain why not.

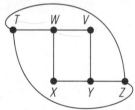

4. a. Represent the floor plan below with a network.
  b. Is it traversable?

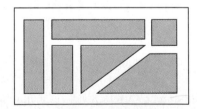

■ **Objective B:** *Make and determine the perspective of drawings. (Lesson 1-5)*

In 5 and 6, draw **a.** in perspective; **b.** not in perspective.

5. a cube   **6.** a table

In 7 and 8, **a.** tell whether the picture is drawn in perspective or not in perspective. **b.** If the figure is drawn in perspective, trace it and show a vanishing point.

7.   shoe box

size: 7
color: bl

8.

PROPERTIES deal with the principles behind the mathematics.

■ **Objective C:** *Give the dimensions of figures and objects. (Lesson 1-2)*

In 9 and 10, tell how many dimensions each object has. Ignore small thicknesses.

9. a mirror   **10.** a tightrope

In 11–14, write the number of dimensions for each figure. Assume the points are ordered pairs.

11. point   **12.** plane
13. line   **14.** space

Objective D: *Given a property of points and lines, tell whether it is true for each of the four descriptions of points: dots, locations, ordered pairs, and nodes. (Lessons 1-1, 1-2, 1-3, 1-4)*

In 15-19, fill in the table with A if the statement is always true, S if sometimes true, N if never true.

Description of Point

	Dot	Location	Ordered Pair	Node

15. A point has no size.

16. A line contains infinitely many points.

17. Between two points on a line there is a third point.

18. Two points determine a line.

19. Two different lines can have two points in common.

Objective E: *Recognize the use of undefined terms and postulates. (Lessons 1-6, 1-7)*

20. In an attempt to define a simple word, you find the original word used in the definition. What is this called?

21. Name three undefined geometric terms.

22. What are the two major reasons for having postulates?

23. Why is the Point-Line-Plane Postulate needed?

In 24-33, a postulate from arithmetic or algebra is applied. Name the postulate.

24. $\frac{2}{7}$ = two sevenths

25. $4(x + y) = 4x + 4y$

26. When $z > 10$, $-5z < -50$.

27. If $|x| = 5$, then $|x| - 3 = 2$.

28. $8.3 + .09 = .09 + 8.3$

29. Since $25\% < 50\%$, $125\% < 150\%$.

30. If x and y are positive and $x + y = 13$, then $x < 13$.

31. If $a + b = 15$ and $15 = c - 12$, then $a + b = c - 12$.

32. If $x^2 + y^2 = 40$ and $y^2 = 7$, then $x^2 + 7 = 40$.

33. Since $1.5 = \frac{3}{2}$, then $1.5y = \frac{3y}{2}$.

Objective F: *Apply properties of betweenness. (Lessons 1-8, 1-9)*

34. If Q is between P and R, then
    $\underline{\quad?\quad} + \underline{\quad?\quad} = \underline{\quad?\quad}$.

35. a. On a number line, graph the set of numbers satisfying $x \geq -3$.
    b. What one-dimensional figure best describes the graph?

36. On the number line below, if $AC = 15$, $BD = 29$, and $AD = 31.8$, find BC.

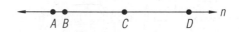

37. In the triangle below, $XW = 46$, $YZ = 39$, and $YW = 6.5$. Find XZ.

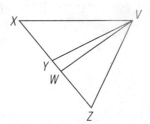

38. Two points are 6 units apart on a number line. The coordinate of one point is -62. What are the possible coordinates of the other?

39. Point Q on a number line has coordinate 11. Find all possibilities for the coordinate of R so that $QR = 17$.

40. If $AB = 19$, $BC = 8$, and $AC = 11$, then __?__ is between __?__ and __?__.

41. If $XY = 10$, $YZ = 6$, and Y is between X and Z, then $XZ = $ __?__.

■ **Objective G:** *Determine whether a triangle can be formed with sides of three given lengths.* *(Lesson 1-9)*

In 42-47, can the numbers be the lengths of three sides of a triangle?

42. 14, 15, 30   **43.** 2, 4, 6

44. 0.8, 0.9, 1.0   **45.** $\frac{1}{3}, \frac{1}{4}, \frac{1}{5}$

46. 2.3, 1.1, 1.1   **47.** 15, 30, 40

48. Two sides of a triangle have lengths 4 cm and 7 cm. How long can the third side be?

49. You are told two sides of a triangle have lengths 1″ and 10″. **a.** Is this possible? **b.** If so, what are possible lengths for the third side? If not, why not?

USES deal with applications of mathematics in real situations.

■ **Objective H:** *Apply distance to real situations.* *(Lesson 1-2)*

50. A student placed a meter stick on a desk. The front of the desk was aligned to the 13 cm mark, and its back to the 56 cm mark. How wide is the desk?

51. A thermometer reading was ⁻6° at Billings and 2° at Fargo. How far apart are these temperatures?

52. Jason took a plane from St. Louis to Kansas City and flew 234 miles. Zach took a train from St. Louis to Kansas City and rode 253 miles. Jessica drove 245 miles from St. Louis to Kansas City. Why are all of these distances different?

53. Use the road mileage chart for Florida below. If you drive from Jacksonville to Miami through Tampa, how much longer is it than going directly from Jacksonville to Miami?

	J	M	T
Jacksonville (J)		356	198
Miami (M)	356		254
Tampa (T)	198	254	

■ **Objective I:** *Apply the Triangle Inequality in real situations.* *(Lesson 1-9)*

54. It is 151 miles from Chicago to Peoria and 289 miles from Chicago to St. Louis. From only this information, what can you say about the distance from Peoria to St. Louis?

55. It is a fifteen-minute walk from Rudy's place to Vanessa's place. It is a 25-minute walk from Vanessa's place to Theo's place. At this rate, by walking, how long would it take to get from Rudy's place to Theo's place?

56. Vinh lives 3 blocks from the fire station and 12 blocks from school. How far apart are the fire station and the school?

57. The Earth is 4.3 light years from the star system Alpha Centauri, and 6.1 light years from Barnard's Star, the two closest star systems to us. From this information only, how far are these systems from each other?

■ **Objective J:** *Determine distance on a number line. (Lesson 1-2)*

In 58 and 59, using the number lines below, find *AB*.

58.

59.

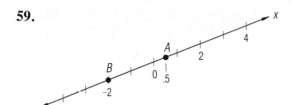

In 60 and 61, calculate $|11 - c|$ if

60. $c = 15$;   **61.** $c = -31$.

In 62-65, give the distance between two points with the given coordinates.

62. 2 and 9   **63.** -31 and 47

64. -14 and -90   **65.** *x* and *y*

■ **Objective K:** *Graph points and lines in the coordinate plane. (Lesson 1-3)*

In 66 and 67, graph the set of points satisfying the equation.

66. $4x - y = 8$ **67.** $y = -2x + 1$

68. Graph $y = -2x$ and $4x - 3y = 10$ on the same set of axes.

In 69-72, classify the line as vertical, horizontal, or oblique.

69. $5x + 3y = -19$ **70.** $x = 11$

71. $y = 3x$ **72.** $y = 3$

73. Give an equation for the horizontal line containing (5, 1).

74. Give an equation for the vertical line containing (-2, 10).

Definitions and If-then Statements

What is a cookie? According to this column from *USA Weekend*, May 23-25, 1986, the answer is not so simple.

Careful definitions are one of the features of mathematical reasoning. In this chapter, important aspects of that reasoning are applied to simple geometric figures, to some of the other mathematics you know, and to everyday critical thinking.

You could look it up, but that might not help

If it looks like a cookie and tastes like a cookie, it is a cookie, right? Not so fast...

Some of the simplest, everyday things turn out to be not so simple when you try to define them. Everybody knows what "time" is, for example. But if your life depended on coming up with a clear definition of time, you would be in a lot of trouble.

In the news, there are plenty of references to "terrorists," But anybody who tries to spell out what is meant by the word "terrorist" runs into difficulty. We all know what a "terrorist" is, but the United Nations has been unable to come up with a working definition. The State Department and the Pentagon have different definitions, and at least one Congressional Committee finally decided that there is no way of defining the word "terrorist" without making value judgments that not everybody is going to agree with.

One man's "terrorist" is another's "freedom fighter." It's impossible to pass laws against terrorism if you can't spell out with some precision what it is you are talking about.

Definitions are important in the law, of course. In Wilmington, Del., right now, there is a big legal battle being fought in the U.S. District Court. Several giant cookie companies are fighting over the recipe for so-called "dual textured" cookies. That means cookies that are crispy on the outside and soft and chewy on the inside. Procter & Gamble claims it discovered the process, pat-

ented it in 1983, and that Nabisco has infringed on the patent.

Nabisco, Keebler and Frito-Lay claim they were making cookies that were crispy on the outside and chewy on the inside before P&G got its patent. So the Nabisco, Keebler and Frito-Lay lawyers asked P&G to define their terms. Among the terms they wanted defined were "cookie" and "dough."

Now I know what the word cookie means and so do you. My 2-year-old Jamie knows what a cookie is and can ask for it by name.

But the definition turns out to be so important in this case that here are these high-priced lawyers, these learned counselors asking the judge, Joseph Longobardi, to please tell them what a "cookie" is, and what "dough" is.

Judge Longobardi is not a man who shies away from an intellectual exercise, but he declined to oblige the opposing lawyers in their request.

"It should not be the court's burden to supply definitions of the terms," he told them in a memo.

If a wise jurist like Judge Longobardi doesn't want to have to render definitions for such relatively simple concepts as "cookie" and "dough," no wonder the U.N. is bogged down with "terrorist."

If we truly don't know the meaning of "dough," if "cookie" truly is something mysterious, it is surely no wonder that we so often blunder when we're dealing with much more serious matters. ❑

CHARLES OSGOOD

In 1986, Charles Osgood was the anchor of *CBS Sunday Night News*. He is editor and anchor of *Newsbreak* and *The Osgood File* on CBS Radio.

2-1

The Need for Definitions

There are many ways to use the word triangle. How would you define a triangle?

You are probably wondering why the column page 59 discussing cookies was put in a book on geometry. The reason is that the column discusses definitions. Careful definitions are found throughout mathematics. When ideas are not carefully defined, people may not agree with what is written about them. Would Nabisco and Procter & Gamble agree on what is meant by a "dual textured cookie"? Do you think everyone in your class would agree on what is (and what is not) a "triangle"? Do you think everyone in the world would agree on what a "circle" is?

Many of the terms that you have seen before this year, including those for the two-dimensional figures shown below, are carefully defined in mathematics and in this book. The drawing above each term pictures one figure of the type the definition should include.

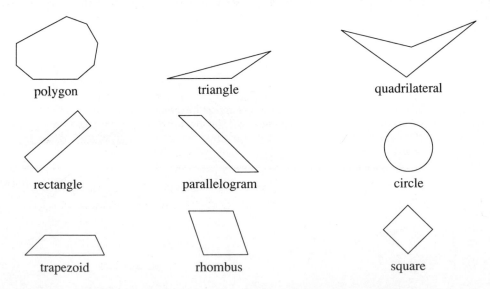

polygon   triangle   quadrilateral

rectangle   parallelogram   circle

trapezoid   rhombus   square

You may be skeptical. You may think, "Why is a definition needed for a rectangle? Everyone knows what a rectangle is." Experience has shown that this is not the case. You may not even agree with us! Try this.

Which of the following do you think should be called rectangles? Make choices in your mind before reading on.

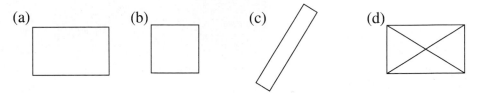

(a)   (b)   (c)   (d)

Almost everyone believes (a) is a rectangle. So do we. Many people think (b) is not a rectangle, because it is a square. Many people think (c) is not a rectangle because it is tilted, or because it is long and thin. Many people think (d) is not a rectangle because there are extra segments drawn. Our view, which agrees with the view of most mathematicians, is that (a), (b), and (c) are rectangles, but (d) is not. That is, all squares are rectangles. A rectangle may be very thin. A rectangle tilted is still a rectangle. But adding segments changes it: (d) is more than a rectangle.

In this lesson, we give only one definition. It distinguishes between sets of points that have "dents" and those that do not. Sets of points that do not have "dents" in them are called *convex sets*.

> **Definition:**
>
> A **convex set** is a set in which all segments connecting points of the set lie entirely in the set.

A set that is not convex is called, quite appropriately, a **nonconvex** set.

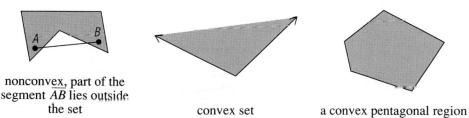

nonconvex, part of the
segment AB lies outside
the set   convex set   a convex pentagonal region

The word "convex" is also used in describing lenses. Lenses which are not convex use the word *concave*.

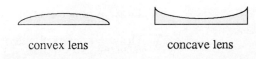

convex lens   concave lens

Questions

In 1–3, refer to the article on the opening page of the chapter.

Covering the Reading

1. What word did a Congressional committee have trouble defining?

2. What does "dual textured" mean?

3. What is the problem that led to a lawsuit involving the cookie companies?

4. Why is it important to carefully define ideas?

5. How many triangles are pictured in this lesson?

6. Draw a figure that you think is almost, but not quite, a rectangle.

In 7–9, is the set convex?

7.   8.   9.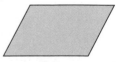

Applying the Mathematics

10. Draw a nonconvex 4-sided region.

11. Draw a convex 8-sided region.

12. The word *midpoint* will be carefully defined in Lesson 2-5. But before reading that lesson, in which of the following pictures do you think point S is the midpoint of $\overline{RT}$?

(a) • R   • S   • T

(b) • R   • S   • T

(c) • R   • S   • T

(d) • R   • S • T

13. The word "quadrilateral" has two parts: "quadri" and "lateral." They come from the Latin *quattuor,* meaning "four," and *latus,* meaning "side." So a quadrilateral is meant to be a four-sided figure.

  a. Which of figures I, II, III, IV, and V do you think are quadrilaterals?

  b. If you think the figure is not a quadrilateral, tell why you think so.

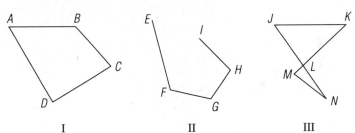

I   II   III

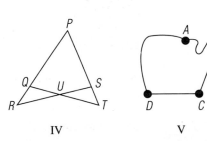

IV   V

14. Which of the following do you think is a picture of a circle?

(a)   (b)

(c)   (d)

15. The points (1, 4), (1, 5), (3, 5), (3, 4), and (1, 4) are connected in that order. Do you think the result should be called a rectangle?

16. An orange is cut with one slice of a sharp knife into two pieces. Do you think each piece should be called "half an orange"?

17. A cube is drawn below. The points A, B, C, and D are connected in order. They form a four-sided figure $ABCD$ in which each angle is a right angle. Should $ABCD$ be called a rectangle?

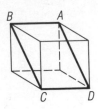

Review

18. Draw a single figure satisfying all of the following conditions.
    (1) P is between T and V.
    (2) $PM = 2 \cdot PV$
    (3) Q is not on $\overleftrightarrow{TV}$.
    (4) $QP = PT$ *(Lesson 1-8)*

19. The line $3x + 4y = 6$ contains the point $(10, a)$. What is a?
(Lesson 1-3)

20. Give the number of sides of each of these polygons. *(Previous course)*
    a. pentagon   **b.** octagon
    c. decagon   **d.** triangle
    e. heptagon   **f.** quadrilateral

In 21 and 22, solve. *(Previous course)*

21. $x - 23 = 180 - x$

22. $y = 6(90 - y)$

23. Solve for m: $225z = 15m$. *(Previous course)*

Exploration

24. Consider the article that opens this chapter.
    a. How would you define "cookie"?
    b. How would you define "terrorist"?

LESSON

2-2

If-then Statements

As seen from the Osgood article and in the previous lesson, precise language is often important. The meaning of words is crucial in understanding mathematics. Not only must words such as "rectangle" or "circle" be defined, but you must know meanings for conjunctions such as "and" and "or" and symbols such as "+," "<," or $\overleftrightarrow{AB}$.

The small word "if" is among the most important words in the language of logic and reasoning. It is used in everyday language, but not always carefully. In mathematics it is used *very carefully*. Recall that a hexagon is a six-sided polygon, and consider the following **if-then statement:**

If a figure is a hexagon, then it is a polygon.

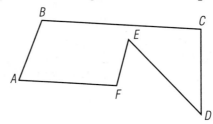

In an if-then statement, the clause following the "if" is called the **antecedent.** The clause following the "then" is the **consequent.** (**Hypothesis** and **conclusion** are alternate names for antecedent and consequent.) The entire if-then statement is called a **conditional.** In the above conditional, the antecedent is *a figure is a hexagon*. The consequent is *it is a polygon*. Notice that both the antecedent and consequent are complete sentences.

The drawing above shows a hexagon, an *instance* of the antecedent. An **instance** of a sentence is a situation for which the sentence is true. For this instance of the antecedent, the consequent of the conditional is true also. The figure is also a polygon.

Now consider the following conditional:

If Y is between X and Z, then $XY < YZ$.

The antecedent is *Y is between X and Z*. To get some idea what this conditional means, you should draw instances of the antecedent. Two are drawn below. In the left instance, the consequent is true: *XY* is less than *YZ*. In the instance at the right, however, the consequent is not true: *XY* is not less than *YZ*. The drawing is not an instance of the consequent. The right drawing shows that the conditional is false. It is a *counterexample* to the conditional.

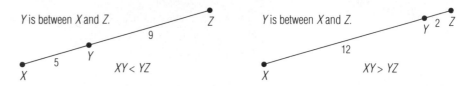

Definition:

A **counterexample** to a conditional is a situation for which the antecedent (*if* part) is true and the consequent (*then* part) is false.

Proving a conditional false is often easy: you need to find just one counterexample.

Example 1 Show that the conditional "If $x^2 = 9$, then $x = 3$" is false.

> **Solution** You need to look for a counterexample. Look for a situation in which $x^2 = 9$ is true but $x \neq 3$. Such a situation is $x = -3$. When x has the value -3, the antecedent $x^2 = 9$ is true but the consequent $x = 3$ is false. You can say that $x = -3$ is a counterexample to the conditional.

Here is the famous conditional known as *Goldbach's Conjecture*. (Christian Goldbach was a German mathematician who lived from 1690 to 1764.)

If n is an even number greater than 2,
then there are always two primes whose sum is n.

You can rather easily find situations for which both the antecedent and consequent are true. Let $n = 4$; 4 is the sum of the primes 2 and 2. Let $n = 6$; 6 is the sum of the primes 3 and 3. Let $n = 8$; 8 is the sum of the primes 3 and 5. Let $n = 100$; 100 is the sum of the primes 41 and 59. This conjecture has been checked for all even numbers from 2 to well over 100,000,000. No counterexample has ever been found.

Unfortunately, a conditional cannot be called true by finding 100 or even a million situations in which the antecedent and consequent are both true. It must be proved true. Goldbach's Conjecture has not yet been proved true.

Conditionals can be written without the words "if" and "then." The following are equivalent to "If a figure is a hexagon, then it is a polygon."

All hexagons are polygons.
Every hexagon is a polygon.
A figure is a polygon if it is a hexagon.

This last statement just has the antecedent, signaled by the word "if," after the consequent.

When statements follow the pattern "All A are B," or "When A occurs, B occurs," they can be rewritten in if-then form as "If something is an A, then something is a B."

Example 2 Rewrite the statement "All triangles have three sides" in if-then form.

   Solution Think of the "something" as a figure: "If a figure is a triangle, then it has three sides."

Single letters can stand for sentences. For instance, with the conditional

If a figure is a hexagon, then it is a polygon,

let h = "a figure is a hexagon" and let p = "a figure is a polygon." Then the conditional may be rewritten:

If h, then p.

A still shorter way of writing this is to use the symbol $\Rightarrow$, which is read "implies."

$$h \Rightarrow p$$
$$h \text{ implies } p$$

With this notation, we can rewrite the definition of counterexample given above. A counterexample to a general conditional $p \Rightarrow q$ is a situation for which p is true and q is false.

In 1 and 2, copy the statement. Underline the antecedent once and the consequent twice.

1. If a parallelogram has a right angle, then it is a rectangle.

2. Fruit kabob is divine if it is made with watermelon.

3. Let s = "A figure is a square."
   p = "A figure is a polygon."
$s \Rightarrow p$ refers to what sentence?

4. An instance of a sentence is a situation for which the sentence is __?__ .

5. Define: counterexample to a conditional.

6. A counterexample to $a \Rightarrow c$ is a situation for which a is __?__ and c is __?__ .

7. State Goldbach's Conjecture.

8. Consider the statement "If $AB = 10$ and $BC = 4$, then $AC = 14$."
   a. Draw an instance of the antecedent for which the consequent is true.
   b. Draw a counterexample to this statement.

9. How many counterexamples are needed to show that a conditional is false?

10. Show that this conditional is false: If $x^2 = 16$, then $x = -4$.

In 11 and 12, rewrite in if-then form.

11. Every square is a quadrilateral.

12. All Irish setters are dogs.

13. Show that the consequent in Goldbach's Conjecture is true when $n = 40$.

14. *Multiple choice.* Pick the counterexample to the if-then statement "If a figure is a hexagonal region, then it is convex."

(a)   (b)   (c)   (d)

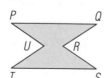   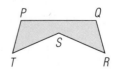

15. Suppose $p \Rightarrow q$ is true. Is it possible to have a counterexample to $p \Rightarrow q$?

In 16 and 17, **a.** find a situation for which both the antecedent and consequent are true. **b.** Find a counterexample to the statement.

16. If you are in Toledo, then you are in the United States.

17. If a line contains (2, 3), then it is oblique.

Review

18. Which figures below do you think should *not* be called "triangles"? For each figure you think is not a triangle, explain why you think it isn't. *(Lesson 2 1)*

a.   **b.**   **c.**    **d.**

19. Characterize each region as convex or nonconvex. *(Lesson 2-1)*

a. 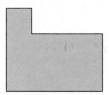   **b.**    **c.**

20. **a.** Draw a convex pentagonal region.
    b. Draw a nonconvex pentagonal region. *(Lesson 2-1)*

21. Two sides of a triangle have length $4x$ and $13x$. What are the possible lengths for the third side? *(Lesson 1-9)*

In 22 and 23, solve. *(Previous course)*

22. $15x - 22 + 17x + 1 = 180$ **23.** $90 > 32 + z > 0$

Exploration

24. Consider the antecedent "A network has five nodes."
    a. Make a true conditional with this antecedent.
    b. Make a false conditional with this antecedent.

25. Repeat Question 24 for the antecedent "A person is 14 years old."

26. The words "antecedent" and "consequent" are derived in part from the Latin words *ante* and *sequens*. What do these Latin words mean and how is this related to their mathematical meanings?

LESSON

2-3

If-then Statements in Computer Programs

Recall that a diagonal of a polygon is a segment connecting two nonconsecutive vertices of the polygon.

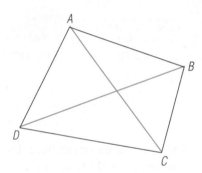

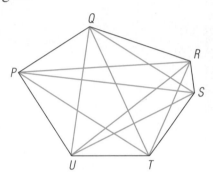

$\overline{AC}$ and $\overline{BD}$ are the two diagonals of quadrilateral *ABCD*.

hexagon *QRSTUP* and its nine diagonals

When polygons have many sides, it is tedious to count to find the number of diagonals. Fortunately, there is a simple formula. If *n* is the number of sides of the polygon and *d* the number of diagonals, then

$$d = \frac{n(n-3)}{2}.$$

A program can instruct a computer to calculate a value of *d* given a value of *n*. Consider the following BASIC (Beginners All-purpose Symbolic Instructional Code) computer program.

```
10  PRINT "COMPUTE NUMBER OF DIAGONALS IN POLYGON"
20  PRINT "ENTER THE NUMBER OF SIDES"
30  INPUT N
40  IF N >= 3 THEN PRINT "THE NUMBER OF DIAGONALS IS ";
    N *(N − 3)/2
50  END
```

The 10, 20, 30, 40, and 50 are **line numbers.** The computer performs the instructions in the order of the line numbers. Any natural number can be a line number.

The PRINT in lines 10 and 20 instructs the computer to display exactly what is inside the quotation marks. In line 30, INPUT N tells the computer to take the value typed in by a user as the value of N.

Line 40 is an if-then statement. (The $>=$ in line 40 is the computer symbol for $\geq$.) The computer performs the consequent *only* if the antecedent is true. In line 40, if the value input by the user is greater than or equal to 3, then the antecedent is true. Then the computer will first print THE NUMBER OF DIAGONALS IS, and next calculate $N(N - 3)/2$ and print the result of that calculation.

To run this program on a computer, type in the program exactly as indicated. Then type RUN. When the program gets to line 30, you will see a ? on the screen. That is the computer asking for the value for N. Respond by typing the value you want.

■ ■ ■ ■ ■ ■ ■ ■ ■

Example Write what will be printed or shown on the screen when the program on the preceding page is run and

a. N is given the value 7;

b. N is given the value 2.

Solution

a. First the computer prints the messages in lines 10 and 20, and asks for a value of N. When the user enters 7, the computer substitutes 7 for N. In line 40, the antecedent is true ($7 \geq 3$), so the computer prints THE NUMBER OF DIAGONALS IS, then calculates $7 \cdot (7 - 3)/2$ and prints 14. So you will see

```
COMPUTE NUMBER OF DIAGONALS IN POLYGON
ENTER THE NUMBER OF SIDES
? 7
THE NUMBER OF DIAGONALS IS 14
```

b. The computer substitutes 2 for N. At line 40, because the antecedent is false when N = 2, it skips the consequent. It then goes on to line 50. The final result is

```
COMPUTE NUMBER OF DIAGONALS IN POLYGON
ENTER THE NUMBER OF SIDES
? 2
```

Many people, especially programmers, would fix the program on the preceding page to account for situations such as part **b** of the Example. If a number less than three is input at line 30, there should be a message to indicate that a polygon must have at least three sides.

A more subtle problem is that the program will also accept a mixed number such as 3.62 as an input value of N and calculate the number of diagonals (1.1222). Fixing these problems is part of what is called "debugging."

In computer programming, a false antecedent causes the machine to ignore the *then* part of the conditional. Outside of computer programming, conditionals with false antecedents are treated differently. Consider the following true conditional:

If a quadrilateral is a square, then its diagonals have the same length.

What if the antecedent is false and a given quadrilateral is *not* a square? The above statement can tell us nothing. In fact, as the following pictures show, some non-square quadrilaterals have diagonals that are the same length, some do not.

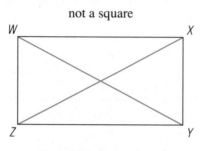
not a square

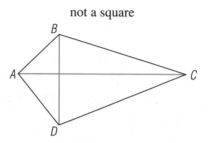
not a square

diagonals of same length   diagonals not of same length

When the antecedent of an if-then statement is false, nothing can be determined about the truth of the consequent.

If you reason from a false statement, you may be able to deduce strange things. Assume, for the moment, that $1 = 2$. Then using properties of algebra, you can deduce that any two numbers are equal! Here we show: If $1 = 2$, then $131 = 177$.

$$
\begin{array}{rcll}
1 &=& 2 & \\
46 \cdot 1 &=& 46 \cdot 2 & \text{Multiplication Property of Equality} \\
46 &=& 92 & \text{arithmetic} \\
46 + 85 &=& 92 + 85 & \text{Addition Property of Equality} \\
131 &=& 177 & \text{arithmetic}
\end{array}
$$

Does $131 = 177$? Of course not. But the conditional "If $1 = 2$, then $131 = 177$" is true. It has been proved true.

In a like manner the conditional "If $1 = 2$, then $3 = 3$" can be proved.

$$
\begin{array}{rcll}
1 &=& 2 & \\
2 &=& 1 & \text{Symmetric Property of Equality} \\
1 + 2 &=& 2 + 1 & \text{Addition Property of Equality} \\
3 &=& 3 & \text{arithmetic}
\end{array}
$$

This illustrates that when p is a false antecedent, both true and false consequents q can be deduced. So mathematicians agree that if p is false, the conditional $p \Rightarrow q$ is true regardless of what q is.

Questions

Covering the Reading

1. How does a BASIC computer program act when the antecedent of a conditional is true?

2. How does a BASIC computer program act when the antecedent of a conditional is false?

3. What is the purpose of the number assigned to each line of a BASIC computer program?

In 4–6, refer to the program in the lesson. Tell what will be printed when the program is run and the indicated value of N is substituted.

4. N = 1   5. N = 100   6. N = 3

7. If a polygon has more than 4 sides, it must have more than two diagonals. What does this statement tell you about polygons that have 4 or fewer sides?

8. **a.** In mathematics, is this statement true or false? If 1 = 2, then 30 = 40.
   b. Show steps to reason that if 1 = 2, then 30 = 40.

9. *True* or *false*?   If Paris is in Germany, then London is in France.

Applying the Mathematics

10. **a.** Diane read an ad: If you use Wonderlashes, your eyes will be more beautiful. Diane used a cheaper brand of artificial eyelashes, and her eyes became more beautiful. Did the ad lie to Diane?
   b. Flora read the same ad as Diane. Flora already had beautiful eyes, and she used Wonderlashes, but her eyes didn't get any more beautiful. Did the ad lie to Flora?

11. **a.** Mr. Woodward heard an ad: "If you want a cleaner house, then you'll use Magikleen." Mr. Woodward wanted a cleaner house, but did not use Magikleen. Is the ad true?
   b. How is the answer to part **a** changed if the word "you'll" is changed to "you might"?

12. Consider this computer program.

```
10  PRINT "INVENTORY OF ELECTRO-ROBOTS"
15  PRINT "ENTER THE NUMBER OF ELECTRO-ROBOTS"
20  INPUT N
25  PRINT "PROFIT EQUALS "; 5 * N − 1500
30  IF N < 300 THEN PRINT "ORDER MORE ELECTRO-
    ROBOTS."
35  END
```

   a. What is printed if N = 400?
   b. What is printed if N = 20? ⟨

13. This program calculates values from a formula you have studied in previous years.

```
10  INPUT R
20  LET A = 3.14159 * R * R
30  IF R > 0 THEN PRINT R, A
40  END
```

   a. Identify the formula.
   b. For what values of R will nothing be printed?

In 14–16, rewrite in if-then form. *(Lesson 2-2)*

Review

14. A polygon has 9 diagonals if it is a hexagon.

15. The volume of a cube with side s is s^3.

16. Every vertical line has an equation of the form $x = h$.

17. Consider the conditional: If $|x| = 10$, then $x = 10$.
   a. If this conditional is $p \Rightarrow q$, what is p?
   b. Find a counterexample to this conditional. *(Lesson 2-2)*

18. Consider this statement:
   If D is on $\overline{XY}$, $XD = 11.2$, and $XY = 26.7$, then $DY = \underline{\ ?\ }$.
   a. Fill in the blank.
   b. Make a drawing of this situation. *(Lessons 2-2, 1-8)*

19. Show that the conditional "If a network is traversable, then it has exactly two odd nodes" is false. *(Lesson 2-2)*

20. In the figure below, C is between B and D. If $BC = 4 \cdot CD$ and $BD = 12$, what is the value of BC? *(Lesson 1-9)*

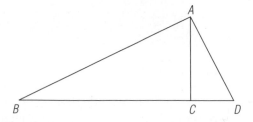

21. Two sides of a triangle are 16 and 41. If x is the length of the third side, graph all possibilities for x on a number line. *(Lesson 1-9)*

In 22 and 23, solve. *(Previous course)*

22. $50z + 3 = 67z + 1$ **23.** $180 > q + 19 > 90$

24. Let N take the values 3, 4, 5, 6, 7, 8, 9, and 10.
   a. Find $d = \dfrac{N(N - 3)}{2}$ for each N.
   b. Plot the ordered pairs *(N, d)* in a graph.
   c. The points all lie on what curve? *(Previous course)*

Exploration

25. The program given here instructs the computer to print the number of diagonals of polygons with any number of sides from 3 to 20.

```
10  PRINT "NUMBER OF DIAGONALS IN POLYGONS"
20  FOR N = 3 TO 20
30  PRINT "THE NUMBER OF SIDES IS "; N
40  PRINT "THE NUMBER OF DIAGONALS IS "; N * (N - 3)/2
50  NEXT N
60  END
```

Modify this program to give the number of diagonals of polygons with any number of sides from 3 to 50. Run your program.

26. a. Debug the program on page 70 by adding lines that will print an appropriate message if the input is less than 3.
   b. Test your program.

Converses

Here is a true if-then statement.

If you are in Los Angeles, then you are in California.

LA ⇒ C

Switching the antecedent and consequent results in a false statement.

If you are in California, then you are in Los Angeles.

C ⇒ LA

The statements $p \Rightarrow q$ and $q \Rightarrow p$ are called *converses* of each other.

Definition:

The **converse** of $p \Rightarrow q$ is $q \Rightarrow p$.

Example 1 Consider the conditional:
If a line is horizontal, then it has an equation of the form $y = k$.

a. Write the converse.
b. Is the original statement true? Is the converse true?

Solution

a. The antecedent is "a line is horizontal." The consequent is "it has an equation of the form $y = k$." Switch these to form the converse. The converse is: "If a line has an equation of the form $y = k$, then it is horizontal."

b. Both the original statement and its converse are true.

Knowing that $p \Rightarrow q$ is true *does not* tell you whether $q \Rightarrow p$ is true or false. So unless you have other evidence, you cannot tell whether the converse of a true statement is true. Here are examples.

"If you are in Los Angeles, then you are in California."

$p \Rightarrow q$ truc
$q \Rightarrow p$ false

"If a line is horizontal, then it has an equation of the form $y = k$."

$p \Rightarrow q$ true
$q \Rightarrow p$ true

Example 2 Mrs. Wilson's will stated: "Every one of my children shall receive ten percent of my estate." When Mrs. Wilson died, Sheri received ten percent of Mrs. Wilson's estate. Is Sheri a child of Mrs. Wilson?

Solution When put in if-then form, the will states "If someone is Mrs. Wilson's child, then he or she shall receive ten percent of the estate." The *converse* is "If someone receives ten percent of the estate, then that person is Mrs. Wilson's child." This converse describes Sheri's situation. Since you cannot tell if the converse of a true statement is true or false, it is impossible to tell whether Sheri is Mrs. Wilson's child.

Sometimes $p \Rightarrow q$ is false. When this happens, $q \Rightarrow p$ may be true or it may be false. Here are examples.

"If $x^2 = 9$,   "If a man has blue eyes,   "If a figure is a circle,
then $x = 3$."   then he weighs over 150 lb."   then it is a rectangle."
$p \Rightarrow q$ false $p \Rightarrow q$ false $p \Rightarrow q$ false
$q \Rightarrow p$ true $q \Rightarrow p$ false $q \Rightarrow p$ false

Thus, unless you have other evidence, accepting the converse of a false statement as false is also using incorrect reasoning. The truth or falsity of $p \Rightarrow q$ does not tell you whether $q \Rightarrow p$ is true or false. You must examine converses as independent statements.

Example 3 Suppose p = a rectangular floor has perimeter 18 feet
               q = a rectangular floor has area 20 square feet.
Show that both $p \Rightarrow q$ and its converse are false.

Solution $p \Rightarrow q$ is the statement: If a rectangular floor has perimeter 18 feet, then its area is 20 square feet. A counterexample will show it is false. Here is a figure whose perimeter is 18 ft and whose area is not 20 sq ft.

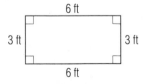

The converse is the statement $q \Rightarrow p$: If a rectangular floor has area 20 sq ft, then its perimeter is 18 ft. Here is a counterexample. It has the right area, but the wrong perimeter.

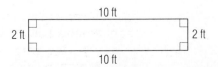

Converses are present whenever equations are solved in algebra. You reason $p \Rightarrow q$ when you solve an equation. You reason the converse $q \Rightarrow p$ when you check the solution. Both $p \Rightarrow q$ <u>and</u> $q \Rightarrow p$ must be true for an equation to be solved correctly. This is why a check is necessary.

■ ■ ■ ■ ■ ■ ■ ■

Example 4   Let p: $6x - 10 = 20$.
Let q: $x = 5$.

    a. Is $p \Rightarrow q$ true?
    b. Is $q \Rightarrow p$ true?

Solution

a. To show $p \Rightarrow q$ is true, solve the equation $6x - 10 = 20$. Justifications for the major steps are given.

$6x = 30$	Addition Property of Equality
$x = 5$	Multiplication Property of Equality

b. To show $q \Rightarrow p$ is true, you need to show if $x = 5$, then $6x - 10 = 20$. This is the check.

$$6 \cdot 5 - 10 = 30 - 10 = 20$$

Distinguishing between a statement and its converse can be tricky. You should be very careful when doing the Questions.

Questions

Covering the Reading

1. Define: converse.

In 2 and 3, the statement is true.
a. Write the converse.   **b.** Tell whether the converse is true.

2. If a line is vertical, then it has an equation of the form $x = h$.

3. If you are a teenager, then you are at least 13 years old.

4. *Multiple choice.*   Suppose a statement is true. Then its converse:
    (a) must be true;
    (b) must be false;
    (c) may be either true or false.

5. Suppose p = a rectangular floor has perimeter 26 feet
               q = a rectangular floor has area 42 square feet.
    a. Show that $p \Rightarrow q$ is false.
    b. Show that the converse of $p \Rightarrow q$ is false.

6. Ms. Hibrough saw an advertisment which read, "Everyone who attends the dance will receive Eau D'or perfume." Ms. Hibrough received some Eau D'or perfume. Did she attend the dance?

In 7–11, **a.** write $p \Rightarrow q$ and $q \Rightarrow p$. **b.** Tell whether these conditionals are true or false.

7. p: $2x + 31 = 4 - x$
   q: $x = -9$

8. p: the perimeter of a particular square is 40 cm.
   q: the area of the same square is 100 cm^2.

9. A, B, and C are collinear points.
   p: $AB + BC = AC$.
   q: B is between A and C.

10. p: $s^2 = 40,000$
    q: $s = 200$

11. p: B is between A and C.
    q: A is between C and B.

12. Refer to Example 3. Find an instance of p for which the consequent q is true.

13. Mr. Chu had lived under communist rule in mainland China but recently immigrated to the province of Ontario in Canada. He knew that communist countries always have socialized medicine. He found out that Ontario has socialized medicine. He concluded that Ontario's provincial government is communist. Is his reasoning correct?

14. a. How many diagonals does an *n*-sided polygon have?

  b. How many diagonals does an octagon have? *(Lesson 2-3)*

15. Refer to the following computer program.

```
10   PRINT "COMPUTE SUM OF ANGLE MEASURES IN
     POLYGON"
20   PRINT "ENTER THE NUMBER OF SIDES"
21   INPUT N
30   IF N >=3 THEN PRINT "THE SUM OF THE ANGLE
     MEASURES (IN DEGREES) IS "; (N − 2) * 180
40   END
```

  a. What will be printed when N = 6?

  b. What will be printed when N = 1? *(Lesson 2-3)*

In 16 and 17, write in if-then form. *(Lesson 2-2)*

16. A figure is a quadrilateral whenever it is a square.

17. Any person born in New York City is a U.S. citizen.

In 18 and 19, graph on a number line and describe the graph. *(Lesson 1-9)*

18. all numbers x satisfying $x \geq 7$

19. all numbers y satisfying $3 \leq y \leq 3.01$

20. Give one reason for undefined terms. *(Lesson 1-6)*

In 21 and 22, Alpha, Beta, and Gamma are three toll booths on a highway. A headquarters building is planned with one of its functions being to collect money from the booths. To save on gas, the sum of the distances from that building to the booths should be as small as possible. Pictured at the left are three mileage markers. (They are like coordinates on a number line; for example, Alpha is 10.3 miles from the end of the highway.) *(Lesson 1-2, Previous course)*

21. Is it more cost efficient to put the headquarters at Alpha, or at Beta, or at Gamma?

22. a. What is the mean of the mileage markers?

  b. What is the median of the mileage markers?

  c. Is it more cost efficient to put the headquarters at the mean or the median?

23. Make up a nonmathematical conditional that is false, but whose converse is true.

38.6 miles

31.5 miles

10.3 miles

2-5

Good Definitions

Good definitions in geometry, just as good definition in a photograph, help to clarify what is being discussed. Without good definition(s), the subject can be a blur.

Osgood's column discussing cookies on the first page of the chapter illustrates the need for precise definitions outside mathematics. By now, you should be convinced that careful definitions are needed inside mathematics in order for everyone to agree on what they are talking about.

In Chapter 1, we gave good definitions for several words, including "distance," "between," and "segment." In this lesson, we give other careful (or good) definitions. These good definitions have the following properties.

A good definition must:
 I. include only words either commonly understood, defined earlier, or purposely undefined;
 II. accurately describe the idea being defined;
 III. include no more information than is necessary.

Consider the term "midpoint." We want "midpoint" to refer to a special point on a segment, the "halfway point." Such points are important. In a commercial flight over water, if there is trouble before the halfway point, the plane goes back to its point of origin. If there is trouble after that point, the plane goes on to its destination. Here is a good definition.

> **Definition:**
>
> The **midpoint** of a segment AB is the point M on $\overline{AB}$ with $AM = MB$.

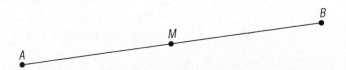

The definition of midpoint uses only words commonly understood (The, of, a, is, . . .), defined earlier (segment, $\overline{AB}$, AM, ...), or purposely undefined (point). We can trace the phrase "midpoint of a segment" back to these earlier or undefined terms.

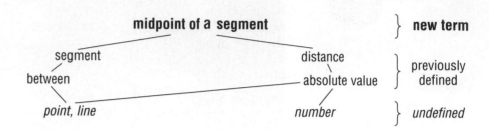

The definition of midpoint distinguishes the midpoint of a segment from other points that are not midpoints. From the definition, the midpoint must be on the segment. Below, $AM = MB$ but M is not on $\overline{AB}$. So M is not the midpoint of $\overline{AB}$. However, since $AM = MB$, we say that M is **equidistant** from A and B.

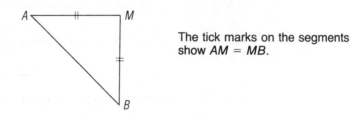

The tick marks on the segments show $AM = MB$.

Some true statements about midpoints are not good definitions. You should be able to tell why they are not good.

■ ■ ■ ■ ■ ■ ■ ■

Example 1   Why is each of these statements not a good definition of "midpoint"?

a. The midpoint of a segment is a point between the endpoints.
b. The midpoint M of $\overline{AB}$ is the point M on $\overline{AB}$ between A and B, the same distance from A and B, and with $MA = MB$.
c. The midpoint M of $\overline{AB}$ is the intersection of $\overline{AB}$ and a bisector of $\overline{AB}$.

Solution

a. The statement does not accurately describe midpoint (violates property II).
b. The statement contains too much information (violates property III).
c. The statement uses a term, "bisector," not previously defined or understood (violates property I).

A good definition does the job of two conditionals. First, it tells you the characteristics of the defined term. For *midpoint*:

If M is the **midpoint** of $\overline{AB}$, then M is on $\overline{AB}$ and AM = MB.

  defined term $\Rightarrow$ characteristics of term
  (in antecedent)

This is the *meaning* half of the definition, because it tells you what the term means.

Second, a good definition tells you the characteristics that allow you to use the defined term. For *midpoint*:

If M is on $\overline{AB}$ and AM = MB, then M is the **midpoint** of $\overline{AB}$.

  characteristics of term $\Rightarrow$ the defined term
               (in consequent)

This is the *sufficient condition* half of the definition, because it tells you when you can use the name of the new term.

Notice that the meaning half and the sufficient condition half of a definition are converses of each other and both are true.

This can be expressed symbolically. In a definition, the meaning half is

$$p \Rightarrow q$$

where p contains the term being defined. The sufficient condition half is

$$q \Rightarrow p.$$

The definition consists of both of these: $p \Rightarrow q$ and $q \Rightarrow p$. We then write $p \Leftrightarrow q$, and say p **if and only if** q. So, for the definition of midpoint, we can say:

M is the **midpoint** of $\overline{AB}$ if and only if M is on $\overline{AB}$ and AM = MB.

■ ■ ■ ■ ■ ■

Example 2 Let p = "A is between C and D."
     Let q = "CA + AD = CD."
     Write $p \Leftrightarrow q$ in words.

     Solution A is between C and D if and only if CA + AD = CD.

Now consider a familiar figure, the circle. Here is a good definition of *circle*.

Definition:

A **circle** is the set of all points in a plane at a certain distance (its radius) from a certain point (its center).

This definition can be reworded to describe each point on a circle. The **circle with center *C* and radius *r*** is the set of all points *P* in a plane with $PC = r$. A circle with center *C* is often called **circle *C*** or $\odot C$.

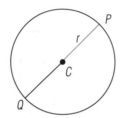

Circle with center *C*, radius *r*
$PC = r$
P is on the circle.
C, the center, is not on the circle.

■ ■   ■   ■   ■   ■ ■ ■

Example 3 Use the above definition of circle.

  a. Write the meaning of circle.
  b. Write the sufficient condition for a circle.
  c. Write the definition of circle as a biconditional (in if-and-only-if form).

Solution

a. The meaning is a conditional with the defined term "circle" in the antecedent: If a figure is a circle, then it is the set of all points in a plane at a certain distance from a certain point.
b. The sufficient condition is the converse of the meaning: If a figure is the set of all points in a plane at a certain distance from a certain point, then it is a circle.
c. Connect the antecedent and consequent with the words *if and only if*: A figure is a circle if and only if it is the set of all points in a plane at a certain distance from a certain point.

As in English, terms in mathematics may have more than one meaning. The term "radius of a circle" is one such term. It means *the distance* from the center to a point on the circle. It also can mean *a segment* connecting the center with a point on the circle. The situation almost always will indicate which meaning is appropriate. The same is true for the term **diameter of a circle,** which can mean either (a) a segment connecting two points on the circle and which contains the center of the circle, or (b) the length of that segment, which is twice the radius.

1. List three properties of a good definition.

2. Define: midpoint of a segment.

3. The definition of "midpoint of a segment" uses two ideas that have been defined earlier. What are they?

4. Break the definition of "midpoint" into its meaning and sufficient condition halves.

5. When $a \Rightarrow b$ and $b \Rightarrow a$, we write a _?_ b.

6. The symbol "$\Leftrightarrow$" is read _?_.

7. If point Q is on circle C with radius r, then $QC =$ _?_.

8. What two meanings does the word "diameter" have?

9. Given: Q is the midpoint of $\overline{RT}$ and $RT = 14$. Fill in each blank with a number. (Hint: draw a picture.)
   a. $RQ =$ _?_
   b. $TQ =$ _?_
   c. $TQ =$ _?_ $\cdot RT$
   d. $\dfrac{RQ}{RT} =$ _?_

10. Why is each of these *not* a good definition of *circle*?
    a. A circle is the set of points at a certain distance from a certain point and it goes around the center.
    b. A circle is a plane section of a sphere.
    c. A circle is the set of points away from a certain point.

11. Refer back to Question 14 of Lesson 2-1. According to the definition of circle, why is choice (d) not a circle?

In 12–15, halves of some previous definitions are written in if-then form. Tell whether the statement is the meaning or the sufficient condition half. (After each question is the lesson where the original definition appears.)

12. If S is space, then S is the set of all possible points. *(Lesson 1-6)*

13. If A is between B and C, then $\overrightarrow{AB}$ and $\overrightarrow{AC}$ are opposite rays. *(Lesson 1-8)*

14. If points lie on the same line, then they are collinear. *(Lesson 1-5)*

15. If two lines are parallel, then they have no points in common or are identical. *(Lesson 1-7)*

16. Let $p =$ "The lawn mower needs gas," and $q =$ "The lawn mower doesn't start on 3 pulls." Write $p \Leftrightarrow q$ out in words.

17. Write the definition of "convex set" from Lesson 2-1 in if-and-only-if form.

18. *Multiple choice.* The shaded portion of the figure at the left is the **interior of the circle** with center A, radius r. Which of these is a good definition of "interior of a circle"?
 (a) The interior of a circle with center A is the set of points inside the circle.
 (b) The interior of a circle with center A, radius r, is the set of points whose distance from A is less than r.

19. In the figure at the left, T is the midpoint of $\overline{DQ}$. $DT = TQ$. Let m be any plane, line, ray, or segment containing T and containing *no* other points of $\overline{DQ}$. m is called a **bisector** of $\overline{DQ}$. Write a good definition of "bisector of a segment."

20. M is equidistant from A and B. $AM = 4x + 10$ and $BM = 5x - 7$. Find x.

Review

In 21–23, a true statement is given. **a.** Give its converse. **b.** Is the converse true? *(Lesson 2-4)*

21. If $x = -\frac{2}{3}$, then $x^2 = \frac{4}{9}$.

22. When you read this book, you are studying geometry.

23. If $\overrightarrow{AB}$ and $\overrightarrow{AC}$ are opposite rays, then A is between B and C.

24. A line in a computer program reads
   30   IF X >= 25 THEN PRINT 3*X − 75
 What will the computer do at this line if X has the value
 a. 20;   **b.** 25;   **c.** 30? *(Lesson 2-3)*

25. Find a counterexample to the conditional "If P, Q, and R are on the same line and $PQ = 20$ and $QR = 6$, then $PR = 26$." *(Lesson 2-2)*

Exploration

26. Sometimes the meaning of a word can be found by taking it apart. For instance, *geometer* originally meant "Earth measurer," from *geo* meaning Earth and *meter* meaning measure. What do these words mean?
 a. geology   **b.** geothermal
 c. geography   **d.** geocentric

2-6

Unions and Intersections of Figures

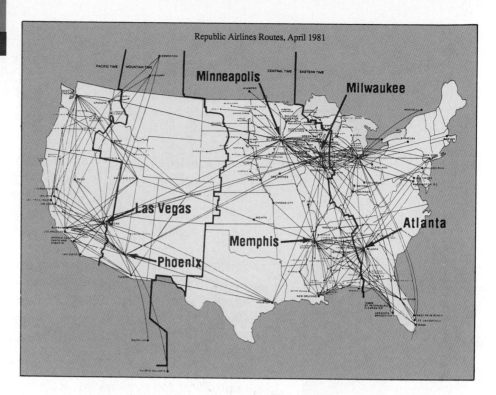

Network of airline routes of Republic Airlines in April, 1981.

Points, lines, segments, and rays are the building blocks of more complex figures. The two most common ways of combining figures or any other sets is to take their *union* or their *intersection*.

Definitions:

The **union of two sets A and B,** written **A ∪ B,** is the set of elements which are either in A or in B, or both.
The **intersection of two sets A and B,** written **A ∩ B,** is the set of elements which are in both A and B.

Here are some examples of unions and intersections of sets.

Set	A	B	A ∪ B	A ∩ B
Example 1	{4, 6, 8}	{10, 6, 4}	{4, 6, 8, 10}	{4, 6}
Example 2	set of numbers x with $x \geq 3$	set of numbers x with $x \leq 7$	set of all real numbers	set of numbers x with $3 \leq x \leq 7$
Example 3	rectangle $PQRS$	diagonals PR and QS	rectangle with diagonals	points P, Q, S, R

Both the union and intersection of figures occur in practical situations. The next example is with networks. An airline has a *route* between two cities when it flies between them. The set of all routes of an airline forms a network. Shown on page 87 is the network for Republic Airlines in April, 1981.

■ ■ ■ ■ ■ ■ ■ ■ ■■

Example 4   In the late 1970s, North Central Airlines (based in Minneapolis) and Southern Airlines (based in Memphis) merged to form Republic Airlines. Let N = the network of routes for North Central Airlines and S = the network for Southern Airlines. What did N ∪ S and N ∩ S mean in this merger?

Solution   N ∪ S consisted of the routes either in North Central or Southern Airlines or both. It became the starting network of the new merged airline, Republic. N ∩ S consisted of the routes in both North Central and Southern Airlines. It was the overlap between them and indicated places where the new merged airline might think of eliminating repetition of flights.

Look closely at the network for Republic on page 87. The nodes are cities and the arcs are routes. The clusters around Milwaukee and Atlanta show where North Central and Southern had the majority of their routes. Notice that there is a third cluster of routes on the west coast. This is because a third airline, Air West, was later merged into Republic. If W stands for the network for Air West, the routes of Republic became W ∪ N ∪ S.

Unions and intersections are important in geometry. Often we speak of *intersections* of lines. Below, the intersection of lines ℓ and m is point P.

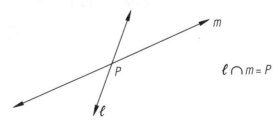

$$\ell \cap m = P$$

If figures have no points in common, then their intersection is the **null set** or **empty set.** That set is written $\varnothing$, or { }. Below are parts of discrete lines s and t. They cross but do not have any points in common.

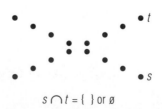

$$s \cap t = \{ \ \} \text{ or } \varnothing$$

Complicated figures, such as the Republic Airlines network, are often unions of simpler figures. A triangle is the *union* of simpler figures; specifically, it is the union of three segments.

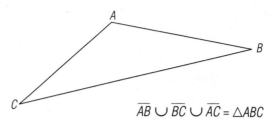

$$\overline{AB} \cup \overline{BC} \cup \overline{AC} = \triangle ABC$$

Questions

Covering the Reading

1. Define: union of two sets A and B.

2. Define: intersection of two sets A and B.

In 3 and 4, find A ∪ B and A ∩ B.

3. A = {-3, 2, 5, 8}, B = {-3, 0, 2}

4. A = solution set to $x \geq 40$, B = solution set to $x \leq 50$

5. Choose the correct words from those in parentheses. The Republic Airline route network is the (union, intersection) of the networks of (two, three) airlines.

6. If W stands for the network of Air West and N for the network of North Central Airlines, what is the meaning of W ∩ N?

7. Suppose m is the line and n is the circle pictured below. What are the elements of $m \cap n$?

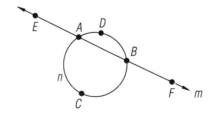

8. *SPED* and *PACE* below are rectangles.
   a. *SPED* ∩ *PACE* = __?__   b. *SPED* ∪ *PACE* = __?__

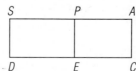

9. A symbol for the null set is __?__ or __?__ .

10. Line ℓ has equation $4x - 3y = 12$. Line m has equation $2x + 5y = 6$. Graph ℓ and m on the same pair of axes. From the graph, determine the coordinates of $\ell \cap m$.

In 11–13, describe G $\cup$ H and G $\cap$ H.

11. G = set of residents of Indonesia.
    H = set of residents of Jakarta, Indonesia.

12. G = ages of people who are eligible to drive in your state.
    H = ages of people who are eligible to vote in your state.

13. G = set of students in your geometry class.
    H = set of students in other geometry classes.

In 14 and 15, x is triangle *GHI* pictured below and y is triangle *IJG*. Name the segments of:

14. x $\cap$ y;   15. x $\cup$ y.

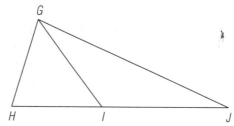

16. Refer to the figure in Question 7. Suppose one of the points from *A, B, C, D, E,* or *F* is chosen at random. What is the probability that it will
    a. lie on line *m*?
    b. lie on circle *n*?
    c. lie on *m* $\cap$ *n*?

17. Tell why each of the following is not a good definition of speed limit. *(Lesson 2-5)*
    a. A speed limit tells how fast you must go.
    b. A speed limit gives the highest speed you can go. If you go faster the police may give you a speeding ticket. On some roads it may be dangerous to go faster than the speed limit.
    c. A speed limit is the maximum legal speed to avoid prosecution under the state's legislative sanctions.

18. Write as two conditionals: *P* is on circle *O* with radius *r* if and only if *PO* = *r*. *(Lessons 2-5, 2-2)*

19. Is the statement "If Q is the set of elements in both set A and set B, then Q is the intersection of sets A and B," the meaning or sufficient condition half of the definition of the intersection of two sets? *(Lesson 2-5)*

20. Draw a convex hexagonal region. *(Lesson 2-1)*

21. Draw a nonconvex decagonal region. *(Lesson 2-1)*

22. a. Write the converse of the statement, "If B is on $\overrightarrow{AC}$, but not between A and C, then $AC = AB - BC$."
  b. Is the statement true?
  c. Is its converse true? *(Lessons 2-4, 1-9)*

23. Give the antecedent and consequent of this statement: Should you work more than 40 hours a week, you will receive time-and-a-half for overtime. *(Lesson 2-2)*

24. Solve for x and check: $x = 2(180 - x)$. *(Previous course)*

25. Graph all possibilities for q on a number line: $22 + q > 180$. *(Previous course)*

Exploration

26. Here is a puzzle that combines some ideas of union, intersection, and networks (from *Mathematical Puzzles of Sam Loyd*, edited by Martin Gardner).

It is told that three neighbors who shared a small park, as shown in the sketch, had a falling out. The owner of the large house, complaining that his neighbors' chickens annoyed him, built an enclosed pathway from his door to the gate at the bottom of the picture. Then the man on the right built a path to the gate on the left, and the man on the left built a path to the gate on the right. None of the paths crossed. Can you draw the three paths correctly?

2-7

Terms Associated with Polygons

Here is a polygon puzzle.

Move 4 of the 16 toothpicks to create three overlapping squares.

Triangles and other polygons are basic to the study of geometry. So good definitions are necessary. In the last lesson, there is the statement "a triangle is the union ... of three segments." This statement is not a good definition because there are unions of three segments that do not look like the figures we want to be triangles.

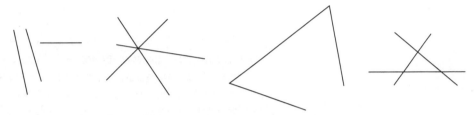

unions of three segments that are not triangles

Clearly a triangle is not the union of *any* three segments. Each segment must intersect the others. Also, the intersections should be at endpoints. These criteria help not only to get a good definition of "triangle," but also the more general term *polygon*.

Definition:

A **polygon** is the union of three or more segments in the same plane such that each segment intersects exactly two others, one at each of its endpoints.

Breaking up the definition clarifies what is and what is not a polygon. A polygon is ...

a union of three or more segments,

yes   no   no

in the same plane.

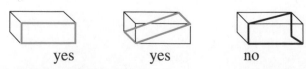

yes   yes   no

Each segment intersects exactly two others.

yes   no   no

Intersections are only at the endpoints of the segments.

yes   no   no

To describe polygons, terminology is needed. The segments which make up a polygon are its **sides.** The endpoints of the sides are the **vertices** of the polygon. The singular of vertices is **vertex.** A polygon can be named by giving its vertices in order. Many names are possible; two names for the polygon shown here are *POLYGN* and *GYLOPN*.

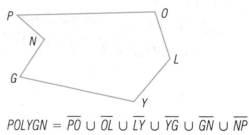

$$POLYGN = \overline{PO} \cup \overline{OL} \cup \overline{LY} \cup \overline{YG} \cup \overline{GN} \cup \overline{NP}$$

Consecutive vertices are endpoints of a side. For instance, *G* and *Y* are consecutive vertices of *POLYGN*. **Consecutive sides** are sides which share an endpoint, for instance $\overline{PO}$ and $\overline{OL}$ above. A **diagonal** is a segment connecting nonconsecutive vertices. Two of the diagonals of *POLYGN* are $\overline{NY}$ and $\overline{NL}$. Neither they nor any other diagonals of *POLYGN* are drawn above.

A polygon with *n* sides is called an ***n*-gon.** When *n* is small, there are special names: a **triangle** has 3 sides; a **quadrilateral** has 4, a **pentagon** has 5, a **hexagon** has 6, a **heptagon** has 7, an **octagon** has 8, a **nonagon** has 9, and a **decagon** has 10. The boundaries of many things are polygons; below is an outline of a house whose boundary is an 8-gon or octagon. A number of such houses were built in the last century.

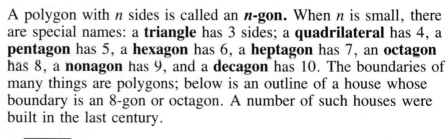

From its definition, every polygon lies entirely in one plane. It separates the plane into three sets—the polygon, its interior, and its exterior. The union of a polygon and its interior is a **polygonal region.**

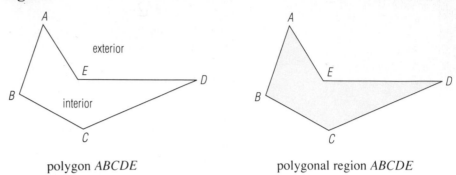

polygon *ABCDE*   polygonal region *ABCDE*

A polygon is **convex** if and only if its corresponding polygonal region is convex. Many commonly used polygons, such as squares and parallelograms, are convex.

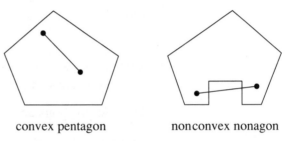

convex pentagon   nonconvex nonagon

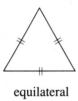

equilateral

Triangles with special characteristics are given specific names. When lengths of the three sides are considered, three possibilities occur: all are equal, two are equal, or no two are equal. An **equilateral triangle** has all three sides equal. An **isosceles triangle** has two (or more) sides of equal length. (An equilateral triangle is also isosceles.) A triangle with no sides of the same length is called **scalene.**

isosceles
(two sides equal)

The classification of triangles by sides is shown below in a **family tree** or **hierarchy.** Each name includes all the shapes below it to which it is connected. Thus an equilateral triangle is an isosceles triangle, a triangle, a polygon, and a figure, but an equilateral triangle is not a scalene triangle.

scalene
(no sides equal)

figure
|
polygon
|
triangle
/   \
isosceles   scalene
|
equilateral

Questions

In 1–4, why is each figure not a polygon?

1.   **2.** 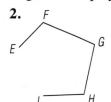 **3.** 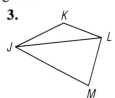 **4.**

5. Use the polygon *ABCDE* below.
   a. Name its vertices.
   b. Name a pair of consecutive sides.
   c. Name a pair of consecutive vertices.

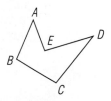

6. a. How many vertices has an octagon?
   b. How many vertices has an *n*-gon?

7. How do polygons and polygonal regions differ?

8. When is a polygon considered to be convex?

In 9–12, characterize the polygonal regional as convex or nonconvex.

9.   **10.**   **11.**   **12.**

13. *Multiple choice.* Which figure is shaped like a nonconvex quadrilateral?
   (a)   (b)   (c)   (d)

14. Draw a convex hexagon.

15. Arrange from most general to most specific: isosceles triangle, figure, polygon, equilateral triangle, triangle, two-dimensional figure.

16. Draw a convex 12-gon.

17. Draw a union of five segments that is not a pentagon.

18. How many diagonals does a pentagon have?

In 19 and 20, the figure includes segments which form more than one polygon. Name the convex polygons.

19.

20.

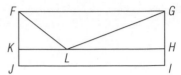

21. Write the sufficient condition half of the definition of a polygon. (Hint: Begin "If a figure is … .")

In 22 and 23, use the four conditions for a polygon:
  I. a union of three or more segments
  II. in the same plane
  III. each segment intersects exactly two others
  IV. intersections are only at the two endpoints.

22. Draw a figure satisfying conditions I, II, and III, but not IV.

23. Draw a figure satisfying conditions I, III, and IV, but not II.

In 24 and 25, how does the given dictionary definition of *polygon* differ from the definition given in this lesson? (Each of these dictionaries gives more than one definition of *polygon*.)

24. "A closed plane figure having many (more than four) angles and sides." (*American College Dictionary,* 1953 edition)

25. "A closed figure on a sphere bounded by great circle arcs." (*Webster's New Collegiate Dictionary,* 1977 edition)

26. S = {-5, 0, 5, 10} and T = {-3, 0, 3}. *(Lesson 2-6)*
  a. Find S ∪ T.
  b. Find S ∩ T.

27. Draw an example of two convex sets C and D whose union C ∪ D is nonconvex. *(Lessons 2-6, 2-1)*

28. a. On a number line, suppose *A* has coordinate 19, *B* has coordinate 8, and *M* has coordinate 13.5. Verify that *M* is the midpoint of $\overline{AB}$ by showing that *AM* = *MB*.
  b. If *M* has coordinate -2, *A* has coordinate -43, and *B* has coordinate 39, verify that *M* is the midpoint of $\overline{AB}$.
  c. If *A* has coordinate *x* and *B* has coordinate *y*, then what is the coordinate of *M,* the midpoint of $\overline{AB}$? *(Lessons 2-5, 1-2)*

29. On Interstate 80, Des Moines is 1849 miles from Sacramento. Salt Lake City is between them, 638 miles from Sacramento. If you wanted to drive halfway from Des Moines to Salt Lake City on this highway, **a.** how far would you have to drive and **b.** how far would you be from Sacramento? *(Lessons 2-5, 1-2)*

30. Give the symbol for each. *(Lesson 1-8)*
   a. line through points X and Y
   b. line segment with endpoints X and Y
   c. distance between X and Y

31. Some names for polygons are no longer used or are used only rarely. For each of the following names of polygons, guess how many sides the polygon has, and then check your guesses by looking in a large dictionary.
   a. dodecagon
   b. duodecagon
   c. enneagon
   d. pentadecagon
   e. quadrangle
   f. tetragon
   g. trigon
   h. undecagon

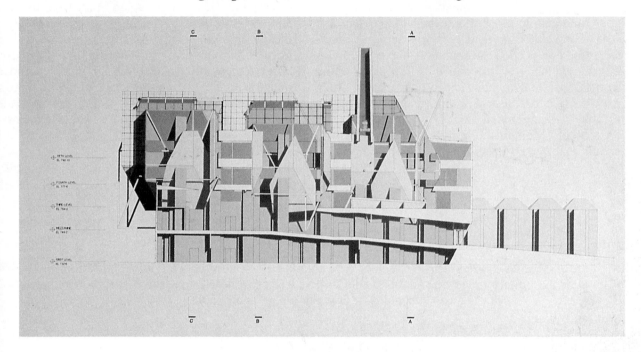

Summary

Every if-then statement (conditional) has an antecedent, the "if" part, and a consequent, the "then" part. If the antecedent is p and the consequent is q, the conditional is $p \Rightarrow q$. This chapter is concerned with the following questions: (1) How can you tell if $p \Rightarrow q$ is false? (2) How are $p \Rightarrow q$ and $q \Rightarrow p$ related? (3) What happens when both $p \Rightarrow q$ and $q \Rightarrow p$ are true? In this chapter, these ideas are applied to segments, circles, and polygons, and also to algebra and everyday reasoning.

(1) How can you tell if $p \Rightarrow q$ is false? A counterexample is needed. A counterexample is a situation for which p is true and q is false. Reasoning from a false statement leads to conclusions which may be true or false. For this reason, computers skip the consequents of any conditional with a false antecedent. Mathematicians consider as true any conditional $p \Rightarrow q$ in which p is false.

(2) $p \Rightarrow q$ and $q \Rightarrow p$ are converse statements. The truth of one does not tell you anything about the truth of the other.

(3) The statement $p \Rightarrow q$ and its converse $q \Rightarrow p$ together form the biconditional $p \Leftrightarrow q$. We then say "p if and only if q." Every definition can be reworded as an "if and only if" statement and can be separated into two if-then statements, the meaning (where the term being defined is in the antecedent) and the sufficient condition (the converse of the meaning). Good definitions are accurate descriptions which involve only words defined earlier, words commonly understood, or words purposely undefined; and good definitions include no more information than is necessary. Good definitions are needed in many fields, not only in mathematics.

Vocabulary

Many terms were defined in this chapter.
For the starred terms (*) below, you should be able to produce a *good* definition.
For the other terms, you should be able to give a general description and a specific example,
including a drawing where appropriate.

Lesson 2-1
convex set
nonconvex set

Lesson 2-2
conditional
if-then statement, $\Rightarrow$
antecedent, if part
consequent, then part
instance of a sentence
*counterexample to a
  conditional
Goldbach's Conjecture

Lesson 2-4
*converse

Lesson 2-5
*midpoint, equidistant
meaning half of a definition
sufficient condition half of
  a definition
if and only if
biconditional, $\Leftrightarrow$
*circle, $\odot$
center, radius,
  diameter of a circle
bisector

Lesson 2-6
*union of sets, $\cup$
*intersection of sets, $\cap$
null set, empty set, $\varnothing$, { }

Lesson 2-7
*polygon, side of polygon
vertex of polygon
consecutive vertices
consecutive sides
diagonal, n-gon
triangle, quadrilateral,
  pentagon, hexagon,
  heptagon, octagon,
  nonagon, decagon
polygonal region
convex polygon
*equilateral triangle
*isosceles triangle
*scalene triangle
hierarchy, family tree

Progress Self-Test

Directions: Take this test as you would take a test in class. Use a ruler and a protractor. Then check your work with the solutions in the Selected Answers section in the back of the book.

1. Tell which property of a good definition is violated by this "bad" definition: The **midpoint of a segment** AB is the point M on $\overline{AB}$ for which $AM = MB$, $\frac{1}{2} AB = AM$, and $\frac{1}{2} AB = MB$.

2. Draw a nonconvex quadrilateral region.

3. In the following statement, underline the antecedent once and the consequent twice: Two angles have equal measure if they are vertical angles.

4. Rewrite in if-then form: Every trapezoid is a quadrilateral.

In 5 and 6, use the figure below. If r is rectangle *ABCD* and t is triangle *ADC,* name the segments of

5. r ∪ t;   6. r ∩ t.

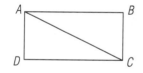

7. Let p = "There are over 10 books on that shelf." q = "The shelf falls." Write $p \Leftrightarrow q$ in words.

8. Consider the statement: If a figure is a triangle, then it is a polygon.
   a. Is the statement true?
   b. Write the converse of this statement.
   c. Show that the converse is false by drawing a counterexample.

9. Mr. Hawkins told his class, "If you do your homework every night, you will be guaranteed a passing grade." Liane, a student in Mr. Hawkins' class, received a passing grade. Did Liane do homework every night?

In 10 and 11, consider this program.

```
10   INPUT V
20   IF V > 5 THEN PRINT V * V
30   IF V <= 5 THEN PRINT "TOO SMALL"
40   END
```

10. What will be printed if 6 is entered for V?

11. What will be printed if V is given the value 5?

12. In the following if-then statement from the definition of convex set, tell whether the conditional is the meaning half or the sufficient condition half.

    If S is a set in which a segment connecting any two points of S lies entirely in S, then S is convex.

13. M is the midpoint of $\overline{AB}$. N is the midpoint of $\overline{MB}$. If $AB = 40$, what is the length of $\overline{AN}$?

14. Match each term with the most appropriate drawing.
    a. hexagon
    b. quadrilateral
    c. octagon

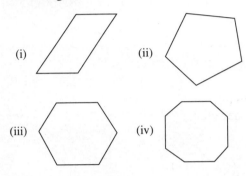

(i)   (ii)

(iii)   (iv)

15. Define: isosceles triangle.

16. Draw a nonconvex hexagon.

17. Draw the hierarchy relating the following: polygon, equilateral triangle, scalene triangle, triangle.

18. Pictured here is a floor plan of the Baha'i House of Worship in Wilmette, Illinois. What is the name given to the polygon outlined?

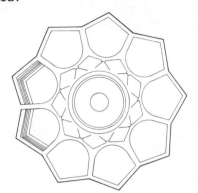

Chapter Review

Questions on **SPUR** Objectives

SPUR stands for **S**kills, **P**roperties, **U**ses, and **R**epresentations.
The Chapter Review questions are grouped according to the
SPUR Objectives for this chapter.

SKILLS deal with the procedures used to get answers.

■ **Objective A:** *Distinguish between convex and nonconvex regions. (Lessons 2-1, 2-7)*

In 1–3, characterize each region as convex or nonconvex.

1.   **2.**   **3.**

■ **Objective B:** *Draw and identify polygons.*
(Lesson 2-7)

4. Draw an equilateral triangle.

5. Draw an isosceles triangle.

6. Draw a convex octagonal region.

7. Draw a nonconvex nonagonal region.

8. Match each term with the most appropriate drawing.
a. decagon   **b.** pentagon   **c.** quadrilateral

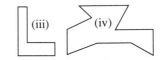

9. Trace the polygon (i) in Question 8 above. Draw the polygon formed by connecting the midpoints of consecutive sides.

PROPERTIES deal with the principles behind the mathematics.

■ **Objective C:** *Write the converse of a conditional.*
(Lesson 2-4)

In 10–12, **a.** write the converse of the statement.
b. Tell whether the converse is true.

10. If $x = 3$, then $x^2 = 9$.

11. If $AM = MB$, then M is the midpoint of $\overline{AB}$.

12. All Hawaiians live in the U.S.

■ **Objective D:** *Apply the properties of a good definition. (Lessons 2-1, 2-5)*

13. Why is it important to carefully define terms?

14. "Polygon" is defined using what three previously defined terms?

In 15 and 16, tell which property of a good definition is violated by these "bad" definitions.

15. The midpoint M of $\overline{AB}$ is a point such that $AM = BM$.

16. A triangle is a closed path with three sides.

17. Here is a definition of a *secant to a circle:*
A secant to a circle is a line which intersects the circle in two points.
This definition makes use of five undefined or previously defined terms. Name them.

18. Break the definition of secant in Question 17 into its meaning and sufficient condition halves.

■ **Objective E:** *Write and interpret statements in "if-then" form. (Lesson 2-2)*

In 19–21, rewrite in "if-then" form.

19. Every radius is a segment.

20. All hexagons have 9 diagonals.

21. Given $AB = 7$, you can conclude $BA = 7$.

In 22 and 23, copy the statement and underline the antecedent once and consequent twice.

22. A figure is a rectangle if it is a square.

23. If p, then q.

In 24 and 25, refer to this statement: If a figure is a union of four segments, then it is a quadrilateral.

24. Draw an instance of the antecedent for which the consequent is also true.

25. Draw a counterexample.

■ **Objective F:** *Determine the union and intersection of sets. (Lesson 2-6)*

26. If A = {2, 5, 9} and B = {5, 13, 9}, find A ∩ B.

27. Let D = the solution set to $n \le 15$, and E = the solution set to $n \ge -15$.
   a. Describe D ∩ E.
   b. Describe D ∪ E.

28. Triangle *MNO* below is x and triangle *MOP* is y. Name the segments of:
   a. x ∩ y;   **b.** x ∪ y.

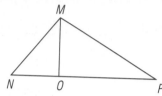

■ **Objective G:** *Use logical ($p \Rightarrow q$) notation.*
(Lessons 2-2, 2-3, 2-4)

29. Let p = "$\triangle ABC$ is equilateral."
        q = "$\triangle ABC$ has three 60° angles."
   Write in words. **a.** $q \Rightarrow p$;   **b.** $p \Leftrightarrow q$.

In 30 and 31, p and q may be any statements.

30. If $p \Rightarrow q$ is true, must $q \Rightarrow p$ be true?

31. A counterexample for $p \Rightarrow q$ is a situation in which p is __?__ and q is __?__ .

USES deal with applications of mathematics in real situations.

■ **Objective H:** *Apply properties of if-then statements in real situations. (Lessons 2-3, 2-4)*

32. A sign on the highway states: "The fine for littering is $100." Mr. Woodson was stopped by police on the highway and fined $100. Was he guilty of littering?

33. A person says: "If the moon is made of green cheese, I'll eat my hat." According to the logic of mathematics, is the statement true or false?

■ **Objective I:** *Identify polygons used for real objects. (Lesson 2-7)*

34. The edge of a tape dispenser is magnified and drawn below. What polygon is this shape?

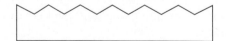

35. An umpire has just swept off home plate in the picture below. What polygon is the shape of home plate?

REPRESENTATIONS deal with pictures, graphs, or objects that illustrate concepts.

■ **Objective J:** *Read computer programs with IF-THEN statements. (Lesson 2-3)*

In 36–38, consider this program.

```
10   PRINT "COMPUTE NUMBER OF
     DIAGONALS IN POLYGON"
20   INPUT N
30   IF N >= 3 THEN PRINT "THE NUMBER
     OF DIAGONALS IS "; N * (N - 3)/2
40   END
```

36. What will be printed if N is given the value 1?

37. What will be printed if N is given the value 20?

38. What will be printed if N is given the value 3?

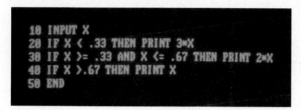

In 39 and 40, consider this program.

```
10   INPUT X
20   IF X < .33 THEN PRINT 3 * X
30   IF X >= .33 AND X <= .67 THEN PRINT
     2 * X
40   IF X > .67 THEN PRINT X
50   END
```

39. What will be printed if X is given the value 0.4?

40. What will be printed if X is given the value 20?

■ **Objective K:** *Draw hierarchies of triangles and polygons. (Lesson 2-7)*

41. Draw the hierarchy relating the following: figure, triangle, isosceles triangle, scalene triangle.

42. Draw the hierarchy relating the following: polygon, triangle, hexagon, isosceles triangle, equilateral triangle.

Angles and Lines

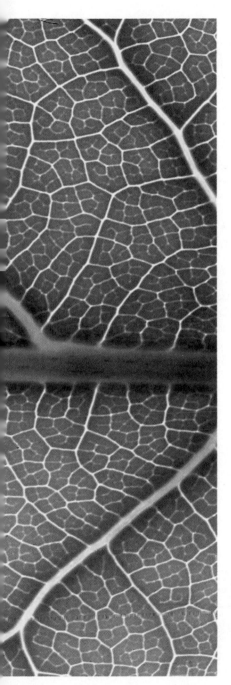

Lines all look the same except for their direction, or *tilt*. Angles give a way of measuring the tilt of a line, and also of measuring the differences in the tilts or directions of two lines. Angles occur everywhere, in both living and inanimate objects. Three examples are pictured here.

The leaf exhibits a network of veins. From the largest vein in the middle, smaller and smaller veins branch out. For particular species of trees, these veins are set at characteristic angles, and often the smaller veins are parallel.

When mud dries, it cakes and separates, often at angles that have measures of 90°, showing perpendicular segments.

Folding chairs have legs which make angles with each other and with the plane of the floor.

In geometry, angles are found in all sorts of figures. They occur whenever lines intersect. And they are found in all polygons. There are also angles between curves and between planes, but in this chapter we concentrate on the basic angles of the plane—those formed by lines and those found in polygons.

There are simple relationships between angles, parallel lines, and perpendicular lines, and surprising connections with the slopes of lines you studied in algebra. These too are studied in this chapter.

Angles and Their Measures

Definition:

An **angle** is the union of two rays that have the same endpoint.

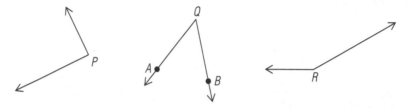

Pictured above are three angles. The **sides** of angles are the two rays; the **vertex** is the common endpoint of the two rays. The symbol for angle is ∠.

Angles may be formed by segments, as in the polygons in the photographs on the previous page, but you should still consider the sides of the angle to be rays.

Angles are named in various ways. When there is only one angle at a given vertex, the angle can be named by the vertex. Above are pictured ∠P, ∠Q, and ∠R.

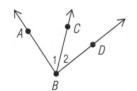

When several angles have the same vertex, each one needs a unique name. At the left there are three angles. Each can be named by giving a point on each side, with the vertex point in between: ∠ABC, ∠CBD, and ∠ABD. The smaller angles can also be named by numbers: ∠1 is ∠ABC, ∠2 is ∠CBD.

Pictured below are two special angles. ∠STV is a straight angle, and ∠XWY is a zero angle. They are special because some different properties apply to them. In identifying angles in a given figure or problem, both straight and zero angles *are ignored unless specifically mentioned.*

∠STV is a straight angle.   ∠XWY is a zero angle.

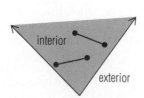

Every angle other than a zero angle separates the other points of the plane into two sets. Except for a straight angle, exactly one of the two sets is convex. The convex set is called the **interior** of the angle and the nonconvex set is the **exterior.**

For a straight angle, both sets are convex and either set may be its interior. A zero angle has no interior.

The **measure** of an angle indicates the amount of openness of the angle. For example, suppose you want to know how wide your angle of vision is. To say it is large is not precise enough to compare your angle with someone else's. The unit of measure used in this book is the **degree,** denoted °. A 1° angle is determined by dividing a circle into 360 equal parts and taking the angle determined by two consecutive subdivision points and the center. The circle itself has a measure of 360°.

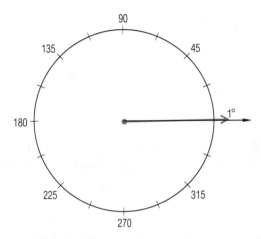

an angle with measure equal to one degree

Since other units of measure for angles are not used in this book, the ° sign is sometimes omitted with angle measures. Thus we can say that the measure of the angle is a unique real number from 0 to 180.

A tool commonly used to measure angles is the **protractor.** It usually contains a scale from 0 to 180 that stretches over a half circle. The **center** V and **base line** $\overleftrightarrow{RV}$ are marked. Angles are measured by performing the three steps shown in the diagram, which shows how to measure ∠AVB.

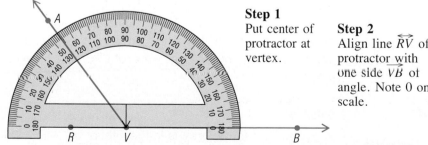

Step 1
Put center of protractor at vertex.

Step 2
Align line $\overleftrightarrow{RV}$ of protractor with one side $\overrightarrow{VB}$ of angle. Note 0 on scale.

Step 3
Read the measure where the other side ($\overrightarrow{VA}$) intersects the protractor.

The steps show that ∠AVB measures about 126. The symbol **m∠AVB** means the measure of angle AVB. So we write m∠AVB ≈ 126.

The basic properties of angles and their measures are assumed.

Angle Measure Postulate:

a. Unique measure assumption
Every angle has a unique measure from 0° to 180°.

b. Two sides of line assumption
Given any ray $\overrightarrow{VA}$ and any number x between 0 and 180, there are unique rays $\overrightarrow{VB}$ and $\overrightarrow{VC}$ such that $\overline{BC}$ intersects line $\overleftrightarrow{VA}$ and m∠BVA = m∠CVA = x.

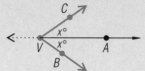

c. Zero angle assumption
If $\overrightarrow{VA}$ and $\overrightarrow{VB}$ are the same ray, then m∠AVB = 0.

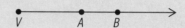

d. Straight angle assumption
If $\overrightarrow{VA}$ and $\overrightarrow{VB}$ are opposite rays, then m∠AVB = 180

e. Angle Addition Property
If $\overrightarrow{VC}$ (except for point V) is in the interior of ∠AVB, then m∠AVC + m∠CVB = m∠AVB.

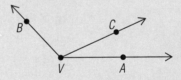

In drawings, an angle's measure is often written in its interior. For instance, in the drawing below at the left, m∠APB = 45.

Example In the drawing at the left, determine

a. m∠APC;   **b.** m∠CPD.

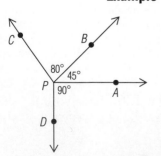

Solution

a. $\overrightarrow{PB}$ (except for point P) is in the interior of ∠APC. Using the Angle Addition Property,

$$m∠APC = m∠APB + m∠BPC$$
$$= 45 + 80$$
$$= 125.$$

b. The measures of the angles about *P* add to 360°. (Think of *P* as the center of a circle.) The given angles add to 215°.
m∠*CPD* = 360 − 215 = 145

A special case of the Angle Addition Property occurs with straight angles. Suppose $\overrightarrow{VA}$ and $\overrightarrow{VB}$ are opposite rays. Then, because of the straight angle assumption, m∠*AVB* = 180. By the Angle Addition Property, m∠1 + m∠2 = 180. For instance, if m∠1 = 43, then m∠2 = 180 − 43 = 137. If m∠1 = *x*, then m∠2 = 180 − *x*. This situation often occurs since it happens whenever lines intersect.

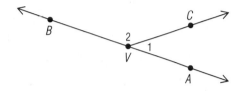

Questions

Covering the Reading

1. Choose the correct words. An angle is the (intersection, union) of two (rays, segments) with the same (endpoint, midpoint).

2. Pictured at the left is the union of two rays. Why does this not picture an angle?

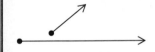

3. Use the angle shown at the right.
   a. Name the vertex of the angle.
   b. Name the sides.
   c. Give 5 different names for this angle.

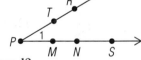

4. In this book, in what unit are angles measured?

5. m∠*A* is short for __?__ .

In 6 and 7, use the drawing of a protractor shown below. Find the approximate measure of each angle.

6. a. ∠*PQS*   **b.** ∠*SQR*

7. a. ∠*SQT*   **b.** ∠*TQR*

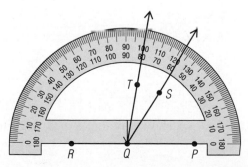

8. Use the drawing below.
   a. Name two straight angles.
   b. Name two angles with measure 0.
   c. m∠CED + m∠CEB = __?__
   d. If m∠1 = x, m∠2 = __?__.

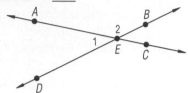

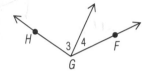

9. Use the figure at the left.
   a. If m∠3 = 80 and m∠4 = 40, then m∠FGH = __?__.
   b. What property did you apply to get the answer to **a**?

10. In the situation pictured below, find the value of x.

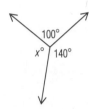

Applying the Mathematics

11. In this photograph of three hexagonal cells of a beehive, the three angles with vertex A have the same measure.
    a. Name these angles.
    b. What is that measure?

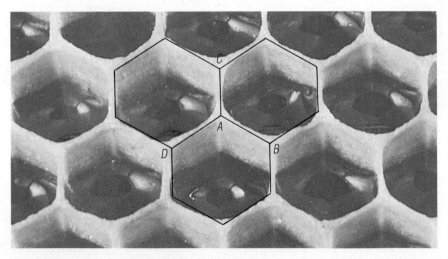

In 12 and 13, use a protractor.

12. a. Draw a 166° angle.
    b. Shade the interior of the angle you have drawn.

13. a. Draw two angles with measure 47° that share a common side.
    b. What part of the Angle Measure Postulate assures that this can be done?

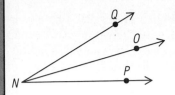

14. Refer to the figure at the left. Suppose $m\angle QNO = 9x - 2$ and $m\angle ONP = 4x + 7$. If $m\angle QNP = 83$, find x and draw a more accurate figure.

15. If you bend your elbow, an angle is formed by the ulna (a bone leading to your wrist) and the humerus (the bone from the shoulder).
   a. When your arm is straight, what is the measure of this angle?
   b. Approximate the measure of the smallest angle you can make with your ulna and humerus.

In 16-18, **a.** guess the measure of the angle. **b.** Measure each with a protractor and compare with your estimate. (You are doing well if your estimate is within 10°.)

16.

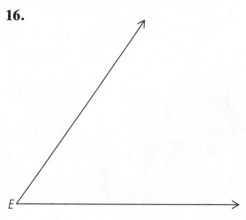

17.

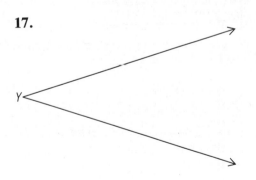

18.

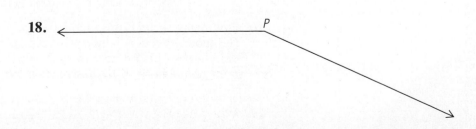

19. The points of a compass are labeled clockwise in degrees like a protractor. Airport runways are numbered with their compass direction, except that the final zero is dropped. The runway heading north is labeled 36 at the bottom, for 360°. North-south and east-west runways are labeled as shown below.

   a. The Orchard Airport Expansion Project planners want to add a runway labeled 32. Draw a possible runway.

   b. What number would be at the other end of the runway numbered 32?

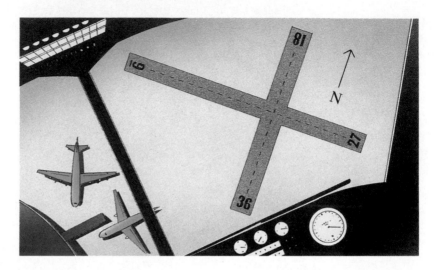

Review

20. In at most how many points do the diagonals of a convex hexagon intersect? *(Lesson 2-7)*

21. In at least how many points do the diagonals of a convex hexagon intersect? *(Lesson 2-7)*

22. An angle is a union of two rays. What are the possible *intersections* of two rays? *(Lesson 2-6)*

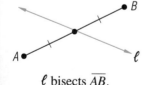

ℓ bisects $\overline{AB}$.

23. Here is a definition of *bisector of a segment*: A line, ray, or segment is a bisector of $\overline{AB}$ if and only if it contains the midpoint of $\overline{AB}$ and no other points of $\overline{AB}$.

   a. Write the meaning half of this definition.

   b. Write the sufficient condition half of this definition. *(Lesson 2-5)*

Exploration

24. Degrees can be divided into minutes and seconds.

   a. From a dictionary or other source, find out how many minutes are in one degree.

   b. How many seconds are in one degree?

   c. The moon covers an angle of about 30 minutes in the sky. How many moons placed next to each other would extend from one point on the horizon to the point on the opposite side of the horizon?

3-2

Types of Angles

Semaphore signals are determined by the angles at which the flags are held.

Angles may be classified by measure into one of five types.

Definitions:

If m is the measure of an angle, then the angle is:

a. **zero** if and only if $m = 0$;
b. **acute** if and only if $0 < m < 90$;
c. **right** if and only if $m = 90$;
d. **obtuse** if and only if $90 < m < 180$;
e. **straight** if and only if $m = 180$.

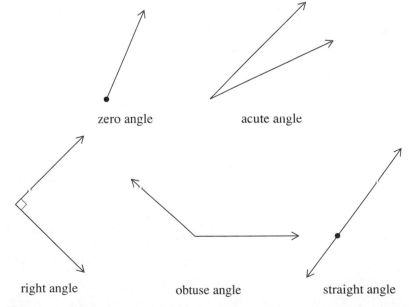

zero angle   acute angle

right angle   obtuse angle   straight angle

To identify a right angle, a "⌐" is drawn in the angle to form a square.

Pairs of angles are special if the sum of their measures is 90 or 180.

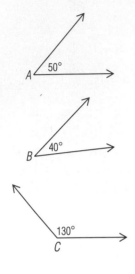

Definitions:

If the measures of two angles are m_1 and m_2, then the angles are:
a. **complementary** if and only if $m_1 + m_2 = 90$;
b. **supplementary** if and only if $m_1 + m_2 = 180$.

In the figures at the left, $\angle A$ and $\angle B$ are complementary angles while $\angle A$ and $\angle C$ are supplementary angles. It is also said that $\angle A$ and $\angle B$ are **complements** and $\angle A$ and $\angle C$ are **supplements.** At the left, $\angle A$ is a complement to $\angle B$ and a supplement to $\angle C$. If the measure of an angle is x, then any complement to it has measure $(90 - x)$ and any supplement has measure $(180 - x)$.

Example 1 An angle has 3 times the measure of a complement to it. Find the measure of the angle.

Solution Let the angle have measure x. Its complement must have measure $90 - x$. But from the given information, three times the measure of the complement equals x. Thus,

$$x = 3(90 - x)$$
$$x = 270 - 3x$$
$$4x = 270$$
$$x = 67.5.$$

The measure of the angle is 67.5°.

Check $90 - 67.5 = 22.5$. Since 67.5 is $3 \cdot 22.5$, it checks.

Pairs of angles may also be classified by their positions relative to each other.

Definitions:

Two non-straight and non-zero angles are:
a. **adjacent angles** if and only if a common side ($\overrightarrow{OB}$ in the left figure on page 115) is interior to the angle formed by the non-common sides ($\angle AOC$);
b. a **linear pair** if and only if they are adjacent and their non-common sides are opposite rays;
c. **vertical angles** if and only if their sides form two lines.

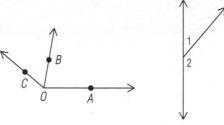

| $\angle COB$ and $\angle BOA$ | $\angle 1$ and $\angle 2$ are | $\angle 3$ and $\angle 5$ are vertical angles. |
| are adjacent angles. | a linear pair. | $\angle 4$ and $\angle 6$ are vertical angles. |

Identification of adjacent angles can be tricky. Below, angles D and E are not adjacent. They do not have a common side since $\overrightarrow{DE} \neq \overrightarrow{ED}$. Angles 7 and 8 below are not adjacent because $\overrightarrow{ZY}$ is not in the interior of $\angle XZW$.

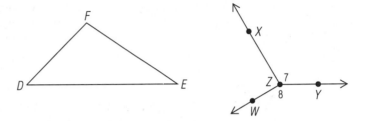

Examine angles 1 and 2 at the top of the page, a linear pair of angles. Their measures add to 180°, since the opposite rays form a line. So they are also supplementary. This argument works for any linear pair. It proves a theorem which you will use later, so we give it a name.

Linear Pair Theorem:

> If two angles form a linear pair, then they are supplementary.

Finally, examine the vertical angles 5 and 3 above. Each forms a linear pair with $\angle 6$. So, by the Linear Pair Theorem, they are supplementary. Thus $m\angle 5 + m\angle 6 = 180$ and $m\angle 3 + m\angle 6 = 180$. From the Substitution Property of Equality, $m\angle 5 + m\angle 6 = m\angle 3 + m\angle 6$. Adding $-m\angle 6$ to each side, $m\angle 5 = m\angle 3$. So the vertical angles have the same measure. This argument works for any vertical angles and proves a second theorem.

Vertical Angle Theorem:

> If two angles are vertical angles, then they have equal measures.

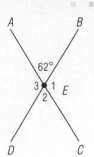

■ ■ ■ ■ ■ ■ ■ ■

Example 2   Find the measures of as many angles as you can in the figure at the left, given m∠AEB = 62.

Solution   With this information, the measures of all drawn angles with vertex *E* can be found. Using the Vertical Angle Theorem, m∠2 = 62. Since ∠AEB and ∠1 form a linear pair, by the Linear Pair Theorem they are supplementary. Thus m∠1 = 180 − 62 = 118. By a similar argument, m∠3 = 118.

■ ■ ■ ■ ■ ■ ■ ■

Example 3   Given ∠5 and ∠6 are complementary and adjacent angles, with m∠5 = 47.

a. Sketch a possible situation.
b. Find m∠6.

Solution

a. Since ∠5 and ∠6 are adjacent, they have a common side, so a figure could look like that drawn below.

b. Since ∠5 and ∠6 are complementary,
           m∠5 + m∠6 = 90.
Substitute 47 for m∠5.
               47 + m∠6 = 90
So m∠6 = 43.

This lesson concludes with one last definition concerning angles.

Definition:

$\overrightarrow{VR}$ is a **bisector** of ∠PVQ if and only if $\overrightarrow{VR}$ is in the interior of ∠PVQ and m∠PVR = m∠RVQ.

Informally, an angle bisector splits an angle into two angles of equal measure.

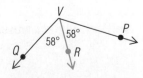

$\overrightarrow{VR}$ bisects ∠PVQ.

1. When classified by measure, there are five types of angles. Name them.

2. An angle has 4 times the measure of a supplement to it. Find the measure of the angle.

In 3 and 4, refer back to the picture of vertical angles on page 115.

3. Does ∠6 appear to be zero, acute, obtuse, right, or straight?

4. Does ∠5 appear to be zero, acute, obtuse, right, or straight?

In 5–7, use the figure at the left.

5. ∠1 and ∠3 are __?__ angles.

6. If m∠1 = 121, find:
   a. m∠2;   **b.** m∠3;   **c.** m∠4.

7. If m∠1 = x, find:
   a. m∠2;   **b.** m∠3;   **c.** m∠4.

8. ∠V and ∠W are supplementary, and m∠V = 103.
   a. Find m∠W.
   b. Is ∠V acute, obtuse, or right?
   c. Is ∠W acute, obtuse, or right?

In 9–11, sketch a possible drawing of ∠1 and ∠2.

9. ∠1 and ∠2 are supplementary and adjacent.

10. ∠1 and ∠2 are complementary and not adjacent.

11. ∠1 and ∠2 are adjacent, complementary, and have the same measure.

12. In the figure below, m∠APE = 180.
   a. ∠OPE is supplementary to __?__.
   b. Name another pair of supplementary angles.

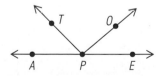

13. **a.** Write the converse of the Linear Pair Theorem.
   b. Draw a counterexample to the converse.
   c. What can you conclude about the converse?

14. Let m be the measure of an angle which is less than its complement. Find all possibilities for m.

15. A triangle is called an **acute, right,** or **obtuse triangle** depending on the measure of its largest angle. Without measuring, does the triangle appear to be acute, right, or obtuse?

a.

b.

c.

16. Use the figure at the right. If $\overrightarrow{BC}$ is the bisector of $\angle ABD$, find $m\angle ABD$.

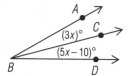

17. The famous Leaning Tower of Pisa has been shifting on its foundation since it was built in the 12th century. At this time the smallest angle it makes with the ground measures about 85°. What is x, the measure of the largest angle it makes with the ground?

Review

18. Measure $\angle D$ below. *(Lesson 3-1)*

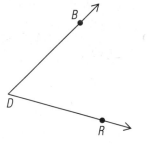

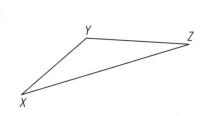

19. Measure $\angle Z$ above. *(Lesson 3-1)*

20. The plane pictured below is heading in a direction 10° north of east, written 10° N of E, as indicated by the ray. How many degrees would it have to turn in order to head due north? *(Lesson 3-1)*

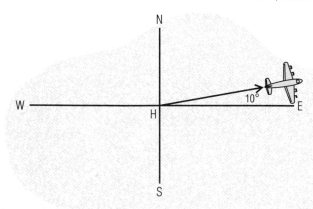

21. Give the number of sides of each type of polygon. *(Lesson 2-7)*
 a. octagon   **b.** hexagon
 c. pentagon   **d.** triangle
 e. quadrilateral   **f.** heptagon
 g. nonagon   **h.** decagon
 i. 35-gon   **j.** *n*-gon

22. Give a counterexample to this statement: If A has 3 elements and B has 2 elements, then A ∪ B has 5 elements. *(Lessons 2-6, 2-2)*

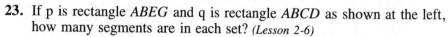

23. If p is rectangle *ABEG* and q is rectangle *ABCD* as shown at the left, how many segments are in each set? *(Lesson 2-6)*
 a. p ∪ q   **b.** p ∩ q

24. Below are conditionals from the definitions of this lesson. Tell whether they are meanings or sufficient conditions. *(Lesson 2-5)*
 a. If *x* is the measure of an angle and $x = 180$, then the angle is a straight angle.
 b. If m_1 and m_2 are the measures of two supplementary angles, then $m_1 + m_2 = 180$.
 c. If two angles are vertical angles, then their sides form two lines.

Exploration

25. The words "acute" and "obtuse" have nonmathematical meanings, as in these sentences.
 a. A person has an *acute* sense of smell.
 b. That argument is *obtuse*.
 What do these words mean in these sentences and how do they relate to the corresponding names for angles?

26. The words "compliment" and "complement" sound alike but mean different things. They are called *homonyms*.
 a. What is the meaning of "compliment"?
 b. Give a homonym for "right."
 c. Find other mathematical terms that have homonyms.

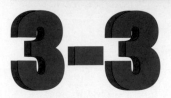
Justifying Conclusions

Recall that you can show that an if-then statement is false by producing a counterexample to it. However, to show that it is true, a *proof* is needed.

Definition:

The **proof** of an if-then statement is a sequence of justified conclusions, leading from the antecedent to the consequent.

To understand this definition, you need to know specifically what is meant by *justified conclusions*. That is what this lesson is about. In the last lesson, two statements were proved—first the Linear Pair Theorem and then the Vertical Angle Theorem. Below, the proof of the Vertical Angle Theorem from the last lesson is repeated, but with the sequence of conclusions and the justifications for them numbered. Notice how each statement follows from previous ones. Notice also that each geometric conclusion is justified either by (1) a particular definition, (2) a particular postulate, or (3) a theorem that has already been proved. These are the only justifications that are allowed in a proof.

Recall the statement of the Vertical Angle Theorem to be proved: *If two angles are vertical angles, then they have equal measures.* We begin with the antecedent of the statement: Angles 3 and 5 are vertical angles.

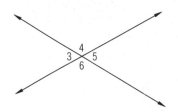

Conclusion 1: Angles 3 and 6 form a linear pair. Angles 5 and 6 form a linear pair.
Justification for 1: If two angles have a side in common and the noncommon sides are opposite rays, then the angles form a linear pair. (definition of linear pair—sufficient condition)

Conclusion 2: $\angle 3$ and $\angle 6$ are supplementary.
$\angle 5$ and $\angle 6$ are supplementary.
Justification for 2: If two angles form a linear pair, they are supplementary. (Linear Pair Theorem)

Conclusion 3: $m\angle 3 + m\angle 6 = 180$.
$m\angle 5 + m\angle 6 = 180$.
Justification for 3: If two angles are supplementary, then the sum of the measures of the angles is 180. (definition of supplementary angles—meaning)

Conclusion 4: $m\angle 3 + m\angle 6 = m\angle 5 + m\angle 6$.
Justification for 4: Substitution Property of Equality ($m\angle 5 + m\angle 6$ has been substituted for 180 in the first part of conclusion 3.)

Conclusion 5: $m\angle 3 = m\angle 5$.
Justification for 5: Addition Property of Equality ($-m\angle 6$ has been added to both sides of the equation of conclusion 4.)

Conclusion 5 is the consequent of the theorem. The measures of vertical angles are equal. The proof shows that the statement is true based on the definitions and postulates agreed upon.

Theorems such as the Linear Pair Theorem and the Vertical Angle Theorem may look rather obvious. So why are they proved? Mathematicians generally have three reasons for proving theorems.

The first reason is very important: What is obvious to one person may not be obvious to another person. Sometimes people disagree.

A second reason for proving statements is also important: If a statement cannot be proved after many people have worked on it for a long time, it is quite possible that either (1) the statement cannot be proved or disproved from the postulates, or (2) the statement is not true even though it looks true.

A third reason for proof is that unexpected results can be verified. For instance, in Chapter 1 you learned Euler's Theorem concerning traversable networks. The Pythagorean Theorem also is not an obvious theorem, but it will be proved later in this book. In algebra, the Quadratic Formula is proved, and that formula is not at all obvious.

Simplifying expressions, solving equations, and applying techniques are all series of justified steps. If the given information *(p)* and the conclusion following from it *(q)* are important enough, then the statement $(p \Rightarrow q)$ is labeled as a theorem. Showing that from the given *p*, the conclusion *q* follows *proves the conditional* $p \Rightarrow q$.

In the Questions, you are asked to provide a justification for one conclusion, the first conclusion one might make from given information. The given *p* is the antecedent; the conclusion *q* is the consequent. The justification is a particular definition, postulate, or theorem which asserts that *p* implies *q*. In Example 1 the justification is a definition. Later in this course, the sequences of justified conclusions may have many steps.

Example 1   Given: X is the midpoint of $\overline{MT}$ as pictured at the right.

Conclusion: $XM = XT$.
Justify this conclusion.

Solution   The "Given" is the antecedent and the "Conclusion" is the consequent of the conditional: "If X is the midpoint of $\overline{MT}$, then $XM = XT$." This is the meaning half of the definition of midpoint. We thus write as the justification: definition of midpoint (meaning).

In Example 2, the justification is a theorem already proved.

Example 2   Given: ∠AEC and ∠DEB are vertical angles as pictured below.
Conclusion: m∠AEC = m∠DEB.
Justify this conclusion.

Solution   The given statement and the conclusion are instances of the antecedent and the consequent of the Vertical Angle Theorem. So the justification is: The Vertical Angle Theorem.

In Example 3, the justification is one of the postulates from algebra mentioned in Lesson 1-7.

Example 3   Given: $x + y = 180$. Justify the conclusion $y = 180 - x$.

Solution $-x$ has been added to both sides of $x + y = 180$ to get the conclusion. The Addition Property of Equality says you can add the same number to both sides of an equality without changing the solutions. So the justification is: the Addition Property of Equality.

To name or categorize figures, a common justification is to use the sufficient condition half of the definition of that kind of figure.

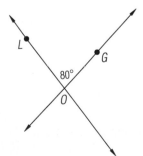

Example 4   Given: m∠LOG = 80.
Justify the conclusion that ∠LOG is an acute angle.

Solution   "If m∠LOG = 80, then ∠LOG is an acute angle." This is an instance of the sufficient condition half of the definition of acute angle. Answer: definition of acute angle (sufficient condition).

To find justifications, you obviously need to be familiar with the definitions, postulates, and theorems that you have had. In the back of the book is a list of postulates and a list of theorems. At the back of each chapter is a vocabulary list with the terms you need to know. At this point you can only use justifications that have been presented prior to this lesson. As each new theorem, definition, or postulate is presented in the text, they become added to the list of possible justifications.

Covering the Reading

1. Define: proof.

2. Name the three kinds of statements which can be used as justifications in a proof.

3. Can a postulate from algebra be used as a justification in geometry?

In 4 and 5, consider the drawing as given.

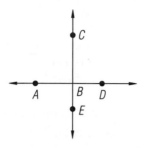

4. *Multiple choice.* Which statement justifies the conclusion?
   Given: m∠ABC = 90.
   Conclusion: ∠ABC is a right angle.
   (a) definition of complementary angles (meaning)
   (b) definition of complementary angles (sufficient condition)
   (c) definition of right angle (meaning)
   (d) definition of right angle (sufficient condition)

Applying the Mathematics

5. State the justification for the conclusion.
   Given: ∠ABC and ∠EBD are vertical angles.
   Conclusion: m∠ABC = m∠EBD.

6. If an important conditional is proved true, it is called a(n) __?__ .

7. Give three reasons why mathematicians feel it is important to have proofs.

8. *Multiple choice.* In going from $4x + 3 = 12$ to $4x = 9$, what is the major justification?
   (a) Associative Property of Addition
   (b) Additive Identity Property of Zero
   (c) Definition of Opposites
   (d) Addition Property of Equality

In 9 and 10, **a.** make a conclusion based on the given information.
b. Give the justification for that conclusion.

9. $4y = 32$

10. In the figure below, I is between E and F.

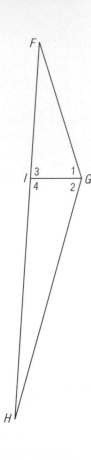

In 11 and 12, *multiple choice*. Use the figure at the left. Which statement justifies the conclusion?

11. Given: m∠1 = 73; m∠2 = 74.
Conclusion: m∠FGH = 147.
(a) Angle Addition Property
(b) Linear Pair Theorem
(c) definition of obtuse angle (meaning)
(d) Vertical Angle Theorem

12. Given: ∠3 and ∠4 form a linear pair.
Conclusion: ∠3 and ∠4 are supplementary angles.
(a) Angle Addition Property
(b) Linear Pair Theorem
(c) definition of supplementary angles (meaning)
(d) definition of supplementary angles (sufficient condition)

In 13–15, state the justification for the conclusion. Use the figure at the left.

13. Given: ∠3 and ∠4 are supplementary angles.
Conclusion: m∠3 + m∠4 = 180.

14. Given: $\overrightarrow{GI}$ bisects ∠FGH.
Conclusion: m∠1 = m∠2.

15. Given: m∠1 = m∠2.
Conclusion: $\overrightarrow{GI}$ bisects ∠FGH.

Review

In 16–18, give the definition.

16. acute angle *(Lesson 3-2)*

17. segment *(Lesson 1-8)*

18. circle *(Lesson 2-5)*

19. A complement of ∠T has five times the measure of ∠T. What is m∠T? *(Lesson 3-2)*

20. $\overrightarrow{HF}$ and $\overrightarrow{HI}$ are opposite rays. Find m∠FHG. *(Lesson 3-2)*

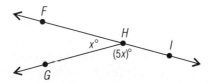

21. An angle is 13° less than its complement. Find its measure. *(Lesson 3-2)*

22. Let v be the measure of an obtuse angle. Graph all possibilities for v on a number line. *(Lesson 3-2)*

23. $\overrightarrow{XW}$ bisects right angle YXZ. What is the measure of ∠YXW? *(Lesson 3-2)*

24. ∠2 and ∠3 are vertical angles. If m∠2 = 12q and m∠3 = 4z, solve for q in terms of z. *(Lesson 3-2)*

25. If m∠*ABC* = 101 in the situation below, find m∠*DBC*. *(Lesson 3-1)*

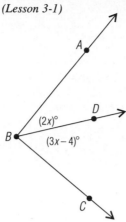

$(2x)°$

$(3x - 4)°$

In 26 and 27, rewrite each statement as a conditional. *(Lesson 2-2)*

26. All squares are rectangles.

27. Two angles cannot be both acute and supplementary.

Exploration

28. The given information is from outside mathematics.
   a. Make a conclusion from the given information.
   b. How sure (in percent) are you of your conclusion?
      i. Today is Monday.
      ii. Last week the football team won its game.
      iii. You toss a coin nine times and it shows "heads" each time.

3-4

Parallel Lines

Lines have **tilt.** The tilt of a line can be measured by an angle it makes with some line of reference. Often the reference line is horizontal. A road might be described as having a *grade* of 7°, which means that the angle it makes with the horizontal has a measure of 7°.

Now consider angles formed when *two* lines *m* and *n* are intersected by a third line, a **transversal.** Eight angles are formed, as numbered below; four by *m* and the transversal, four by *n* and the transversal. Any pair of angles in similar locations with respect to the transversal and each line is called a pair of **corresponding angles.** In the drawing, angles 1 and 5 are corresponding angles, as are angles 2 and 6, 3 and 7, and 4 and 8.

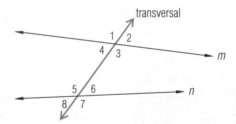

Recall that two coplanar lines are parallel if and only if they are the same line or they do not intersect. (In symbols, $\ell \parallel m \Leftrightarrow \ell = m$ *or* $\ell \cap m = \varnothing$.) If two lines have the same tilt, that is, if they make the same angle with a transversal, you would definitely think they are parallel.

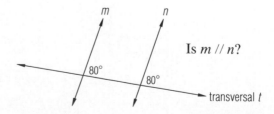

Yet, on Earth, two north-south streets make the same angle with any east-west street, but they would intersect at the North Pole (and

South Pole!) if extended. Also, in perspective drawings, some parallel lines meet at a vanishing point. Assumptions about parallel lines are needed to ensure that the geometry you are studying is not the geometry of the curved surface of Earth or the geometry of perspective drawings. The first postulate says that lines with the same tilt are parallel.

Corresponding Angles Postulate:

> If two coplanar lines are cut by a transversal so that two corresponding angles have the same measure, then the lines are parallel.

When using this postulate as a justification, you may abbreviate it:
$$\text{corr.} \angle s = \Rightarrow \text{ // lines.}$$

The second postulate is the converse of the first.

Parallel Lines Postulate:

> If two lines are parallel and are cut by a transversal, corresponding angles have the same measure.

This postulate may be abbreviated: // lines $\Rightarrow$ corr.$\angle s$ =.

Information about linear pairs and vertical angles can be used with the Parallel Lines Postulate to determine measures of angles formed by parallel lines.

■ ■ ■ ■ ■ ■ ■ ■

Example 1 s // t as pictured below. (The >s on the lines s and t indicate that s is parallel to t.) What is m$\angle 8$?

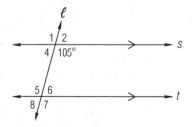

Solution Here are the steps in the thinking, with justifications.

m$\angle 7 = 105$	because // lines $\Rightarrow$ corr. $\angle s$ =. (Parallel Lines Postulate)
m$\angle 7$ + m$\angle 8 = 180$	because of the Linear Pair Theorem.
105 + m$\angle 8 = 180$	because of substitution.
m$\angle 8 = 75$	because of the Addition Property of Equality.

In the coordinate plane, the tilt of a nonvertical line is indicated by the number called the *slope* of the line. You learned about slope in algebra; some ideas are reviewed here.

Definition:

The **slope** of the line through (x_1, y_1) and (x_2, y_2), with $x_1 \neq x_2$, is $\dfrac{y_2 - y_1}{x_2 - x_1}$.

The slope is the change in *y*-values divided by the corresponding change in *x*-values. It tells how many units the line goes up or down for every unit the line goes to the right. The slope of a horizontal line is equal to zero, while the slope of a vertical line is undefined.

Example 2   Find the slope of the line through (7, 5) and (2, 4).

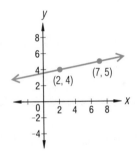

Solution   Use the definition. Here $(x_1, y_1) = (7, 5)$ and $(x_2, y_2) = (2, 4)$, so the slope $= \dfrac{4 - 5}{2 - 7} = \dfrac{-1}{-5} = \dfrac{1}{5}$.

Check   The line goes up $\dfrac{1}{5}$ unit for each unit you move to the right. Thus, as you move right 5 units (from 2 to 7), the line goes up 1 unit (from 4 to 5). So it checks.

Example 3   Find the slope of the line with equation $4x + 3y = -12$.

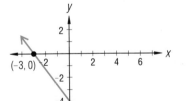

Solution   Find two points on the line. We find (-3, 0) and (6, -12). Now use the definition of slope with these two points.

slope $= \dfrac{-12 - 0}{6 - -3} = \dfrac{-12}{9} = \dfrac{-4}{3}$

Check   This line should go down 4 units for every 3 units moved to the right. An accurate·graph shows it does.

Since slope is a measure of the tilt of a line, the next theorem should come as no surprise. A proof requires quite a bit of algebra and is omitted.

Parallel Lines and Slopes Theorem:

Two nonvertical lines are parallel if and only if they have the same slope.

All vertical lines, of course, are parallel as well. Thus, to determine whether lines are parallel, you only have to know their slopes.

The Parallel Lines and Slopes Theorem is two conditionals. When using it to justify that lines are parallel, you can abbreviate it: = slopes $\Rightarrow$ // lines. When using it to justify equal slopes, write: // lines $\Rightarrow$ = slopes.

Suppose two lines ℓ and n are each parallel to a third line m. Then, because // lines $\Rightarrow$ = slopes, ℓ and m have the same slope, and so do m and n. Thus ℓ and n have the same slope. Then, since = slopes $\Rightarrow$ // lines, ℓ and n are parallel. This argument proves a simple theorem.

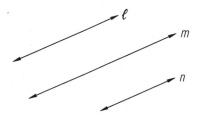

Transitivity of Parallelism Theorem:

In a plane, if ℓ // m and m // n, then ℓ // n.

In words, if two lines are parallel to a third line, then they are parallel to each other.

Questions

Covering the Reading

In 1–3, refer to the drawing below. Consider line ℓ as a transversal to lines m and n.

1. $\angle 5$ and __?__ are corresponding angles.

2. $\angle 1$ and __?__ are corresponding angles.

3. If m$\angle 4$ = m$\angle 6$, what is wrong with the drawing?

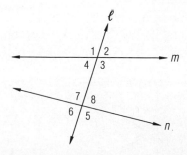

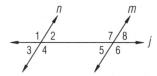

In 4 and 5, use the drawing at the left.

4. If $\overline{AB} \parallel \overline{CD}$ and m$\angle ABE = 80$, find m$\angle DCB$.

5. *True* or *false*?   If m$\angle ABC = $ m$\angle FCD$, then $\overline{AB} \parallel \overline{CD}$.

6. *True* or *false*?   The Corresponding Angles Postulate is true on the surface of the earth.

In 7 and 8, find the slope of the line containing the two points.

7. (1, 4) and (6, 2)   **8.** (3, -7) and (-7, 3)

9. If two nonvertical lines are parallel, what can you say about their slopes?

In 10 and 11, find the slope of a line parallel to the line with the given equation.

10. $y = 4x - 5$ **11.** $12x - 3y = 10$

12. For what lines is slope not defined?

13. What justifies the fact that when two lines are parallel to the same line they are also parallel to each other?

Applying the Mathematics

In 14 and 15, use the figure below. $m \parallel n$.

14. If m$\angle 1 = 122$, find the measures of as many other angles as you can.

15. a. Name all angles with the same measure as $\angle 6$.
     b. Name all angles supplementary to $\angle 6$.

In 16 and 17, use the figure below. A, B, C, and D are collinear. $\overline{BE} \parallel \overline{CF}$.

16. If m$\angle ABE = 106$, then m$\angle$ _?_ $= 106$.

17. $\angle EBC$ and _?_ are corresponding angles.

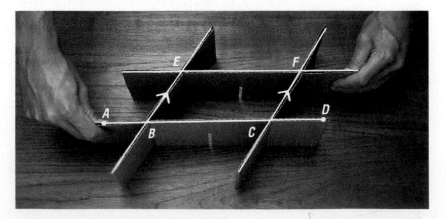

18. Use the coordinate plane sketched below.
    a. Which line has the largest slope?
    b. Which line has negative slope?

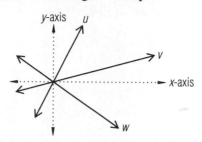

19. *True* or *false*?   The slope of the line containing (x_1, y_1) and (x_2, y_2) equals the slope of the line containing (x_2, y_2) and (x_1, y_1).

20. Which would probably be easier to climb, a cliff with a grade of 65° or one with a grade of 80°?

In 21 and 22, state the justification for the conclusion.

21. Given: $m\angle 1 = m\angle 6$ as shown at the right.
    Conclusion: $\ell \parallel m$.

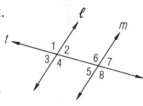

Review

22. Given: the figure at the right.
    Conclusion: $m\angle 2 = m\angle 3$. *(Lessons 3-3, 3-2)*

23. Draw an obtuse scalene triangle. *(Lessons 3-2, 2-7)*

24. M is the midpoint of $\overline{AB}$. N is the midpoint of $\overline{MB}$. Fill in the blanks with numbers. (Hint: Draw a picture.)
    a. If $AB = 5$, then $MN = \underline{\ ?\ }$.
    b. If $AN = x$, then $NB = \underline{\ ?\ }$. *(Lesson 2-5)*

25. M is the midpoint of $\overline{RS}$. If M has coordinate -2 and S has coordinate 31, find the coordinate of R. *(Lessons 2-5, 1-2)*

Exploration

26. With a ruler, draw three rays $\overrightarrow{OP}$, $\overrightarrow{OQ}$ and $\overrightarrow{OR}$. Let A be any point on $\overrightarrow{OP}$. Let B be any point on $\overrightarrow{OQ}$. Let C be any point on $\overrightarrow{OR}$. Draw six lines: $\overleftrightarrow{AB}$, $\overleftrightarrow{BC}$, $\overleftrightarrow{AC}$, $\overleftrightarrow{PQ}$, $\overleftrightarrow{PR}$, and $\overleftrightarrow{QR}$. Verify the incredible discovery of Gerard Desargues in the early 1600s, that either (1) $\overleftrightarrow{AB} \parallel \overleftrightarrow{PQ}$, $\overleftrightarrow{AC} \parallel \overleftrightarrow{PR}$, or $\overleftrightarrow{BC} \parallel \overleftrightarrow{QR}$; or (2) the three points of intersection of these pairs of lines are collinear. (This result is known as Desargues' Theorem.)

A bookcase is pictured above. There are many right angles in the
bookcase (though, due to perspective, they don't all look that way).
The angles at the corner of this page are right angles. Right angles
are very common. As you know, the sides of right angles are called
perpendicular.

> **Definition:**
>
> Two segments, rays, or lines are **perpendicular** if and only if
> the lines containing them form a 90° angle.

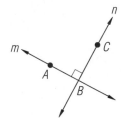

Perpendicular lines need not be horizontal and vertical. $\angle ABC$ above
is a right angle, so m and n are perpendicular. The ⌐ sign in the
drawing indicates perpendicularity. The symbol $\perp$ is read "is perpen-
dicular to." You can write $m \perp n$, $\overline{AB} \perp \overleftrightarrow{BC}$, $\overleftrightarrow{AB} \perp \overleftrightarrow{BC}$, or $m \perp \overleftrightarrow{BC}$
to indicate perpendicularity.

When lines form one right angle, the Vertical Angle and Linear Pair
Theorems force the other three angles to be right angles. So you can
put the ⌐ symbol by any of the angles.

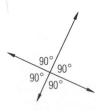

The two edges of this page are each perpendicular to the bottom edge. If the edges are extended, corresponding 90° angles appear. By the Corresponding Angles Postulate, the side edges are parallel. This argument proves a useful theorem.

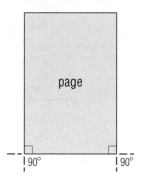

Two Perpendiculars Theorem:

If two coplanar lines ℓ and m are each perpendicular to the same line, then they are parallel to each other.

In symbols, if ℓ ⊥ n and m ⊥ n, then ℓ // m. "Is perpendicular to" does not satisfy the transitive property.

Suppose you are given these lines as shown below with one perpendicular relation (ℓ ⊥ m) and one parallel relation (m // n) among the lines. There are 90° angles where ℓ intersects m. Since // lines ⇒ corr. ∠s =, there are also 90° angles where ℓ intersects n. So ℓ ⊥ n. This simple argument proves: if ℓ ⊥ m and m // n, then ℓ ⊥ n.

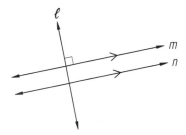

In words, this relation is stated as follows.

Perpendicular to Parallels Theorem:

In a plane, if a line is perpendicular to one of two parallel lines, then it is perpendicular to the other.

As you think of parallel lines as having the same tilt, so you may think of two perpendicular lines as having the most different tilts imaginable. Since you know that parallel lines have the same slope, you might expect that the slopes of two perpendicular lines are about as different as two related numbers can be. What numbers are most different? Opposites? Reciprocals? In fact, the slopes of perpendicular lines are both. Each slope is the opposite of the reciprocal of the other. In symbols, if the slope of a given line is m, the slope of any line perpendicular to it is $-\frac{1}{m}$. Since $m \cdot -\frac{1}{m} = -1$, the next theorem is simply stated as follows.

Perpendicular Lines and Slopes Theorem:

Two nonvertical lines are perpendicular if and only if the product of their slopes is -1.

A proof of this theorem requires quite a bit of algebra, and is omitted.

If one of two perpendicular lines is vertical (with undefined slope), it is perpendicular to a horizontal line (with 0 slope). Since one of the lines has undefined slope, there is no product of slopes in this case.

Example A line has slope 5. What is the slope of a line perpendicular to it?

Solution All lines perpendicular to a given line are parallel (Two Perpendiculars Theorem), thus they have the same slope. Let that slope be s. By the Perpendicular Lines and Slopes Theorem,
$$5s = -1.$$
Solving the equation, $\qquad s = -\frac{1}{5}.$

Check Note that $-\frac{1}{5}$ is the opposite of the reciprocal of the given slope 5.

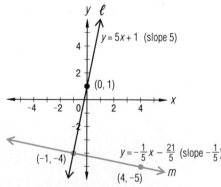

An instance of the Example is graphed above. Line ℓ has equation $y = 5x + 1$. Line m has equation $y = -\frac{1}{5}x - \frac{21}{5}$. $y = 5x + 1$ contains $(0, 1)$ and $(-1, -4)$ and has slope 5. $y = -\frac{1}{5}x - \frac{21}{5}$ contains $(-1, -4)$ and $(4, -5)$ and has slope $-\frac{1}{5}$. Lines ℓ and m are perpendicular.

In Lessons 3-4 and 3-5 you have seen how parallel and perpendicular lines can be determined either through angle measures or by slopes. The table below shows how parallelism and perpendicularity relate to the ideas in Chapters 1 and 2 of points as locations and points as ordered pairs.

	a point as a location	a point as an ordered pair (x, y)
line		$Ax + By = C$
measure of tilt of line	angle measure	slope
parallel lines	corresponding angles = in measure	slopes equal
perpendicular lines	lines form 90° angles	product of slopes = −1

Questions

Covering the Reading

1. **a** Define: perpendicular lines.
   b. Write the meaning half of the definition.

2. Trace line ℓ below. Draw a line through point P perpendicular to ℓ.

3. What are the *two* symbols indicating perpendicularity?

4. **a.** Trace the figure below. Draw a line t perpendicular to line m.
   b. If $m \parallel n$, must t also be perpendicular to n?

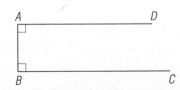

5. In the drawing below, $\overline{AD} \perp \overline{AB}$ and $\overline{BC} \perp \overline{AB}$. What theorem justifies the conclusion that $\overline{AD} \parallel \overline{BC}$?

6. In the drawing below, $\ell \parallel m$ and $m \perp n$. What theorem justifies the conclusion that $\ell \perp n$?

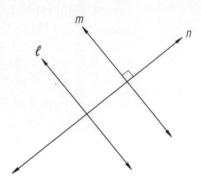

7. A line has slope $\frac{2}{3}$. What is the slope of a line perpendicular to it?

8. A line has slope x. What is the slope of a line perpendicular to it?

9. Write the two conditionals making up the Perpendicular Lines and Slopes Theorem.

10. Line s is perpendicular to line t below. What is the slope of s?

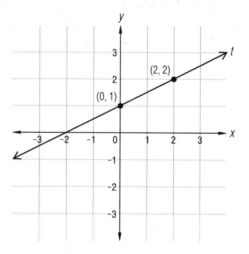

11. Below, $\overrightarrow{AD} \perp \overrightarrow{AC}$. Answer with numbers.
   a. $m\angle DAC = $ ___?___
   b. $m\angle DAE = $ ___?___

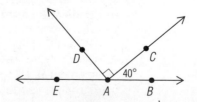

12. Why are street intersections often planned so the streets are perpendicular, even when one has to be bent to do so, as in the diagram below?

In 13 and 14, use the figure below, given $\overline{QR} \parallel \overline{SU}$, $\overline{QT} \parallel \overline{UP}$, and $\overline{QT} \perp \overline{TU}$ as indicated.

13. Justify each conclusion using one of the following justifications.
   $\parallel$ lines $\Rightarrow$ corr. $\angle$s =
   corr. $\angle$s = $\Rightarrow \parallel$ lines
   $\ell \perp n$ and $m \perp n \Rightarrow \ell \parallel m$
   $\ell \perp m$ and $m \parallel n \Rightarrow \ell \perp n$
   $\ell \perp m \Rightarrow 90°$ angle
   $90°$ angle $\Rightarrow \ell \perp m$
   a. m$\angle S$ = m$\angle PQR$ **b.** $\overline{QT} \perp \overline{QR}$
   c. m$\angle SQT$ = m$\angle P$ **d.** m$\angle QTU$ = 90

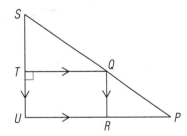

14. If m$\angle PQR$ = 65, give the measure of each angle.
   a. $\angle S$ **b.** $\angle TQR$
   c. $\angle TQS$ **d.** $\angle P$

15. A line has equation $9y + 2x = 180$. What is the slope of any line perpendicular to this line?

16. Consider this statement: If $\overline{AB} \perp \overline{BC}$ and $\overline{BC} \perp \overline{CD}$, then $\overline{AB} \perp \overline{CD}$.
   a. Draw an instance of this statement in a plane, or tell why the drawing is impossible.
   b. Draw an instance of this statement in space, or tell why the drawing is impossible.

17. Lines *r*, *s*, and *t* intersect as shown below. m∠1 = 70 and *s* ∥ *r*. Find the measures of angles 2 through 8. *(Lesson 3-4)*

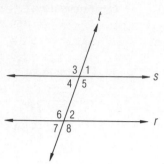

18. A line contains (4, -7) and (-10, -9). Find its slope. *(Lesson 3-4)*

In 19-21, use the figure below. State the justification for the conclusion. *(Lessons 3-4, 3-3, 3-2)*

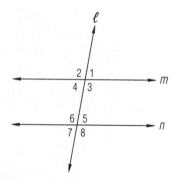

19. Given: m∠3 = m∠8.
Conclusion: *m* ∥ *n*.

20. Given: the figure.
Conclusion: ∠7 and ∠8 are supplementary angles.

21. Using a protractor, find m∠6. *(Lesson 3-1)* ⌐

22. Which of the if-then statements of Question 13 refers to the meaning half of the definition of perpendicular lines? *(Lesson 2-5)*

23. In the figure below, identify the points on ⊙A ∩ ⊙B. *(Lesson 2-6)*

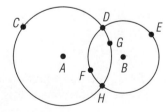

24. Draw the figure of Question 23 using a compass. *(Previous course)*

25. Draw a 24° angle. *(Lesson 3-1)*

26. Mazes or labyrinths are puzzles where you try to find a path from the start to the finish. Mazes are usually designed so the walls are either horizontal or vertical.
    a. Try to find the way from the START to the FINISH in the maze pictured below. (From *The Dell Big Book of Crosswords and Pencil Puzzles #5*, Dell Publishing Co., 1985)
    b. Design your own maze.

3-6

Constructing Perpendiculars

You are in a park when someone gets hurt and needs help. (Below is drawn a picture of this situation as seen from the air.) You want to run to the nearest road as fast as you can to flag down a car. What is the shortest route to the road?

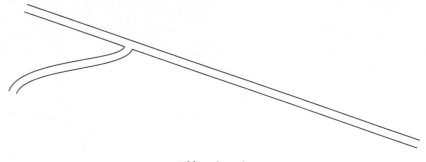

● Your location

The answer is that you should run along the line through your location perpendicular to the road.

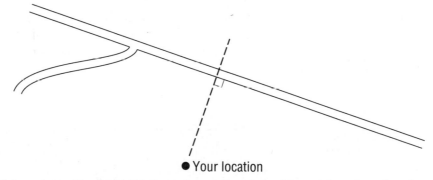

● Your location

This perpendicular may be accurately placed by either drawing it or constructing it. In a **drawing,** you may use any tools. You can use a ruler, a protractor, a computer drawing program, a compass, a T square, or any other tool.

A **construction** is a precise way of drawing which uses specific tools and follows specific rules. From the time of the ancient Greeks, only two tools have been permitted in making a construction. They are the **unmarked straightedge** and the **compass.**

Use of these tools follows three specific rules.

Point rule:

> A point must either be given or be the intersection of figures that have been already constructed.
> *If a figure is given, you can assume as many points are given as will determine the figure.*

Straightedge rule:

> A straightedge can draw the line $\overleftrightarrow{AB}$ through two points A and B.
> *A ruler can substitute for the straightedge, but the marks on the ruler must be ignored.*

Compass rule:

> A compass can draw a circle with center at a point A and containing a second point B.
> *Also, a compass can be lifted keeping the same radius.*

Constructing a geometric figure is like playing a game with rules telling you what is legal and what is illegal. In this book we describe a construction by showing you the steps in it. A sequence of steps leading to a desired end is called an **algorithm.** When we describe a construction, we show you the algorithm for it.

One of the most important constructions is of the line passing through the midpoint of a segment and perpendicular to it. This is the **perpendicular bisector** or ⊥ **bisector** of the segment. (A **bisector** of a segment is its midpoint or any plane, line, ray, or segment which intersects it at its midpoint only.)

unmarked straightedge and compass

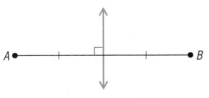

the ⊥ bisector of $\overline{AB}$

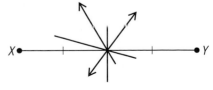

some of the many bisectors of $\overline{XY}$

Example 1   Construct the perpendicular bisector of a given segment $\overline{AB}$.

Solution   Here are the algorithm steps.
Step 1.   ⊙A containing B (Compass rule)
Step 2.   ⊙B containing A (Compass rule)
Step 3.   ⊙A and ⊙B intersect at
                new points C and D.   (Point rule)
Step 4. $\overleftrightarrow{CD}$ (Straightedge rule)

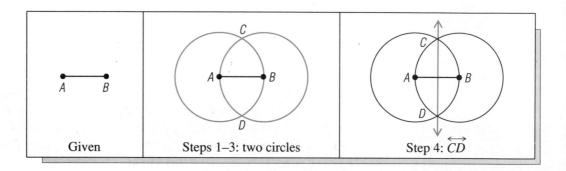

| Given | Steps 1–3: two circles | Step 4: $\overleftrightarrow{CD}$ |

A bonus is that the midpoint of $\overline{AB}$ has also been constructed. It is the intersection of $\overline{AB}$ and $\overleftrightarrow{CD}$ in Step 4.

The steps in Example 1 will give the ⊥ bisector of any given segment. Although at this point you cannot prove that this algorithm works, later in this course you will have enough information to do so. For now, you should be able to repeat the steps of the construction for any segment $\overline{AB}$.

The construction of the perpendicular bisector is a building block for many other constructions.

Example 2   Construct the line perpendicular to $\overleftrightarrow{AP}$ through point P on the line.

Solution 1   The idea is to locate the point B on the other side of P from A, so that P is the midpoint of $\overline{AB}$. Then construct the ⊥ bisector of $\overline{AB}$. That is the desired line. Here is an algorithm for this construction.

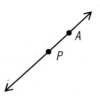

Step 1.   ⊙P containing A (Compass rule)
Step 2.   ⊙P intersects $\overleftrightarrow{AP}$ at A and B.   (Point rule)
Steps 3–6.   Construct the ⊥ bisector of $\overline{AB}$ as in Example 1.
Step 3.   ⊙A containing B (Compass rule)
Step 4.   ⊙B containing A (Compass rule)
Step 5.   ⊙B intersects ⊙A at D and E.   (Point rule)
Step 6. $\overleftrightarrow{DE}$ (Straightedge rule)

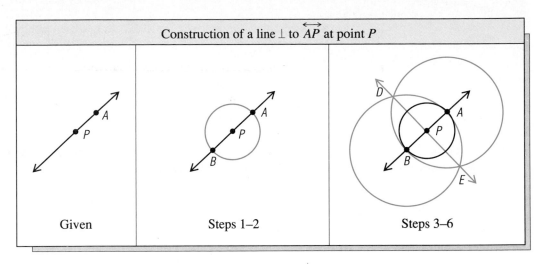

Construction of a line ⊥ to $\overleftrightarrow{AP}$ at point P

| Given | Steps 1–2 | Steps 3–6 |

A **subroutine** is an algorithm you already know that you use in another algorithm. Computer programs often have subroutines. It saves having to write the same steps over and over again. Since Steps 3–6 of Solution 1 are the ⊥ bisector construction, you can write the algorithm in a shorter way. Steps 1 and 2 are the same as in Solution 1. But Step 3 is different.

Solution 2 Step 1. ⊙P containing A
Step 2. ⊙P intersects $\overleftrightarrow{AP}$ at A and B.
Step 3. Subroutine: $\overleftrightarrow{DE}$, the ⊥ bisector of $\overline{AB}$.

What about the injured person in the park? In Question 11 you are asked to follow an algorithm to construct the unique line perpendicular to a given line through a point not on that line. That line gives the path you should take.

Questions

Covering the Reading

1. What tools may you use in drawings?

2. What tools may you use in constructions?

3. What are the three rules of a construction?

4. In constructions, what points can be used?

5. What is an algorithm?

6. What is the perpendicular bisector of a segment?

In 7 and 8, use the figure at the left.

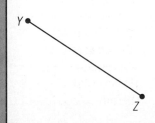

7. Trace $\overline{YZ}$. Draw a bisector that is not a perpendicular bisector.

8. Trace $\overline{YZ}$. Construct its perpendicular bisector.

9. Trace the line below. Construct the perpendicular to ℓ through point Q.

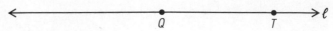

10. What is a subroutine?

11. Trace the figure below. Then follow this algorithm to construct the perpendicular to $\overleftrightarrow{AC}$ from P.
Step 1.　$\odot P$ containing A
Step 2.　$\odot P$ intersects $\overleftrightarrow{AC}$ at A and B.
Step 3.　Subroutine: $\overleftrightarrow{DE}$, the $\perp$ bisector of $\overline{AB}$.
P lies on $\overleftrightarrow{DE}$.

12. Give the rule justifying the first two steps in Question 11.

13. Trace the figure below. Use the algorithm of Question 11 to construct the perpendicular to $\overleftrightarrow{QR}$ through T.

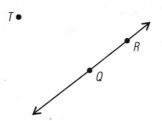

14. Trace the road and the clubhouse dot. Construct the shortest path from the clubhouse to the road.

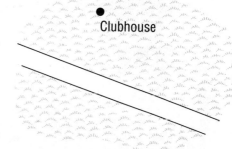

15. Trace $\overline{AB}$ below. Follow the steps. What have you constructed?
Step 1.　$\odot A$ containing B
Step 2.　$\odot B$ containing A
Step 3.　$\odot A$ and $\odot B$ intersect at C and D.
Step 4.　$\overline{AC}, \overline{BC}$

144

16. a. Measure $\overline{GH}$, $\overline{GI}$, $\overline{GJ}$, $\overline{GK}$, $\overline{GL}$, and $\overline{GM}$ to the nearest millimeter.
 b. Which is the shortest?

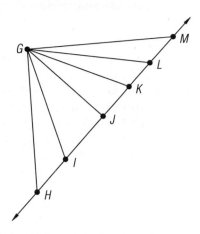

Review

17. Break the definition of perpendicular lines into its meaning and sufficient condition halves. *(Lessons 3-5, 2-5)*

18. a. What is the slope of the line with equation $x - 2y = 15$?
 (Lesson 3-4)
 b. What is the slope of a line perpendicular to it? *(Lesson 3-5)* ·

19. In the figure at the left, $\ell \parallel m$. If $m\angle 6 = m\angle 1 + 12$, find $m\angle 1$. *(Lessons 3-4, 3-2)*

20. Fill in the table with $\ell \parallel n$, $\ell \perp n$, or *can't tell*. *(Lessons 3-5, 3-4)*

	$m \parallel n$	$m \perp n$
$\ell \parallel m$	?	?
$\ell \perp m$	?	?

Exploration

21. Because the rules for constructions are quite specific, there are some figures that can be drawn but cannot be constructed. The Greeks were very puzzled by this and three problems became famous. They are called "squaring the circle," "duplicating the cube," and "trisecting an angle." Find out what one of these problems was.

Summary

To show $p \Rightarrow q$ is true, you must show that whenever p is true, so is q. One way to do this is to give a general property for which $p \Rightarrow q$ is a special case. This general property is a justification for the truth of $p \Rightarrow q$. The justification must be a postulate, a definition, or a theorem already proved. Then q is a conclusion from p; q has been proved from p; q follows from p.

The basic properties of angles are found in the Angle Measure Postulate. Angles may be classified by their measure as zero, acute, right, obtuse, or straight. Some pairs of angles are vertical angles, in which case their measures are equal. If they form a linear pair, then they are supplementary.

The later results of this chapter stem from two assumptions: the Corresponding Angles Postulate and the Parallel Lines Postulate. These postulates lead to the following theorems:

Transitivity of Parallelism Theorem:
If $\ell \parallel m$ and $m \parallel n$, then $\ell \parallel n$.

Two Perpendiculars Theorem:
If $\ell \perp m$ and $n \perp m$, then $\ell \parallel n$.
Perpendicular to Parallels Theorem:
If $\ell \perp m$ and $m \parallel n$, then $\ell \perp n$.

The word "construction" has a special meaning in geometry. Perpendicular lines, perpendicular bisectors, reflection images, and angle bisectors can all be constructed following specific rules of construction laid down by the ancient Greeks. With these rules, only given or intersecting points of figures can be used and only a straightedge and compass are allowed. In contrast, any instruments, even computers, can be used to make drawings.

In the coordinate plane, the tilt of a nonvertical line is measured by its slope. Nonvertical lines are parallel if and only if they have the same slope. Nonvertical lines are perpendicular if and only if the product of their slopes is -1.

Vocabulary

Below are the new terms and phrases for this chapter. You should be able to give a general description and specific example of each. For those terms that are starred, you should be able to give a *good* definition. You should also be able to rewrite each named theorem or postulate in if-then or if-and-only-if form, as appropriate.

Lesson 3-1
*angle, vertex of angle
sides of angle
$\angle$, $\angle A$, $\angle ABC$, $\angle 1$
interior of angle, exterior of angle
measure of angle, m$\angle ABC$
degree, °, protractor
Angle Measure Postulate
Angle Addition Property

Lesson 3-2
*zero angle, *acute angle,
*right angle, *obtuse angle,
*straight angle
*complementary angles

*supplementary angles
complements, supplements
*adjacent angles, *linear pair
*vertical angles
Linear Pair Theorem
Vertical Angle Theorem

Lesson 3-3
*proof, conclusion, justification

Lesson 3-4
transversal, corresponding angles
*slope
Corresponding Angles Postulate
Parallel Lines Postulate
Parallel Lines and Slopes Theorem
Transitivity of Parallelism Theorem

Lesson 3-5
*perpendicular, $\perp$, $\neg$
Two Perpendiculars Theorem
Perpendicular to Parallels Theorem
Perpendicular Lines and
    Slopes Theorem

Lesson 3-6
drawing, construction
Point rule in constructions
Straightedge rule in constructions
Compass rule in constructions
algorithm
*perpendicular bisector, *bisector
subroutine

Progress Self-Test

Directions: Take this test as you would take a test in class. Use a ruler, compass and a protractor. Then check your work with the solutions in the Selected Answers section in the back of the book.

1. Sketch two angles ∠1 and ∠2 that are a linear pair.

In 2–4, refer to the figure below.

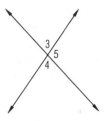

2. If m∠3 = 77, find m∠4.

3. Because of their positions, ∠3 and ∠4 are called __?__ .

4. If m∠3 = 2x, then m∠5 = __?__ .

5. A movie goer has to look 15° above eye level to see the movie screen. How many more degrees would the movie goer have to bend his or her head to be staring straight up at the ceiling?

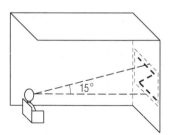

6. ∠1 and ∠2 are complementary. If m∠1 = 5x − 7 and m∠2 = 4x + 16, find m∠1.

7. Use a protractor to find the measure of ∠A below.

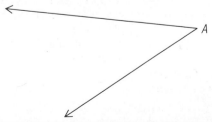

8. Draw a 72° angle.

In 9 and 10, use the figure below.

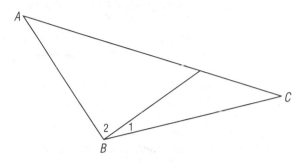

9. If m∠ABC = 110 and m∠2 = 4 · m∠1, find m∠1.

10. *Multiple choice.* Tell which property justifies the conclusion: m∠1 + m∠2 = m∠ABC.
(a) definition of supplementary angles (meaning)
(b) definition of supplementary angles (sufficient condition)
(c) Linear Pair Theorem
(d) Angle Addition Property

11. Let m∠1 = 21 + x. If ∠1 is acute, graph all possibilities for x on a number line.

12. $\overrightarrow{BC}$ is the bisector of angle ABD below. If m∠ABC = 14y − 3 and m∠CBD = 37 − y, what is y?

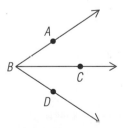

In 13 and 14, complete the statement.

13. If two lines are perpendicular to the same line, then they are __?__ .

14. If two lines are parallel to the same line, then they are __?__ .

In 15 and 16, consider $\overline{AB}$ drawn below.

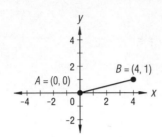

15. What is its slope?

16. What is the slope of the perpendicular bisector of $\overline{AB}$?

In 17 and 18, a line has equation $2x - y = 6$.

17. What is the slope of this line?

18. What is the slope of any line perpendicular to this line?

In 19 and 20, if $\ell \parallel m$ below, give the measure of the indicated angle.

19. $\angle 4$ 20. $\angle 5$

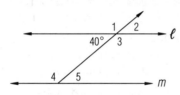

21. *Multiple choice.* Hank has to get quickly to the street for help. Which path should he take?
   (a) w (b) x
   (c) y (d) z

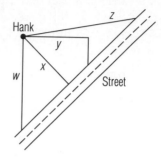

22. Trace the figure below. Construct the perpendicular to $\overleftrightarrow{RT}$ containing T.

23. Justify the conclusion.
   Given: Q is the midpoint of $\overline{OP}$.
   Conclusion: $OQ = QP$

Chapter Review

Questions on **SPUR** Objectives

SPUR stands for **S**kills, **P**roperties, **U**ses, and **R**epresentations.
The Chapter Review questions are grouped according to the
SPUR Objectives for this chapter.

SKILLS deal with the procedures used to get answers.

■ **Objective A:** *Draw and analyze drawings of angles. (Lessons 3-1, 3-2)*

In 1 and 2, use the drawing below.

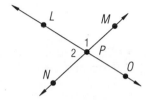

1. **a.** Name a straight angle.
   b. Name an angle with measure 0°.
   c. Name a linear pair.
   d. Give two other names for ∠1.

2. Does ∠2 appear to be acute, right, or obtuse?

In 3 and 4, sketch possible angles 5 and 6.

3. ∠5 and ∠6 are supplementary and adjacent.

4. ∠5 and ∠6 are complementary and have the same measure.

In 5 and 6, refer to the figure below.
Find **a.** m∠1, **b.** m∠3, **c.** m∠4:

5. if m∠2 = 78;

6. if m∠2 = 3x.

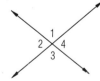

■ **Objective B.** *Draw angles with a given measure and measure drawn angles. (Lesson 3-1)*

In 7 and 8, measure the angles to the nearest degree using a protractor.

7. Angle R ı

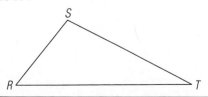

8.

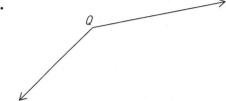

9. Draw two angles with measure 58° that share a common side.

10. Draw an angle with measure 92°.

■ **Objective C:** *Use algebra to represent and find measures of angles. (Lessons 3-1, 3-2)*

11. Let *m* be the measure of an acute angle. Graph all possibilities for *m* on a number line.

12. Point *D* is in the interior of ∠ABC. If m∠ABD = 5t and m∠DBC = 3t and m∠ABC = 72, find the value of *t*.

13. Let m∠3 = 12 − x. If ∠3 is straight, what is *x*?

14. Let m∠4 = 31 + y. If ∠4 is obtuse, graph the possible values for *y* on a number line.

In 15 and 16, ∠1 and ∠2 below form a linear pair.

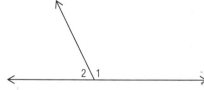

15. If m∠2 is one-fourth m∠1, find the measures of ∠1 and ∠2.

16. If m∠1 = 7x − 6 and m∠2 = 5x + 18, find m∠1 and m∠2.

In 17 and 18, use the figure below.

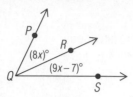

17. If m∠*PQS* = 40, find *x*.

18. If $\overrightarrow{QR}$ is the bisector of ∠*PQS*, find m∠*PQS*.

19. Lines ℓ and *m* intersect as in the diagram below. Find *y*.

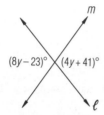

20. An angle has a measure 9 times that of its complement. What is the measure of the angle?

21. An angle's measure is 42° less than the measure of a supplement to it. What is the measure of the angle?

22. Let *q* be the measure of an angle which is less than its supplement. Find all possibilities for *q*.

23. ∠5 and ∠6 are vertical angles. If m∠5 = 17*z* and m∠6 = 2*w*, solve for *w* in terms of *z*.

■ **Objective D:** *Determine measures of angles formed by parallel lines and transversals.* (*Lesson 3-4*)

In 24 and 25, use the figure below where *s* ∥ *t*.

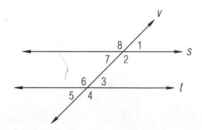

24. If m∠1 = 83, find the measures of angles 2 through 8.

25. If m∠2 = 3 · m∠5, find m∠2.

■ **Objective E:** *Perform the following constructions with a straightedge and a compass: perpendicular bisector, ⊥ from point to line, ⊥ to line at point.* (*Lesson 3-6*)

In 26–30, first trace the figure.

26. Construct the perpendicular bisector of $\overline{AB}$ below.

27. Construct the ⊥ to $\overleftrightarrow{AB}$ above through *B*.

28. Construct the perpendicular to line *m* below through *R*.

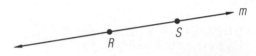

29. Construct the perpendicular to $\overleftrightarrow{AB}$ below from *Q*.

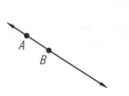

30. Construct the line ⊥ to $\overline{WV}$ through *U*.

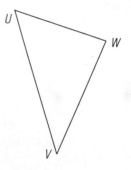

31. a. Follow the algorithm below and perform this construction on any 3 points on a circle of your choosing.

Step 1. $\overleftrightarrow{XY}$

Step 2.   Subroutine:
$\overleftrightarrow{PQ}$, the $\perp$ bisector of $\overline{XY}$

Step 3. $\overleftrightarrow{XZ}$

Step 4.   Subroutine:
$\overleftrightarrow{RS}$ the $\perp$ bisector of $\overline{XZ}$

Step 5. $\overleftrightarrow{PQ}$ intersects $\overleftrightarrow{RS}$ at T, the desired point.

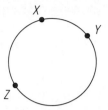

b. What is point T?

c. Give the rule justifying steps 1, 3, and 5 in part **a** above.

Properties deal with the principles behind the mathematics.

■ **Objective F:** *Give justifications for conclusions involving different figures.* (*Lessons 3-2, 3-3, 3-4, 3-5*)

In 32–34, *multiple choice.*   Which statement justifies the conclusion?

32. Given: m$\angle ABD$ = m$\angle DBC$ in the figure below.
Conclusion: $\overrightarrow{BD}$ bisects $\angle ABC$.
(a) Angle Addition Property
(b) definition of angle bisector (meaning)
(c) definition of angle bisector (sufficient condition)
(d) Linear Pair Theorem

33. Given: A is on a circle with radius 5 and center C.
Conclusion: AC = 5.
(a) definition of a circle (meaning)
(b) definition of a circle (sufficient condition)
(c) definition of distance (meaning)
(d) definition of distance (sufficient condition)

34. Given: $\angle 3$ and $\angle 5$ are vertical angles.
Conclusion: m$\angle 3$ = m$\angle 5$.
(a) definition of acute angle (meaning)
(b) definition of acute angle (sufficient condition)
(c) Linear Pair Theorem
(d) Vertical Angle Theorem

In 35 and 36, *multiple choice.*   Choose the correct justification from this list.
(a) If $\ell \parallel m$ and $m \perp n$, then $\ell \perp n$.
(b) If $\ell \perp m$ and $m \perp n$, then $\ell \parallel n$.
(c) If $\ell \parallel m$ and $m \parallel n$, then $\ell \parallel n$.

35. Given: $\overline{MJ} \perp \overline{JK}$
$\overline{MJ} \parallel \overline{KL}$.
Conclusion: $\overline{KL} \perp \overline{JK}$.

36. Given: $\overline{MJ} \perp \overline{JK}$
$\overline{KL} \perp \overline{JK}$.
Conclusion: $\overline{JM} \parallel \overline{KL}$.

In 37–39, justify the conclusion.

37. Given: $\angle 4$ and $\angle 5$ are a linear pair.
Conclusion: m$\angle 4$ + m$\angle 5$ = 180.

38. Given: A and B are distinct points.
Conclusion: There is only one line containing A and B.

39. Given: the figure below.
Conclusion: m$\angle EFG$ + m$\angle GFH$ = m$\angle EFH$.

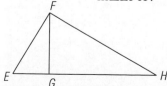

■ **Objective G:** *Apply angle measure to describe real situations.* (Lessons 3-1, 3-2)

40. The latitude of a point P on Earth is often described as the measure of the angle PCE, where C is the center of the earth and E is the point on the equator directly north or south of P. On a diagram like the one below, draw a point Q at 35° latitude.

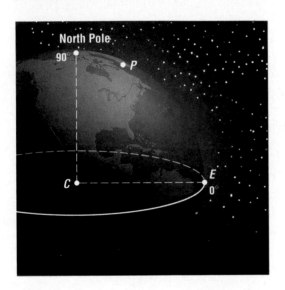

In 41 and 42, trace the diagram at the right.

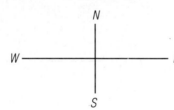

41. Draw a ray going in the direction 20° S of W.

42. A plane is taking off to go 30° E of S. How much would it have to turn to fly due north?

43. A nail is being driven into a wall to hang a picture. If the measure of the smaller angle is 45°, what is the measure of the larger angle?

■ **Objective H:** *Apply constructions and drawings in real situations.* (Lesson 3-6)

44. Some girls are having a race to the river. Trace the river's edge and the starting point and *draw* the shortest path to run.

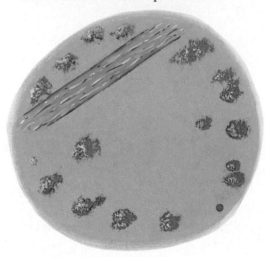

45. A scale drawing of a football field is being made. Many lines perpendicular to $\overleftrightarrow{AB}$ are needed. Trace $\overleftrightarrow{AB}$ and construct the $\perp$ to $\overleftrightarrow{AB}$ through C.

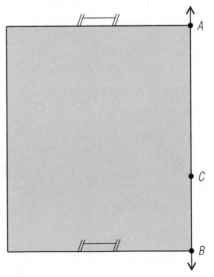

■ **Objective I:** *Determine the slope of a line from its equation or given two points on it.* *(Lesson 3-4)*

46. Give the slope of the line through (-5, -2) and (6, 1).

47. Give the slope of the line through (4, -3) and (-3, 4).

In 48 and 49, find the slope of the line with the given equation.

48. $y = -\frac{3}{5}x + 11$

49. $5x - 3y = 45$

50. Which line below has the greater slope, $2y = x + 1$ or $25y = 5x + 1$?

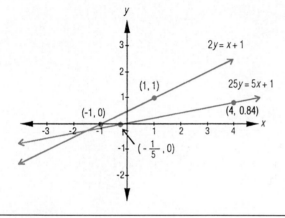

51. Which line has the greater slope, $y = 3x$ or $x = 3y$?

■ **Objective J:** *Determine the slope of a line parallel or perpendicular to a given line.* *(Lessons 3-4, 3-5)*

52. If a line has slope 10, each line parallel to it has slope __?__ and each line perpendicular to it has slope __?__ .

53. If a line has slope $-\frac{2}{3}$, each line parallel to it has slope __?__ and each line perpendicular to it has slope __?__ .

54. Line m goes through points (8, -1) and (-6, -3). If line n is perpendicular to m, what is the slope of n?

55. *Multiple choice.* The lines with equations $y = 2x + 1$ and $y = -2x + 1$ are
(a) parallel;
(b) perpendicular;
(c) neither parallel nor perpendicular.

Reflections

Hermann Rorschach, a Swiss psychiatrist born in 1884, invented a technique for investigating the inner workings of the human mind. He presented ink blots to people and asked them to describe what images they saw. What people saw was supposed to indicate how they thought of themselves and the world in which they lived.

Rorschach ink blots are reflection-symmetric figures like the one shown above.

Reflection-symmetric figures are common in the world of business also. Many companies have logos or trademarks that are reflection-symmetric. Can you name the company associated with the trademark at the right?

Many living creatures have reflection-symmetric shapes. Examples include starfish, manta rays, the leaves and fruits of many trees, beetles, and butterflies. Stars, orbits of planets, sound waves, and crystals are also reflection-symmetric. Because geometry studies these and other real things, many important shapes in geometry are reflection-symmetric. You will examine some of these shapes and their properties in this chapter.

Reflecting Points

The inkblot on the first page of this chapter is an example of a figure and its *reflection image*. It provides still another application of perpendicular lines. Examine the figure below. Think of the picture at the left as the original. It is called the **preimage.** The *reflection image* at the right can be drawn by folding over the line *m* and then tracing. Line *m* is called the **reflecting line** or **line of reflection.**

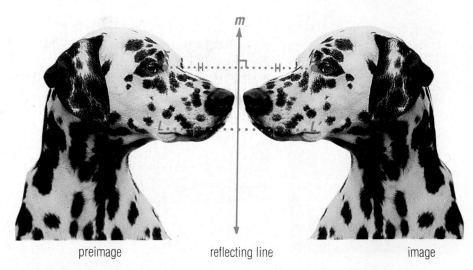

preimage   reflecting line   image

The apostrophe (') indicates corresponding points; E' (read "E prime") corresponds to E. Line *m* is the perpendicular bisector of the segments connecting the corresponding eyes E and E' and the corners of the lips L and L'.

Definition:

For a point P not on a line m, the **reflection image of P over line m** is the point Q if and only if m is the perpendicular bisector of $\overline{PQ}$.

For a point P on m, the **reflection image of P over line m** is P itself.

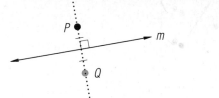

P is not on m.
Q is the reflection image of P.

P is on m.
P is its own reflection image.

In the figures above, let P' be the image of P. Then, at the left, $Q = P'$. At the right, $P = P'$.

Recall that drawing is different than constructing. For *drawing* reflection images of complicated figures, folding and tracing is a good procedure. So is putting a mirror on the reflecting line and sighting the image behind the mirror. For individual points, a quick way of drawing utilizes a protractor.

Example 1   Draw the reflection image P' of point P over line m.

Solution   Here is an algorithm.
1. Place your protractor so that its 90° mark and the center of the protractor are on m.
2. Slide the protractor along m so that the edge line (the line through the 0° and 180° marks) goes through P.
3. Measure the distance d from P to m along the edge line. You may wish to draw the line lightly.
4. Locate P' on the other side of m along the edge, the same distance from P.

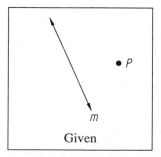

Given

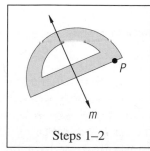

Steps 1–2

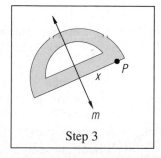

Step 3

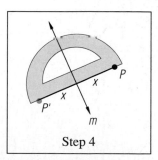

Step 4

Reflection images can also be constructed following the rules for constructions, as shown on the next page.

Example 2 Construct the reflection image of point *B* over line *m*.

Solution Shown are steps in the algorithm of the construction.
Step 1. Identify a point on *m*. Call it *Q*.   (Point rule)
Step 2. ⊙*B* containing *Q*   (Compass rule)
Step 3. ⊙*B* intersects *m* in *Q* and *S*.   (Point rule)
Step 4. ⊙*Q* containing *B*   (Compass rule)
Step 5. ⊙*S* containing *B*   (Why?)
Step 6. ⊙*Q* intersects ⊙*S* in *B* and *B′*.   (Point rule)

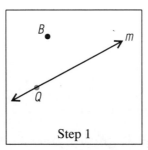

Step 1

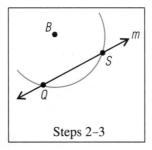

Steps 2–3

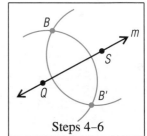

Steps 4–6

Connecting *B* and *B′* yields a bonus, the ⊥ to *m* through *B*.

You can use abbreviations instead of writing statements like "*P* is the reflection image of *R* over line *m*" and "*A′* is the reflection of *A*." Use the lower case letter r to refer to a reflection. When discussing reflections in general, or when the reflecting line is obvious, you can write

$$r(A) = A'$$

for "The reflection image of *A* is *A′*." It is read "r of *A* equals *A′*." When you want to emphasize the reflecting line *m,* write

$$r_m(Q) = P$$

for "The reflection image of *Q* over line *m* is *P*." It is read "r of *Q* over line *m* equals *P*."

Example 3 The reflection image of *A* over line *m* is *B*. Name *B* in two ways using reflection notation.

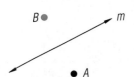

Solution You can write *B* = r(*A*) since the reflecting line is obvious. Or specify the line: *B* = r*m*(*A*).

Reflecting images are often needed for points in the coordinate plane. If the reflecting line is one of the axes, the image is found using the definition of reflection.

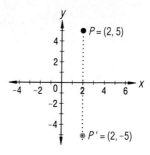

Example 4 Find the image of (2, 5) when reflected over the *x*-axis.

Solution Draw a coordinate plane and let $P = (2, 5)$. Since P is 5 units from the *x*-axis, its image will be 5 units away on the other side. So $P' = (2, -5)$.

In Example 4, $P' = r_x(P)$. So you could write $r_x(P) = (2, -5)$ or $r_x(2, 5) = (2, -5)$.

Questions

Covering the Reading

1. A figure that is to be reflected is called the ___?___.

2. Trace the figure below onto your paper. Then find its reflection image over line *m* by folding and tracing.

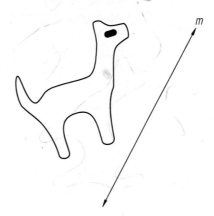

3. Suppose *B* is the reflection image of *A* over line *m*. How are *m*, *A*, and *B* related?

4. When a point *P* is on the reflecting line ℓ, then the reflection image of *P* is ___?___.

5. Trace the drawing at the left.
   a. *Draw* the reflection image of *Q* over line ℓ.
   b. *Construct* the reflection image of *P* over line ℓ.

6. What is the justification for Step 5 in Example 2?

7. What letter is used to denote a reflection?

8. If *P* is a point, write in words:
   a. $r(P)$ **b.** $r_m(P)$.

In 9 and 10, trace the drawing, then draw or construct the reflection images of the points over line *m*.

9.

10.

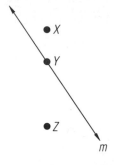

11. In the figure at the right, give the coordinates of:
   a. $r_x(P)$;
   b. $r_y(P)$.

12. Find the image of (-4,1) when reflected over
   a. the *x*-axis;
   b. the *y*-axis.

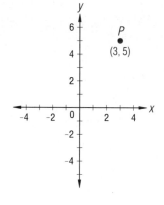

13. Find the image of (*c, d*) when reflected over **a.** the *x*-axis;
   b. the *y*-axis

14. a. *B, C,* and *D* are three reflection images of point *A*. Match each image with the correct reflecting line.

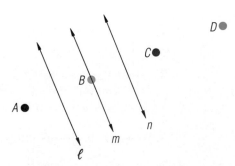

   b. Name each image of *A* using reflection notation.

160

15. Below, $r_\ell(P) = T$. Construct ℓ.

• *T*

• *P*

16. Trace the figures below. Find the line so that one of the figures is the reflection image of the other.

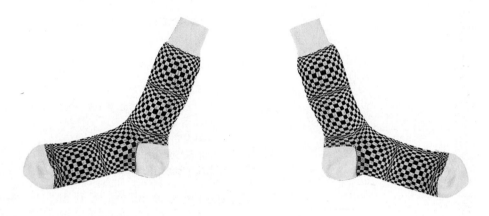

17. a. Decipher the message below.
   b. Which letter is written incorrectly?

HELP! I'M TRAPPED
INSIDE THIS PAGE!

In 18 and 19, trace the figure below.

Review

• *A*

B   *C*

18. Construct the perpendicular to $\overleftrightarrow{BC}$ through point *A*. *(Lesson 3-6)*

19. Construct the ⊥ bisector of $\overline{BC}$. *(Lesson 3-6)*

20. Use the coordinate plane below.
  a. Is $\ell \parallel m$? Justify your answer.
  b. Is $\ell \perp n$? Justify your answer. *(Lessons 3-5, 3-4)*

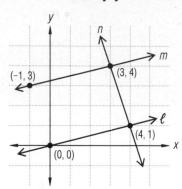

21. *Multiple choice.* The lines with equations $x + 2y = 6$ and $2x - y = 8$ are
  (a) parallel
  (b) perpendicular
  (c) neither parallel nor perpendicular. *(Lessons 3-5, 3-4)*

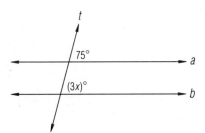

22. Use the figure at the left. E is on $\overline{VG}$. *(Lessons 3-3, 3-2)*
  Given: $m\angle G = 30$, $m\angle GEO = 150$. Justify each conclusion.
  a. $m\angle VEO = 30$
  b. $\overline{EO} \parallel \overline{GL}$

23. In the figure below, $a \parallel b$. Find x. *(Lesson 3-4)*

24. Draw three possible pictures of the antecedent in this sentence. (Make your pictures look different from each other.) Then write in as many consequents as you think are true.

  If $r_\ell(A) = B$ and $r_\ell(C) = D$, then __?__ .

Reflecting Figures

Power-generating windmills reflected in a pond

In Lesson 4-1 each point in the image dog corresponds to a single point in the preimage dog. The reflection image of the dog is the set of all the individual image points. This is why tracing works. In general, the **reflection image of a figure** is the set of all the reflection images of points in the figure.

Below is ∠AEH and its image, ∠A'E'H'. Individual points of ∠AEH are black and their reflection images are shown in blue.

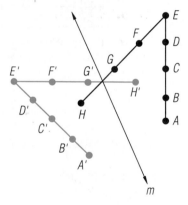

Several striking features of this figure are evident. Look at the *collinear* points E, D, and C. Their images E', D', and C' are also collinear. Also, D is *between* E and C, and its image, D', is between the images of E and C. This observation is true also for F, G, and H. Is it true for E, G, and A?

Look at $\overline{EA}$ and $\overline{E'A'}$. The unique *distance* EA is the same as the distance E'A'. Also, the measure of ∠AEH is equal to the measure of its image angle, ∠A'E'H'. (You could measure the segments and angles to verify this.)

Each of these observations notes a property of the preimage that is also a property of the image. We say the property is **preserved** by reflections.

The order of the parts in the Reflection Postulate is a logical order. Points must have images before there can be collinearity. Images of collinear points must be collinear before betweenness can be preserved. Betweenness precedes distance and the rays necessary to have angles. But most people remember the entire postulate in an alphabetical order, as follows:

Every reflection is a 1-1 correspondence that preserves angle measure, betweenness, collinearity, and distance.

Since most figures in geometry are infinite sets of points, you cannot construct their images by reflecting *every* point. Shortcuts are necessary. Suppose you want to reflect $\overline{AB}$ over m at the left. First note that $\overline{AB}$ is completely determined by the two points A and B. Find the images of A and B. Call them X and Y, so $r_m(A) = X$ and $r_m(B) = Y$ as shown. Every other point of $\overline{AB}$ is between A and B. Since reflections preserve betweenness, the images must lie between X and Y. So, draw $\overline{XY}$, and you have the image of $\overline{AB}$. Using reflection notation, write $r_m(\overline{AB}) = \overline{XY}$.

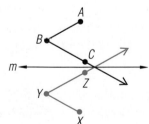

The same idea holds for angles and rays. Angles can be determined by a vertex and two points, one on each side. So, if $r(A) = X$, $r(B) = Y$, and $r(C) = Z$, the reflection image of $\angle ABC$ is $\angle XYZ$. Write $r(\angle ABC) = \angle XYZ$. Also, $r(\overrightarrow{BC}) = \overrightarrow{YZ}$.

Figure Reflection Theorem:

If a figure is determined by certain points, then its reflection image is the corresponding figure determined by the reflection images of those points.

Example 1   Draw the reflection image of △EFG over line m.

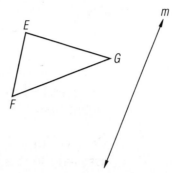

Solution   The three noncollinear points E, F, and G determine △EFG. Locate the images of E, F, and G. r(E) = E', r(F) = F', r(G) = G'. Draw △E'F'G'. r(△EFG) = △E'F'G'.

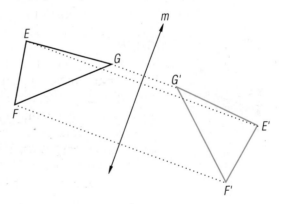

Check   Since reflections preserve distance, the corresponding sides should have the same length. Measuring shows EG = E'G', FG = F'G', and EF = E'F'. Another way of checking is by measuring the angles. Since reflections preserve angle measure, m∠E should equal m∠E', m∠G should equal m∠G', and m∠F should equal m∠F'.

When a figure intersects the reflecting line, the image must intersect the reflecting line in the *same* point or points. In Example 2, the preimage intersects the reflecting line at two points. This makes checking the image easier since the image of a point on the reflecting line is the point itself.

Example 2   Draw the reflection image of △*PAW* over line *m*.

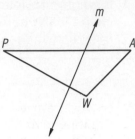

Solution   Find the images of *A*, *P*, and *W*. Connect them.

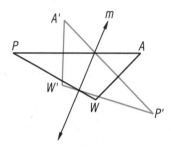

Check $\overline{AP}$ and $\overline{A'P'}$ should intersect *m* at the same point. So should $\overline{WP}$ and $\overline{W'P'}$

Questions

Covering the Reading

1. Name four properties that reflections preserve.

2. Can a point have two different reflection images over the same line?

3. In the figure below, *V* is between *A* and *Z*. If the reflection images of these points are *A'*, *V'*, and *Z'*, what is true?

   A●

   V●

   Z●

4. Since reflections preserve distance, if $D = r_\ell(C)$ and $B = r_\ell(A)$, then $AC = \underline{\ ?\ }$.

5. $m\angle ABC = 50$, $m\angle DEF = 100$.
   a. Can $\angle DEF$ be a reflection image of $\angle ABC$?
   b. Why or why not?

6. State the Figure Reflection Theorem.

7. If $r_m(X) = Z$, $r_m(T) = S$, then $r_m(\overline{XT}) = \underline{\ ?\ }$.

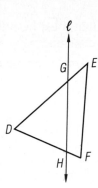

8. Trace the drawing at the left.
   a. Draw $r_\ell(\triangle DEF)$.
   b. Check by measuring that the sides of $\triangle DEF$ and its image are of equal lengths.

9. a. In Question 8, which sides of the image $\triangle D'E'F'$ intersect the reflecting line?
   b. Where do they intersect the line?

10. Trace the drawing below.
    a. Draw $r_w(\angle ABC)$.
    b. Check that $m\angle ABC = m\angle A'B'C'$ using a protractor.

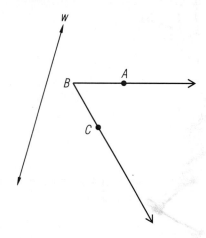

Applying the Mathematics

11. Trace the drawing below. Then reflect the figure over line w.

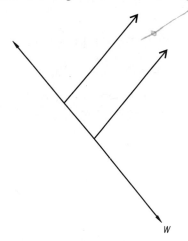

12. a. How many image points are needed to draw the image of pentagon $ABCDE$ at the right over line m?
    b. If $m\angle ABC = 130$, what is the measure of $\angle A'B'C'$ (its reflection image)?

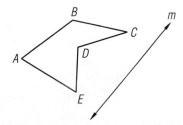

13. How many image points are needed to draw the image of an angle?

In 14 and 15, what is the fewest number of points that must be reflected before you can draw the image of the entire figure over line *w*?

14.

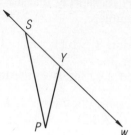

15. $\overline{GH}$ is a diameter of the circle.

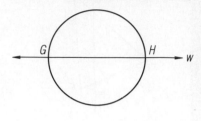

16. Copy the drawing below.
   a. Draw $r_x(\triangle ABC)$.
   b. Give the coordinates of the images of the vertices.

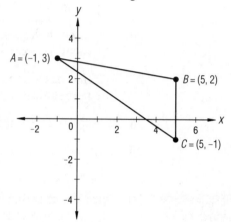

In 17–20, the reflection image of $\triangle MNO$ over line ℓ is $\triangle QRS$.
$r_\ell(M) = Q$, $r_\ell(N) = R$, $r_\ell(O) = S$. Choose the correct justification for the conclusion from the choices at the right.

17. $NO = RS$

18. $m\angle NMO = m\angle RQS$

19. $\ell \perp \overline{MQ}$

20. ℓ bisects $\overline{MQ}$.

(a) Reflections preserve angle measure.

(b) Reflections preserve betweenness.

(c) Reflections preserve collinearity.

(d) Reflections preserve distance.

(e) definition of reflection image

In 21–23, copy the drawing. Then sketch where the reflecting line *m* should be so that *XYZ* is the reflection image of *ABC* over *m*.

21.

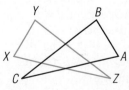

22.

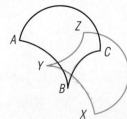

23.

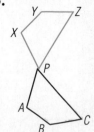

In 24 and 25, trace the figure first.

24. Construct the reflecting line m for which the reflection image of B, at the left below, is A. *(Lessons 4-1, 3-6)*

25. Trace the line $\overleftrightarrow{PQ}$ at the right above. Construct the line n perpendicular to $\overleftrightarrow{PQ}$ through P. *(Lesson 3-6)*

26. Write the definition of perpendicular bisector as an if-and-only-if statement. *(Lessons 3-6, 2-5)*

27. If a line has slope -3, each line parallel to it has slope __?__ and each line perpendicular to it has slope __?__. *(Lessons 3-5, 3-4)*

28. If $p \Rightarrow q$ is true and p is false, what can be concluded? *(Lesson 2-3)*

29. Write the Transitive Property of Equality. *(Lesson 1-7)*

30. Trace the drawing. Given that A' is the reflection image of A over a line m, construct the image of $\angle 1$ over line m.

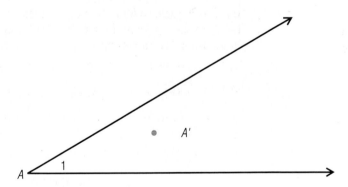

Drawing or constructing figures can be time-consuming and difficult. If you do not have a good compass, your circles may start in one place and end in another. Pencil lines have thickness and if a ruler slips just a little, the entire drawing may be off.

Computers have changed the way many people draw. Nowadays, many of the Saturday morning television cartoons are drawn with the aid of a computer. Many commercials on TV use computer graphics. Manufacturers use computer drawings to help design new products.

Because a construction can be described by an algorithm, constructions are quite suited to computers. We call any computer software that enables figures to be constructed an **automatic drawing tool** or **automatic drawer.** Most automatic drawers enable you to construct, draw, or measure segments, angles, polygons, and circles of various sizes.

The area in which an automatic drawer can draw is called the **window.** Above the window is a **menu** bar of instructions and options. Below is pictured a screen from one such piece of software.

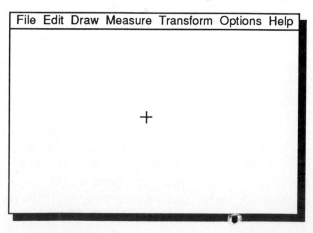

Example 1 Use an automatic drawer to create a picture of two parallel lines and a transversal.

Solution On many drawers, you can proceed as follows:
1. Choose two points. (Many automatic drawers label points in alphabetical order, so call them *A* and *B*.)
2. Draw the line through *A* and *B*.
3. Choose a third point not on $\overleftrightarrow{AB}$. (Call it *C*.)
4. Draw a line through *C* parallel to $\overleftrightarrow{AB}$.
5. Draw $\overleftrightarrow{AC}$.

Below we show how the window might look after each of the steps above.

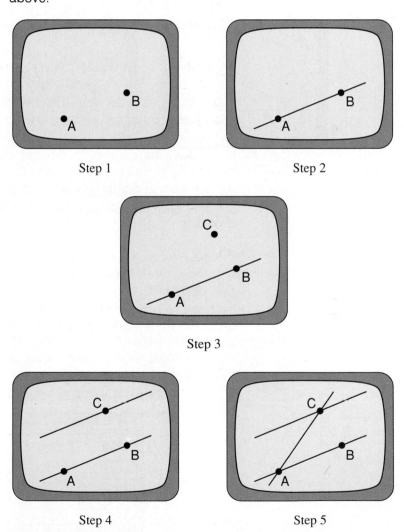

Step 1   Step 2

Step 3

Step 4   Step 5

Most automatic drawers can draw reflection images. However, because the points are limited to the positions of the pixels on the computer screen, the images may not be drawn exactly. For instance, there might not be a pixel in the exact spot for a reflection image of a point over a given line. Still, the computer drawing will be very close.

Example 2 Use an automatic drawer to draw the reflection image of a triangle over one of its sides.

Solution You can usually proceed as follows:
1. Draw a triangle, or choose three points and instruct the drawer to draw the segments connecting them. Call it △*ABC*.
2. Choose a side, say $\overline{AC}$, and instruct the drawer to reflect *B*, the vertex not on $\overline{AC}$, over that side.
3. Connect the images of the vertex points.

Depending on your choice of positions of the three points and line, you might have pictures that look like the following.

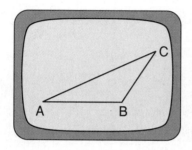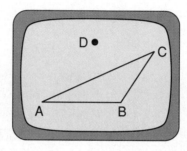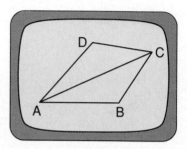

Because most automatic drawers allow you to measure segments and angles, they can be used to verify postulates or theorems.

Example 3 Use the drawing of Example 2 to verify that reflections preserve angle measure.

Solution Ask the automatic drawer to give you the measure of angle *BAC*. Then ask it for the measure of angle *DAC*. These should be equal. Do the same for the other corresponding angles, recording the measures. You should get three pairs of equal measures. Sample output from one automatic drawer is shown below.

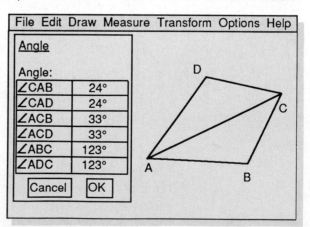

File Edit Draw Measure Transform Options Help

Angle

Angle:	
∠CAB	24°
∠CAD	24°
∠ACB	33°
∠ACD	33°
∠ABC	123°
∠ADC	123°

Cancel   OK

The freedom to choose the position of points and lines and the ease of erasing parts of drawings make automatic drawers a simple tool to use. They are particularly helpful for making complicated drawings, and for exploring. Below are two designs. The one on the left was made from reflecting $\triangle ABC$ from Example 2 over side $\overline{AB}$; the one on the right was made by reflecting the figure on the left over line $\overleftrightarrow{CD}$. The reflection can be done even though the line $\overleftrightarrow{CD}$ is not displayed.

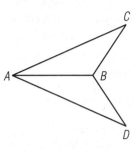
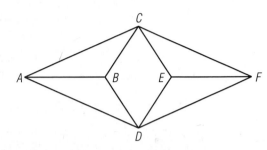

If your automatic drawer is connected to a printer, you may be able to get it to print out the drawings you create. This is called **hard copy.** Otherwise you should copy the drawings you get onto a sheet of paper.

Questions

Covering the Reading

1. What is an automatic drawer?

2. Why do many people like to use automatic drawers?

In 3 and 4, refer to Examples 2 and 3.
3. a. Measure $\overline{AB}$, $\overline{BC}$, $\overline{AD}$, and $\overline{DC}$ using a ruler.
   b. What part of the Reflection Postulate have you verified?

4. a. Trace $\triangle ABC$, and reflect it over $\overline{BC}$. Let $r_{\overline{BC}}(A) = D$.
   b. Draw $r_{\overline{DC}}(ABDC)$.

In 5–7, use your automatic drawer to draw a figure like the one at the left in which $D = r_{\overleftrightarrow{AB}}(C)$ and $E = r_{\overleftrightarrow{AB}}(F)$.

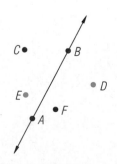

5. a. Measure $\overline{DE}$ and $\overline{CF}$. How do their lengths compare?
   b. Which part of the Reflection Postulate have you verified?

6. a. Measure $\overline{AF}$ and $\overline{AE}$. How do their lengths compare?
   b. Which part of the Reflection Postulate have you verified?

7. a. Measure $\angle EDB$ and $\angle FCB$. How do they compare?
   b. Which part of the Reflection Postulate have you verified?

8. Use an automatic drawer to draw a figure like the one at the right.

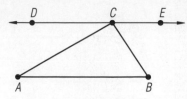

   a. Draw a triangle ABC.
   b. Draw a line $\overleftrightarrow{DE}$ through C parallel to $\overline{AB}$, with C between D and E.
   c. Find m$\angle DCA$, m$\angle ACB$, m$\angle BCE$, m$\angle CAB$, and m$\angle CBA$.
   d. Name two pairs of angles in your figure that have equal measures.

In 9 and 10, use your automatic drawer to draw $\overleftrightarrow{AB} \parallel \overleftrightarrow{DC}$ and $\overleftrightarrow{AD} \parallel \overleftrightarrow{BC}$. If possible, label angles 1 to 8 on the screen, as shown at the left.

9. a. Find the measure of each of angles 1 to 8.
   b. Name all pairs among $\angle 1$ to $\angle 8$ that are corresponding angles.
   c. What postulate do your responses to **a** and **b** verify?

10. a. Find m$\angle 2$ + m$\angle 3$ + m$\angle 6$ + m$\angle 7$.
    b. Compare your answer to part **a** to another student's answer. What might be true about m$\angle 2$ + m$\angle 3$ + m$\angle 6$ + m$\angle 7$ for any set of lines where $\overline{AB} \parallel \overline{DC}$ and $\overline{AD} \parallel \overline{BC}$?

11. Use an automatic drawer.
    a. Draw line $\overleftrightarrow{AB}$. Draw a line through B perpendicular to $\overleftrightarrow{AB}$. Pick a point C on this perpendicular and draw $\overline{AC}$. You should see a right triangle (a triangle with one right angle).
    b. Draw the reflection image of $\triangle ABC$ over $\overline{AC}$. Label $r_{\overline{AC}}(B) = D$.
    c. Reflect the figure now on the screen over $\overline{AB}$. Label $r_{\overline{AB}}(C) = E$ and $r_{\overline{AB}}(D) = F$.
    d. Measure $\overline{BC}$, $\overline{DC}$, $\overline{FE}$, and $\overline{EB}$. What property of reflections guarantees that they must be equal?
    e. Name at least three pairs of angles that are equal in measure.

12. According to the Reflection Postulate, what four properties are preserved under reflections? (Hint: they start with the letters a, b, c, and d.) *(Lesson 4-2)*

In 13 and 14, trace the figure below.

13. Draw the reflection image of quadrilateral $BCDE$ over $\overleftrightarrow{AB}$. *(Lesson 4-2)*

14. Construct the line containing point A perpendicular to $\overleftrightarrow{DE}$. *(Lesson 3-6)*

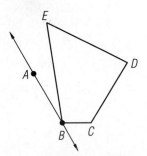

In 15 and 16, $P = (-2, 0)$, $Q = (-4, 3)$, and $R = (2, 7)$.

15. Find the coordinates of the vertices of the image of $\triangle PQR$ when it is reflected over the *y*-axis. *(Lessons 4-2, 4-1)*

16. Show that $\angle PQR$ is a right angle, by proving that $\overleftrightarrow{PQ} \perp \overleftrightarrow{QR}$. *(Lesson 3-5)*

17. Reflect the letter *R* over line ℓ at the left. *(Lesson 4-2)*

18. Match the following angle type with an algebraic description. *(Lesson 3-2)*

a. acute   (i) $m_1 + m_2 = 90$
b. complementary   (ii) $m_1 + m_2 = 180$
c. obtuse   (iii) $m = 0$
d. right   (iv) $m = 90$
e. straight   (v) $m = 180$
f. supplementary   (vi) $90 < m < 180$
g. zero   (vii) $0 < m < 90$

19. Name the angle shown in four different ways. *(Lesson 3-1)*

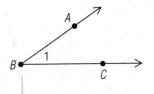

20. Characterize each region as convex or nonconvex. *(Lessons 2-7, 2-1)*

a.   **b.** 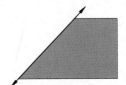   **c.**

21. Given A = {L, I, N, E, S} and B = {P, O, I, N, T, S}. Find A ∩ B. *(Lesson 2-6).*

22. Using an automatic drawer, make the figures below.

a. 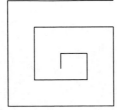   **b.**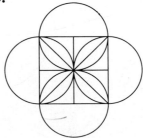

The First Theorem in Euclid's *Elements*

In this detail from Raphael's painting, School of Athens, *the artist has illustrated his concept of Euclid discussing geometry with a group of students.*

You have seen the proofs of a number of theorems. Books differ in the postulates they choose, in the order of theorems they prove, and even sometimes in the definitions of terms they use.

In Europe, it was not always this way. From 250 B.C. until the end of the 1700s, there was essentially only one geometry textbook, Euclid's *Elements*. Developments in geometry ultimately made the *Elements* out-of-date, but in some schools it was used even in the first part of this century. The *Elements* contains some of the greatest logical thinking of all time.

The first theorem in the *Elements* concerns the construction of an equilateral triangle. Recall that an equilateral triangle is defined as a triangle with all three sides having the same length. The task is to construct an equilateral triangle with one side the given segment $\overline{AB}$.

A————————B

Here is an algorithm:

Step 1. ⊙A containing B
Step 2. ⊙B containing A
Step 3. ⊙A and ⊙B intersect at C and D.
Step 4. $\overline{AC}$, $\overline{BC}$

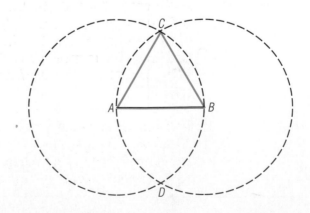

There is a natural question: How do you know that these steps construct an equilateral triangle? To answer this question, a proof is needed. Recall that a proof of $p \Rightarrow q$ is a sequence of justified statements beginning with p and ending with q. It is customary to call p the **given** and q **what is to be proved,** or just simply the **to prove** or **prove.** Here is a statement of Euclid's first theorem.

Theorem:

The triangle constructed in the above construction is an equilateral triangle.

Thus the given p is the segments and circles that are constructed, and q is the statement that $\triangle ABC$ is equilateral.

Here is Euclid's proof of this theorem. By the definition of circle (the meaning of $\odot A$), $AB = AC$. By the definition of circle (the meaning of $\odot B$), $AB = BC$. Thus, by the Transitive Property of Equality, all three sides are equal. And then, by the definition of equilateral triangle (sufficient condition), $\triangle ABC$ is equilateral.

Euclid wrote in paragraphs. Some teachers like to display proofs in *two-column form.* Here is Euclid's proof, rewritten in that form. The conclusions are in the left column and the justifications for them are in the right column. We write the given above the conclusions.

Given: the segments and angles in the above construction.

Conclusions	Justifications
1. $AB = AC$	definition of circle (meaning of $\odot A$)
2. $AB = BC$	definition of circle (meaning of $\odot B$)
3. $AB = AC = BC$	Transitive Property of Equality
4. $\triangle ABC$ is equilateral.	definition of equilateral triangle (sufficient condition)

Example 1 on the next page contains a proof. In it, p is the statement $m \parallel n$ and q is the statement $m\angle 1 = m\angle 7$. So we start with $m \parallel n$ and finish with the equality of angle measures $m\angle 1 = m\angle 7$. Example 1 illustrates a very common way of doing this. Each angle measure is shown equal to the same third measure. Then, as in Euclid's proof, the Transitive Property of Equality is used.

This thinking, which you do in your head, we show in a step called "Analyze." You do not have to write down this step. We put what you should write in **special bold type.** There are many ways of writing a proof; your teacher may prefer one way over another.

Example 1 **Given:** *(p): m ∥ n* and angles as numbered in the figure below.
Prove: *(q):* m∠1 = m∠7.

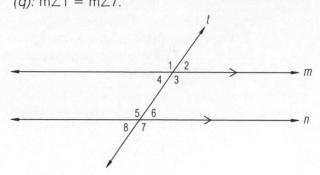

Analyze Angles 1 and 5 are corresponding angles formed by parallel lines. Angles 5 and 7 are vertical angles. That's enough.

Write **Given: *m ∥ n.***

Conclusions	Justifications
1. m∠1 = m∠5	∥ lines ⇒ corr. ∠s =
2. m∠5 = m∠7	Vertical Angle Theorem
3. m∠1 = m∠7	Transitive Property of Equality (steps 1 and 2)

Many teachers would say you do not have to rewrite the given above the conclusions if you have already written it once in introducing the problem.

In Example 1, you were given a figure. There are certain things you can assume from a figure. You can assume lines and angles intersect as shown, that points are in the order as shown, and that angles are marked as shown. For instance, in the figure below you can assume that *ℓ, m,* and *n* are all lines, that *ℓ* and *m* intersect at *B*, that *E, D, B,* and *C* all lie on *m,* that *A* and *B* lie on *ℓ,* and that *F* is not on *ℓ, m,* or *n.*

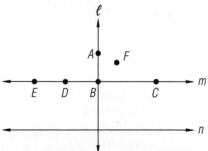

However, unless specifically given, you cannot assume lines are ∥ or ⊥, or that distances or angle measures are equal. For instance, you *cannot* assume from the figure above that *ℓ* is perpendicular to *m* or *n* or that *m* is parallel to *n,* even though they look it. You cannot tell the measure of ∠*ABC.* You cannot assume that *F* is between *A* and *C* or that $\overrightarrow{BF}$ bisects ∠*ABC,* or that *DE = DB,* even though all these may look true. Only if given, or after you have proved these things, can you take them as so.

Here is another proof which utilizes the Transitive Property of Equality.

Example 2   **Given:** B is the midpoint of $\overline{AC}$.
C is the midpoint of $\overline{BD}$.
Prove: $AB = CD$.

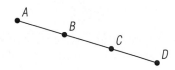

Analyze   From midpoints come equal distances. BC is a distance equal to AB and CD.

Write   **Given: B is the midpoint of $\overline{AC}$, C is the midpoint of $\overline{BD}$.**

Conclusions	**Justifications**
1. $AB = BC$	definition of midpoint (meaning)
2. $BC = CD$	definition of midpoint (meaning)
3. $AB = CD$	Transitive Property of Equality (steps 1 and 2)

Questions

Covering the Reading

1. Define: equilateral triangle.

2. **a.** Trace $\overline{MT}$. Then construct an equilateral triangle with $\overline{MT}$ as one side.
   b. How many different triangles could you construct?

3. In circle O below, what is the justification for the conclusion $OA = OB$?

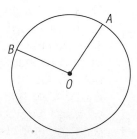

4. What caused people to stop using Euclid's *Elements* as a geometry text?

5. Use the drawing at the right.
Given: *m* ‖ *n*.
Justify each conclusion.
a. m∠2 = m∠6
b. m∠6 = m∠8
c. m∠2 = m∠8

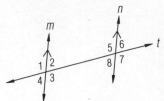

In 6–11, refer to the figure below at the right. Can you assume the listed information from the figure?

6. *r* intersects *p* at *C*.

7. *r* ‖ *s*

8. m∠*EGF* = 90

9. m∠*BCA* = m∠*FGA*

10. *G* is the midpoint of $\overline{FH}$.

11. *p* ⊥ *r*

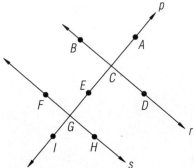

Applying the Mathematics

12. Here is a flowchart display of the proof of Example 1. One justification is already placed in a rectangle. Place the appropriate justifications in the other two rectangles.

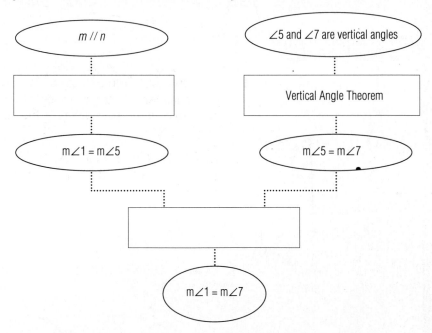

13. In Question 12, which of the five statements (in the ovals) is given from the figure of Example 1?

In 14–16, write proofs as in the Examples of this lesson.

14. Use the figure at the right.
Given: $\ell \parallel m$.
Prove: $m\angle 4 = m\angle 8$.

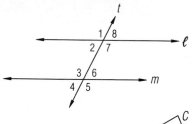

15. Use the figure at the right.
Given: $m\angle CBD = m\angle D$.
Prove: $m\angle ABE = m\angle D$.

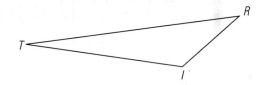

16. Given: $\triangle ABC$ is equilateral.
$\triangle BCD$ is equilateral.
Prove: $AB = DC$.

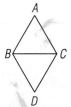

17. a. Reflect $\triangle TRI$ below over line $\overleftrightarrow{RI}$. Let U be the image of T.
b. Why does $TI = UI$? *(Lessons 4-3, 4-2)*

18. a. If two lines are perpendicular to the same line, then they are __?__.
(Lesson 3-5)
b. If two lines are parallel to the same line, then they are __?__.
(Lesson 3-4)

19. The roof below is supported by $\overline{BE}$ and the top of the wall $\overline{CF}$. If
$m\angle DCF = 145$ and $\overline{BE}$ is parallel to $\overline{CF}$, what must $m\angle ABE$ be?
(Lesson 3-4)

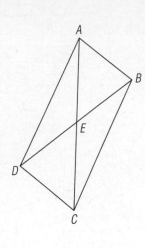

In 20–22, justify each conclusion. *(Lessons 3-3, 3-2, 2-7, 1-7)*

20. Given: The diagonals of quadrilateral *ABCD* at the left intersect at *E*. m∠*BEA* = 50.
Conclusion: m∠*AED* = 130.

21. Given: $3x - 4y = 5$.
Conclusion: $-4y = -3x + 5$.

22. Given: $-4y = -3x + 5$.
Conclusion: $y = \dfrac{-3x + 5}{-4}$.

23. Duplicate Euclid's construction (page 176) using an automatic drawer. Draw $\overline{AD}$ and $\overline{BD}$. Measure the angles and sides of the triangles formed. What can you conclude?

Exploration

24. Either by hand or with an automatic drawer, start with a triangle such as the one below and construct the perpendicular segment from *A* to $\overline{BC}$, the ⊥ segment from *B* to $\overline{AC}$, and the ⊥ segment from *C* to $\overline{AB}$. How are these constructed segments related?

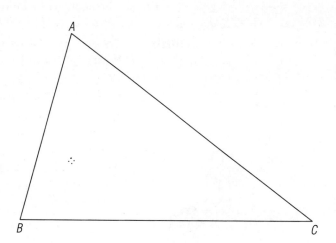

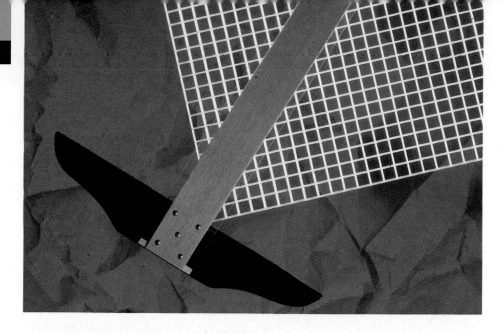

LESSON 4-5

The Perpendicular Bisector Theorem

Like any other definitions, postulates, or theorems, you can use properties of reflections as justifications in proofs.

Example 1   **Given:** P is on the perpendicular bisector m of segment $\overline{AB}$.
Prove: $PA = PB$.

Analyze   Think of the perpendicular bisector m as a reflecting line. Then B is the image of A. P is on m, so P is the image of itself. Use the postulate that reflections preserve distance.

Write   **Given: m is the $\perp$ bisector of $\overline{AB}$. P is on m.**

Conclusions	Justifications
1. $r_m(P) = P$	definition of reflection (sufficient condition)
2. $r_m(A) = B$	definition of reflection (sufficient condition)
3. $PA = PB$	Reflections preserve distance.

The result proved in Example 1 can be written as an if-then statement. It is so important it is labeled as a theorem.

Perpendicular Bisector Theorem:

If a point is on the perpendicular bisector of a segment, then it is equidistant from the endpoints of the segment.

The Perpendicular Bisector Theorem has a surprising application. It can help locate the center of a circle.

Example 2   Construct the circle through the three noncollinear points A, B, and C

Solution

Step 1.   Subroutine: *m*, the perpendicular bisector of $\overline{AB}$
Step 2.   Subroutine: *n*, the perpendicular bisector of $\overline{BC}$
Step 3.   *m* and *n* intersect at O. (Point Rule)
Step 4.   ⊙O containing A   (Compass rule)

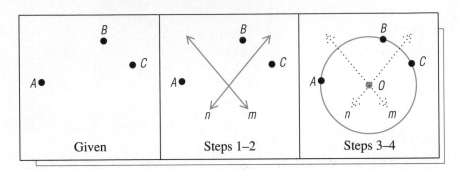

Given   Steps 1–2   Steps 3–4

If *m* and *n* intersect, it can be proven that this construction works. Because of the Perpendicular Bisector Theorem with line *m*, $OA = OB$. With line *n*, this theorem also justifies the conclusion $OB = OC$. By the Transitive Property of Equality, the three distances OA, OB, and OC are all equal. Thus ⊙O with radius OA contains points B and C also.

Questions

Covering the Reading

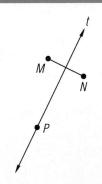

1. In the figure at the left, *t* is the ⊥ bisector of $\overline{MN}$. Justify each conclusion.
    a. *P* is the reflection image of *P* over *t*.
    b. $r_t(N) = M$
    c. $PM = PN$

2. What statement is proved by the reasoning of Question 1?

3. Choose the correct words in parentheses. Any point on the (bisector, perpendicular bisector) of a segment is equidistant from the (endpoints, midpoint) of the segment.

4. Trace the three points *A*, *B*, and *C* below. Construct a circle containing points *A*, *B*, and *C*.

A●

B●   ●C

5. Trace the three points J, K, and L below. Construct a circle containing all three points.

●
J

●
K

●
L

Applying the Mathematics

6. Use the figure below.
   Given: e is the $\perp$ bisector of $\overline{VW}$.
            f is the $\perp$ bisector of $\overline{WX}$.
   Prove: $VC = CX$.

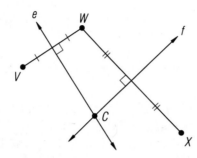

7. Use the figure below.
   Given: $r_{\overleftrightarrow{QR}}(C) = D$.
   Prove: $CQ = DQ$.

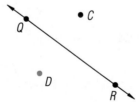

8. A tree stands midway between two stakes. Guy wires are attached from the stakes to the same point up the tree. Explain why the two guy wires must have the same length.

9. Use the figure at the right.
Given: △ABC is equilateral.
$\overline{C}$ is the midpoint of $\overline{AD}$.
Prove: $BC = CD$. *(Lesson 4-4)*

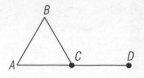

10. Draw a figure and state the justification for the conclusion.
Given: $r_\ell(\angle ABC) = \angle DEF$.
Conclusion: $m\angle ABC = m\angle DEF$. *(Lesson 4-2)*

K M
N
W X

11. Which of the letters at the left does *not* look the same as its reflection image over a vertical line? *(Lesson 4-2)*

12. Write as an if-then statement: Reflections preserve betweenness.
(Lesson 4-2)

13. Lincoln Avenue intersects the parallel streets Washington and Jefferson. Which of the eight angles at the corners have equal measures? *(Lesson 3-4)*

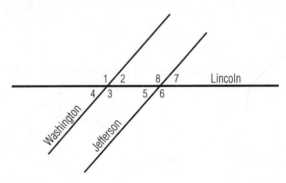

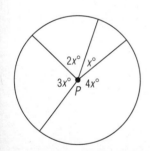

14. Suppose the angles about point P have measures as indicated in the drawing at the left.
a. What is the measure of the largest angle?
b. Are any of the angles complementary?
c. Are any of the angles supplementary? *(Lesson 3-2)*

15. Trace the figure below.
a. Draw the circle through the three vertices of △VWX.
b. Is the center of the circle inside or outside the triangle?
c. What determines whether the center will be inside or outside? (If you have an automatic drawer, experiment with triangles of different shapes.)

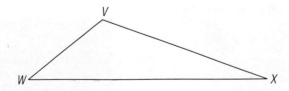

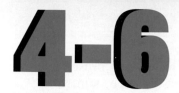

Reflecting Polygons

In Lesson 4-2, the shorthand r(△*ABC*) = △*XYZ* was introduced for the statement "The reflection image of △*ABC* is △*XYZ*." This notation is used for polygons as well as triangles. As with triangles, when you use the r( ) notation for polygons, the order of the vertices is important.

$r_t(ABCD) = MVWS$ is read "The reflection image of polygon *ABCD* over line *t* is polygon *MVWS*."

From this it is understood that $r_t(A) = M$, $r_t(B) = V$, $r_t(C) = W$, and $r_t(D) = S$. The reasons for this are the Figure Reflection Theorem and the fact that a polygon is determined by its vertices.

Example Draw $r_m(ABCDE)$.

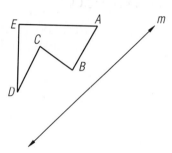

Solution Draw the images of *A*, *B*, *C*, *D*, and *E*. Call them *A'*, *B'*, *C'*, *D'*, and *E'*. Then draw $\overline{A'B'}$, $\overline{B'C'}$, $\overline{C'D'}$, $\overline{D'E'}$, and $\overline{E'A'}$.

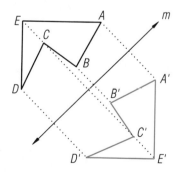

Because of the Figure Reflection Theorem, $r_m(ABCDE) = A'B'C'D'E'$.

In the Example, $r_m(A) = A'$. Thus *m* is the perpendicular bisector of $\overline{AA'}$, by the definition of reflection. Since $\overline{AA'}$ and $\overline{A'A}$ are the same segment, *m* is the perpendicular bisector of $\overline{A'A}$. Thus $r_m(A') = A$. Similarly, $r_m(B') = B$, $r_m(C') = C$, $r_m(D') = D$, and $r_m(E') = E$. Putting this all together, $r_m(A'B'C'D'E') = ABCDE$. That is, if $r_m(A) = A'$, then $r_m(A') = A$ for points; and if $r_m(ABCD...) = A'B'C'D'...$, then $r_m(A'B'C'D'...) = ABCD...$ for polygons and other figures.

LESSON 4-6 Reflecting Polygons **187**

Flip-Flop Theorem:

If F and F' are points or figures and r(F) = F', then r(F') = F.

Look back at the above Example. Although reflections preserve angle measure, betweenness, collinearity, and distance, something is not preserved. The image $A'B'C'D'E'$ looks reversed from the preimage $ABCDE$. Now we explore that reversal.

Imagine that $ABCDE$ in the Example encloses a garden. Imagine further than you begin at A and walk around the garden to B, to C, to D, to E, and back to A. The garden is always on your *right* as you go around it. Do the same with the corresponding points on the image polygon. Begin at A' and go to B', C', D', and E'. This time the garden is always on your *left*.

When you think of the vertices of a polygon in order, as above, you have assigned an **orientation** to the polygon. Every polygon has two orientations. The orientation for which the interior is on the right is called **clockwise.** When the interior is on the left, the orientation is **counterclockwise.**

With convex polygons these names fit with intuition. Clockwise is the direction the hands move on nondigital clocks. However, for nonconvex polygons, the orientation names are not as descriptive.

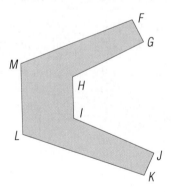

FGHIJKLM is clockwise but *GHIJ* seems to go in the wrong direction.

Orientation depends on the order in which the vertices are given. Back in the Example, when the orientation of $ABCDE$ was clockwise, the orientation of the image polygon, *taking the letters in the same order,* was counterclockwise. Had we chosen $EDCBA$ as the order of vertices in the first figure, then the orientation of the preimage would have been counterclockwise. The orientation of the image would have been the orientation of $E'D'C'B'A'$, clockwise.

In general, a figure and its reflection image always have opposite orientations. We take the word "orientation" as undefined, and add the following part to the Reflection Postulate of Lesson 4-2.

Reflection Postulate:

Under a reflection:
f. A polygon and its image, with vertices taken in
corresponding order, have opposite orientations.
Reflections switch orientation.

Questions

Covering the Reading

1. Trace the figure below.
Draw $r_t(WXYZ)$.

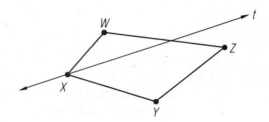

In 2 and 3, draw a picture of each situation.

2. $r_k(LOVE) = BATH$

3. $r_\ell(\triangle ABC) = \triangle ADE$

4. a. If $r_m(A) = C$, then $r_m(C) = \underline{\ ?\ }$.
b. What theorem justifies your answer to part **a**?

5. a. Is *TXWA* below oriented clockwise or counterclockwise?
b. What is the orientation of *XWAT*?
c. Which way is *WXTA* oriented?

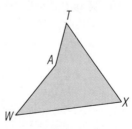

6. How are the orientations of a figure and its reflection image related?

7. *True* or *false*? Until you know the order of vertices, you cannot tell
whether a polygon is oriented clockwise or counterclockwise.

8. A triangle is drawn so that tracing its vertices *T, A, B* (in that order)
yields a clockwise motion. What type of motion results if the vertices
are traced in the following orders?
a. *B, A, T*　　　　　　　　　**b.** *A, T, B,*
c. *T, B, A*　　　　　　　　　**d.** *B, T, A*

9. If r(*ONE*) = *SIX*, give:
    a. r(*N*)   **b.** r(∠*EON*)   **c.** r($\overrightarrow{NO}$)   **d.** r($\overline{EO}$).

10. Police Officer Hugh Hunter follows a clockwise path *ABCDXTZA* when he walks his beat. If Officer Marlene Snyder walks the same streets, beginning at *D*, but with a counterclockwise orientation, name the path she takes.

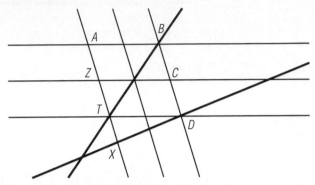

11. What is the orientation of the path run by a batter in baseball as he or she runs around the baseball diamond?

12. Given: r(*ABCD*) = *EFGH* and the length of $\overline{BD}$ is 12 cm. Make a conclusion.

13. r$_m$(∠*ABC*) = ∠*DEF*. r$_m$(*A*) = *D*, but r$_m$(*C*) ≠ *F*. Draw a figure.

14. Use the figure at the left.
    Given: ℓ is the ⊥ bisector of $\overline{AB}$.
    Fill in the blanks in the proof that r$_\ell$($\overline{AB}$) = $\overline{BA}$.

Conclusions	Justifications
1. r$_\ell$(*A*) = *B*	**a.** ?
2. **b.** ?	Flip-Flop Theorem
3. **c.** ?	Figure Reflection Theorem

15. *Z* is the reflection image of *A* over line ℓ below. Match each conclusion with its justification. *(Lessons 4-2, 3-1)*

    a. $\overline{ZA}$ ⊥ ℓ (i)   definition of bisector (meaning)
    b. ℓ bisects $\overline{ZA}$.   (ii)   definition of midpoint (meaning)
    c. *M* is the midpoint of $\overline{ZA}$.   (iii) definition of reflection (meaning)
    d. *AM* = *MZ*

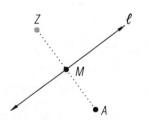

16. Given: *M* is the midpoint of $\overline{AB}$.
             AN = *AM*.
    Prove: *AN* = *MB*. *(Lesson 4-4)*

17. Use the figure below.

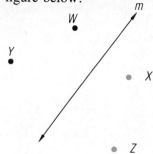

Given: $r_m(W) = X$, $r_m(Y) = Z$.
Fill in the justifications in this proof that $\overline{WX} \parallel \overline{YZ}$.
(Lessons 4-5, 4-1, 3-5)

Conclusions	Justifications
1. $\overline{WX} \perp m$	**a.** ?
2. $\overline{YZ} \perp m$	**b.** ?
3. $\overline{WX} \parallel \overline{YZ}$	**c.** ?

In 18 and 19, let $A = (7, -2)$, $B = (3, 4)$, $C = (-5, 0)$, and $D = (0, -8)$.

18. Graph $ABCD$ and its reflection image over the y-axis.
(Lessons 4-2, 4-1)

19. a. Find the slope of $\overleftrightarrow{AB}$.
 b. Find the slope of a line perpendicular to $\overleftrightarrow{AB}$.
 (Lessons 3-5, 3-4)

20. *True* or *false*?   A supplement of an acute angle is always an obtuse angle. *(Lesson 3-2)*

21. Give a counterexample to this statement: If $m\angle A = x$, then the measure of a complement to $\angle A$ cannot be x. *(Lessons 3-2, 2-2)*

Exploration

22. Many objects come in different orientations. For instance, there are right-handed golf clubs and left-handed golf clubs. Name at least three other objects that come in different orientations.

Reflection-Symmetric Figures

When a figure is reflected over a line, either of two situations may arise. In the first case, as pictured below at the left, the preimage and image are *distinct*. This is the most common case.

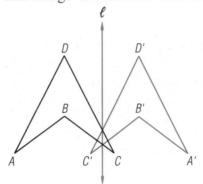

$$r_\ell(ABCD) = A'B'C'D'$$

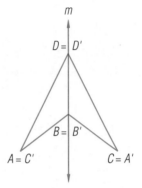

$$r_m(ABCD) = A'B'C'D' = CBAD$$

In the second case, pictured at the right, the image of quadrilateral *ABCD* is itself. The preimage and image *coincide*. Note, however, that $r_m(A) = C$, $r_m(B) = B$, $r_m(C) = A$, and $r_m(D) = D$. Thus, $A'B'C'D' = CBAD$ and $r_m(ABCD) = CBAD$. The figure is called *reflection-symmetric*, and the reflecting line is called a *symmetry line* for the figure.

> **Definition:**
>
> A plane figure F is a **reflection-symmetric figure** if and only if there is a line m such that $r_m(F) = F$. The line m is a **symmetry line** for the figure.

With symmetric figures, it is absolutely necessary to name the images so that preimage and image points correspond. For example, in the figure above at the right, write $r_m(ABCD) = CBAD$, *not* $r_m(ABCD) = ABCD$. Although the quadrilateral and its image are the same set of points, their orientations are different. *ABCD* is oriented counterclockwise while *CBAD* is clockwise oriented.

The union of any figure and its reflection image is always a figure that is symmetric to the reflecting line. The ink blot in the opening to this chapter is an example of such reflection-symmetric figures.

Example Draw what appears to be a symmetry line for each capital letter shown below.

a. **A**   b. **C**   c. **X**   d. **N**

Solutions In **a** and **b** there is one line of symmetry. In **c** there are two: one horizontal and one vertical. In **d** there are no symmetry lines.

a. **A**   b. **C**   c. **X**   d. **N**

Many simple figures are reflection-symmetric. Every segment is reflection-symmetric to its perpendicular bisector. Specifically, if ℓ is the $\perp$ bisector of $\overline{AB}$, $r_\ell(\overline{AB}) = \overline{BA}$. Every segment $\overline{AB}$ has a second symmetry line, namely $\overleftrightarrow{AB}$, the line containing it. Specifically, $r_{\overleftrightarrow{AB}}(A) = A$, $r_{\overleftrightarrow{AB}}(B) = B$, and so $r_{\overleftrightarrow{AB}}(\overline{AB}) = \overline{AB}$. No other symmetry lines are possible for a segment, since endpoints must have endpoints as reflection images.

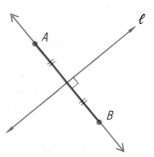

Segment Symmetry Theorem:

A segment has exactly two symmetry lines:
1. its perpendicular bisector, and
2. the line containing the segment.

Angles also possess reflection symmetry. Consider $\angle ABC$ with its bisector $\overrightarrow{BD}$ so that $m\angle ABD = m\angle CBD$.

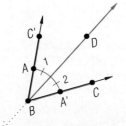

Imagine folding $\angle ABC$ along $\overrightarrow{BD}$. Since $m\angle 1 = m\angle 2$, $\overrightarrow{BC}$ will fold (reflect) onto $\overrightarrow{BA}$ even though C does not necessarily fold onto A.

Similarly $\overrightarrow{BA}$ reflects onto $\overrightarrow{BC}$ (but A does not necessarily reflect onto C). Thus the image of $\angle ABC$ is itself.

The following two theorems summarize this discussion.

Side-Switching Theorem:

If one side of an angle is reflected over the line containing the angle bisector, its image is the other side of the angle.

Angle Symmetry Theorem:

The line containing the bisector of an angle is a symmetry line of the angle.

In the next chapter, certain polygons are examined for symmetry. All of their symmetries can be traced back to symmetries of angles or segments.

Questions

Covering the Reading

1. Define: reflection-symmetric figure.

In 2−5, the figure has at least one symmetry line. Trace the figure and draw all symmetry lines.

2.

3.

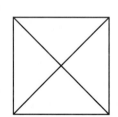

4.

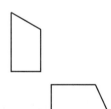

5.

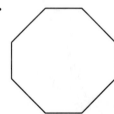

6. Alchemists used these symbols during the Middle Ages. How many symmetry lines does each have?

    a. Copper   **b.** Tin   **c.** Lead

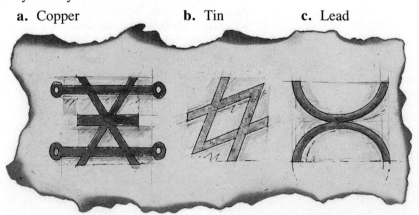

In 7 and 8, trace. Then draw all lines of symmetry for the given figure.

7. $\overline{AB}$

8. $\angle CDE$

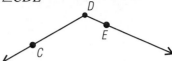

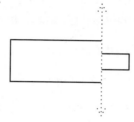

9. Use the drawing at the left. Give the reflection image of each figure over the line $\overleftrightarrow{FH}$.
 a. $\overrightarrow{FJ}$
 b. $\overrightarrow{FG}$
 c. $\angle JFG$

10. Complete this statement of the Side-Switching Theorem. If m is the bisector of $\angle ABC$, then $r_m(\overrightarrow{BA}) = \underline{\ ?\ }$.

Applying the Mathematics

In 11–13, copy the figure and complete its shape so that the result is symmetric to the dotted line.

11.

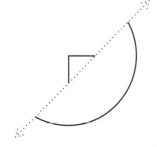

12.

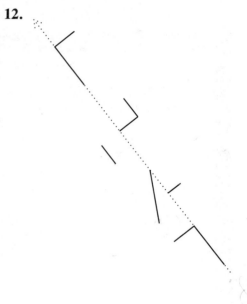

13.

14. In the figure below, ℓ is the perpendicular bisector of $\overline{TU}$. $VT = 8$ and $WT = 5$.
 a. Find the length of $\overline{UV}$.
 b. $r_\ell(\triangle TUV) = \underline{\ ?\ }$

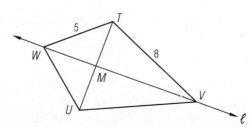

15. a. Trace the figure at the right.
Draw $r_{\overleftrightarrow{AC}}(ABCD)$.
   b. *True* or *false*?   The figure at
the right has no symmetry lines.

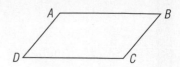

In 16 and 17, follow this algorithm for constructing the bisector of $\angle AOB$.

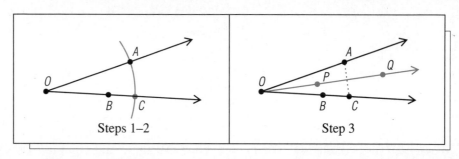

| Steps 1–2 | Step 3 |

Step 1. $\odot O$ containing A
Step 2. $\odot O$ intersects $\overrightarrow{OB}$ at C.
Step 3.   Subroutine: $\overleftrightarrow{PQ}$, the $\perp$ bisector of $\overline{AC}$

Trace the angle. Use the algorithm to construct its symmetry lines.

16.   **17.**

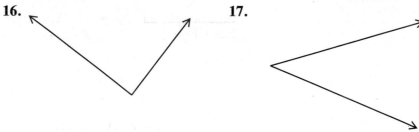

In 18 and 19, *multiple choice*.   *A, B,* and *C* are noncollinear points, with
$m\angle ABC = 40$. Also, $D = r_{\overleftrightarrow{BA}}(C)$ and $E = r_{\overleftrightarrow{BD}}(C)$.

18. $m\angle EBC =$
   (a) 40   (b) 80   (c) 120   (d) 160
   (e) can equal more than one number.

19. $m\angle EBA =$
   (a) 20   (b) 40   (c) 80   (d) 120
   (e) depends on the position of A.

Review

20. If $r(ABCD) = EFGH$, find: *(Lesson 4-6)*
   a. $r(EFGH)$ **b.** $r(C)$ **c.** $r(\triangle ABD)$ **d.** $r(\angle GCH)$.

21. Complete this proof. *(Lesson 4-4)*
Given: $\overrightarrow{OB}$ bisects $\angle AOC$.
$\overrightarrow{OC}$ bisects $\angle BOD$.
Prove: $m\angle AOB = m\angle COD$.

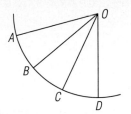

Conclusions	Justifications
1. **a.** ?	1. def. of angle bisector (meaning)
2. $m\angle BOC = m\angle COD$	2. **b.** ?
3. **c.** ?	3. Transitive Property of Equality (steps 1 and 2)

22. Construct a circle containing the three vertices of $\triangle PAT$ below. *(Lesson 4-2)*

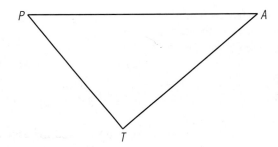

23. Line m goes through points $(3, -1)$ and $(-7, 4)$. Find the slope of line n if $m \perp n$. *(Lessons 3-5, 3-4)*

24. At the right, *ABCDEF* is a hexagon with diagonals $\overline{AD}$, $\overline{BF}$, and $\overline{CE}$. $m\angle 1 = 70$ and $m\angle 2 = 70$.
  a. Which other numbered angles measure 70°? *(Lesson 3-4)*
  b. *True* or *false*? $\angle 4$ and $\angle 6$ are complementary angles. *(Lesson 3-2)*

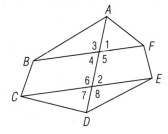

Exploration

25. Is there any angle which has more than one symmetry line? If so, draw such an angle. If not, why is there no such angle?

26. a. Draw two non-perpendicular intersecting lines. The resulting figure has two symmetry lines. Draw these lines.
  b. Repeat part **a** with two other lines.
  c. How are these symmetry lines related to each other?

Summary

The reflection image of the point A over the line m is the point B if and only if m is the perpendicular bisector of $\overline{AB}$. In symbols, $r_m(A) = B$. If A is on line m, then $r_m(A) = A$.

The basic properties of reflections are assumed in the Reflection Postulate. Other important properties can be deduced:

Flip-Flop Theorem:
If $r(F) = F'$, then $r(F') = F$.

Figure Reflection Theorem:
If a figure is determined by certain points, its reflection image is determined by the images of those points.

Perpendicular Bisector Theorem:
If P is on the perpendicular bisector of $\overline{AB}$, then $PA = PB$.

Side-Switching Theorem:
If m is the bisector of $\angle ABC$, then $r_m(\overrightarrow{BA}) = \overrightarrow{BC}$.

Reflection images of points are easy to locate if the reflecting lines are the x-axis or the y-axis.

Sometimes a figure F and its reflection image $r_m(F)$ coincide. When this is the case, m is called a symmetry line for the figure. Every segment has two symmetry lines, its perpendicular bisector and itself. Every angle has one, the line containing its bisector.

Vocabulary

Below are the new terms and phrases for this chapter. You should be able to give a general description and specific example of each. For those terms that are starred, you should be able to give a precise definition. You should also be able to rewrite each named theorem or postulate in if-then or if-and-only-if form, as appropriate.

Lesson 4-1
preimage
reflecting line
line of reflection
*reflection image of a point
r, r(P), $r_m(P)$

Lesson 4-2
reflection image of a figure
Reflection Postulate (a)–(e)
preserved property
Figure Reflection Theorem
$r_m(ABC)$

Lesson 4-3
automatic drawer
automatic drawing tool
window, menu, hard copy

Lesson 4-4
given
to prove, prove, what is
   to be proved
Proof Writing: Analyze, Write

Lesson 4-5
Perpendicular Bisector Theorem

Lesson 4-6
Flip-Flop Theorem
orientation
clockwise
counterclockwise
Reflection Postulate (f)

Lesson 4-7
*reflection-symmetric figure
*symmetry line
Segment Symmetry Theorem
Side-Switching Theorem
Angle Symmetry Theorem

Progress Self-Test

Directions: Take this test as you would take a test in class. Use a ruler, compass and a protractor. Then check your work with the solutions in the Selected Answers section in the back of the book.

In 1 and 2, given $r_m(A) = B$ and $r_m(C) = D$. Justify each conclusion.

1. $AC = BD$

2. $m \perp \overline{AB}$

In 3–5, polygon F′ below is the reflection image over line m of polygon F.

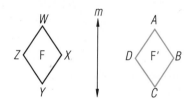

3. $r_m(X) = $ ___?___

4. $r_m(\angle ABC) = $ ___?___

5. What is the orientation of the image of WXYZ?

In 6 and 7, polygon $ABCD$ is symmetric to line n.

6. $r_n(ABCD) = $ ___?___

7. If $m\angle BDA = x$, find $m\angle ACB$.

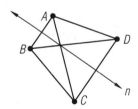

8. Draw the reflecting line m such that $r_m(W) = V$.

9. $\triangle MNP$ below has vertices $M = (2, 0)$, $N = (5, -1)$, and $P = (-3, 4)$. Give the vertices of the reflection image of $\triangle MNP$ over the x-axis.

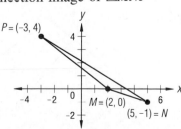

In 10 and 11, trace the figure first.

10. Draw $r_\ell(P)$.

11. Draw $r_m(\triangle CDE)$.

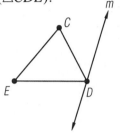

In 12 and 13, trace the figure. Then draw all lines that seem to be symmetry lines.

12.

13.

14. Write the proof.
Given: $m\angle 1 = m\angle 2$.
Prove: $m\angle 3 = m\angle 2$.

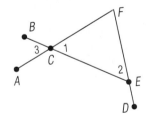

15. Fill in the blanks in this proof.
Given: $r_\ell(W) = X$, $r_\ell(Y) = Z$.
Prove: $\overline{WX} \parallel \overline{YZ}$.

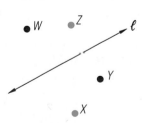

Conclusions	Justifications
1. $\ell \perp \overline{YZ}$	**a.** ___?___
2. $\ell \perp \overline{WX}$	**b.** ___?___
3. $\overline{WX} \parallel \overline{YZ}$	**c.** ___?___

Chapter Review

Questions on **SPUR** Objectives

SPUR stands for **S**kills, **P**roperties, **U**ses, and **R**epresentations.
The Chapter Review questions are grouped according to the
SPUR Objectives for this chapter.

SKILLS deal with the procedures used to get answers.

■ **Objective A:** *Perform drawings and constructions applying the definition of reflection image.*
(Lessons 4-1, 4-3)

In 1–4, trace the figure first.

1. Draw $r_\ell(E)$.

2. Construct $r_m(X)$.

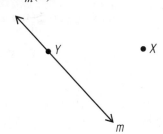

3. Construct the reflecting line ℓ for which $r_\ell(P) = Q$.

4. Draw the reflecting line m for which $r_m(\triangle ABC) = \triangle DEF$.

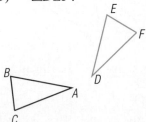

■ **Objective B:** *Draw reflection images of segments, angles, and polygons over a given line.*
(Lessons 4-2, 4-3, 4-6)

In 5–8, trace the figure first. Then draw the reflection image of the given figure over the given line.

5.

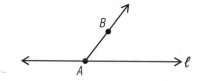

6.

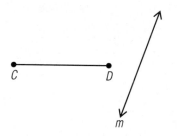

7.

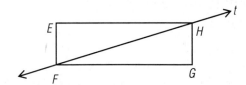

8.

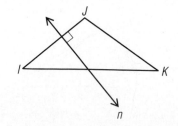

Objective C: *Draw all symmetry lines of segments and angles. (Lesson 4-7)*

In 9–11, draw all symmetry lines.

9.

10.

11.
  •

  •

Objective D: *Determine measures of angles in figures and their reflection images. (Lessons 4-2, 4-6)*

In 12 and 13, use the figure below. $r_{\overleftrightarrow{AD}}(B) = C$.

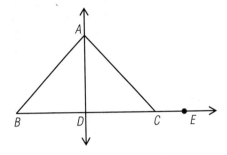

12. If m∠BAD = 42, find m∠BAC.

13. If m∠$B = x$, find m∠ACE.

PROPERTIES deal with the principles behind the mathematics.

Objective E: *Apply properties of reflections to make conclusions, using one or more of the following justifications:*

    definition of reflection
    Reflections preserve distance.
    Reflections preserve angle measure.
    Reflections switch orientation.
    Figure Reflection Theorem
    Flip-Flop Theorem
    Side-Switching Theorem

(Lessons 4-1, 4-2, 4-6, 4-7)

14. If $r_m(A) = B$, then what conclusion follows due to the Flip-Flop Theorem?

15. If $r_\ell(A) = B$, what conclusion follows due to the definition of reflection?

In 16–19, suppose r($CDEF$) = $GHIJ$. Justify each conclusion.

16. r(E) = I

17. r(∠EDF) = ∠IHJ

18. m∠EDF = m∠IHJ

19. $FC = JG$

In 20 and 21, refer to the figure below.

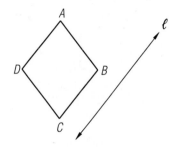

20. What is the orientation of $ADCB$?

21. If $ADCB$ is reflected over line ℓ, what is the orientation of the image?

Objective F: *Apply properties of symmetry to make conclusions about symmetric figures.* *(Lesson 4-7)*

In 22–24, $\overleftrightarrow{XZ}$ is a symmetry line of polygon *WXYZ* below.

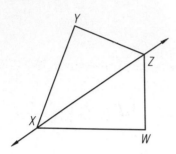

22. Which sides of the polygon have the same length?

23. Which angles of the figure have the same measure?

24. If m∠*WXZ* = 35, which other angle or angles have measure 35°?

In 25–27, polygon r(*FABCDE*) = *FEDCBA*.

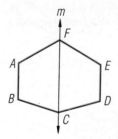

25. *True* or *false*?   *FABCDE* is symmetric to line *m*.

26. Name all angles with the same measure as ∠*D*.

27. *True* or *false*?   *m* bisects ∠*AFE*.

28. **a.** How many symmetry lines has a segment $\overline{PQ}$?
    b. Name them.

Objective G: *Given appropriate information, write proofs, using theorems, postulates, or definitions you have studied in this book as justifications.* *(Lessons 4-4, 4-5)*

In 29 and 30, use the figure below. Justify the conclusion.

29. Given: $r_m(E) = F$.
                $r_m(G) = H$.
    Conclusion 1: $r_m(H) = G$.
    Conclusion 2:   *EH* = *FG*.

30. Given: $r_m(E) = F$.
                $r_m(G) = H$.
    Conclusion 1: $r_m(I) = I$.
    Conclusion 2:   m∠*EGI* = m∠*FHI*.

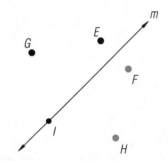

31. Use the figure below.
    Given: *m* ∥ *n*.
    Prove: m∠1 = m∠6.

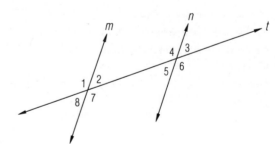

32. Given: △*MOP* in the figure below is equilateral.
             MO = *MN*.
    Prove: *MP* = *MN*.

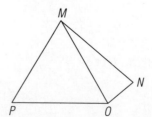

■ **Objective H:** *Locate and make symmetry lines in designs.* *(Lesson 4-7)*

In 33–35, trace the figure. Then draw all lines that would seem to be lines of reflection symmetry.

33.

34.

35.

36. You see this writing in a mirror. What does the original say?

ƎW R HTAM

■ **Objective I:** *Find coordinates of reflection images of points over the coordinate axes.* *(Lessons 4-1, 4-2)*

37. Find the reflection image of (3, 7) over the *x*-axis.

38. A quadrilateral has vertices $A = (3, 7)$, $B = (3, 1)$, $C = (-2, 8)$, and $D = (0, 4)$.

Find and graph the vertices of the reflection image of this quadrilateral over the *y*-axis.

39. Give the image of (a, b) when reflected over the *y*-axis.

40. Give the image of (c, d) when reflected over the *x*-axis.

CHAPTER 5

Polygons

This illustration is made entirely of polygons and segments. It shows the variety of polygons and their power to approximate curves such as those on a face and hands. The chapter begins with properties of some triangles, moves to properties of quadrilaterals, and then finishes with properties that apply to all polygons.

5-1

Isosceles Triangles

In the last chapter, you were asked to draw symmetry lines of figures just by looking at them. Of course, that kind of exercise does not prove that a figure has symmetry. People make mistakes and draw symmetry lines where there aren't any. In this lesson is a proof that isosceles triangles are reflection-symmetric. This symmetry will enable you to deduce some other properties of isosceles triangles.

Recall that isosceles triangles have (at least) two sides of equal length. They are the outlines of rooftops, cones, and many other objects that taper to a point. They occur when the endpoints of two noncollinear radii of a circle are joined.

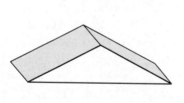  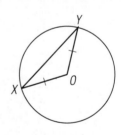

The angle determined by the equal sides in an isosceles triangle is called the **vertex angle** ($\angle A$ in the figure below). The other two angles are the **base angles** ($\angle B$ and $\angle C$). Each base angle is said to be *opposite* one of the equal sides. The side whose endpoints are the vertices of the base angles is called the **base** ($\overline{BC}$).

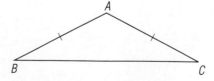

The proof of the next theorem is long. Long proofs are often easier to understand when they are written in paragraphs than when they are in the two-column format of Conclusions and Justifications. You should read the proof very slowly and refer to the drawing as figures are named.

Isosceles Triangle Symmetry Theorem:

> The line containing the bisector of the vertex angle of an isosceles triangle is a symmetry line for the triangle.

Proof

First draw a figure and state the given and the conclusion in terms of that figure.

Given: Isosceles triangle *ABC* with vertex angle *A* bisected by *m*.

Prove: *m* is a symmetry line for $\triangle ABC$.

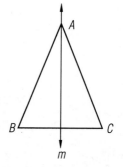

There are three things given. Each leads to conclusions that are used later in the proof. First, since *m* is an angle bisector, because of the Side-Switching Theorem, when $\overrightarrow{AB}$ is reflected over *m*, its image is $\overrightarrow{AC}$. Thus $r_m(B)$ is on $\overrightarrow{AC}$. Let $B' = r_m(B)$. Second, it is given that *A* is on the reflecting line, so $r_m(A) = A$. Hence, since reflections preserve distance, $AB' = AB$. Third, it is given that $\triangle ABC$ is isosceles with vertex angle *A*, so $AB = AC$. Now put all these conclusions together. By the Transitive Property of Equality, $AB' = AC$. So B' and *C* are points on ray $\overrightarrow{AC}$ at the same distance from *A*, and so $B' = C$. That is, $r_m(B) = C$. By the Flip-Flop Theorem, $r_m(C) = B$. So, by the Figure Reflection Theorem, $r_m(\triangle ABC) = \triangle ACB$, which is the sufficient condition for the symmetry of the triangle to line *m*.

In triangles that are not isosceles, no angle bisector is a symmetry line. Below, you can see that the reflection image of *E* over the bisector *m* is not *F*. ($r_m(E)$ is on $\overrightarrow{DF}$. You should estimate its location.)

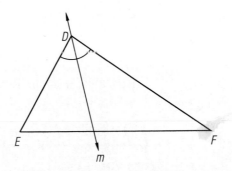

A segment connecting a vertex of a triangle to the midpoint of the opposite side is called a **median** of the triangle. Drawn below are one median, one perpendicular bisector, and one angle bisector of △*DEF*.

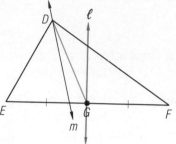

m is the bisector of ∠*EDF*.
ℓ is the ⊥ bisector of $\overline{EF}$.
$\overline{DG}$ is the median from vertex *D*.

For △*DEF*, the median, angle bisector, and ⊥ bisector are on different lines. But examine again isosceles triangle *ABC* with bisector *m* of ∠*A*. Since $r_m(B) = C$, *m* is the ⊥ bisector of $\overline{BC}$. And so *m* contains the midpoint of $\overline{BC}$. And so *m* contains the median from vertex *A*. This proves:

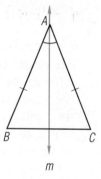

Theorem:

    In an isosceles triangle, the bisector of the vertex angle, the perpendicular bisector of the base, and the median to the base determine the same line.

There's even more. In the proof of the Isosceles Triangle Symmetry Theorem, since $r_m(A) = A$, $r_m(B) = C$, and $r_m(C) = B$, then $r_m(\angle ABC) = \angle ACB$ by the Figure Reflection Theorem. Thus m∠*ABC* = m∠*ACB* because reflections preserve angle measure. This conclusion is a very important theorem.

Isosceles Triangle Theorem:

    If a triangle has two equal sides, then the angles opposite them are equal.

The Isosceles Triangle Theorem is useful in proofs in which you must go from equal sides to equal angles.

Example 1   Given: the figure at the right, with $PQ = QR$.

Prove: $m\angle 2 = m\angle 4$.

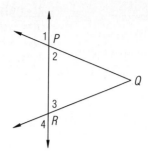

Analyze $PQ = QR$, and so, because of the Isosceles Triangle Theorem, $m\angle 2 = m\angle 3$. Angles 3 and 4 are vertical. Thus the Transitive Property strategy can be used.

Write

Conclusions	Justifications
1. $m\angle 2 = m\angle 3$	Isosceles Triangle Theorem
2. $m\angle 3 = m\angle 4$	Vertical Angle Theorem
3. $m\angle 2 = m\angle 4$	Transitive Property of Equality (steps 1 and 2)

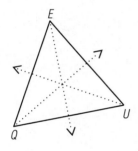

In an equilateral triangle all sides have the same length, so any side of an equilateral triangle may be considered as its base, and any angle its vertex angle. Thus, from the Isosceles Triangle Symmetry Theorem, an equilateral triangle has three symmetry lines. These lines can be thought of as the bisectors of its angles or the perpendicular bisectors of its sides. The lines contain its medians.

Example 2   Prove: If a triangle is equilateral, then it is equiangular (has three equal angles).

Draw   A figure is needed. Use equilateral $\triangle EQU$ at the left above and write a "given" and "prove" for that figure.

Given: Equilateral $\triangle QUE$.

Prove: $m\angle Q = m\angle U = m\angle E$.

Analyze   Take the equal sides two at a time. From each pair, get two equal angles.

Write

Conclusions	Justifications
1. $QE = EU$	definition of equilateral $\triangle$ (meaning)
2. $m\angle Q = m\angle U$	Isosceles $\triangle$ Theorem
3. $EU = QU$	definition of equilateral $\triangle$ (meaning)
4. $m\angle Q = m\angle E$	Isosceles $\triangle$ Theorem
5. $m\angle Q = m\angle E = m\angle U$	Transitive Property of Equality (steps 2 and 4)

In Questions 1 and 2, refer to $\triangle WIN$ in which $IW = IN$.

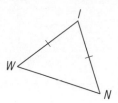

1. Identify:
   a. the base
   b. the vertex angle
   c. the base angles
   d. the angles of equal measure.

2. Describe the location of a symmetry line of $\triangle WIN$.

3. *Multiple choice.*   When a triangle is isosceles, which of the following best describes the bisector of its vertex angle and the perpendicular bisector of its base?
   (a) They are the same line.
   (b) They are parallel.
   (c) They are both perpendicular to the base.
   (d) All of (a)-(c) are true.

4. In $\triangle DEF$ at the right, $DE = EF$ and M is the midpoint of $\overline{DF}$.
   a. $\overline{EM}$ is called a(n) __?__ .
   b. What pairs of angles are equal?

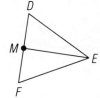

5. Use the figure below. (Hint: Use at least one theorem from this lesson as a justification.)
   Given: $XY = XZ$.
   Prove: $m\angle 1 = m\angle 2$.

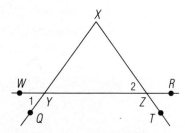

6. *True or false?*
   a. If a triangle is isosceles, then it is equilateral.
   b. If a triangle is equilateral, then it is isosceles.

7. Match the type of triangle with the number of symmetry lines.
   a. equilateral   (i)   1
   b. isosceles   (ii) 2
   c. scalene   (iii) 3
                         (iv) 0

In 8 and 9, use the figure below. $\overleftrightarrow{OE}$ is a symmetry line for $\triangle HEP$.

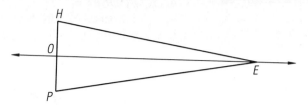

8. Name all pairs of segments with equal lengths.

9. Name all pairs of angles with equal measures.

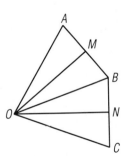

10. In the figure at the left, $\odot A$ and $\odot H$ each have radius AH and $\odot A \cap \odot H = \{M, T\}$.
  a. Is $\triangle AHM$ equilateral, isosceles but not equilateral, or neither isosceles nor equilateral? Justify your answer.
  b. Name all angles in the figure equal in measure to $\angle HMA$.

11. Given: In the figure at the right,
              $\overline{AD}$ and $\overline{BE}$ intersect at C,
              $AB = AC$, and $DC = DE$.
      Prove: $m\angle B = m\angle CED$.

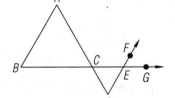

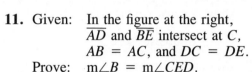

12. At the left, $\triangle AOB$ and $\triangle BOC$ are each isosceles. $\overrightarrow{OM}$ and $\overrightarrow{ON}$ are bisectors of the vertex angles AOB and BOC. If $m\angle AOC = 83$, what is $m\angle MON$?

13. *Multiple choice.*   The horizontal beam $\overline{RS}$ below helps to support other beams. To keep the top beams from collapsing, the vertical support $\overline{QT}$ is used. If the beams $\overline{RT}$ and $\overline{ST}$ are of equal length, which of (a)–(c) is not true?

(a) $\overrightarrow{TQ}$ bisects $\angle RTS$.   (c) $\overrightarrow{TQ} \perp \overline{RS}$
(b) Q is the midpoint of $\overline{RS}$.   (d) All of (a)-(c) are true.

14. $\overleftrightarrow{AD}$ is a symmetry line for polygon *ABCDEF* below.
  a. r(*ABCDEF*) = __?__
  b. Which sides of $\overline{ABCDEF}$ have the same length?
  c. Which angles in the figure have the same measure? *(Lesson 4-7)*

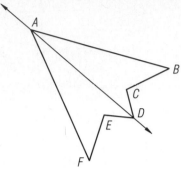

15. If F and G are figures and $r_m(F) = G$, then $r_m(G) = $ __?__ . *(Lesson 4-6)*

16. Give the reflection image of (x, y) over the *y*-axis. *(Lesson 4-1)*

17. Draw a convex nonagon. *(Lesson 2-7)*

18. Draw an obtuse isosceles triangle. *(Lesson 2-7)*

19. Arrange from least to greatest number of sides: rectangle, octagon, pentagon, equilateral triangle, nonagon, 7-gon. *(Lesson 2-7)*

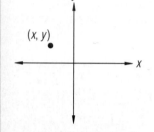

20. Find three meanings of the word *median* other than the one in this lesson.

21. Use a ruler, compass, and protractor or an automatic drawing tool.
  a. Draw an equilateral triangle. Draw all three medians. They should all intersect in a point called the **centroid** of the triangle. Measure the lengths of the medians and distances from the centroid to each of the vertices. What can you conclude?
  b. Draw an isosceles triangle that is not equilateral. Repeat the steps in part **a** for your triangle.
  c. Draw a scalene triangle. Repeat the steps in part **a** again.
  d. Summarize your work by writing a sentence or two that begins "In any triangle, the three medians... ."

5-2

Types of Quadrilaterals

The three-sided polygons, the triangles, were classified by the number of equal sides in Lesson 2-7. The four-sided polygons, the quadrilaterals, are more diverse and the classification is more complicated. There are seven major types: parallelogram, rhombus, rectangle, square, kite, trapezoid, and isosceles trapezoid. Here are definitions and examples for four of them. You should *memorize* these definitions.

$\overline{AB} /\!/ \overline{CD}, \overline{BC} /\!/ \overline{AD}$

Definition:

A quadrilateral is a **parallelogram** if and only if both pairs of its opposite sides are parallel.

$EF = FG = GH = HE$

Definition:

A quadrilateral is a **rhombus** if and only if its four sides are equal in length.

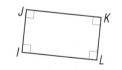

$\angle I, \angle J, \angle K, \angle L$ are right angles.

Definition:

A quadrilateral is a **rectangle** if and only if it has four right angles.

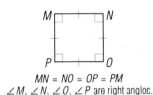

$MN = NO = OP = PM$
$\angle M, \angle N, \angle O, \angle P$ are right angles.

Definition:

A quadrilateral is a **square** if and only if it has four equal sides and four right angles.

From the definitions, you can see that every square is a rhombus since every square has four equal sides. You can also conclude that every square is a rectangle since every square has four right angles. This information is summarized in the network below. This network shows a part of a hierarchy of quadrilaterals.

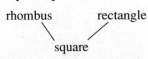

rhombus   rectangle

square

Because two perpendiculars to the same line are parallel, every rectangle is a parallelogram. So we can add "parallelogram" to the hierarchy.

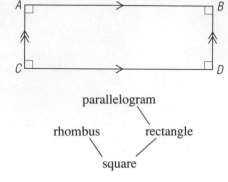

parallelogram

rhombus   rectangle

square

A fifth type of quadrilateral is formed by the union of two isosceles triangles having the same base, with the base removed. The result is a quadrilateral that resembles a *kite* or arrowhead. Pictured here are the convex kite *ABCD* and the nonconvex kite *FORM*.

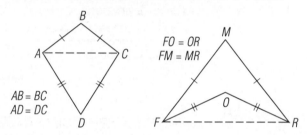

Definition:

A quadrilateral is a **kite** if and only if it has two distinct pairs of consecutive sides of the same length.

From the definitions of kite and rhombus, every rhombus is a kite. This information is added to the hierarchy. You can also now conclude that every square is a kite by reading up the hierarchy from square to rhombus to kite.

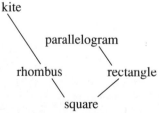

kite

parallelogram

rhombus   rectangle

square

A figure more general than the parallelogram is the *trapezoid*.

Definition:

A quadrilateral is a **trapezoid** if and only if it has at least one pair of parallel sides.

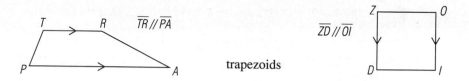

Parallel sides of a trapezoid are called **bases.** In the figures above, $\overline{TR}$ and $\overline{PA}$ are bases and $\overline{ZD}$ and $\overline{OI}$ are bases. Two consecutive angles that share a base are called **base angles.** This terminology enables us to define a special type of trapezoid.

> **Definition:**
>
> A trapezoid is **isosceles** if and only if it has a pair of base angles equal in measure.

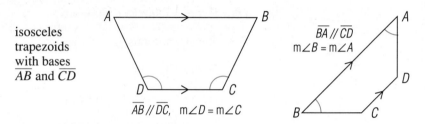

isosceles trapezoids with bases $\overline{AB}$ and $\overline{CD}$

Because a rectangle has opposite sides parallel and all angles equal, every rectangle is an isosceles trapezoid. You can now relate all these seven types of quadrilaterals in the same hierarchy. This is shown by the dark lines below. One other hierarchy relationship can be deduced; every rhombus is a parallelogram. It will be deduced in Lesson 5-4. This is shown in the hierarchy now by a blue line.

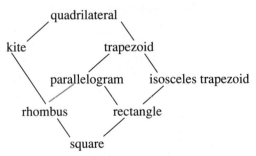

The hierarchy of quadrilaterals is very useful because it allows properties of some quadrilaterals to apply to other quadrilaterals. The general rule is:

> ANY property held by a type of figure in the hierarchy is also held by *all* the types of figures below it to which it is connected.

For example, *square* is below *rhombus* in the hierarchy. Thus any square has all the properties of a rhombus. Squares and rhombuses are below *kite*. Thus they have all the properties of kites. In the next lessons this rule will be used to identify many properties of specific quadrilaterals.

In 1–7, **a.** give a sufficient condition for each figure and **b.** draw an example.

1. parallelogram

2. rhombus

3. rectangle

4. square

5. kite

6. trapezoid

7. isosceles trapezoid

8. Draw a hierarchy of the following quadrilaterals: kite, square, rhombus, rectangle, parallelogram.

In 9–15, *true* or *false*?

9. Every square is a rhombus.

10. Every rhombus is a square.

11. Every square is a kite.

12. Every kite is a rhombus.

13. If a quadrilateral is a trapezoid, then it is a parallelogram.

14. A property of a square is a property of a kite.

15. A property of a trapezoid is a property of a parallelogram.

In 16–19, write in symbols the information marked on the figure. Use this information to name the figure. Be as specific as you can, but do not be fooled by looks.

16.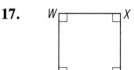

17.

18.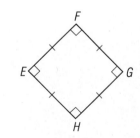

19.

20. Let A = set of all rectangles and B = set of all rhombuses. Describe A ∩ B.

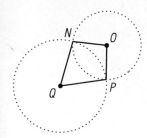

21. Circles O and Q intersect at N and P. Justify each conclusion in this proof that $NOPQ$ is a kite.

Conclusions	Justifications
1. $QN = QP$	**a.** __?__
2. $ON = OP$	**b.** __?__
3. $NOPQ$ is a kite.	**c.** __?__

In 22–24, a real object is given. Name all of the types of quadrilaterals that describe each shape.

22. bedsheet   **23.** warning sign   **24.** trough

25. In $\triangle ABC$, $AB = AC$.
If m$\angle B = 4x - 7$
and m$\angle C = 2x + 13$,
a. find x;
b. find m$\angle B$. *(Lesson 4-2)*

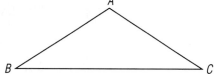

26. Given: $\triangle DEF$ is isosceles with vertex angle F.
          $\triangle EFG$ is isosceles with vertex angle F.
Prove: $DF = FG$. *(Lesson 5-1)*

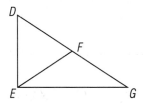

27. Draw a nonconvex hexagon. *(Lesson 2-7)*

28. Which of the types of quadrilaterals on the hierarchy can be nonconvex? Support your answer with drawings.

29. Biologists place living things in a hierarchy. Show a hierarchy containing the following terms: man, cat, animal, mammal, primate, chimpanzee, lion, feline, plant.

30. Think of another hierarchy outside of mathematics different from that in Question 29.

Conjectures

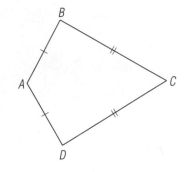

Pictured at the left is a kite, with two distinct pairs of equal sides. By measuring with a protractor, you can verify that $m\angle A = 122$, $m\angle C = 60$, and $m\angle B = m\angle D = 89$.

Does *every* kite have two angles of equal measure? Or is *ABCD* in some way an *unusual* kite? To answer this question, examine some other kites.

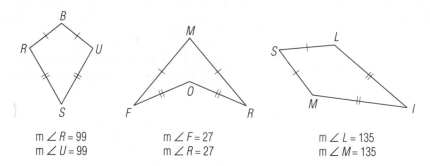

| $m\angle R = 99$ | $m\angle F = 27$ | $m\angle L = 135$ |
| $m\angle U = 99$ | $m\angle R = 27$ | $m\angle M = 135$ |

Each of the three kites above has two angles of equal measure.

A **conjecture** is an educated guess or opinion. The evidence above supports the conjecture "Every kite has at least two angles of equal measure."

To tell whether a conjecture is true or false, mathematicians usually start by examining instances. For conjectures about geometric figures, this means that drawings are made and explored. If even one counterexample is found, the conjecture is not true. If a counterexample is not found, there is evidence that the conjecture is true. Still, for a conjecture to be accepted as true for all cases, it must be proved.

The ancient Greeks tested conjectures with straightedge and compass constructions. Today we still have those tools, but increasingly people are using computers to explore conjectures. In this lesson, you may draw pictures using ruler, compass, and protractor, or you may use a computer with an automatic drawing tool.

To test a conjecture, it often helps to rewrite it in if-then form.

Example 1 **a.** Test this conjecture. "The diagonals of a kite are perpendicular."
b. Do you think the conjecture is true?

Solution

a. In if-then form the conjecture states that "if a figure is a kite, then its diagonals are perpendicular." Draw a variety of figures which satisfy the antecedent of the conjecture. That is, draw some kites. The more different they look, the better. We use the three kites from the previous page.

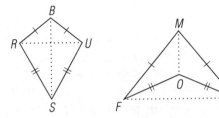

In each case drawn here, the diagonals do seem to form 90° angles at the point of intersection. (For kite *FORM*, the lines containing the diagonals seem to be perpendicular.)
b. You still could think the conjecture is false, but no counterexample is given here. The conjecture seems to be true.

Example 2 Show that the conjecture "The diagonals of a parallelogram have equal length" is false.

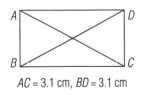

AC = 3.1 cm, BD = 3.1 cm

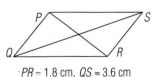

PR = 1.8 cm, QS = 3.6 cm

Solution Restate the conjecture as an if-then statement: If a figure is a parallelogram, then its diagonals have equal length. To prove this statement is false you must find at least one figure satisfying the antecedent, but not the consequent. That is, you must find a parallelogram whose diagonals are not of equal length. At the left are two parallelograms. Notice that in *ABCD* the diagonals are equal; but in *PQRS* they are not. *ABCD* supports the conjecture. *PQRS* is a counterexample to the stated conjecture. It shows that the conjecture is false.

When a conjecture is not true, as in Example 2, you may try to **refine** it. This means to change the statement slightly so that the conjecture is true. In Example 2, the conjecture is true for some parallelograms, namely rectangles. Is it true for any other parallelograms? That conjecture is left for you in Question 7.

When you are asked to make a conjecture, it often helps to organize your work in a table.

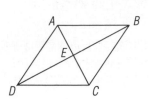

Example 3 Make a conjecture about the diagonals of a rhombus.

Draw some rhombuses (the more different they look, the better), and draw their diagonals.

Because you are not asked to conjecture about any specific property of the diagonals, measure lengths of the diagonals and angles formed by the diagonals. For the rhombuses at the left, some measurements are organized in a table. Lengths are in millimeters.

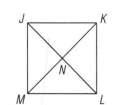

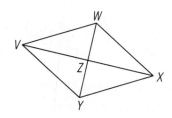

rhombus	ABCD	JKLM	VWXY
lengths of diagonals	AC = 18 BD = 34	JL = 26 KM = 26	VX = 36 WY = 20
lengths from point of intersection of diagonals to vertices	EA = 9 EC = 9 ED = 17 EB = 17	NJ = 13 NL = 13 NM = 13 NK = 13	ZV = 18 ZX = 18 ZW = 10 ZY = 10
angles formed at point of intersection of diagonals	m∠AED = 90 m∠AEB = 90 m∠BEC = 90 m∠DEC = 90	m∠JNK = 90 m∠KNL = 90 m∠LNM = 90 m∠MNJ = 90	m∠VZW = 90 m∠WZX = 90 m∠XZY = 90 m∠YZV = 90

Now look for patterns that hold for *all* the rhombuses. Here are two reasonable conjectures:
(1) The diagonals bisect each other; that is, they intersect at a point which is the midpoint of each segment.
(2) The diagonals are perpendicular.

Conjectures can be related to each other. If the conjecture of Example 1 is true, then so will be conjecture (2) of Example 3. Any property true of all kites is true of all rhombuses.

Questions

Covering the Reading

1. What is a conjecture?

2. To show a conjecture is true, a(n) __?__ is needed.

3. To show a conjecture is not true, a(n) __?__ is enough.

4. Refer to Example 1.
   a. Draw another figure to test the conjecture.
   b. Does your figure support the conjecture?
   c. Do you think the conjecture is true?

5. Refer to Example 2.
   a. Which figure drawn supports the conjecture?
   b. Which figure shows that the conjecture is false?

6. What does *refining a conjecture* mean?

7. Refine the conjecture of Example 2.

In 8 and 9, use the rhombuses drawn in Example 3.

8. Which rhombus provides a counterexample to the conjecture that "the diagonals of a rhombus are equal in length"?

9. Make a conjecture about the angles formed by the diagonals and the sides of a rhombus. Measure the angles first. Record your work in a chart like the one below. (You might want to number the angles to save writing.)

ABCD	*JKLM*	*VWXY*
m∠*DAE* =	m∠*MJN* =	m∠*ZVW* =
m∠*EAB* =	m∠*NJK* =	.
m∠*ABE* =	.	.
m∠*EBC* =	.	.
.	.	
.		
.		

Applying the Mathematics

In 10–13, a conjecture is made. Draw a counterexample to show that it is not true.

10. If $XM = MY$, then M is the midpoint of $\overline{XY}$.

11. If two angles are supplementary, then they have the same vertex.

12. The square of any real number is positive.

13. The three medians in an isosceles triangle are equal in length.

14. a. Test this conjecture on at least three cases: The diagonals of an isosceles trapezoid are equal.
    b. Do you think this conjecture is true?

In 15–17, a conjecture is stated. If a figure is not drawn, you should draw one or more. Finally, choose the answer A, B, C, D, or E that best indicates your feeling about the statement.
(A) The conjecture is definitely true and in my mind needs no proof.
(B) The conjecture may be true, but I need a proof or a similar argument before I'd believe it.
(C) the conjecture doesn't seem true, but I am not sure. Some discussion would help.
(D) the conjecture is probably not true, but I'd be sure only if I had a counterexample.
(E) The conjecture is definitely false. No argument is needed to convince me that it is false.

15. If the midpoints of two sides of a triangle are joined, the segment is parallel to the third side.

16. If the midpoints of the four sides of a rectangle are connected, the resulting figure is a rectangle.

17. In the figure below, *PQR* is a semicircle with center *S*. Point *O* is the center of the larger circle. m∠*POR* = 90. Then the areas of the two shaded regions are equal.

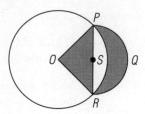

In 18–21, define each term. *(Lessons 5-2, 2-7)*

Review

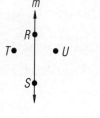

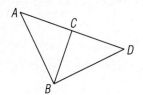

18. square

19. parallelogram

20. rhombus

21. isosceles triangle

22. Given: In the figure at the left, r$_m$(*T*) = *U*
Prove: *RUST* is a kite. *(Lessons 5-2, 4-5)*

23. Arrange in order of most general to most specific: rhombus, polygon, square, quadrilateral, kite. *(Lesson 5-2)*

24. Given: At the left, △*ABC* is isosceles with vertex angle *C*.
△*BCD* is isosceles with vertex angle *C*.
C is on $\overline{AD}$.
Prove: $\overline{BC}$ is a median in △*ABD*. *(Lesson 5-1)*

25. Given: ℓ and *m* are symmetry lines
for quadrilateral *EFGH*. Simplify:
a. r$_ℓ$(*F*)
b. r$_ℓ$(*EFGH*)
c. r$_m$(∠*GEF*). *(Lesson 4-7)*

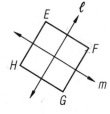

Exploration

26. A *simple closed curve* is a closed curve that does not intersect itself. Here are some examples.

a.   **b.**   **c.**

     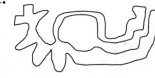

An unsolved conjecture (as of 1989) is that on every simple closed curve there are four points which are the vertices of a square. In curve **a** are four points which might be the vertices of a square. Trace and try to find the square for curves **b** and **c**.

5-4

Properties of Kites

Here again is the hierarchy of quadrilaterals. Remember that any property held by a type of figure in the hierarchy is held by all types below to which it is connected. Since all seven types of quadrilaterals are either kites or trapezoids or both, it is particularly useful to know the properties of these two types.

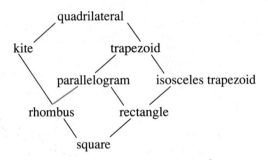

Properties held by all kites will also be properties of rhombuses and squares. These properties will be developed in this lesson. In the next lesson you will learn some properties of trapezoids.

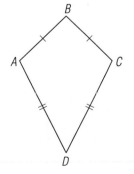

The common vertices of the equal sides of a kite are the **ends** of the kite. In the kite at the left, B and D are ends. All four of a rhombus' vertices are ends. Of all properties of kites, the most powerful is the kite's symmetry.

Kite Symmetry Theorem:

The line containing the ends of a kite is a symmetry line for the kite.

Proof

Draw A figure is needed with the "given" and "prove" restated in terms of that figure.

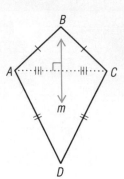

Given: ABCD is a kite with ends B and D.

Prove: $\overleftrightarrow{BD}$ is a symmetry line for ABCD.

Analyze Use the symmetry lines of isosceles triangles ABC and ADC.

Write

Conclusions	Justifications
1. $AB = BC,\ AD = DC$	def. of ends of kite (meaning)
2. $\triangle ABC$ and $\triangle ADC$ are isosceles.	def. of isosceles triangle (sufficient condition)
3. Let m be the $\perp$ bisector of $\overline{AC}$.	A segment has exactly one $\perp$ bisector.
4. $r_m(A) = C,\ r_m(C) = A$	definition of reflection (sufficient condition)
5. m contains B and D.	The $\perp$ bisector of the base of an isosceles triangle is the angle bisector of the vertex angle (so it contains the vertex).
6. $r_m(B) = B,\ r_m(D) = D$	definition of reflection (sufficient condition)
7. $r_m(ABCD) = CBAD$	Figure Reflection Theorem
8. m (which is $\overleftrightarrow{BD}$) is a symmetry line for ABCD.	definition of symmetry line (sufficient condition)

The diagonal determined by the ends ($\overline{BD}$ above) is called the **symmetry diagonal** of the kite. The line $\overleftrightarrow{BD}$ is the $\perp$ bisector of the other diagonal of the kite. Notice that from conclusions 4 and 6 in the proof, $r_m(\angle ABD) = \angle CBD$ and $r_m(\angle ADB) = \angle CDB$ by the Figure Reflection Theorem. Thus $\overline{BD}$ bisects $\angle ABC$ and $\angle ADC$. This is summarized in the following theorem.

Kite Diagonal Theorem:

The symmetry diagonal of a kite is the perpendicular bisector of the other diagonal and bisects the two angles at the ends of the kite.

Example 1

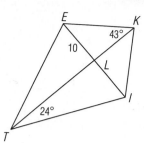

Given kite *KITE* with ends *K* and *T*. If *EL* = 10, m∠*EKT* = 43, and m∠*ITK* = 24, find as many other lengths and angle measures as you can.

Solution   Since $\overleftrightarrow{KT}$ is a symmetry line for the kite, r(∠*EKT*) = ∠*IKT* so m∠*IKT* = 43. Also r(∠*ITK*) = ∠*ETK* so m∠*ETK* = 24. By angle addition, m∠*ETI* = 48 and m∠*EKI* = 86. Since r(*E*) = *I*, $\overleftrightarrow{KT}$ is the ⊥ bisector of $\overline{EI}$, making *LI* = 10 and *EI* = 20. The four angles with vertex *L* have measure 90.

The Kite Diagonal Theorem applies to rhombuses and squares because of their positions in the hierarchy. Another important property of kites is that the two angles not bisected by the symmetry diagonal are equal in measure. You are asked to finish a proof of this in Question 9.

A rhombus is a kite, any of whose vertices can be ends. Thus a rhombus has two symmetry diagonals. In rhombus *RHOM* below, $\overline{RO}$ is the perpendicular bisector of $\overline{HM}$ and $\overline{HM}$ is the perpendicular bisector of $\overline{RO}$. Thus *X* is the midpoint of $\overline{HM}$ and $\overline{RO}$.

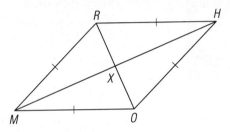

Rhombus Symmetry Theorem:

> Every rhombus has two symmetry lines, the lines containing its diagonals.

Example 2

In rhombus *RHOM* above, if m∠*RHM* = 23 and m∠*MRH* = 134, find as many other angle measures as you can.

Solution   Each diagonal bisects the angles at the vertices it connects. Thus m∠*ORH* = $\frac{1}{2}$ · 134 = 67. Opposite angles are equal in measure due to the rhombus' symmetry. All the angles surrounding *X* are right angles. All of the angle measures are given in the figure below.

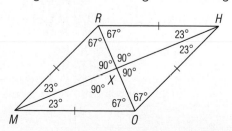

In 1–3, refer to the hierarchy of quadrilaterals. Answer *always*, *sometimes,* or *never*.

1. A figure is a parallelogram if it is a rectangle.

2. Every square is a trapezoid.

3. If a figure is a rhombus, then it is a square.

4. To which types of quadrilaterals on the hierarchy of quadrilaterals does the Kite Symmetry Theorem apply?

5. Refer to kite *KITE* at the right.
KI = IT and *KE = ET*.
a. Name the ends of *KITE*.
b. Name the symmetry line.
c. $r_{\overleftrightarrow{IE}}(\angle IKE) =$ ___?___

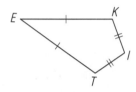

6. At the left, *RH = HO = OM = MR*.
a. IS *RHOM* a kite?
b. If so, name its ends. If not, why not?
c. How many lines of symmetry has RHOM?

7. Use kite *ABCD* below. If *BE* = 15, m∠*BCA* = 30, and m∠*DAC* = 50, find as many other angle measures and lengths as you can.

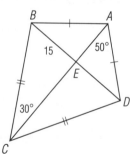

*Associates Building
Chicago, Illinois*

8. In rhombus *QRST* at the left, m∠*SQR* = 51 and m∠*QRS* = 78. Find as many other angle measures as you can.

9. Complete the proof that non-end angles of a kite have equal measure.
Given: Kite *ABCD* with ends *B* and *D*.
Prove: m∠*A* = m∠*C*.

Conclusions	Justifications
1. $\overline{BD}$ is a symmetry diagonal of *ABCD*.	**a.** ___?___
2. $\overleftrightarrow{BD}$ is the ⊥ bisector of $\overline{AC}$.	**b.** ___?___
3. $r_{\overleftrightarrow{BD}}(A) = C$, $r_{\overleftrightarrow{BD}}(C) = A$	**c.** ___?___
4. $r_{\overleftrightarrow{BD}}(B) = B$, $r_{\overleftrightarrow{BD}}(D) = D$	**d.** ___?___
5. $r_{\overleftrightarrow{BD}}(\angle BAD) = \angle BCD$	**e.** ___?___
6. m∠*BAD* = m∠*BCD*	**f.** ___?___

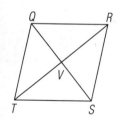

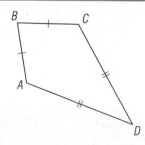

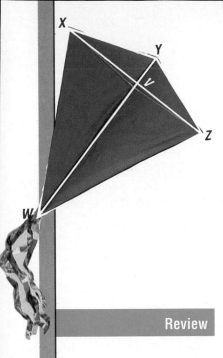

10. Complete the following paragraph proof that the opposite angles of a rhombus are equal. Use the diagram from Question 6.
    a. The reflection image of ∠M over $\overleftrightarrow{RO}$ is __?__, so m∠M = __?__ because reflections preserve __?__.
    b. Similarly, the reflection image of ∠R over __?__ is ∠O, so m∠O = m∠R.

11. a. Draw a nonconvex kite ABCD with ends B and D.
    b. Does the proof of Question 9 work for this kite?
    c. Is the Kite Diagonal Theorem true for nonconvex kites?

12. Two sticks $\overline{XZ}$ and $\overline{WY}$ were lashed together to form the kite at the left. If XZ = 20″, WY = 30″, and VY = 7″, find
    a. XV   b. VZ
    c. WV   d. m∠YVZ.

Review

13. Give a counterexample to show that the following conjecture is not true: If the midpoints of the sides of a rhombus are connected in order, the resulting figure is a square. *(Lesson 5-3)*

14. If the conjecture in Question 13 is refined by replacing the word "square" with "rectangle," do you think the conjecture is true? *(Lesson 5-3)*

In 15 and 16, define the term. *(Lesson 5-2)*

15. trapezoid   16. isosceles trapezoid

17. Name all types of quadrilaterals which are isosceles trapezoids. *(Lesson 5-2)*

18. Draw an example of this situation. LOVE is a quadrilateral oriented clockwise. r_m(LOVE) = HATE. (Caution: There can only be one point E.) *(Lesson 4-6)*

19. Trace the needed parts in the picture at the left. Construct the shortest path from C to the highway. *(Lesson 3-6)*

20. In the figure below, m ∥ n. Find x. *(Lesson 3-4)*

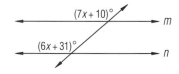

In 21 and 22, use the figure at the left. *(Lesson 3-2, Previous course)*

21. If m∠ABC = 8x − 7 and m∠EBD = 3x + 68, find x.

22. If m∠ABC = 2y + 3 and m∠CBD = 4y + 9, find m∠ABC.

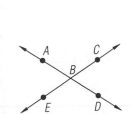

Exploration

23. Design and build a "flat" kite that flies (not a box kite). Does your shape agree with the mathematical definition of kite?

5-5

Properties of Trapezoids

Because of the hierarchy of quadrilaterals, any property of a trapezoid holds for parallelograms, rhombuses, rectangles, squares, and isosceles trapezoids. In the trapezoid below, $\overline{AB} \parallel \overline{DC}$. $\overline{AD}$ has been extended beyond A to point E. This forms the linear pair $\angle 1$ and $\angle 2$. Now follow the reasoning.

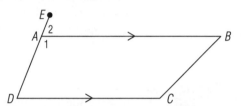

Conclusions	Justifications
1. $m\angle 1 + m\angle 2 = 180$	Linear Pair Theorem
2. $m\angle 2 = m\angle D$	$\parallel$ lines $\Rightarrow$ corr. $\angle$s =
3. $m\angle 1 + m\angle D = 180$	Substitution (step 2 into step 1)
4. $\angle 1$ and $\angle D$ are supplementary.	definition of supplementary (sufficient condition)

This argument could be repeated with $\angle B$ and $\angle C$ and with any trapezoid. The result is the following theorem:

Trapezoid Angle Theorem:

In a trapezoid, consecutive angles between a pair of parallel sides are supplementary.

Notice how the Trapezoid Angle Theorem is applied to other figures. A pair of the consecutive angles between parallel sides is marked in each figure below.

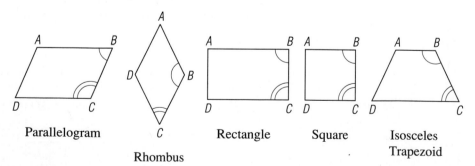

Parallelogram   Rhombus   Rectangle   Square   Isosceles Trapezoid

In all cases shown, angles B and C are supplementary.

Example 1 In trapezoid *TRAP* below, $\overline{TR} \parallel \overline{AP}$. If m∠*A* = 82, find the measures of as many other angles as you can.

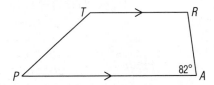

Solution From the Trapezoid Angle Theorem, angles *A* and *R* are supplementary. So 82 + m∠*R* = 180. So m∠*R* = 98. No other angle measures can be found. However, the Trapezoid Angle Theorem tells you that m∠*P* + m∠*T* = 180.

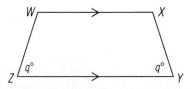

Recall that an isosceles trapezoid is defined to be a trapezoid with a pair of base angles of equal measure. Above is an isosceles trapezoid with bases $\overline{WX}$ and $\overline{YZ}$. Let m∠*Y* = m∠*Z* = *q*. According to the Trapezoid Angle Theorem, m∠*W* = 180 − *q* and m∠*X* = 180 − *q*. So m∠*W* = m∠*X*. This argument proves:

Theorem:

In an isosceles trapezoid, both pairs of base angles are equal in measure.

The isosceles trapezoid is also related to the isosceles triangle in a way that is shown below. Let △*ABC* be isosceles with vertex angle *A* and base $\overline{BC}$. Draw $\overleftrightarrow{DE} \parallel \overline{BC}$. Then you can prove that *DECB* is an isosceles trapezoid. (See Question 9.) Since an isosceles triangle is symmetric, you would expect that an isosceles trapezoid is symmetric as well.

Isosceles Trapezoid Symmetry Theorem:

The perpendicular bisector of one base of an isosceles trapezoid is the perpendicular bisector of the other base and a symmetry line for the trapezoid.

Proof

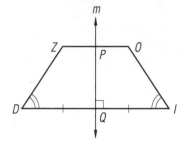

Use *ZOID* as marked at the left with $m\angle I = m\angle D$. Let m be the $\perp$ bisector of $\overline{ID}$. We need to show that m is also the $\perp$ bisector of $\overline{ZO}$. This will imply that m is a symmetry line for the trapezoid.

Since m is the $\perp$ bisector of $\overline{ID}$, $r_m(D) = I$ and $r_m(I) = D$. We want to show that $r_m(Z) = O$. Since reflections preserve angle measure, you know that $r_m(\overrightarrow{DZ}) = \overrightarrow{IO}$, so $r_m(Z)$ lies on $\overrightarrow{IO}$. Since *ZOID* is a trapezoid, $\overline{ZO} \parallel \overline{DI}$; thus $\overline{ZO} \perp m$ by the Perpendicular to Parallels Theorem. Thus by the definition of reflection, $r_m(Z)$ lies on $\overleftrightarrow{ZO}$. Since $r_m(Z)$ lies on $\overrightarrow{IO}$ and $\overleftrightarrow{ZO}$, and $\overrightarrow{IO}$ and $\overleftrightarrow{ZO}$ intersect at O, $r_m(Z)$ must be the point O. By the Flip-Flop Theorem, $r_m(O) = Z$. Thus by the Figure Reflection Theorem, $r_m(ZOID) = OZDI$, and m is a symmetry line of *ZOID*. Also, since $r_m(Z) = O$, m is the $\perp$ bisector of $\overline{OZ}$.

A **corollary** to a theorem is a theorem that is easily proved from the first theorem. The Isosceles Trapezoid Symmetry Theorem has a beautiful corollary. Since $r_m(Z) = O$, and $r_m(D) = I$, and reflections preserve distance, $ZD = OI$. This proves:

Isosceles Trapezoid Theorem:

In an isosceles trapezoid, the non-base sides are equal in measure.

▪ ▪ ▪ ▪ ▪ ▪ ▪ ▪

Example 2   *WXYZ* at the left is an isosceles trapezoid with bases $\overline{WX}$ *and* $\overline{YZ}$. Fill in as many lengths and angle measures as you can.

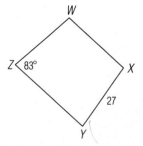

Solution   From the Isosceles Trapezoid Theorem, $WZ = XY$ so $WZ = 27$. From the Trapezoid Angle Theorem, $m\angle W = 180 - 83 = 97$. Since each pair of base angles has the same measure, $m\angle X = m\angle W = 97$ and $m\angle Y = m\angle Z = 83$.

A rectangle can be considered as an isosceles trapezoid in two ways. Either pair of parallel sides can be the bases. Thus another corollary of the Isosceles Trapezoid Symmetry Theorem is:

Questions

In 1–3, refer to the hierarchy of quadrilaterals. To which types of quadrilaterals does the theorem apply?

1. Trapezoid Angle Theorem

2. Isosceles Trapezoid Symmetry Theorem

3. Rectangle Symmetry Theorem

4. In trapezoid *ZOID* below, $\overline{ZD} \parallel \overline{OI}$, m∠Z = 68, and m∠I = 95.
   a. Name the bases of *ZOID*.
   b. Name the two pairs of base angles.
   c. Find the measure of as many other angles as you can.

The cane fields at a sugar mill in Kauai, Hawaii form trapezoids.

5. Use the figure above. Let *ZOID* be an isosceles trapezoid with bases $\overline{OI}$ and $\overline{ZD}$. If $\overline{OZ}$ = 12 cm and m∠O = 125, find as many other lengths and angle measures as you can.

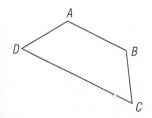

6. Isosceles trapezoid *ABCD* at the left has bases $\overline{AB}$ and $\overline{DC}$. Trace it and construct *m,* a symmetry line for the trapezoid.

7. What is a corollary?

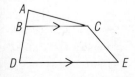

8. At the left, *B* is between *A* and *D*. *BCED* is a trapezoid with $\overline{BC} \parallel \overline{ED}$. Justify each statement in this proof of the Trapezoid Angle Theorem.
   a. m∠ABC = m∠D
   b. m∠ABC + m∠CBD = 180
   c. m∠D + m∠CBD = 180

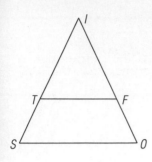

9. Given: △*ISO* at the left is isosceles with *IS = IO*.
$\overline{TF} \parallel \overline{SO}$.
Justify each step in this proof that *SOFT* is an isosceles trapezoid.

Conclusions	Justifications
1. *SOFT* is a trapezoid.	**a.** _?_
2. m∠*S* = m∠*O*	**b.** _?_
3. *SOFT* is an isosceles trapezoid.	**c.** _?_

10. Quadrilateral *PARL* at the right is a parallelogram. If m∠*R* = 27.3, find the measures of as many other angles as you can.

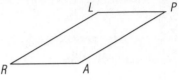

11. Trace rectangle *RECT* below, and draw all its symmetry lines.

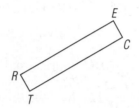

12. Given: *ABCD* below is an isosceles trapezoid with bases $\overline{AB}$ and $\overline{DC}$.
a. Prove: *AC = BD*. (Hint: use symmetry and reflections.)
b. State the result in words as a theorem.

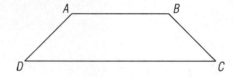

13. *True* or *false*?
a. The diagonals of an isosceles trapezoid are equal in measure.
b. The diagonals of a rectangle are equal in measure.
c. The diagonals of a square are equal in measure.

14. a. What theorem of this lesson tells you that the top view of most beds has two symmetry lines?
b. Why do you think most beds are shaped this way?

Review

15. In the kitc at the left, *I* and *E* are ends. If *KI* = 4, *KR* = 3, *ET* = 8, m∠*RIT* = 49, and m∠*KET* = 44, find as many other lengths and angle measures as you can. *(Lesson 5-4)*

16. In the kite at the left, justify the following conclusions:
(Lessons 5-4, 4-7, 4-1)
a. $\overleftrightarrow{IE}$ is a symmetry line for the kite.
b. $\overleftrightarrow{IE}$ is the ⊥ bisector of $\overline{KT}$.
c. $r_{\overleftrightarrow{IE}}(R) = R$

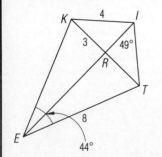

17. At the left is a nonconvex kite.
    a. Name its ends.
    b. Does it have a symmetry line?
    c. Does the Kite Diagonal Theorem hold for this kite? *(Lesson 5-2)*

18. Given: Isosceles triangle *LOV*
             at the right with vertex angle *L*.
             $\overline{LE}$ is a median.
    Justify each conclusion.
    a. $LO = LV$
    b. $LE = LE$
    c. *E* is the midpoint of $\overline{OV}$.
    d. $EV = OE$ *(Lessons 5-1, 3-3, 2-7, 1-7)*

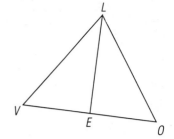

19. a. Name four properties preserved by reflections. *(Lesson 4-2)*
    b. Name one property not preserved by reflections. *(Lesson 4-6)*

In 20 and 21, use the figure at the right.

20. Trace the figure. Draw $r_{\overleftrightarrow{BD}}$ ($\triangle ABC$).
    (Lesson 4-2)

21. If $m\angle ADB = 3x - 2$ and
    $m\angle CDB = 9x - 10$, then
    a. find *x*;
    b. find $m\angle CDB$. *(Lesson 3-2)*

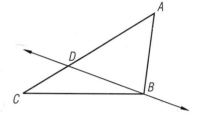

22. Refer to the figure below. (It is not drawn accurately.)
    a. Solve for *y*.
    b. Is *m* ∥ *n*? Explain why or why not. *(Lessons 3-4, 3-2)*

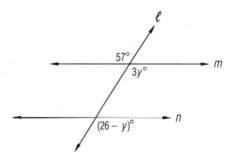

23. Test this conjecture. If the midpoints of the sides of an isosceles trapezoid are connected in order, the resulting figure is a rhombus.

5-6

Alternate Interior Angles

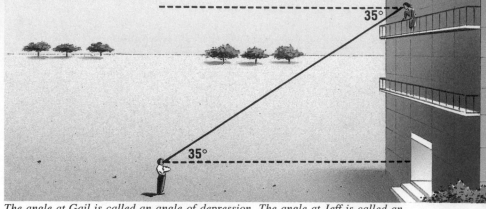

The angle at Gail is called an angle of depression. The angle at Jeff is called an angle of elevation. They are alternate interior angles and are equal in measure.

This lesson completes the hierarchy for quadrilaterals by proving that all rhombuses are parallelograms. To do so, it is first necessary to describe and justify some properties of parallel lines.

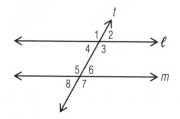

When two lines are cut by a transversal, the four angles between the lines ($\angle 3$, $\angle 4$, $\angle 5$, and $\angle 6$ in the picture) are called **interior angles.** The other four angles are called **exterior angles.** Angles 4 and 6 are called **alternate interior angles** (they are on alternate sides of the transversal), as are angles 3 and 5.

The alternate interior angles are like the angles in the letter Z. If the top and bottom of the Z are parallel, the angles look equal in measure. The proof relies on the Parallel Lines Postulate. The proof is short and is one you should be able to do.

> **// Lines ⇒ AIA = Theorem:**
>
> If two parallel lines are cut by a transversal, then alternate interior angles are equal in measure.

Proof

Draw   Two parallel lines cut by a transversal are needed. Number alternate interior angles as $\angle 1$ and $\angle 2$ and state the given and prove in terms of the figure.

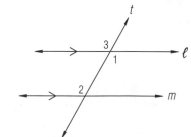

Given: $\ell \parallel m$.
Prove: $m\angle 1 = m\angle 2$.
Analyze   Both $\angle 1$ and $\angle 2$ equal $\angle 3$ in measure. So the Transitive Property is used.

Write	Conclusions	Justifications
	1. $m\angle 1 = m\angle 3$	**Vertical Angle Theorem**
	2. $m\angle 3 = m\angle 2$	**// lines ⇒ corr. $\angle$s =**
	3. $m\angle 1 = m\angle 2$	**Transitive Property of Equality** (steps 1 and 2)

Example 1   In the figure below, $n \parallel p$. If $m\angle 3 = 43$ and $m\angle 4 = 57$, find the measures of angles 1 and 2.

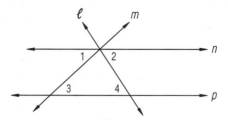

Solution   Angles 1 and 3 are alternate interior angles with m as a transversal. Thus, $m\angle 1 = m\angle 3 = 43$. Similarly, angles 2 and 4 are alternate interior angles with ℓ as a transversal and thus $m\angle 2 = m\angle 4 = 57$.

The converse of the $\parallel$ Lines $\Rightarrow$ AIA $=$ Theorem is true also. You will prove it in Question 11.

AIA $=$ $\Rightarrow$ $\parallel$ Lines Theorem:

If two lines are cut by a transversal and form alternate interior angles of equal measure, then the lines are parallel.

Example 2   Given the figure below (not drawn to scale) with angles as marked. *True* or *false*?
  a. $\overline{AB} \parallel \overline{CD}$
  b. $\overline{AD} \parallel \overline{BC}$

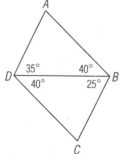

Solution   a. True. $\overline{BD}$ serves as a transversal for sides $\overline{AB}$ and $\overline{CD}$. (Note the Z formed by $\overline{AB}$, $\overline{BD}$, and $\overline{DC}$.) $\angle ABD$ and $\angle BDC$ are alternate interior angles with the same measure, so $\overline{AB} \parallel \overline{CD}$.
b. False. $\overline{BD}$ is a transversal, but alternate interior angles $\angle ADB$ and $\angle CBD$ have different measures, so $\overline{AD}$ is not parallel to $\overline{BC}$.

The AIA $=$ $\Rightarrow$ $\parallel$ Lines Theorem enables you to finish the hierarchy of quadrilaterals. The proof of the next theorem is not short, but take your time and try to follow it.

Theorem:

If a quadrilateral is a rhombus, then it is a parallelogram.

Proof

Draw A rhombus is needed.
The figure is shown at the right.

Given: *RHOM* is a rhombus.
Prove: *RHOM* is a parallelogram.

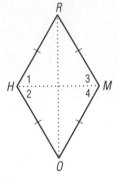

Analyze Since *RH* = *HO* = *OM* = *MR*, you need to show $\overline{RM} \parallel \overline{OH}$ and $\overline{RH} \parallel \overline{OM}$. A rhombus is a kite in two ways, so either diagonal is a symmetry line. This creates many equal angles, including alternate interior angles, which is enough to show that both pairs of opposite sides are parallel.

Write $\overleftrightarrow{HM}$ **is a symmetry diagonal for kite *RHOM* with ends *H* and *M*. ∠1 and ∠3 are reflection images of ∠2 and ∠4. Thus m∠1 = m∠2 and m∠3 = m∠4. Also, since △*HRM* is isosceles, m∠1 = m∠3. Transitivity gives m∠1 = m∠4, where ∠1 and ∠4 are alternate interior angles for $\overleftrightarrow{HR}$ and $\overleftrightarrow{OM}$ formed by transversal $\overleftrightarrow{HM}$. By the AIA = ⇒ ∥ Lines Theorem, $\overleftrightarrow{HR} \parallel \overleftrightarrow{OM}$. In the same manner using isosceles triangle *HOM*, alternate interior angles 2 and 3 are equal and $\overline{RM} \parallel \overline{HO}$. Thus by the sufficient condition half of the definition of a parallelogram, *RHOM* is a parallelogram.**

We call the connections between quadrilaterals the *Quadrilateral Hierarchy Theorem*.

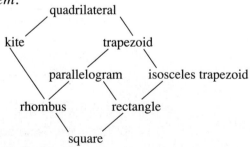

Quadrilateral Hierarchy Theorem:

If a figure is of any type on the hierarchy, it is also of all types connected above it.

236

The Quadrilateral Hierarchy Theorem is helpful in many proofs.

■ ■ ■ ■ ■ ■ ■ ■

Example 3   **Given:**   *ABCD* is a square.
Prove: $\overline{AB} \parallel \overline{CD}$.

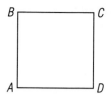

Solution 1   The proof is short. Here it is written in two columns.

Write Conclusions	Justifications
1. *ABCD* is a parallelogram.	Quadrilateral Hierarchy Theorem
2. $\overline{AB} \parallel \overline{CD}$	definition of parallelogram (meaning)

Solution 2   Here is a paragraph proof.

Since *ABCD* is a square, it is a parallelogram by the Quadrilateral Hierarchy Theorem. Because opposite sides of a parallelogram are parallel, $\overline{AB} \parallel \overline{CD}$.

Questions

Covering the Reading

In 1–4, use the figure at the left.
1. **a.** Name the interior angles.
   b. Name the alternate interior angles.

2. If $\ell \parallel m$, which angles equal $\angle 7$ in measure?

3. If $\ell \parallel m$, which angles are supplementary to $\angle 3$?

4. *True* or *false*?   If m$\angle 2$ = m$\angle 6$, then $\ell \parallel m$.

5. Write in words:
   a. AIA = $\Rightarrow \parallel$ Lines Theorem
   b. $\parallel$ Lines $\Rightarrow$ AIA = Theorem
   c. Statement **a** is the ? of statement **b**.

In 6–8, *true* or *false*?
6. Every parallelogram is a kite.

7. All rectangles are trapezoids.

8. If a figure is an isosceles trapezoid, then it is a square.

9. Given: *ABCD* is a rhombus.
   Prove: $\overline{AD} \parallel \overline{BC}$.

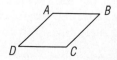

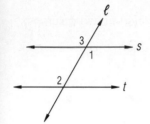

10. Refer to the figure for Questions 1–4.
   a. Which pairs of angles do you think are **alternate exterior** angles?
   b. If $\ell \parallel m$, are these pairs of angles equal in measure, supplementary, or complementary?

11. Complete this proof of the AIA $= \Rightarrow \parallel$ Lines Theorem.
   Given: $m\angle 1 = m\angle 2$.
   Prove: $s \parallel t$.

Conclusions	Justifications
1. $m\angle 3 = m\angle 1$	**a.** ___?___
2. $m\angle 3 = m\angle 2$	**b.** ___?___
3. $s \parallel t$	**c.** ___?___

In 12–14, use the figure below where $\ell \parallel m$.

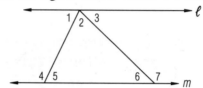

12. a. $m\angle 1 + m\angle 2 + m\angle 3 = $ ___?___
   b. If $m\angle 1 = 35$, what is $m\angle 5$?
   c. If $m\angle 1 + m\angle 2 = 145$, what is $m\angle 7$?

13. If $m\angle 5 = 45$ and $m\angle 6 = 40$, find the measures of as many other numbered angles as you can.

14. *Multiple choice.* If $m\angle 4 = x$, then $m\angle 2 + m\angle 3 = $
   (a) x (b) $90 - x$ (c) $180 - x$ (d) $\dfrac{180 - x}{2}$.

15. In the figure below, $\overleftrightarrow{BD} \parallel \overleftrightarrow{FI}$. If $m\angle EGH = 57$ and $m\angle EHG = 43$, find the measures of all other angles in the figure.

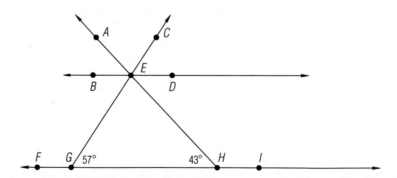

16. One angle of an isosceles trapezoid has measure 7 times another.
   a. Find the measures of all angles of the figure.
   b. Draw an example. *(Lesson 5-5)*

17. Consider the lines with equations $y = 2x + 1$ and $y = 2x - 1$.
   a. Are these lines parallel?
   b. Are these lines perpendicular? *(Lessons 3-5, 3-4)*

18. Graph points $A = (0, 0)$, $B = (10, 0)$, $C = (7, 3)$, and $D = (2, 3)$. What kind of a figure is $ABCD$? *(Lessons 5-2, 3-4, 1-3)*

19. If you take a square sheet of paper and fold it onto itself along a diagonal, what kind of figure is formed? *(Lesson 5-1)*

20. $\overleftrightarrow{EF}$ and $\overleftrightarrow{GH}$ are symmetry lines for $ABCD$ at the right. *(Lessons 4-7, 4-2, 4-1)*

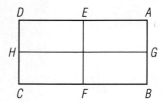

    a. $r_{\overleftrightarrow{GH}}(A) = \underline{\quad?\quad}$
    b. $r_{\overleftrightarrow{EF}}(ABCD) = \underline{\quad?\quad}$

21. Below, $WXYZ$ is an isosceles trapezoid with base angles X and Y. If $m\angle X = -2q + 71$ and $m\angle Y = -5q + 32$, find $m\angle X$. *(Lesson 5-5)*

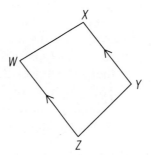

22. Measure the three angles of $\triangle TRI$ to the nearest degree. *(Lesson 3-1)*

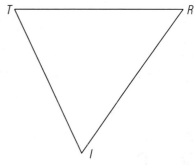

23. According to the Angle Measure Postulate, every angle has a unique measure from $\underline{\quad?\quad}$ to $\underline{\quad?\quad}$. *(Lesson 3-1)*

24. State the Angle Addition Property. *(Lesson 3-1)*

25. Give a counterexample to this conditional: If a triangle is isosceles, then it is acute. *(Lessons 2-7, 2-2)*

26. **a.** Other than Z, which printed capital letters usually contain alternate interior angles? Print them.
    b. Which printed capital letters usually contain corresponding angles? Print them.

5-7

Sums of Angle Measures in Polygons

In the early 1800s, the great mathematician Karl Friedrich Gauss wondered whether the theorems of Euclidean geometry were true over long distances. And so he measured the angles between three mountaintops in Germany to see if they added to 180°. Gauss found that the sum of the angles in his measurements was very close to 180°, within the limits of the accuracy of his instruments. He was checking the truth of a theorem known to the ancient Greeks. It also probably has been known to you for some time. Here is a proof.

Triangle-Sum Theorem:

> The sum of the measures of the angles of a triangle is 180°.

The statement of the Triangle-Sum Theorem can be rewritten as a conditional: If a figure is a triangle, then the sum of the measures of its angles is 180.

Proof

Draw   Draw a △*ABC* and restate the antecedent and consequent in terms of that triangle.

Given: △*ABC*.

Prove: m∠*A* + m∠*B* + m∠*C* = 180.

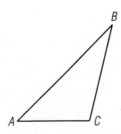

Analyze Much of what has been assumed and so far proved about angle measures relates to parallel lines. Use that knowledge by drawing a line parallel to a side through the third vertex. This creates alternate interior angles and it creates a straight angle which is 180°

Write

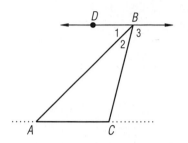

Conclusions	Justifications
1. Draw $\overleftrightarrow{BD}$ with m∠1 = m∠A.	**Angle Measure Postulate**
2. $\overleftrightarrow{BD}$ ∥ $\overleftrightarrow{AC}$	**AIA = ⇒ ∥ Lines Theorem**
3. m∠3 = m∠C	**∥ Lines ⇒ AIA = Theorem**
4. m∠1 + m∠2 = m∠DBC	**Angle Addition Postulate**
5. m∠DBC + m∠3 = 180	**Linear Pair Theorem**
6. m∠1 + m∠2 + m∠3 = 180	**Substitution** (step 4 into step 5)
7. m∠A + m∠ABC + m∠C = 180	**Substitution** (steps 1 and 3 into step 6)

■ ■ ■ ■ ■ ■ ■■

Example In △ABC, the angles are in the *extended ratio* 1:2:3. This means they have measures 1x, 2x, and 3x. Find their measures.

Solution Draw a picture.

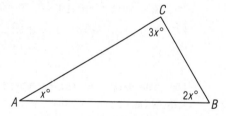

From the Triangle-Sum Theorem,
$$m∠A + m∠B + m∠C = 180.$$
Substituting, $\quad\quad x + 2x + 3x = 180$
$$6x = 180$$
$$x = 30.$$
So m∠A = 30, m∠B = 60, and m∠C = 90.

Check 30, 60, and 90 are in the extended ratio 30:60:90 or 1:2:3.

You might wonder why Gauss climbed the mountaintops in the first place. He was trying to imagine a geometry without the Corresponding Angles Postulate. Without that postulate, he could not prove the theorems about alternate interior angles, and so he would not have the Triangle-Sum Theorem. Within a generation, other mathematicians developed geometries like those Gauss imagined, so-called **non-Euclidean geometries.** In their geometries, the sum of the measures of the angles of a triangle is not 180°.

In a plane, two perpendiculars to the same line cannot intersect to form a triangle, but this can happen on a sphere. The surface of the earth can be approximated as a sphere. A triangle formed by two longitudes (north-south lines) and the equator is isosceles with two right base angles! Since there is a third angle at the North Pole, the measures add to more than 180°. Thus neither the Two Perpendiculars Theorem nor the Triangle-Sum Theorem works on the surface of the earth.

North Pole

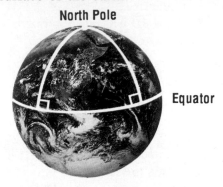

Equator

In a plane, the Triangle-Sum Theorem enables the sum of the measures of the angles of any convex polygon to be calculated. Quadrilaterals are an obvious place to start.

Let S = the sum of the measures of the angles of $QUAD$ below.
$$S = m\angle U + m\angle A + m\angle D + m\angle Q$$

Drawing $\overline{AQ}$ splits $\angle A$ and $\angle Q$ into four smaller angles. Now by the Angle Addition Postulate and substitution,
$$S = m\angle U + (m\angle 1 + m\angle 2) + m\angle D + (m\angle 3 + m\angle 4).$$

Rearrange the terms in this sum to put those in the same triangles together.
$$S = \underbrace{(m\angle U + m\angle 1 + m\angle 3)}_{180} + \underbrace{(m\angle 2 + m\angle 4 + m\angle D)}_{180}$$
$$= \qquad\qquad 180 \qquad\qquad + \qquad\qquad 180$$
$$= 360$$

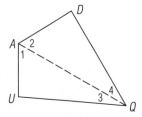

This argument proves:

Quadrilateral-Sum Theorem:

The sum of the measures of the angles of a convex quadrilateral is 360°.

The sum of the measures of the angles of a convex *n*-gon can be determined in a similar manner. Consider the polygons displayed below.

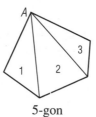
5-gon

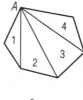
6-gon

7-gon

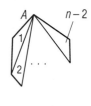
n-gon

Choose a vertex on each. Call it *A*. Draw the diagonals from *A*. For the 5-gon, the two diagonals form 3 triangles. The sum of the measures of the angles is $3 \cdot 180°$ (180° in each triangle).

For the 6-gon, there are 4 triangles; for the 7-gon, 5 triangles; and for the *n*-gon, there are $n - 2$ triangles. The sums of the measures of the angles are thus

6-gon	$4 \cdot 180°$
7-gon	$5 \cdot 180°$
n-gon	$(n - 2) \cdot 180°$

This argument can be formalized to prove the Polygon-Sum Theorem.

Polygon-Sum Theorem:

> The sum of the measures of the angles of a convex polygon of *n* sides is $(n - 2) \cdot 180°$.

Questions

Covering the Reading

1. Here is a slightly different drawing for a proof of the Triangle-Sum Theorem. $\ell \parallel \overline{AB}$ below. Justify each statement.

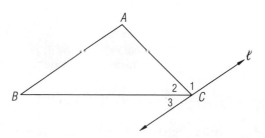

   a. $m\angle A = m\angle 1$
   b. $m\angle B = m\angle 3$
   c. Since $m\angle 1 + m\angle 2 + m\angle 3 = 180$, then
   $m\angle A + m\angle 2 + m\angle B = 180$.

In 2 and 3, refer to △EFG at the right.

2. If m∠F = 115 and m∠G = 40, find m∠E.

3. If the angles of a triangle are in the extended ratio 1:3:5, find their measures.

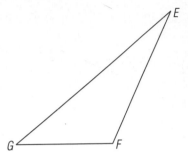

4. Given: Rectangle *ABCD* at the right.
   Fill in the blanks with numbers.
   a. m∠1 = ___?___
   b. m∠2 = m∠__?__
   c. m∠2 + m∠6 = ___?___
   d. m∠3 + m∠5 = ___?___
   e. m∠3 + m∠4 + m∠5 = ___?___
   f. m∠1 + m∠2 + m∠3 + m∠4 + m∠5 + m∠6 = ___?___

5. In convex quadrilateral *HIJK*, m∠H + m∠I + m∠J + m∠K = ___?___ .

6. State the Polygon-Sum Theorem.

7. a. Give an example of a situation in which the measures of the angles of a triangle do not add to 180°.
   b. What are geometries called in which this happens?

Applying the Mathematics

In 8–11, given is a type of figure.
   a. Give the sum of the measures of the angles of that figure.
   b. Identify the theorem in this lesson that justifies your answer.

8. convex kite

9. isosceles triangle

10. 10-gon

11. 20-gon

12. Refer to the triangulated polygons pictured on the previous page.
   a. *True* or *false*? Each side of the polygon which does not contain vertex *A* is part of exactly one triangle.
   b. How many sides of the *n*-gon do not contain vertex *A*?
   c. Into how many triangles does an *n*-gon triangulate?

13. A surveyor measures angles of a lot in degrees and minutes. There are 60 minutes in a degree. What should be the value of *x*?

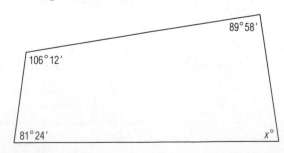

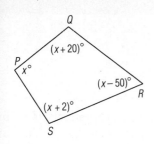

Q

$(x+20)°$

P

$x°$

$(x-50)°$

R

$(x+2)°$

S

14. In the quadrilateral at the left:
   a. Find x.
   b. Find the measures of the four angles.

15. **a.** Each angle of an equilateral triangle has what measure?
   b. Explain how you got your answer to part **a**.

16. One angle of a triangle is a right angle. The third angle is three times the smallest angle. What are their measures?

17. One angle of an isosceles triangle has measure 39°. What are *all* the possible measures of the other angles?

Review

18. Draw, from memory, the hierarchy of quadrilaterals. The diagram at the left below is a hint. *(Lesson 5-6)*

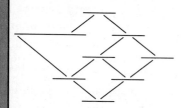

19. Given: $m\angle D = m\angle CBE$.
   $\overleftrightarrow{AB} \parallel \overline{DE}$.
   Prove: **a.** *ABED* is an isosceles trapezoid.
   b. $\angle A$ and $\angle D$ are supplementary.
   (Lessons 5-6, 5-5, 5-2)

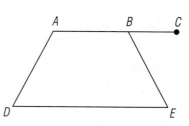

A   B   C

D   E

In 20 and 21, define the term. *(Lesson 5-2)*

20. rhombus   **21.** trapezoid

22. Write the Isosceles Triangle Theorem as an if-then statement.
   (Lessons 5-1, 2-2)

23. *P*, *Q*, and *R* below are ships. From ship *Q*, ship *P* is 30°N of E and ship *R* is 10°S of E. From ship *R*, ship *P* is 15°W of N. From the captain's viewpoint on ship *P*, what is the position of the other two ships? *(Lesson 3-1)*

Exploration

24. Find a globe. Estimate the sum of the measures of the angle of the triangle determined by Los Angeles, London, and Rio de Janiero.

Summary

In this chapter you studied many polygons and their properties. The simplest polygon, with 3 sides, is the triangle.

Triangles can be classified by the number of equal sides (shown below on the left), or by the size of the largest angle (shown below on the right).

Every isosceles triangle has at least one line of symmetry. That line is the bisector of the vertex angle, is the perpendicular bisector of the base, and contains the median to the opposite side. An equilateral triangle has three lines of symmetry. A scalene triangle has no line of symmetry.

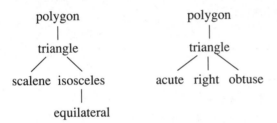

A hierarchy for common quadrilaterals is below.

The importance of this hierarchy is that any property true for all figures of some type is true for all figures of every type below it to which it is connected. Thus the Kite Symmetry Theorem applies to rhombuses and squares as well. The Trapezoid Angle Theorem can be applied to all special types of quadrilaterals except kites. Similarly, the Isosceles Triangle Symmetry Theorem applies to equilateral triangles as well.

From examining figures, if a property appears to be true, a conjecture is made. If a counterexample is then found, the conjecture is false. For a conjecture to be true and become a theorem, a proof of it must be found. Mathematicians, in their research, are constantly forming conjectures and searching for counterexamples or proofs.

In this chapter, two theorems about alternate interior angles are proved. They can be summarized in one if-and-only-if statement: Two lines cut by a transversal are parallel ⇔ the alternate interior angles formed have the same measure. This theorem is applied to deduce the Triangle-Sum Theorem, which in turn is used to prove the Quadrilateral-Sum Theorem and to develop the formula that $S = (n - 2) \cdot 180°$ for the sum of the measures of the interior angles of any n-gon.

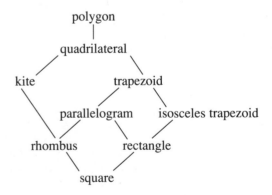

Vocabulary

Below are the new terms and phrases for this chapter.
(Some you have studied in previous years, but we repeat them here for reference.)
You should be able to give a general description and specific example of each.
For those terms that are starred (*), you should be able to give a precise definition.

Lesson 5-1
median of a triangle
vertex angle
base angles of an isosceles triangle
Isosceles Triangle Symmetry Theorem
Isosceles Triangle Theorem

Lesson 5-2
*parallelogram
*rhombus
*rectangle
*square
*kite
*trapezoid
bases, base angles
*isosceles trapezoid

Lesson 5-3
conjecture
refining a conjecture

Lesson 5-4
ends of a kite
symmetry diagonal
Kite Symmetry Theorem
Kite Diagonal Theorem
Rhombus Symmetry Theorem

Lesson 5-5
corollary
Trapezoid Angle Theorem
Isosceles Trapezoid Symmetry Theorem
Isosceles Trapezoid Theorem
Rectangle Symmetry Theorem

Lesson 5-6
interior angles, exterior angles
alternate interior angles
// Lines $\Rightarrow$ AIA $=$ Theorem
AIA $= \Rightarrow$ // Lines Theorem
Quadrilateral Hierarchy Theorem

Lesson 5-7
non-Euclidean geometries
Triangle-Sum Theorem
Quadrilateral-Sum Theorem
Polygon-Sum Theorem
extended ratio

Progress Self-Test

Directions: Take this test as you would take a test in class. Use a ruler, compass, and protractor. Then check your work with the solutions in the Selected Answers section in the back of the book.

In 1 and 2, *true* or *false*?

1. Every square is a rectangle.

2. Every kite has two lines of symmetry.

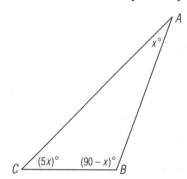

3. Use △*ABC* as drawn above.
   a. Find *x*.
   b. Find the measures of the three angles. (Note: △*ABC* is not drawn accurately.)

4. Angle *W* of an isosceles trapezoid *WXYZ* with base $\overline{WX}$ has measure 100°.
   a. Draw such a trapezoid.
   b. Find the measure of as many other angles as you can.

5. Find the sum of the measures of the angles in a convex decagon.

In 6–8, refer to the figure at the right. △*MNP* and △*NOP* are equilateral.

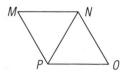

6. Find the measure of each angle.
   a. ∠*M*   **b.** ∠*MNO*

7. *True or false?* Quadrilateral *MNOP* is a rhombus. Justify your answer.

8. **a.** How many symmetry lines does *MNOP* have?
   b. Name them.

9. *ABCD* below is a parallelogram. Justify each conclusion.
   a. m∠*A* + m∠*B* = 180
   b. m∠*D* = m∠*DCE*

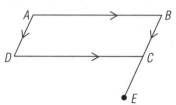

10. Given: *AB = BC*.
    Prove: m∠*A* = m∠*ECD*.

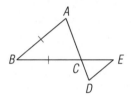

11. In the figure below, ℓ ∥ *m*.
    If m∠5 = 9*z* − 52 and m∠3 = 2*z* + 45,
    a. find *z*;   **b.** find m∠3.

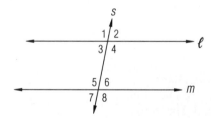

12. Draw an isosceles obtuse triangle.

In Question 13, a conjecture is made. **a.** Is it *true* or *false*? **b.** If it is false, draw a counterexample. If it is true, tell why it is true.

13. If two angles are supplementary, then they form a linear pair.

14. **a.** What polygon is the shape of the top of most briefcases?
    b. Why do you think it is this shape?

15. Draw the hierarchy relating the following: polygon, pentagon, parallelogram, rectangle, rhombus.

Chapter Review

Questions on **SPUR** Objectives

SPUR stands for **S**kills, **P**roperties, **U**ses, and **R**epresentations.
The Chapter Review questions are grouped according to the
SPUR Objectives for this chapter.

SKILLS deal with the procedures used to get answers.

■ **Objective A:** *Draw polygons satisfying various conditions. (Lessons 5-1, 5-3, 5-4, 5-5)*

In 1–4, draw an example of the figure using ruler, compass, or protractor.

1. a scalene right triangle
2. an isosceles acute triangle
3. a kite that is not a rhombus
4. a trapezoid that is not isosceles

In 11 and 12, $s \parallel t$ as pictured below at the right.

11. If $m\angle 3 = 2x - 11$ and $m\angle 6 = -x + 46$, find $m\angle 3$.

12. If $m\angle 1 = 6x - 5$ and $m\angle 7 = 2x + 5$, find $m\angle 1$.

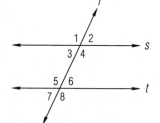

■ **Objective B:** *Apply the Trapezoid Angle Theorem and the theorems about alternate interior angles. (Lessons 5-5, 5-6)*

In 5 and 6, use trapezoid *TRAP* below.

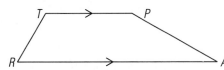

5. If $m\angle T = 2 \cdot m\angle R$, find the measure of as many angles as you can.

6. If $m\angle A = 8x - 12$ and $m\angle P = 15x - 15$, find $m\angle A$.

7. Use isosceles trapezoid *NICE* at the right. If $m\angle N = 5x - 7$ and $m\angle E = 11x - 79$,
   a. find $m\angle E$;
   b. find $m\angle C$.

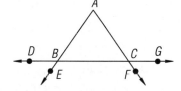

In 8–10, use the figure at the right where $\ell \parallel m$.

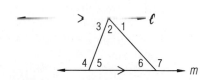

8. If $m\angle 1 + m\angle 5 = 140$, find $m\angle 2$.
9. If $m\angle 7 = 117$ and $m\angle 3 = 60$, find $m\angle 2$.
10. If $m\angle 5 = m\angle 6$, what other pairs of angles have equal measures?

■ **Objective C:** *Find unknown measures of angles using the Isosceles Triangle, Triangle-Sum, Quadrilateral-Sum, and Polygon-Sum Theorems. (Lessons 5-1, 5-7)*

In 13 and 14 use the figure below in which $AB = AC$.

13. If $m\angle ABC = 42$, find $m\angle GCF$.

14. If $m\angle DBE = x$, find $m\angle ACG$.

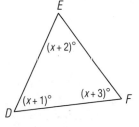

15. Two angles of a triangle have measures 43° and 91°. Find the measure of the third angle.

16. One angle in an isosceles triangle is 72°. What are the possible measures of the other angles?

17. In $\triangle DEF$ at the right:
    a. find x;
    b. find the measures of the three angles of the triangle.

18. Find the measures of all four angles of quadrilateral *RSTU*.

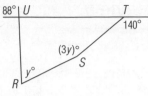

19. What is the sum of the measures of the interior angles of a convex octagon?

20. A convex polygon has *n* sides. From one vertex all possible diagonals are drawn.
  a. How many diagonals are drawn?
  b. Into how many triangular regions do the diagonals divide the *n*-gon?
  c. What is the sum of the measures of the angles of the *n*-gon?

PROPERTIES deal with the principles behind the mathematics.

■ **Objective D:** *Classify special polygons by their properties.* *(Lessons 5-1, 5-2)*

21. Arrange from general to specific: rhombus, quadrilateral, polygon, square, parallelogram.

22. Arrange from least to greatest number of sides: 6-gon, heptagon, kite, scalene triangle, octagon.

In 23 and 24, from the indications, what quadrilateral is pictured? Be as specific as possible.

23. 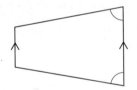   **24.**

In 25 and 26, *true* or *false*? If false, give a counterexample.

25. Every square is a parallelogram.

26. Every parallelogram is a rectangle.

In 27 and 28, refer to the quadrilateral at the right in which *AB = BC* and *DA = DC*.

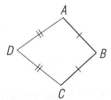

27. Does the figure have any symmetry lines?

28. Name two angles with equal measures.

29. *Multiple choice.* Suppose that in △*DEF* the bisector of ∠*D* coincides with the median to side *EF*. What type of triangle is *DEF*?
  (a) acute   (b) right
  (c) isosceles   (d) obtuse

30. Draw a triangle with 3 lines of symmetry.

■ **Objective E:** *Identify properties of triangles and quadrilaterals.* *(Lessons 5-1, 5-4, 5-5)*

In 31–34, *true* or *false*?

31. Every trapezoid has at least one line of symmetry.

32. The diagonals of a rhombus bisect each other.

33. The perpendicular bisector of one base of an isosceles trapezoid is the perpendicular bisector of the other.

34. The perpendicular bisector of the base of an isosceles triangle contains the angle bisector of the vertex angle.

■ **Objective F:** *Evaluate conjectures.* *(Lesson 5-3)*

In 35–37, a conjecture is stated. Explore it with drawings. Choose the answer A, B, C, D, or E below which best indicates your feeling about the statement.
  (A) The conjecture is definitely true and in my mind needs no proof.
  (B) The conjecture may be true, but I need a proof or a similar argument to believe it.
  (C) The conjecture doesn't seem true, but I am not sure. Discussion would help.
  (D) The conjecture is probably not true, but I'd be sure only if I had a counterexample.
  (E) The conjecture is definitely false. No argument is needed to convince me.

35. If two angles are vertical angles, then they are both acute.

36. If two angles form a linear pair, then the bisectors of those angles form a right angle.

37. It is possible for two squares to intersect in exactly five points.

In 38 and 39, a conjecture is made. **a.** Is it *true* or *false*? **b.** If it is false, draw a counterexample.

38. If *M* is the midpoint of $\overline{AB}$, then *AM* = *MB*.

39. All adjacent angles are supplementary.

■ **Objective G:** *Write proofs using the properties of triangles and quadrilaterals.*
(Lessons 5-1, 5-2, 5-4, 5-5, 5-6)

40. Given: *ABCD* is a square.
Prove: $\overline{BC} \parallel \overline{AD}$.

41. Given: m∠*F* = m∠*FHI* in the figure below.
Prove: *EFHG* is a trapezoid.

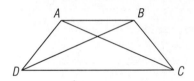

42. Given: Isosceles trapezoid *ABCD* with bases $\overline{AB}$ and $\overline{CD}$.
Prove: *AC* = *BD*. (Hint: Use symmetry.)

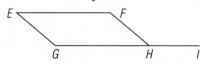

43. Given: △*ABC* is isosceles with vertex angle *BAC*.
△*ACD* is isosceles with vertex angle *ACD*.
Prove: *AB* = *CD*.

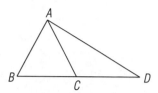

44. Complete the justifications in the following proof.
Given: kite *KITE* with ends *I* and *E*.
Prove: *KX* = *TX*.

Conclusions	Justifications
1. $\overleftrightarrow{IE}$ is the ⊥ bisector of $\overline{KT}$.	**a.** ?
2. *X* is the midpoint of $\overline{KT}$.	**b.** ?
3. *KX* = *TX*	**c.** ?

45. Given: ⊙*O* and ⊙*P*.
Prove: *OQPR* is a kite.

USES deal with applications of mathematics in real situations.

■ **Objective H:** *Explain why everyday objects are shaped like certain polygons.* *(Lesson 5-2)*

46. a. What polygon is the shape of most notebook paper?
b. Why do you think it is this shape?

47. The four bases on a baseball field are vertices of a polygon. **a.** What is the name of this polygon? **b.** What are its dimensions? **c.** Why are the bases placed this way?

48. Pictured below are several road signs.
a. Name the polygon that best describes each.
b. Why are road signs different shapes and colors?

REPRESENTATIONS deal with pictures, graphs, or objects that illustrate concepts.

■ **Objective I:** *Draw hierarchies of polygons.* *(Lesson 5-2)*

49. Draw the hierarchy relating the following: rectangle, square, rhombus, parallelogram.

50. Draw the hierarchy relating the following: figure, quadrilateral, isosceles trapezoid, trapezoid, parallelogram, rectangle.

Transformations and Congruence

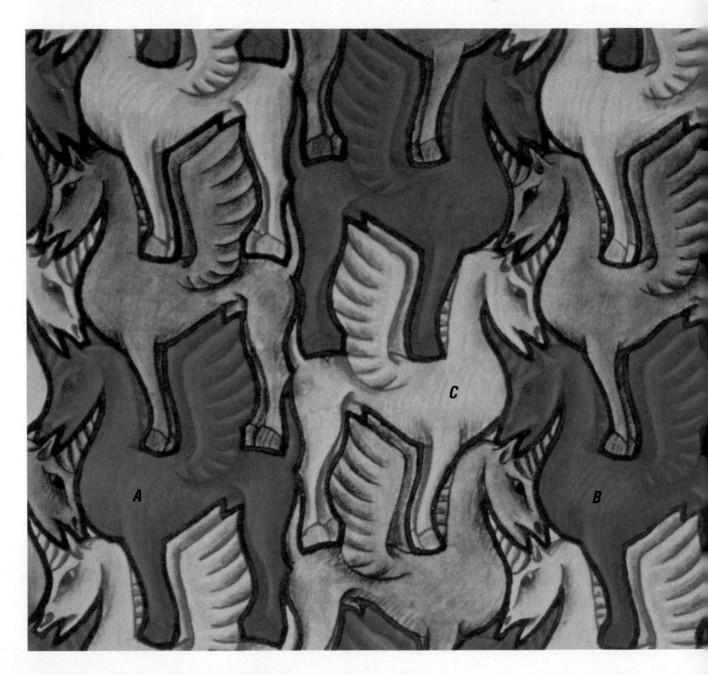

The drawing at the left, called a *tessellation,* is one of the many tessellations drawn by the Dutch artist Maurits Escher (1898–1973). This tessellation was designed by piecing together unicorns of the same size and shape. We say that the unicorns are all *congruent* to each other.

Unicorns *A* and *B* are related to each other by a *slide* or *translation.* Each is a translation image of the other. (The translation is horizontal.) On the other hand, unicorns *A* and *C* have different orientations. But they are not related by a single reflection. They are related by another kind of transformation, a *walk* or *glide reflection.*

It is natural to ask for all the possible ways in which the various unicorns could be related to each other. In this chapter, you will learn that there are four types of transformations in the plane which yield congruent figures: reflections (flips), rotations (turns), translations (slides), and glide reflections (walks). These were first categorized in 1831 by the French mathematician Michel Chasles (1793–1880).

The first use of transformations dates back to the ancient Greeks about the time of Euclid. However, not until Euler (in 1776) did anyone identify all the kinds of transformations in space that could yield congruent figures. It is interesting that the three-dimensional analysis of congruence was accomplished before the two-dimensional. This is probably because the congruent objects seen daily are three-dimensional.

Studying these various transformations helps a person to become more aware of the movements of objects such as gears (which rotate), imprints (which flip), and conveyer belts (which slide). More complicated movements, such as those done by robots, can be taken apart into their component moves and analyzed.

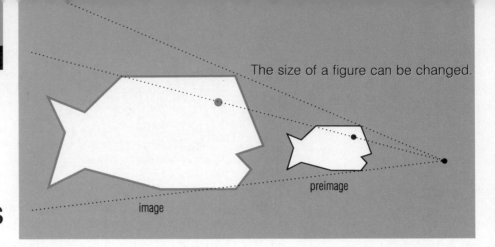

The size of a figure can be changed.

image

preimage

In Chapter 4 you studied reflections. Reflections are important because they describe how figures are related. But there are many things which can be done to figures other than reflecting them over lines. In the figures above and below, the dotted lines connect points in the preimages (black) to their images (blue) and are meant to suggest what is happening to specific points on the figure.

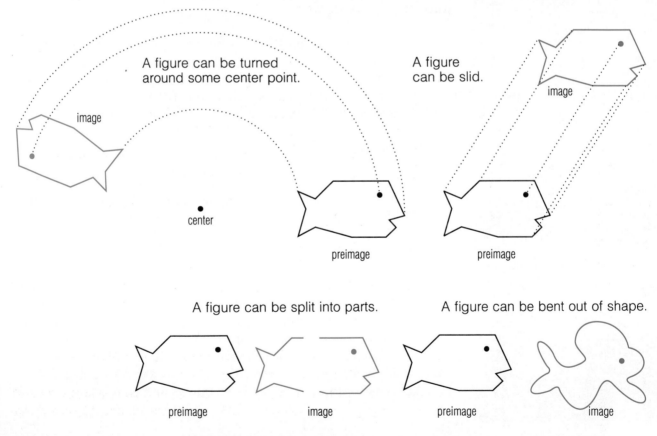

A figure can be turned around some center point.

image

center

preimage

A figure can be slid.

image

preimage

A figure can be split into parts.

preimage   image

A figure can be bent out of shape.

preimage   image

In each of these operations on figures, there is a preimage and an image. Sometimes the image looks identical to the preimage, at other times not. But in each case, the figure has been *transformed*. The operation applied to the figure is called a *transformation*.

The sufficient conditions for a transformation are satisfied by any reflection. Thus *every reflection is a transformation.*

A transformation is often called a **mapping;** a transformation *maps* a preimage onto an image. If the transformation is called T, then the image of a point P is written **T(P),** which is read "T of P."

One way to describe a transformation is by a *rule* which tells how to locate the image of any point. For the reflection r_ℓ, the rule is rather long: If P is on ℓ, then $r_\ell(P) = P$. If P is not on ℓ, then $r_\ell(P)$ is the point such that ℓ is the $\perp$ bisector of the segment connecting P and $r_\ell(P)$. In a coordinate plane, the rule for a transformation can be given by a formula.

Example A transformation T maps (x, y) onto $(x - 8, y - 12)$.
a. Find T(6, 11).
b. If $J = (6, 11)$, $K = (15, 15)$, and $L = (15, 9)$, graph T($\triangle JKL$).
c. Conjecture about the kind of transformation T is.

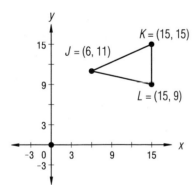

Solution

a. From the given, T$(x, y) = (x - 8, y - 12)$.
To find T(6, 11), substitute 6 for x, 11 for y.
$$T(6, 11) = (6 - 8, 11 - 12) = (-2, -1)$$

b. To find T($\triangle JKL$), find the images of J, K, and L. Call the images J', K', and L'. These are the vertices of the image, which is a triangle. J' was found in part **a.**
$$J' = T(J) = (-2, -1)$$
$$K' = T(K) = T(15, 15) = (15 - 8, 15 - 12) = (7, 3)$$
$$L' = T(L) = T(15, 9) = (15 - 8, 9 - 12) = (7, -3)$$

c. Graphing shows that $\triangle J'K'L'$ is the same size and shape as $\triangle JKL$. It appears to have been slid 8 units to the left and 12 units down.

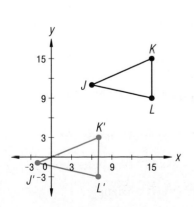

Some transformations with simple rules give rise to distorted images. Drawn below is the front of a house and its image under the transformation S, where $S(x, y) = (2x, x + y)$. (To save space, only the outside vertices are named.) Although distorted, this image is not very different from a perspective view of the house and, in fact, some early work with transformations was done to understand artists' perspective drawings. Collinearity and betweenness are preserved, so you can still discern the house. But angle measures and distances are not preserved, so the image house is distorted.

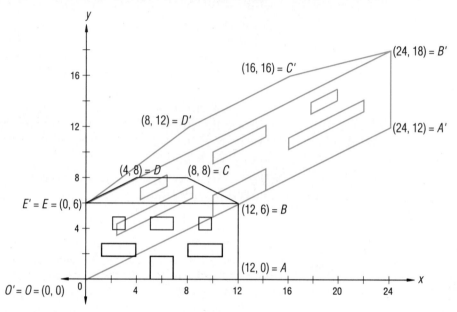

The T( ) notation for transformations is similar to notation used with other mathematics. For example, the number of elements of a set S is often written as N(S). The probability of an event E is often written as P(E).

Covering the Reading

Questions

1. Define: transformation.

2. A transformation can be described by giving a(n) __?__ which tells how to locate the image of any point.

In 3–8, *true* or *false*?

3. It is correct to say that a transformation *maps* a preimage onto an image.

4. In any transformation, a preimage point has exactly one image.

5. In any transformation, an image point has exactly one preimage.

6. In any transformation, the image of a triangle is a triangle.

7. Every transformation is a reflection.

8. Every transformation preserves angle measure.

9. Refer to the Example. The midpoint of $\overline{KL}$ is (15, 12). Call this point M.
   a. What are the coordinates of T(M)?
   b. Let $M' = $ T(M). Is M' the midpoint of $\overline{K'L'}$?

10. Some of the early work with transformations was done to understand what kind of drawings of artists?

11. Suppose T(x, y) = ($x + 2$, $y - 3$). Let $N = $ (10, 7), $O = $ (0, 0), and $P = $ (-4, 3).
   a. Graph $\triangle NOP$ and its image under T.
   b. Which word(s) best describes the transformation T: reflection, slide, turn, or size change?

12. The door of the preimage house pictured on the previous page has vertices (5, 0), (5, 2), (7, 2), and (7, 0). Find the vertices of the image door under the transformation S.

Applying the Mathematics

13. Explain how you know that the transformation S on page 256 does not preserve angle measure.

14. A transformation T has the rule T(x, y) = (10 − x, y). This transformation preserves betweenness so you can find the image of segments using only their vertices. Let $A = $ (0, 0), $B = $ (3, 4), and $C = $ (-1, -6).
   a. Draw $\triangle ABC$ and its image under T.
   b. Describe the transformation T.

15. A transformation S maps (x, y) onto (-y, x).
   a. Draw the quadrilateral with vertices $Q = $ (2, 1), $U = $ (5, 1), $A = $ (5, 8), and $D = $ (2, 6).
   b. Draw S($QUAD$) and label it $Q'U'A'D'$.
   c. Which word best describes S: reflection, slide, or turn?

Review

16. Recall that, when outcomes occur randomly, the probability of an event is the number of successful outcomes divided by the number of possible outcomes. Let P(E) be the probability of an event E.
   a. What is P(heads in a toss of a fair coin)?
   b. What is P(a randomly selected day falls on a weekend)?
   (Previous course)

17. *Multiple choice.* The angles other than the right angle in a right triangle are
   (a) acute and supplementary
   (b) acute and complementary
   (c) obtuse and supplementary
   (d) obtuse and complementary
   (e) none of the above. *(Lessons 5-7, 3-2)*

18. Let N(S) be the number of elements in a set S.
   a. Calculate N(set of even integers from 1 to 10).
   b. Calculate N(set of even integers from 1 to 100).
   (Previous course)

19. A right triangle is also isosceles. **a.** Is this possible? **b.** If not, why not? If so, what can be determined about the measures of the angles in this triangle? *(Lessons 5-7, 5-1)*

20. One angle of a rhombus has measure 55°. Find the measures of as many other angles of the rhombus as you can. *(Lessons 5-5, 5-4)*

21. Using ruler and protractor, draw a scalene acute triangle. *(Lesson 5-1)*

22. The **distance between two parallel lines** is the length of a perpendicular segment connecting two points on them.

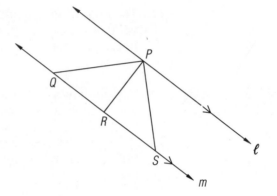

Multiple choice. Which seems to be the distance between ℓ and *m*? *(Lesson 3-6)*
   (a) *PQ*   (b) *PR*   (c) *PS*

23. Below, $\overrightarrow{AC}$ bisects ∠*BAD*, m∠*DAE* = $\frac{1}{2}$ · m∠*CAD*, and m∠*BAE* = 80. Find m∠*DAE*. *(Lesson 3-1)*

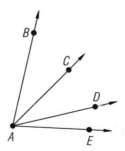

Exploration

24. Explore the transformation with rule T(*x*, *y*) = (2*x*, *y*) by finding images of common figures under T. (Hint: Use points in all quadrants.)

Translations

In the figure below, $\triangle ABC$ has been slid about 7 cm up and to the right to produce the image $\triangle A''B''C''$ (read "A double prime, B double prime, C double prime"). This transformation is known as a *translation* or slide.

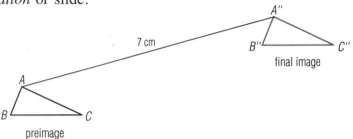

New transformations can result from successive applications of one type of transformation. The transformation from $\triangle ABC$ to $\triangle A''B''C''$ can be the result of two successive reflections over parallel lines. The drawing below shows $\triangle ABC$, its reflection image $\triangle A'B'C'$ over line ℓ, and a third triangle $A''B''C''$ which is the reflection image of $\triangle A'B'C'$ over a parallel line m.

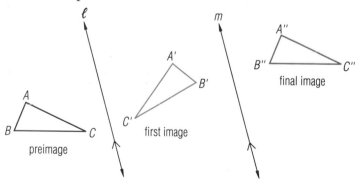

The relationships between these three triangles can be stated in symbols.

$$r_\ell(\triangle ABC) = \triangle A'B'C'$$
$$r_m(\triangle A'B'C') = \triangle A''B''C''$$

Substituting $r_\ell(\triangle ABC)$ in the second equation for $\triangle A'B'C'$ (they are equal in the first equation), you can write the result of first applying r_ℓ, then applying r_m.

$$r_m(r_\ell(\triangle ABC)) = \triangle A''B''C''.$$

When one reflection r_ℓ is followed by a second reflection r_m, the result of combining those reflections is called the *composite* of the reflections. Any transformations can follow each other.

The composite of S and T may be thought of as "apply transformation S, then apply transformation T to the image you found under S"; it is written $T \circ S$ and is read "T following S." In the drawing on page 259, r_ℓ is the first transformation, r_m the second. You can write either $r_m(r_\ell(\triangle ABC)) = \triangle A''B''C''$ or $r_m \circ r_\ell(\triangle ABC) = \triangle A''B''C''$.

Notice that the transformation applied first is written *on the right*. The reason for this is that with transformations, as in algebra, you must work inside parentheses first. Thus in $r_m(r_\ell(A))$, the transformation r_ℓ should be applied before r_m, and r_ℓ is on the right.

Above, it seems that the composite of the two reflections has the effect of sliding $\triangle ABC$. This can be verified. Have you ever been in a room with two mirrors on opposite walls? (Barber shops and beauty salons often have such rooms.)

If you look in one of the mirrors, you see not only the usual reflection image but also many images of images. Some of these look like slide images. This is why, by using two parallel mirrors, you can see the back of your head.

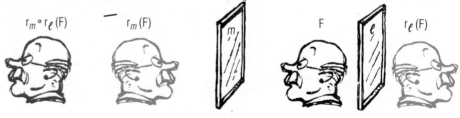

Below is still another example of a composite of two reflections over parallel lines. Again, the preimage looks like it could have been slid onto the image.

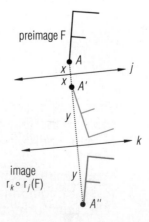

That is, when $m \parallel n$, the transformation $T = r_m \circ r_n$ is a translation.

Since each reflection in a translation preserves angles, betweenness, collinearity, and distance, so does the translation. Also, the translation preserves orientation, because the first reflection switches orientation, and the second switches it back.

A translation is often called a slide because the preimage looks as if it could have been slid onto the image. Thus you can describe a slide by telling how far a preimage is slid and in what direction. The **direction** of a translation is given by any ray from a preimage point through its image point. The **magnitude** of a translation is the distance between any point and its image.

For the transformation on the previous page, $\overrightarrow{AA''}$ is the direction and AA'' is the magnitude. The direction and magnitude of a translation are related to the reflecting lines in a surprisingly simple way.

Proof

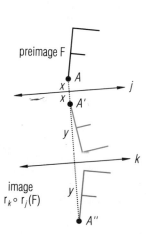

preimage F

j

k

image
$r_k \circ r_j(F)$

Use the figure at the left, concentrating on points A, A', and A''. By the definition of reflection, $\overline{AA'} \perp j$ and $\overline{A'A''} \perp k$. So, by the Two Perpendiculars Theorem, $\overline{AA'} \parallel \overline{A'A''}$. But A' is on each line. So $\overleftrightarrow{AA'} = \overleftrightarrow{A'A''}$ and the three points are collinear. This means $\overleftrightarrow{AA''}$ is perpendicular to both reflecting lines. Notice that the distance between the parallel lines is $x + y$. Thus $AA'' = 2x + 2y$, which is double $x + y$. The proof is similar if A is located in a different position relative to j and k.

Since a translation is defined by reflections, the Figure Reflection Theorem holds for translations. Thus to translate a figure, you only have to translate the points which determine the figure. You can translate a preimage in either of two ways: (1) slide each preimage point the proper distance in the proper direction, or (2) reflect over two parallel lines which are perpendicular to the direction and exactly half the distance apart.

Example   Draw possible reflecting lines for the translation mapping △ABC onto △A'B'C'.

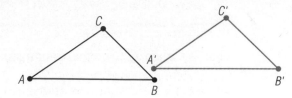

Solution   The reflecting lines are perpendicular to the translation's direction. So first draw *any* line *m* perpendicular to $\overleftrightarrow{AA'}$. Let $AA' = d$. The magnitude *d* of the translation is 2 times the distance between ℓ and *m*. So draw a second line *n* parallel to *m* in the same direction as the translation such that the perpendicular distance between *m* and *n* is $\frac{d}{2}$.

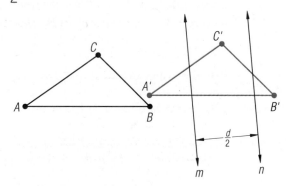

Check   If you do the reflections over the lines *m* and *n*, will it work? That is, does $r_n \circ r_m(\triangle ABC) = \triangle A'B'C'$?
Draw $r_m(\triangle ABC)$. Call it △XYZ. Now reflect △XYZ over *n*. The image of △XYZ should coincide with △A'B'C', which is the case.

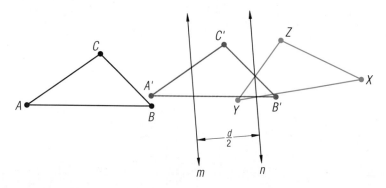

A surprising thing about the solution to the Example is that line *m* could be anywhere in the plane so long as it is perpendicular to $\overleftrightarrow{AA'}$. It does not have to be close to the preimage.

Covering the Reading

1. A translation is the ___?___ of two reflections over parallel lines.

2. Where might you see parallel mirrors in a room? Why are they there?

3. *Multiple choice.* Which of the following symbols stands for the transformation which results from first applying f, then applying s?
   (a) f(s) (b) s(f) (c) f ∘ s (d) s ∘ f

In 4 and 5, use the diagram at the left. Fill in the blank with a named point.

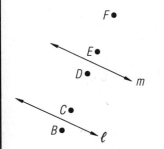

4. **a.** $r_m(F) = $ ___?___
   b. $r_\ell(r_m(F)) = $ ___?___
   c. $r_\ell \circ r_m(F) = $ ___?___

5. **a.** $r_\ell(A) = $ ___?___
   b. $r_m \circ r_\ell(A) = $ ___?___

6. If $\ell \parallel m$, what kind of transformation is $r_\ell \circ r_m$?

7. Name five properties preserved under translations.

8. Which is the more general term: translation or transformation?

9. Horizontal lines ℓ and m are 1 cm apart, as shown. Consider the translation $r_\ell \circ r_m$.
   a. What is its magnitude?
   b. What is its direction?

Applying the Mathematics

10. **a.** Trace this drawing on a sheet of paper. Leave a lot of room at the right and above.

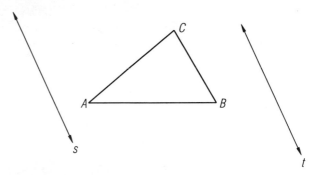

   b. Draw $r_s(\triangle ABC)$. Call it $\triangle A^*B^*C^*$.
   c. Draw $r_t \circ r_s(\triangle ABC)$. Call it $\triangle A'B'C'$.
   d. Verify in your drawing that $\overline{AA'}$, $\overline{BB'}$, and $\overline{CC'}$ are parallel segments of the same length.
   e. *Multiple choice.* How does the length of $\overline{AA'}$ compare with the distance between s and t?
   (i) It is the same.
   (ii) It is twice as much.
   (iii) It is half as much.

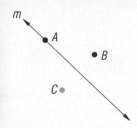

11. At the left, $r_m(B) = C$. What is $r_m \circ r_m(\overline{AB})$?

12. Generalize the result of Question 11.

13. Describe two methods for translating an image 6 inches to the left.

14. When the letter R is reflected over line ℓ, and then line m, its final image is as shown. But someone erased line m. Trace the figure and put line m back.

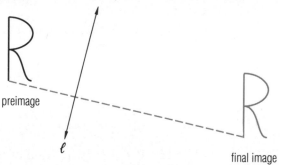

preimage

ℓ

final image

15. Carla has just had her hair cut. With her back to a mirror on the wall, she holds a hand mirror in front of her face.

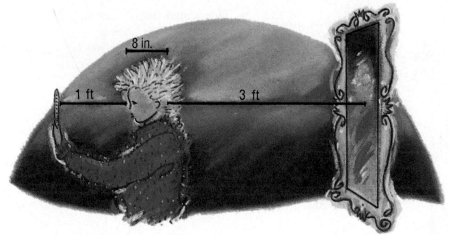

8 in.

1 ft   3 ft

If Carla's eyes are 1 ft from the hand mirror, her head is 8″ thick, and the back of her head is 3′ from the wall mirror, about how far from her eyes will the image of the back of Carla's head appear in her mirror?

16. The transformation with rule $T(x, y) = (x + 2, y + 6)$ is a translation.
    a. Graph $(7, 3)$ and $T(7, 3)$.
    b. Find the slope of the line through $(7, 3)$ and its image. (The slope helps to indicate the direction of the translation.)
    c. Describe in words the effect of T on a figure.

17. a. Suppose the point $(2, 5)$ is translated 4 units to the right and 6 units down. What is its image?
    b. Suppose (x, y) is translated 4 units to the right and 6 units down. What is its image?

18. a. If S is the set of vertices of an octagon, what is N(S)?
  b. If S is the set of diagonals of an octagon, what is N(S)?
    (Lessons 6-1, 2-7)

19. If T(*x*, *y*) = (*x* − 8, 3*y*), what is T(-4, 5)? *(Lesson 6-1)*

20. Given: ℓ ∥ *m* as shown below.
    Prove: m∠1 = m∠8. *(Lessons 4-4, 3-4)*

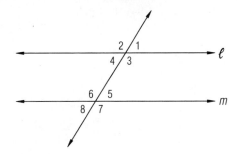

21. *True* or *false*?   *(Lesson 5-5)*
  a. If a figure is a rhombus, then it is a trapezoid.
  b. If a figure is a trapezoid, then it is a rhombus.

22. Trace the diagram below. Draw two different 49° angles with one side $\overrightarrow{PQ}$. *(Lesson 3-2)*

23. Give a good definition for *circle*. *(Lesson 2-5)*

24. If a room has parallel mirrors on opposite walls and you view your image, what happens?

Portrait of Mr. Edward James by the
Belgian surrealist René Magritte.
Magritte is famous for his
paintings of impossible situations.

6-3

Rotations

Sir David Brewster (1781-1868) invented the first kaleidoscope.

In Lesson 6-2, a composite of reflections was done over parallel lines. Kaleidoscopes like the one shown above result from reflections over intersecting lines. In the situation below, the preimage flag is reflected over intersecting lines. The transformation can be described as $r_m \circ r_\ell$ (r_ℓ is done before r_m).

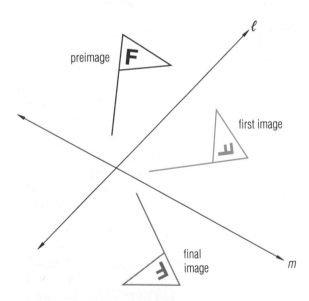

Because each reflection switches orientation, the preimage and final image have the same orientation. Though the final image is almost upside down, it is not backwards. (Turn the page upside down to check.)

The preimage and the final image are related in an astounding way. Cover up the first image. You can *turn* the preimage onto the second image! Moreover, the center of the turn is the intersection of the lines, because that point coincides with its image under each reflection.

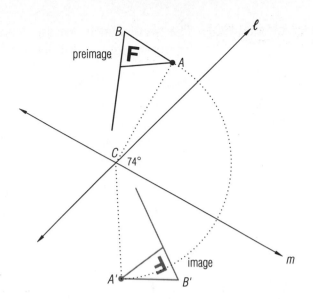

preimage

image

This composite is called a *rotation*.

> **Definition:**
>
> A **rotation** is the composite of two reflections over intersecting lines.

If the reflecting lines are ℓ and m, the **center** of the rotation $r_m \circ r_\ell$ is the point of intersection of the lines. Now measure (with a protractor) $\angle ACA'$ or $\angle BCB'$ in the figure above. The measure of these angles is about 148°. We say that the flag has been rotated 148° **clockwise.** Clockwise is the negative direction; **counterclockwise** is positive. The rotation of the flag has **magnitude** -148°. Magnitudes range from -180° to 180°. (There can be magnitudes outside this range, such as a rotation of 720°. This can always be converted to a rotation in the given range by adding or subtracting a multiple of 360°.)

Now measure the angle between the lines ℓ and m in the figure above. It is 74°, half of 148°. In general, the magnitude of a rotation is easily found from the angle between the reflecting lines. The following theorem illustrates the power of proof to establish results that are not obvious at first glance.

> **Two Reflection Theorem for Rotations:**
>
> The rotation $r_m \circ r_\ell$, where m intersects ℓ, "turns" figures twice the non-obtuse angle between ℓ and m, measured from ℓ to m, about the point of intersection of the lines.

The proof that follows is lengthy. Be sure to go on to read the Example even if you have difficulty following the proof.

Proof

Draw Use the diagram with the flags. But instead of considering the entire flag, consider a single point A at the tip of the flag. $r_\ell(A) = A^*$ and $r_m(A^*) = A'$. Below, the given and prove is written in terms of this diagram.

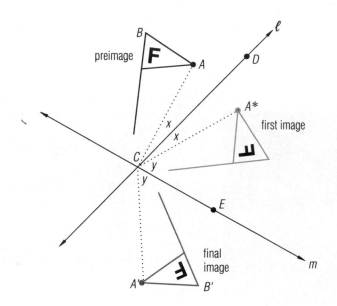

Given: $r_m \circ r_\ell (A) = A'$
  $\ell \cap m = C.$
Prove: (1) $r_m \circ r_\ell (C) = C$
  (2) $m\angle ACA' = 2 \cdot m\angle DCE$
  (3) $AC = A'C.$

Write

(1) C is on both reflecting lines.
So $r_m \circ r_\ell(C) = r_m (r_\ell(C)) = r_m(C) = C$.
(2) By the Figure Reflection Theorem, $r_\ell (\angle ACD) = \angle A^*CD$ and $r_m(\angle A^*CE) = \angle A'CE$. Since reflections preserve angle measure, $m\angle ACD = m\angle A^*CD$ (call it x) and $m\angle A^*CE = m\angle A'CE$ (call it y). From the Angle Addition Property, $m\angle DCE = x + y$ and $m\angle ACA' = 2(x + y)$. By substitution, $m\angle ACA' = 2(m\angle DCE)$.
(3) Since $AC = A^*C$ and $A^*C = A'C$ (reflections preserve distance), $AC = A'C$.

If A were located on one of the lines, or on the other side of ℓ or m, the steps would be a little different, but the result would still hold.

Example   Use two reflections to draw the image of *ABCD* under a rotation with center *P* and magnitude of 48°.

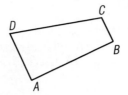

P•

Solution   The angle between reflecting lines must be ½ the magnitude. Since the magnitude is 48°, the angle between the reflecting lines must be 24°.

Step 1.   Draw any line $\overleftrightarrow{PO}$ through *P*.
Step 2.   Draw $\overleftrightarrow{PQ}$ such that m∠*OPQ* = 24 (counterclockwise).
Step 3.   Reflect *ABCD* over $\overleftrightarrow{PO}$. Call the image *A*B*C*D**.
Step 4.   Reflect *A*B*C*D** over $\overleftrightarrow{PQ}$. This is the final image *A'B'C'D'*.

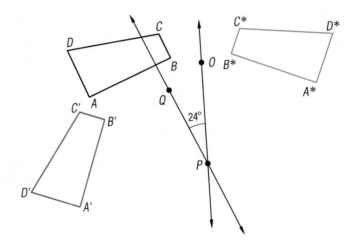

Check 1   Measure ∠*BPB'* and ∠*APA'* to see that each is a 48° angle. Check also that *BP* = *B'P*, *AP* = *A'P*, *CP* = *C'P*, and *DP* = *D'P*.

Check 2   Trace *ABCD*. Turn your tracing 48° counterclockwise about point *P*. It should coincide with *A'B'C'D'*.

In clothing stores you often find intersecting mirrors. These mirrors allow a shopper to see how clothes look from the front, side, and back. The shopper can see the reflection image of a reflection image in the mirrors. In the figure, the shopper is using the left and middle mirrors. This, in effect, turns the shopper twice the angle between the mirrors. Below, the acute angle between the mirrors is 55°, and as a result, the final image of the shopper is rotated 110°. This is enough of a turn to show the shopper what the back of the clothing looks like.

Questions

Covering the Reading

1. The composite of two reflections over two intersecting lines is a(n) __?__ .

2. The center of the rotation in Question 1 is the __?__ of the reflecting lines.

3. *Multiple choice.* If a magnitude of a rotation is negative, then the direction of the rotation is
   (a) clockwise   (b) counterclockwise.

In 4–6, use the figure below. Given $r_\ell(P) = Q$ and $r_m(Q) = P'$. The angle between the lines has measure 37°.

4. What is m∠POP'?

5. Justify each conclusion.
   a. $OP = OQ$
   b. $OQ = OP'$
   c. $OP = OP'$

6. Justify each conclusion.
   a. $r_\ell(\angle POD) = \angle QOD$
   b. m∠POD = m∠QOD

7. To rotate a figure -160°, you could reflect the figure over two lines where the acute angle between the lines has measure __?__ .

8. Name two places in the real world where you can find intersecting mirrors.

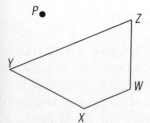

9. Trace the figure at the left. Leave a lot of room. Rotate *WXYZ* -98° about *P* by using two reflections.

10. Trace the figure below.
  a. Draw $r_m \circ r_\ell (\triangle ABC)$.
  b. Use a protractor to determine the magnitude of this rotation.

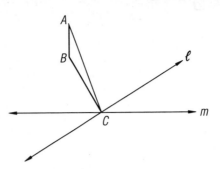

11. Reflect (4, 2) over the *x*-axis. Reflect its image over the *y*-axis.
  a. What is the final image?
  b. What rotation has taken place?

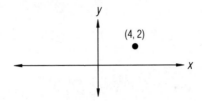

12. Identify the properties that rotations preserve from this list:
  angle measure, betweenness, collinearity, distance, orientation.

In 13–15 below, $r_\ell(\triangle LMN) = \triangle OPQ$ and $r_m(\triangle OPQ) = \triangle RST$. Prove:
13. $MN = ST$.   **14.** $m\angle N = m\angle T$.

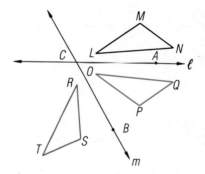

15. Suppose $m\angle NCT = 172$.
  a. What is the magnitude of the rotation with center *C* under which $\triangle RST$ is the image of $\triangle LMN$?
  b. What is the magnitude of the rotation with center *C* under which $\triangle LMN$ is the image of $\triangle RST$?
  c. What is $m\angle ACB$?

16. A view through a kaleidoscope is pictured at the beginning of this lesson. What is the magnitude of the rotation R with center *O* if $R(B) = C$?

17. *Multiple choice.* Translations do *not* preserve
(a) angle measure
(b) collinearity
(c) orientation
(d) All are preserved. *(Lesson 6-2)*

18. In the drawing at the right, *s* ∥ *t*. Trace the drawing and draw $r_t \circ r_s(ABCD)$. *(Lesson 6-2)*

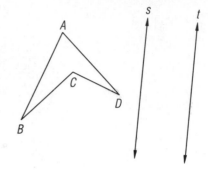

19. If T(*x*, *y*) = (*x* + 43, *y* − 210), what is T(-30, -2)? *(Lesson 6-1)*

20. One angle of an isosceles triangle measures 50°.
a. If this angle is a base angle, what are the measures of the two other angles?
b. If this angle is the vertex angle, what are the measures of the two other angles? *(Lessons 5-7, 5-1)*

21. In rhombus *ABCD* at the left, m∠*A* = *x* and m∠*B* = 3*x* + 3. Find the measure of ∠*D*. *(Lesson 5-5)*

22. Below, *n*-gon *ABCD...L* is pictured.
a. What is *n*?
b. Is *ABCD...L* clockwise or counterclockwise oriented? *(Lesson 4-6)*

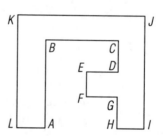

23. In 4 minutes, through how many degrees turns:
a. the minute hand of a clock?
b. the hour hand of a clock? *(Lesson 3-1)*

24. Point *B* is the image of *A* under a rotation.
a. Identify a point which could be the center of the rotation.
b. Identify another point which could be the center.
c. Identify a third point which could be the center.
d. Generalize parts **a, b,** and **c.**

A •

• *B*

Miniature Golf and Billiards

© John Margolies/Esto

When a ball is rolled without spin against a wall, it bounces off the wall as if it had gone through the wall and its path were reflected over the wall. The ball takes the shortest path to its destination. The marked angles are always of equal measure.

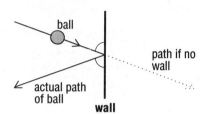

This property is not limited to bouncing balls. It is true of any object traveling without spin which hits a surface. It holds for sound, light, and radio waves which bounce off surfaces. For example, when you look in a mirror to see a person, your eye receives as images only those light waves which bounce off the mirror in your direction. This is shown in the diagram below. You see the person's image in the mirror as if the person were reflected to the other side of the mirror. The image appears to be as far "behind" the mirror as the person is in front of it, and the orientation of the image is reversed.

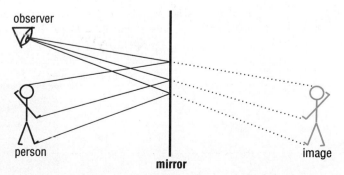

The simple idea of bouncing off a wall has applications also in many sports, including miniature golf and billiards. In miniature golf, the object of the game is to hit a golf ball into a hole. The hole is often placed so that a direct shot into it is impossible. Below is a picture of a miniature golf hole with a golf ball at G and the hole at H.

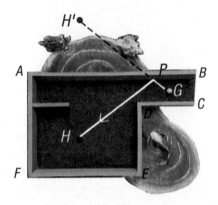

In this situation, a good strategy is to bounce (carom) the ball off a board, as shown below. To find where to aim the ball, reflect the hole H over line $\overleftrightarrow{AB}$. If you shoot for image H', the ball will bounce off $\overline{AB}$ at P and go toward the hole. If its path intersects wall $\overline{CD}$, then another strategy, using at least two caroms, is needed.

The following discussion of billiards shows how to aim when two or more caroms are needed. Billiards is a game played on a table with rubber cushions on its sides and no holes. In 3-cushion billiards the goal is to hit the cue ball so that it bounces off three cushions and then hits another ball. Pictured below is a table with cushions w, x, y, and z, the cue ball C, and another ball B.

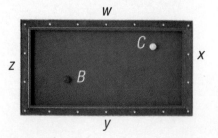

Suppose you want to shoot C off x, then y, then z, and finally hit B. Reflect the target B successively over the sides in *reverse* order: first z, then y, then x. Shoot in the direction of $B''' = r_x \circ r_y \circ r_z (B)$.

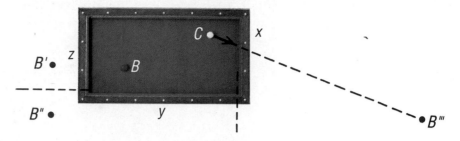

Notice what happens with the shot. (Observe the diagram below.) On the way toward B''', it bounces off side x in the direction of B''. On the way toward B'', it bounces off y in the direction of B'. Finally it hits z, and is reflected to B.

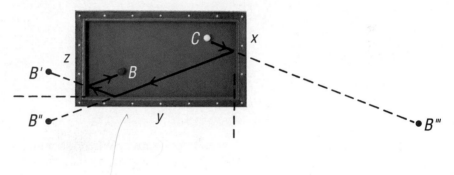

In general, to shoot an object J off wall 1 and then wall 2 and into a second object K, aim at $r_1 \circ r_2 (K)$.

Questions

Covering the Reading

1. A ball B is rolling toward the wall without spin. Trace the figure and draw the rest of the path showing how the ball will bounce off the wall.

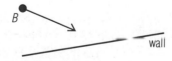

2. Trace this figure. To shoot a ball from A to B off the wall w, where should you aim?

3. Trace the diagram of Hole 3 in the miniature golf course below. Where can you shoot in order to get the ball *G* into the hole *H*?

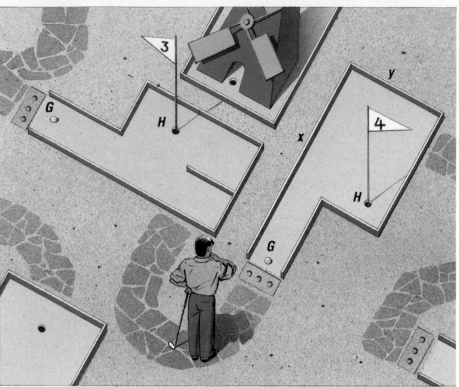

4. Trace Hole 4 above. Where should you aim on wall *x* to shoot a golf ball off sides *x* and *y* and into the hole at *H*?

5. Trace the picture of the billiards table at the left. If you wish to bounce *P* off the top, right, and bottom sides, and then hit *Q,* in what direction should you shoot *P*?

6. A billiard ball travels along the path shown below. Trace the figure and mark all angles that are equal in measure.

7. A laser beam sent from point *S* is to be reflected off two lines *ℓ* and *m* in such a way that it finally passes through point *D*. Trace the figure below. Then construct the path of the laser beam.

8. Find two other paths for getting from the golf ball *G* to the hole *H* in one shot in the first miniature golf picture on page 274.

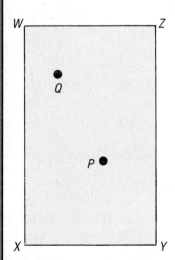

In 9 and 10, pocket billiards is played on a table with rubber cushions on its sides and 6 holes called *pockets*. The goal is to hit the cue ball so it hits an object ball into a pocket. Trace the figure below.

9. If you want to bounce the object ball *B* off wall *y* to go into the upper right corner pocket, where on *y* should the ball bounce?

10. If you want to hit the cue ball *C* off side *x* before hitting object ball *B*, where should you aim?

11. Trace the diagram of the miniature golf hole below. Where should you shoot in order to get the ball *G* into the hole *H*?

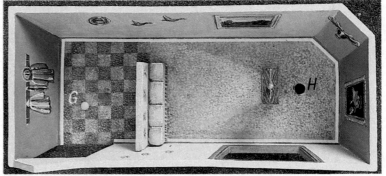

12. A billiards table with sides *w*, *x*, *y*, and *z* is diagrammed at the left on a coordinate plane. A player wants to hit a cue ball at $C = (3, 2)$ into a second ball at $B = (1, 6)$. At what point should the player aim in order to bounce the cue ball off sides *W*, *Z*, and *Y*, in that order?

13. Below is Captain Natalie looking through a periscope at a ship. The line of sight through the periscope from Captain Natalie's eye to the ship is given. What are the measures of angles 1 and 2 at which the mirrors are slanted?

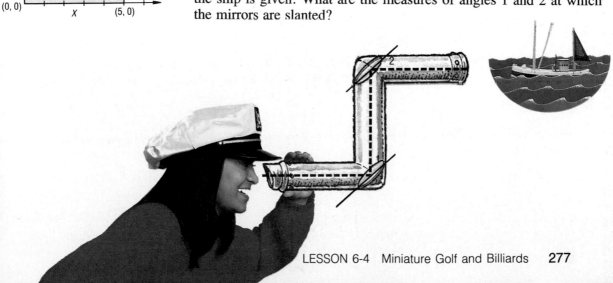

14. *Multiple choice.* Which parallelogram below is not a rotation image of one of the other two? *(Lesson 6-3)*

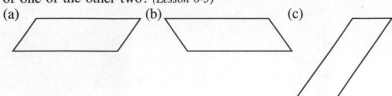

(a)   (b)   (c)

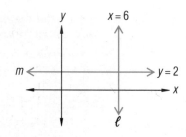

15. Trace the figure at the left. Rotate $\triangle ABC$ 100° about point P by using two reflections. *(Lesson 6-3)*

16. Let P(E) be the probability of an event E. If a number x is randomly picked from {2, 3, 4, 5, 6, 7, 8}, what is P(x is even)? *(Lesson 6-1)*

In 17 and 18, refer to the figure below.

17. Let ℓ be the line with equation $x = 6$. Let m be the line with equation $y = 2$. Give the center and magnitude of the rotation $r_\ell \circ r_m$. *(Lesson 6-3)*

18. Let m be the line with equation $y = 2$. Let n be the x-axis. Give the direction and magnitude of the translation $r_n \circ r_m$. *(Lesson 6-2)*

19. In $\triangle ABC$, the angles are in the extended ratio 2:3:4.
a. Find the measure of the largest angle.
b. Is $\triangle ABC$ acute, right, or obtuse? *(Lesson 5-7)*

20. Design a miniature golf hole in which smart golfers, but not those who don't apply reflections, could make a hole-in-one.

Congruent Figures

Figures are copied everywhere. Teachers photocopy pages for students. Tool and die makers create devices (the "dies") for cutting and forging metal so that manufacturers can make identical parts. Artists use copies of figures to create designs or patterns. Children draw copies of figures by tracing. People look at copies of themselves every time they look in mirrors.

The idea of "copy" is found everywhere in geometry also, and geometers have a special word to describe figures which are copies of each other: *congruent*. To be used in reasoning, like any other idea in mathematics, the word "congruent" needs a careful definition. But recall that good definitions can only use undefined terms or terms previously defined. We cannot define "congruent" as "exact copy" because "copy" has never been defined nor is "copy" an undefined term.

The key to the definition of congruence comes from the idea of tracing. When you make a tracing, you get a copy of an original figure. You can slide (translate) or turn (rotate) the tracing and your copy remains. You can even turn the paper over, reflecting the tracing image. You can do these movements and reflections again and again—what we call *composing* them. Thus we say that two figures are congruent if and only if one can be gotten from the other by these transformations.

Definition (longer form):

Two figures, F and G, are **congruent figures**, written **F ≅ G,** if and only if G is the image of F under a translation, a reflection, a rotation, or any composite of these.

But you have learned that rotations and translations are each composites of two reflections. This enables a shorter definition to be used.

Definition (shorter form):

Two figures F and G are **congruent figures**, written **F ≅ G,** if and only if G is the image of F under a reflection or composite of reflections.

Below are six figures. Each is a reflection image of another. Since $r_\ell \circ r_k$ maps Figure 1 onto Figure 3, Figures 1 and 3 are congruent (sufficient condition). Conversely, since Figure 4 and Figure 6 are congruent, then they can be mapped one onto the other by a reflection or composite of reflections. In this case $r_p \circ r_n$ does the job.

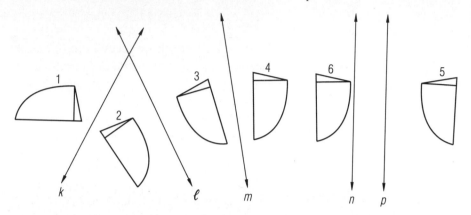

Use the same reflecting line twice and a figure is reflected back onto itself. Thus any figure is congruent to itself. If $F \cong G$, then use the reflecting lines in reverse order and you see that $G \cong F$. When $F \cong G$ and $G \cong H$, use all the reflecting lines of both these congruences to get $F \cong H$. Thus $\cong$ satisfies three properties also satisfied by $=$, called the *equivalence properties*.

Equivalence Properties of $\cong$ Theorem:

For any figures F, G, and H:
Reflexive Property of Congruence: $F \cong F$.
Symmetric Property of Congruence: If $F \cong G$, then $G \cong F$.
Transitive Property of Congruence: If $F \cong G$ and $G \cong H$, then $F \cong H$.

A transformation that is a reflection or composite of reflections is called a **congruence transformation** or **isometry.** "Isometry" comes from the Greek *isos* meaning "equal" and *metron* meaning "measure." Below is a hierarchy of the transformations you have studied so far.

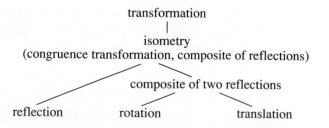

Every reflection preserves angle measure, betweenness, collinearity, and distance. So these properties are preserved by any isometry. The names of these four properties happen to begin with the first four letters of the alphabet.

A-B-C-D Theorem:

Every isometry preserves Angle measure, Betweenness, Collinearity (lines), and Distance (lengths of segments).

When figures are congruent, corresponding parts are images of each other under an isometry. Since every isometry has the A-B-C-D preservation properties, corresponding parts have equal measures. In general:

If two segments are congruent, they have equal lengths.
If two angles are congruent, they have equal measures.

Are the converses of these statements true as well? If segments have equal lengths, then are they congruent? Yes, here is a proof. At the left below, $WX = YZ$.

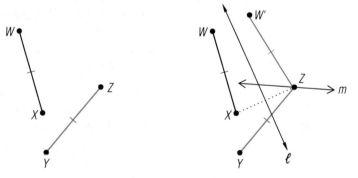

Reflect $\overline{WX}$ over ℓ, the $\perp$ bisector of $\overline{XZ}$, as shown above at the right. Now $WX = W'Z = YZ$. So $\triangle W'ZY$ (not drawn) is isosceles. Now reflect $\overline{W'Z}$ over m, the bisector of $\angle W'ZY$. By the Isosceles Triangle Symmetry Theorem, $r_m(\overline{W'Z}) = \overline{YZ}$. So $r_m \circ r_\ell(\overline{WX}) = \overline{YZ}$ and the segments are congruent by the definition of congruence (sufficient condition).

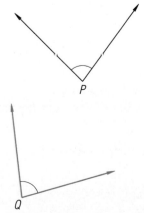

Similarly, if $\angle P$ and $\angle Q$ at the left have the same measure, you can map one onto the other by a composite of reflections. (The first reflecting line can be the $\perp$ bisector of $\overline{PQ}$.) The results of these arguments are two quite useful theorems.

Segment Congruence Theorem:

Two segments are congruent if and only if they have the same length.

Because of these theorems, in this book the phrase *congruent segments* can be substituted for the phrase *segments of equal length*, and *congruent angles* for *angles with the same measure*. For instance, the definition of a square could be restated as: A quadrilateral is a square if and only if it has four congruent sides and four right angles.

Questions

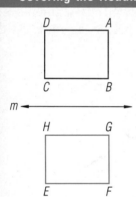

1. Define: congruent figures.

2. *Multiple choice.* Suppose $\angle A$ is congruent to $\angle B$. Which is true?
   (a) $m\angle A + m\angle B = 90$ (b) $m\angle A + m\angle B = 180$
   (c) $m\angle A = m\angle B$ (d) none of these

3. In the figure at the left, $r_m(ABCD) = FGHE$. Assume nothing else about this figure.
   a. $\overline{BC} \cong$ _?_
   b. $\angle CAB \cong$ _?_
   c. $\triangle BCD \cong$ _?_

In 4–6, which equivalence property justifies each statement?

4. If $\overline{AB} \cong \overline{CD}$ and $\overline{CD} \cong \overline{GF}$, then $\overline{AB} \cong \overline{GF}$.

5. If $\triangle MPQ \cong \triangle ABC$, then $\triangle ABC \cong \triangle MPQ$.

6. $\angle QAM \cong \angle QAM$

In 7 and 8, refer to the drawing of the six congruent figures on page 280.

7. **a.** Which transformation maps figure 6 onto figure 4?
   b. Which transformation maps figure 4 onto figure 6?

8. Which transformation maps figure 1 onto figure 5?

9. Give two synonyms for "isometry."

10. Name four properties preserved by isometries.

11. Name three places outside of mathematics where congruent figures may be found.

12. According to the Segment Congruence Theorem, if $AX = BY$, then _?_ .

13. According to the Angle Congruence Theorem, if $\angle C \cong \angle T$, then _?_ .

14. *Multiple choice.* If r($\triangle ABC$) = $\triangle DEF$, then according to the definition of congruence,

   (a) $\overline{AB} \cong \overline{DE}$ (b) m$\angle C$ = m$\angle F$ (c) $\triangle ABC \cong \triangle DEF$.

In 15 and 16, reword the statement using the word *congruent*.

15. An isosceles triangle has two sides of the same length.

16. If two lines are cut by a transversal and alternate interior angles have the same measure, then the lines are parallel.

Applying the Mathematics

17. Draw two congruent nonsymmetric pentagons with the same orientation.

18. Draw a figure congruent to the stick figure at the left and with different orientation.

19. Can two circles not be congruent?

20. If $r_\ell \circ r_m(F) = G$, what transformation maps G onto F?

21. What does the transformation $r_\ell \circ r_\ell$ do to a figure?

22. Explain why any two positions of the minute hand of a clock are congruent to each other.

23. $\triangle ABC$ is isosceles with vertex angle A.
$\triangle CAD$ is isosceles with vertex angle A.
  a. Which segments in the figure are congruent to $\overline{AB}$?
  b. Which angles are congruent to $\angle B$?

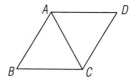

24. Draw two congruent triangles which are neither reflection, rotation, nor translation images of each other.

Review

25. If you want to hit the cue ball C off side x before C hits object ball B, where should you aim? *(Lesson 6-4)*

26. Trace the picture of the miniature golf hole below. Where can you shoot in order to get the ball *G* into the hole *H*? *(Lesson 6-4)*

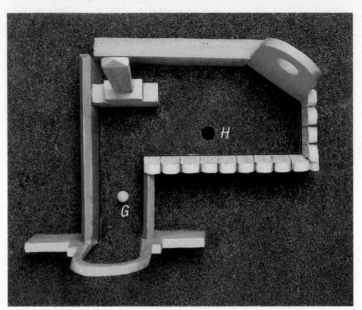

In 27 and 28, use the figure at the left. All triangles in the figure are equilateral.

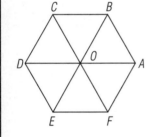

27. Suppose a rotation R has center *O*.
 a. What is its magnitude if R(*B*) = *C*?
 b. What is its magnitude if R(*A*) = *E*? *(Lesson 6-3)*

28. Justify the steps in this proof that *OAFE* is a parallelogram.
 (Lessons 5-6, 5-1, 4-5)

Conclusions	Justifications
1. $OA = AF = OF$	**a.** ?
2. $OF = FE = OE$	**b.** ?
3. $OA = AF = FE = OE$	**c.** ?
4. *OAFE* is a rhombus.	**d.** ?
5. *OAFE* is parallelogram.	**e.** ?

29. Seven angles of an octagon each has measure 150°.
 a. Is this possible?
 b. If so, what is the measure of the eighth angle? If not, why is it not possible? *(Lesson 5-7)*

Exploration

30. Let G be clockwise oriented. F is the image of G under a composite of *n* reflections.
 a. What is the orientation of F when *n* = 3?
 b. What is the orientation of F when *n* = 10?
 c. For what values of *n* will F and G have the same orientation?
 d. For what values of *n* will F and G have opposite orientations?

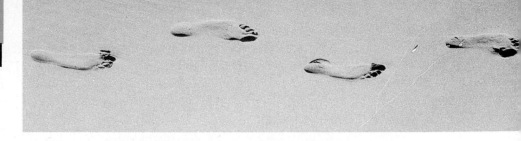

6-6

Isometries

By the definition of congruence you know that for any pair of congruent figures, such as the letter *R*s drawn below, there exists a composite of reflections which maps one image onto the other. But what is the least number of reflections needed? And how can you find the reflecting lines?

Figure I   Figure II

The answer may be surprising. If two figures are oriented the same way, as these are, only two reflections are needed! We do not prove this theorem in this book, but you can verify it with drawings.

Example 1 Draw reflecting lines ℓ and m for a composite of reflections $r_m \circ r_\ell$ which maps Figure I onto Figure II above.

Solution

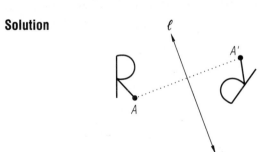

Since the two figures are of the same orientation, it will take two reflections. Select two corresponding points, such as *A* and *A'* above, and let ℓ be the perpendicular bisector of $\overline{AA'}$. Then reflect Figure I over ℓ.

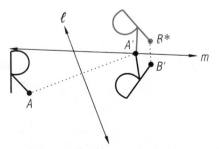

Pick a point from that image (in blue above) and its corresponding point in Figure II. We have labeled these points *B** and *B'*. Let *m* be the perpendicular bisector of $\overline{B^*B'}$. Then $r_m \circ r_\ell$ (Figure I) = Figure II.

The procedure outlined works whether the original figures are rotation or translation images. In Example 1, since ℓ and m intersect, the original figures were rotation images. Now consider congruent figures of different orientations such as Figures III and IV below.

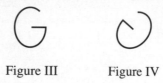

Figure III   Figure IV

There is no single reflection that will map Figure III onto Figure IV. But reflect Figure III over *any* line and its image (Figure III* in blue below) has the same orientation as Figure IV. Now, as was shown on the previous page for letter R, the image, Figure III*, can be mapped onto Figure IV in two reflections. In all, then, Figure III can be mapped onto Figure IV in three reflections.

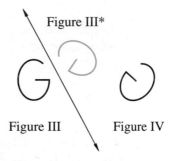

Figure III*

Figure III   Figure IV

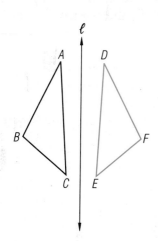

If you reflect over the same line twice, the final image is the same as the original preimage. At the left, $r_\ell (\triangle ABC) = \triangle DFE$ and $r_\ell \circ r_\ell(\triangle ABC) = \triangle ABC$.

If you reflect over ℓ three times, the final image equals the first image.

$$r_\ell \circ r_\ell \circ r_\ell(\triangle ABC) = r_\ell \circ r_\ell(\triangle DFE)$$
$$= \triangle DFE$$

Thus, sometimes the composite of three reflections equals a single reflection.

When the composite of three reflections is not equal to one reflection, an isometry called a **glide reflection** occurs. A glide reflection is the composite of a translation (the "glide" part) and a reflection over a line parallel to the direction of the translation. Informally this is called a *walk* as you can see from the picture below.

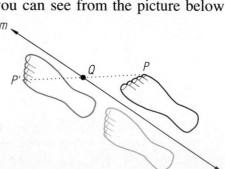

Definition:

Let r_m be a reflection and T be a translation with nonzero magnitude and direction parallel to m. Then $G = T \circ r_m$ is a **glide reflection**.

Successive footprints are very close to being glide reflection images of one another, because each can be mapped onto the other by reflecting over a line and then translating in a direction parallel to that line.

A glide reflection is clearly determined by giving the reflecting line and the magnitude and direction of the translation. The reflecting line has an interesting property. We will give a proof of this property in a later lesson.

Glide Reflection Theorem:

Let $G = T \circ r_m$ be a glide reflection, and let $G(P) = P'$. Then the midpoint of $\overline{PP'}$ is on m.

According to the theorem, in the figure on the bottom of the previous page, since P' is the glide reflection image of P, the intersection of $\overline{PP'}$ and m is Q, the midpoint of $\overline{PP'}$.

The Glide Reflection Theorem suggests a way to find the reflecting line for the reflection or glide reflection that maps one congruent figure onto another. Just connect corresponding points. Since the midpoints of these segments lie on the reflecting line, they determine it.

■ ■ ■ ■ ■ ■ ■ ■

Example 2   Find the reflecting line ℓ of the glide reflection mapping Figure III onto Figure IV on the previous page.

Solution

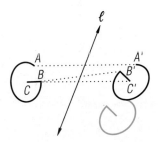

Connect at least two pairs of corresponding points. ℓ is determined by the midpoints of $\overline{AA'}$, $\overline{BB'}$, and $\overline{CC'}$. The image in blue shows the initial reflection of Figure III over ℓ.

All congruent figures can be mapped onto each other by a single reflection, rotation, translation, or glide reflection. These four transformations are all the isometries. The transformation hierarchy from Lesson 6-5 can be extended to include all the isometries.

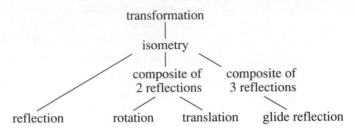

Reflection and glide reflection images have opposite orientation; rotation and translation images the same orientation.

■ ■ ■ ■ ■ ■ ■ ■ ■ ■

Example 3   Examine the tessellation below.

a. Which type of isometry maps figure A onto figure B?
b. Which type of isometry maps figure A onto figure C?

Solution

a. Since A and B have the same orientation, they are related either by a rotation or a translation. A and B can't be related by a translation because they are tilted differently. So B is a rotation image of A. (Can you determine the center of the rotation?)

b. Since A and C have opposite orientations, they are related by a reflection or glide reflection. They are not reflection images of each other, so C must be a glide reflection image of A. The glide reflection line contains the midpoints of segments connecting corresponding points on A and C.

Questions

Covering the Reading

1. When two congruent figures have the same orientation, at most how many reflections are needed to map one onto the other?

2. When two congruent figures have different orientations, at most how many reflections are needed to map one onto the other?

3. Define: glide reflection.

In 4–6, use the tessellation below.

4. Which type of isometry maps figure A onto figure B?

5. Which type of isometry maps figure A onto figure C?

6. Which type of isometry maps figure C onto figure D?

In 7 and 8, trace the figures. Figure I ≅ Figure II. Find the reflecting line ℓ of the glide reflection mapping Figure I onto Figure II.

7.

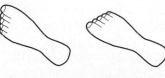

Figure I   Figure II

8.

Figure I

Figure II

In 9 and 10, trace the figures. Figure I ≅ Figure II. Find a composite of reflections $r_m \circ r_\ell$ which maps Figure I onto Figure II.

9.

Figure II

Figure I

10.

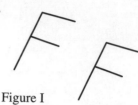

Figure I

Figure II

11. Name the four types of isometries.

12. *True* or *false*?
    For any two figures, there is an isometry mapping one onto the other.

13. **a.** Name four properties preserved by glide reflections.
    b. Name a property that glide reflections do not preserve.

14. Use the transformation $T(x, y) = (x + 6, -y)$.
    a. Find $T(\triangle ABC)$ where $A = (0, 6)$, $B = (-5, 6)$, and $C = (-5, -2)$.
    b. Graph $\triangle ABC$ and $T(\triangle ABC)$ on the same axes.
    c. T is a glide reflection. What is the reflecting line?
    d. What are the magnitude and direction of the translation?

15. **a.** Trace the figure at the left. Perform a glide reflection by reflecting $\triangle ABC$ over line ℓ and then translating the image 4 cm parallel to ℓ.
    b. Is your answer to part **a** unique?

16. Trace the figure below. Let $\ell \parallel m$, $m \perp n$, and $r_\ell \circ r_m \circ r_n(ABCDE) = (FGHIJ)$. Draw ℓ, m, and n.

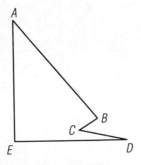

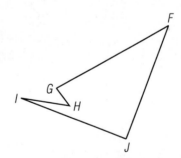

In 17 and 18, justify each conclusion. *(Lesson 6-5)*

17. Given: $AB = CD$.
    Conclusion: $\overline{AB} \cong \overline{CD}$.

18. Given: $\angle EFG \cong \angle HIJ$.
    Conclusion: $m\angle EFG = m\angle HIJ$.

19. Rewrite this statement using the word *congruent:* The bisector of an angle splits it into two angles of the same measure. *(Lesson 6-5)*

290

20. Trace the diagram of this billiards table. If you wish to have *P* bounce off the top, right, and bottom sides, and then hit *Q*, in what direction should you shoot *P*? *(Lesson 6-4)*

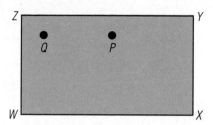

21. Refer to kite *CHIP* at the left. *(Lessons 6-5, 5-4)*
  a. Name its ends.
  b. Name its symmetry line.
  c. $r_{\overleftrightarrow{CI}}(\triangle CIP) = \underline{\ ?\ }$
  d. $\triangle CIP \cong \underline{\ ?\ }$

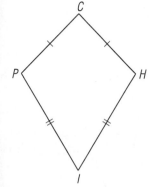

22. Use the figure below.
  Given: $\overleftrightarrow{AG} \parallel \overleftrightarrow{BH}$.
  Prove: $m\angle CDG = m\angle BEF$. *(Lessons 4-4, 3-4)*

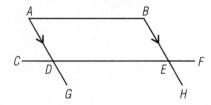

23. Nine times the measure of angle *T* is greater than 801.
  a. Give the possible values of $m\angle T$.
  b. Can $\angle T$ be an acute angle? *(Lesson 3-2, Previous course)*

24. A lot has 50′ of frontage and is *x* feet deep. If the area of the lot is less than 1000 square feet, what is *x*? *(Previous course)*

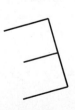

50′

Exploration

25. Below are two congruent reflection-symmetric figures. Find and describe two isometries of different types which will map Figure I onto Figure II.

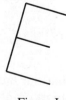

Figure I

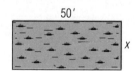

Figure II

6-7

Corresponding Parts in Congruent Figures

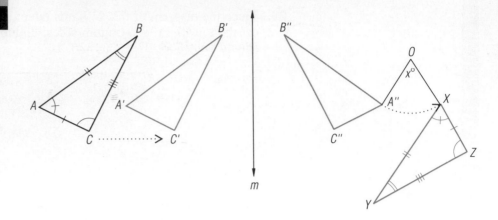

In the figure above, $\triangle ABC$ was translated onto $\triangle A'B'C'$. Then $\triangle A'B'C'$ was reflected over m onto $\triangle A''B''C''$. Lastly, $\triangle A''B''C''$ was rotated about O onto $\triangle XYZ$. Under this composite of transformations, call it T, $\triangle XYZ$ is the image of $\triangle ABC$. So by the definition of congruence, $\triangle ABC \cong \triangle XYZ$.

Specifically, $T(A) = X$, $T(B) = Y$, and $T(C) = Z$. Angles and sides that are images of each other are called *corresponding parts*. Since T can also be described as a composite of reflections (in this case, three reflections), and every composite of reflections preserves distance and angle measure, all the corresponding parts are congruent.

$$\angle A \cong \angle X \qquad \angle B \cong \angle Y \qquad \angle C \cong \angle Z$$

$$\overline{AB} \cong \overline{XY} \qquad \overline{BC} \cong \overline{YZ} \qquad \overline{AC} \cong \overline{XZ}$$

In general, when two figures are congruent, all corresponding angles and sides and other parts of the figures are congruent. This is a *widely used* theorem, and we give it an abbreviated name.

Corresponding Parts in Congruent Figures (CPCF) Theorem:

If two figures are congruent, then any pair of corresponding parts is congruent.

Unless stated otherwise, corresponding parts of a figure refer to sides and angles. With a pair of congruent triangles, there are six pairs of corresponding parts, three pairs of sides and three pairs of angles. However, other corresponding parts in a figure that may exist are bisectors, diagonals, other segments, polygons, or other figures.

Remember that the order of vertices tells you which points are images of which points and, therefore, which parts correspond.

Example 1 $\triangle TOP \cong \triangle JKL$. List the six pairs of congruent parts. Sketch this situation and mark the congruent parts.

Solution $\angle T \cong \angle J$, $\angle O \cong \angle K$, and $\angle P \cong \angle L$.
$\overline{TO} \cong \overline{JK}$, $\overline{OP} \cong \overline{KL}$, and $\overline{TP} \cong \overline{JL}$.

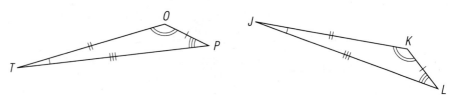

Sometimes it is not so easy to determine corresponding parts from a picture. Then the order of vertices is very helpful. Example 2 demonstrates this.

Example 2 A student was able to prove $ABCD \cong FGAE$. Using the CPCF Theorem, which angle is congruent to $\angle BAD$? Which segment is congruent to $\overline{DB}$ (not drawn)?

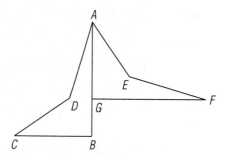

Solution Read the corresponding vertices from the congruence statement, $ABCD \cong FGAE$. $\angle BAD \cong \angle GFE$ and $\overline{DB} \cong \overline{EG}$.

Check The two angles look like the smallest angles in their respective quadrilaterals, and the segments are the shortest diagonals.

Questions

Covering the Reading

1. By the definition of congruence, when are triangles congruent?

2. Unless otherwise stated, corresponding parts refer to __?__.

3. For congruent triangles, there are __?__ pairs of corresponding parts.

4. State the CPCF Theorem.

5. $\triangle ATV \cong \triangle MCI$. What part is congruent to the part named?
   a. $\angle T$ **b.** $\angle VAT$ **c.** $\overline{IC}$

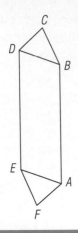

6. Suppose $\triangle ADE \cong \triangle BNO$.
  a. Which sides are congruent?
  b. Which angles are congruent?

7. For the figure at the left, a student was able to prove $ABCDEF \cong DEFABC$. What segment is congruent to $\overline{CD}$?

8. Suppose $\triangle ATV \cong \triangle MCI$ and $AT = 5$ cm. What other distance can be found?

9. Suppose $\triangle MCI \cong \triangle GTE$ and m$\angle ICM = 94$. What other angle measures 94°?

Applying the Mathematics

In 10–13, assume the two triangles in each figure that appear to be congruent are congruent. **a.** Write a congruence statement for each with the vertices in *correct* order. **b.** List, in pairs, all corresponding congruent parts.

10. 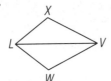 **11.** 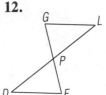 **12.**   **13.**

14. Tell whether or not the task uses the idea of congruence.
  a. sorting records into 33 and 45 rpms
  b. making sure that the rear window of a car fits snugly into the window frame
  c. constructing a circle with diameter equal to the length of $\overline{FY}$
  d. demonstrating that a tall thin glass and a short fat glass can hold the same amount of water
  e. explaining to a Martian that M and *M* are two ways to represent the same letter
  f. figuring out that two jigsaw puzzle pieces fit together

15. Draw two triangles which have the same shape but are not congruent.

16. Draw two triangles which have the same area but are not congruent.

Review

17. Name four kinds of isometries. *(Lesson 6-6)*

18. Name four properties preserved by isometries. *(Lessons 6-6, 6-5)*

19. Consider the line with equation $y = 3x$. *(Lessons 6-3, 6-2, 3-5, 3-4)*
  a. What is the slope of this line under a -90° rotation with center (0, 0)?
  b. What is the slope of this line under a translation?

In 20–22, Figure I $\cong$ Figure II. Which type of isometry maps Figure I onto Figure II? *(Lesson 6-6)*

20.

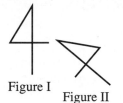

Figure I   Figure II

21.

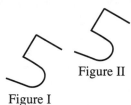

Figure II

Figure I

22.

Figure I   Figure II

23. Rewrite the Isosceles Triangle Theorem using the word *congruent*. *(Lessons 6-5, 5-1)*

24. Let the image of $\triangle DEF$ under a translation be $\triangle D'E'F'$. What property of translations is exemplified by each statement? *(Lessons 6-5, 6-2)*

  a. $\angle FED \cong \angle F'E'D'$
  b. $\overline{E'D'} \cong \overline{ED}$
  c. If B is between E and D, then the image of B under this translation is between E' and D'.

25. If $T(a, b) = (2a, 3b)$, find $T(x, y)$. *(Lesson 6-1)*

26. The measure of an angle is greater than three times the measure of a supplement to it. Is this possible? If so, what is the measure of the angle? *(Lesson 3-2, Previous course)*

Exploration

27. a. Find three characteristics that make Figure I not congruent to Figure II.

Figure I   Figure II

  b. Make up a puzzle like the one in part **a**, or find such a puzzle in a newspaper or magazine.

Summary

This chapter starts with transformations. Two special ones, rotations and translations, are related to reflections in an extraordinary way. A composite of two reflections over parallel lines is a translation. Do the composite over two intersecting lines, and the result is a rotation. The reflecting lines completely determine the magnitude and direction of the translation, or the center and magnitude of the rotation.

Two figures are congruent if and only if one is the image of the other under a reflection or composite of reflections. A transformation which preserves congruence is called an isometry. There are four types of isometries: reflections, rotations, translations, and glide reflections. All isometries preserve angle measure, betweenness, collinearity, and distance. Single rotations and translations preserve orientation, while single reflections and glide reflections reverse orientation.

If two figures are congruent, then all pairs of corresponding parts are congruent. If the parts are segments, then they have the same length. If they are angles, then they have the same measure.

The transformations which underlie the theory of congruence have many applications. In billiards and miniature golf, using reflections and composites of reflections can help a player succeed. The same principles apply to light, sound, and radio waves bouncing off surfaces. Combinations of mirrors are used in kaleidoscopes, periscopes, and other optical instruments, as well as in stores and in the home.

Vocabulary

Below are the new terms and phrases for this chapter. For the starred terms (*) below, you should be able to produce a *good* definition. For the other terms, you should be able to give a general description and specific example of each.

Lesson 6-1
*transformation, mapping
maps, T(P)
distance between two parallel
   lines

Lesson 6-2
*translation, slide
composite of two
   transformations
$T_2 \circ T_1$, $T_2(T_1(P))$, $T_2 \circ T_1(P)$
direction of translation
magnitude of translation
Two Reflection Theorem
   for Translations

Lesson 6-3
*rotation
center of rotation
magnitude of rotation
clockwise, counterclockwise
direction of rotation
Two Reflection Theorem for
   Rotations

Lesson 6-5
*congruent figures, ≅
*congruence transformation
isometry
Equivalence Properties of
   ≅ Theorem

Reflexive Property, Symmetric
   Property, and Transitive
   Property of Congruence
transformation hierarchy
A-B-C-D Theorem
Segment Congruence Theorem
Angle Congruence Theorem

Lesson 6-6
glide reflection, walk
Glide Reflection Theorem

Lesson 6-7
corresponding parts
Corresponding Parts in
   Congruent Figures (CPCF)
   Theorem

Progress Self-Test

Directions: Take this test as you would take a test in class. Use a ruler and a protractor. Then check your work with the solutions in the Selected Answers section in the back of the book.

1. Trace this drawing. $\ell \parallel m$.
  a. Draw $r_\ell \circ r_m (\triangle ABC)$.
  b. Describe this transformation.

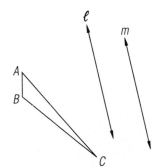

2. *Multiple choice.* In the figure below, $r_\ell \circ r_m (\triangle ABC)$ is which one of these?
  (a) reflection
  (b) rotation
  (c) translation

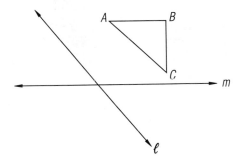

In 3 and 4, in the figure below, $\ell \parallel m$ and $\ell \perp n$.

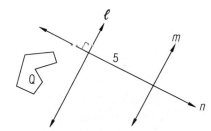

3. Describe the transformation $r_\ell \circ r_m$.
4. Describe the transformation $r_n \circ r_m \circ r_\ell$.

In 5 and 6, $\triangle ABC$ below has been reflected over line m, then its image was reflected over line n.

5. What angle of $\triangle JKL$ has the same measure as $\angle C$?

6. Name all segments whose length is equal to FG.

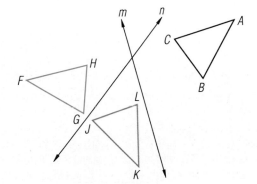

7. Below, $\triangle ABC$ has been reflected over line m. Then its image has been reflected over line ℓ. Fill in the blanks.
$\triangle ABC \cong \underline{\ ?\ } \cong \underline{\ ?\ }$

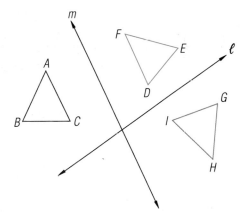

8. According to the CPCF Theorem, what happens if $\triangle ABC \cong \triangle DEF$?
9. Name five properties preserved by translations.
10. Name four kinds of isometries.
11. *True* or *false*? If one figure can be mapped onto another by a series of reflections, then the figures are congruent.

12. Let T be a transformation with the rule
T(x, y) = (x − 3, y + 8). Let A = (10, 5),
B = (13, -2), and C = (7, -3).
   a. Graph △ABC and T(△ABC) on the
   same axes.
   b. Describe this transformation.

13. Suppose V(x) is the number of vertices of a
figure x. What is V(hexagon)?

In 14 and 15, use the miniature golf hole
diagrammed below. The piano keys are part
of the floor.

14. Give the path a ball at G must take to carom
off y and go into the hole at H.

15. Give the path a ball at G must take to bounce
off x and then y and go into the hole at H.

In 16 and 17, Figure I ≅ Figure II. Trace the
figures, then find and describe an isometry that will
map Figure I onto Figure II.

16.

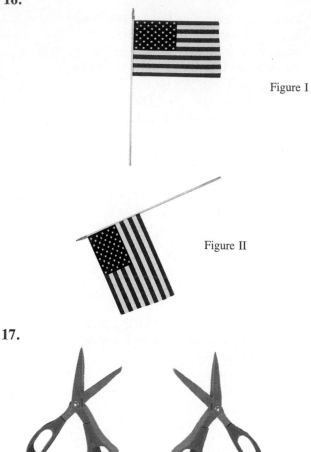

Figure I

Figure II

17.

Figure I   Figure II

Chapter Review

Questions on **SPUR** Objectives

SPUR stands for **S**kills, **P**roperties, **U**ses, and **R**epresentations.
The Chapter Review questions are grouped according to the
SPUR Objectives for this chapter.

SKILLS deal with the procedures used to get answers.

■ **Objective A:** *Draw or identify images of figures under composites of reflections. (Lessons 6-2, 6-3, 6-6)*

In 1 and 2, draw and describe each transformation.

1. $r_a(r_b(\triangle DEF))$.   **2.** $r_b \circ r_a (\triangle DEF)$

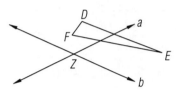

In 3 and 4, use this drawing. $n \parallel m$.

3. a. Draw the image of *ABCDE* under the transformation $r_n \circ r_m$.
    b. Describe this transformation.

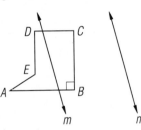

4. a. Draw $r_m \circ r_n$ (*ABCDE*).
    b. Describe this transformation.

5. Trace the figure below. Perform a glide reflection by reflecting *PQRS* over line ℓ and then translating the image $1\frac{1}{2}$ inches parallel to ℓ.

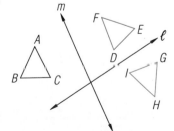

PROPERTIES deal with the principles behind the mathematics.

■ **Objective B:** *Apply properties of reflections to obtain properties of translations and rotations.*
(Lessons 6-2, 6-3)

6. *Multiple choice.* Rotations do *not* preserve
    (a) betweenness   (b) distance
    (c) orientation.   (d) All are preserved.

7. *Multiple choice.* A composite of two reflections
    (a) can never be a reflection
    (b) can never be a rotation
    (c) can never be a translation
    (d) can be any of the tranformations mentioned in (a), (b), and (c).

In 8 and 9, use the figure below.
$r_m(\triangle ABC) = \triangle FED$;
$r_\ell(\triangle DEF) = \triangle IGH$.

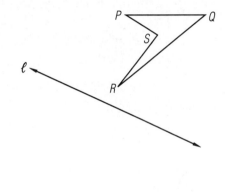

8. What side of $\triangle GHI$ has the same length as $\overline{BC}$?

9. What angle of $\triangle ABC$ has the same measure as $\angle G$?

■ **Objective C:** *Apply the Two Reflection Theorem for Translations and for Rotations.*
(Lessons 6-2, 6-3, 6-6)

In 10–12, $\ell \parallel m$ and $\ell \perp n$.
Describe the transformation.

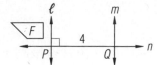

10. $r_\ell \circ r_m$

11. $r_m \circ r_n$

12. $r_m \circ r_\ell \circ r_n$

13. To rotate $\triangle MNO$ 30° about a point C, you can reflect successively over two lines that form an angle of measure __?__ whose vertex is __?__ .

■ **Objective D:** *Determine properties of congruent figures. (Lessons 6-5, 6-6, 6-7)*

In 14 and 15, use the given and figure of Questions 8 and 9.

14. Name all segments congruent to $\overline{FE}$.

15. Name all angles congruent to $\angle A$.

16. *True* or *false*? Congruent figures must have the same orientation.

17. *True* or *false*? A figure and its glide reflection image are always congruent.

18. Define: congruence.

19. Name the four types of isometries.

In 20–22, use the figure below.
$r_s(ABCD) = EHGF$; $r_t(EHGF) = IJKL$.

20. $ABCD \cong$ __?__ $\cong$ __?__

21. $GFEH \cong$ __?__ $\cong$ __?__

22. $ABCD \cong EHGF$ and $EHGF \cong IJKL \Rightarrow ABCD \cong$ __?__ .

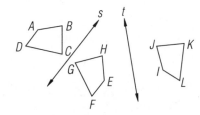

In 23–25, use the figure above. Justify each conclusion.

23. $\overline{AB} \cong \overline{IJ}$

24. $m\angle C = m\angle K$

25. $ABCD \cong ABCD$

USES deal with applications of mathematics in real situations.

■ **Objective E:** *Determine the isometry which maps one figure onto another. (Lessons 6-2, 6-3, 6-6)*

In 26–29, name the type of isometry which maps Figure I onto Figure II.

26.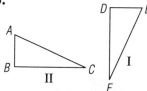

27.

28.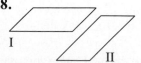

29.

In 30 and 31, use the tessellation below.

30. Which type of isometry maps figure A onto figure B?

31. Which type of isometry maps figure B onto figure C?

Objective F: *Use reflections to find a path from an object to a particular point. (Lesson 6-4)*

In 32 and 33, use the drawing below. Find a path to shoot a ball at *G* into the hole at *H* after bouncing off the named sides.

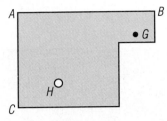

32. $\overline{AB}$

33. $\overline{AB}$ and then $\overline{AC}$

In 34 and 35, use the drawing below.

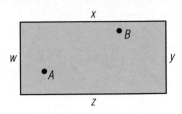

34. Draw the path of a ball that starts at *B* and bounces off *x*, *y*, and *z* in that order, and then hits *A*.

35. Draw a path from *B* that bounces off *x* and *z* in that order, then hits *A*.

REPRESENTATIONS deal with pictures, graphs, or objects that illustrate concepts.

Objective G: *Apply a rule described using T( ) notation. (Lessons 6-1, 6-2, 6-3, 6-6)*

36. A transformation T has the rule T(*x*, *y*) = (*x* + 4, *y* − 2). Let *P* = (7, 3), *Q* = (4, 0), and *R* = (-2, 2).
    a. Graph △*PQR* and its image under T.
    b. What isometry is T?

37. A transformation S has the rule S(*x*, *y*) = (*y*, 2*x*).
    a. Graph the quadrilateral with vertices *A* = (5, 2), *B* = (5, -2), *C* = (-5, -2), and *D* = (-5, 2).
    b. Graph S(*ABCD*) on the same axes and label it *A′B′C′D′*.
    c. Describe the transformation S.

38. Use the transformation T(*x*, *y*) = (-*x*, *y* − 4).
    a. Find T(△*DEF*) where *D* = (-2, -1), *E* = (5, 0), and *F* = (0, 8).
    b. Graph △*DEF* and T(△*DEF*) on the same axes.
    c. Describe this transformation.

39. Let N(S) be the number of elements in set S. What is N({2, 3, 4, 5})?

40. Let P(E) be the probability of an event E. If a number *x* is randomly picked from {1, 2, 4, 5, 7, 8}, what is P(*x* is divisible by 4)?

In 41 and 42, *multiple choice*.

41. At the right, Figure B is the image of Figure A under transformation S. What could be the rule?
    (a) S(*x*, *y*) = (-*x*, -*y*)
    (b) S(*x*, *y*) = (-*y*, -*x*)
    (c) S(*x*, *y*) = (*x*, -*y*)
    (d) S(*x*, *y*) = (-*y*, *x*)

42. Figure D is the image of Figure C under transformation T. What could be the rule?

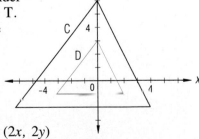

    (a) T(*x*, *y*) = (2*x*, 2*y*)

    (b) T(*x*, *y*) = (*x* + 2, *y* + 2)

    (c) T(*x*, *y*) = (*x* − 2, *y* − 2)

    (d) T(*x*, *y*) = $\left(\dfrac{x}{2}, \dfrac{y}{2}\right)$

Triangle Congruence

Triangles, the simplest of all polygons, have many uses. The supporting structures for many bridges utilize triangles because triangles are rigid. The bridge pictured at the left splits in the middle into two parts which are raised to let tall boats through. The mechanism which raises and lowers the bridge has triangles in its design. Notice that many of the triangles of the bridge are congruent, a feature which ensures the smoothness of the bridge and a pleasant design.

If a person at a point *A* sights an airplane or other object in the sky, that person can only determine the direction of the plane, not how far it is away. But if a person at a second point *B* sights the airplane simultaneously, then the airplane is at the intersection *C* of the two rays and can be located precisely. This method is called *triangulation*, because *A*, *B*, and *C* are vertices of a triangle. For hundreds of years, until satellites gave us accurate maps of the earth with cameras, triangulation was the best way to determine the precise locations of mountain peaks, harbors, and other places not easily reached.

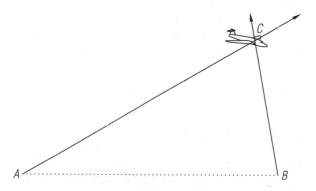

The Lake Street bridge in Chicago provides support for commuter trains.

In this chapter, you will draw or construct triangles given lengths of their sides and measures of their angles. This activity will help you learn the conditions that are sufficient to make pairs of triangles congruent. These conditions, which are formulated as the triangle congruence theorems, have been utilized from the time of the ancient Greeks to deduce properties of polygons. And so, in this chapter, you are studying an old subject with many modern applications.

Drawing
Triangles

Before Ramon built a shed for firewood, he constructed a scale model of the lean-to.

A lean-to roof has only one slanted side. To make such a roof, triangular supports (shown in orange) are often used. In order for the lean-to roof to be a plane, and to fit snugly with the walls, the triangular supports must be congruent. Since roofs and their supports are often made of wood, these triangles cannot be made by machine; they have to be measured and cut.

Ramon was building a lean-to to serve as a shed for firewood on his farm. He cut long pieces of wood into lengths of 2, 4, and 5 feet. Using one piece of each length, he made triangles out of them. He did this by cutting and nailing the ends together. He made four triangular frames for his shed.

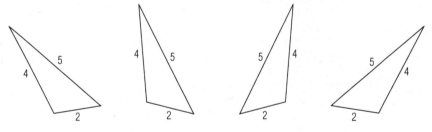

Ramon's frames

Ramon was uncertain as to whether his frames would be congruent, as required by the plan for the shed. Was it possible the angles might have different measures in these triangles? This is a question to be answered in Lesson 7-2, but we explore it here.

Drawing a triangle with sides 2 cm, 4 cm, and 5 cm on a sheet of paper is different than constructing one out of wood. You can't pick up, cut, or nail the sides when they are on paper! Some automatic drawers enable you to enter side lengths and angle measures in a triangle and they then draw a triangle. If you do not have such software, here is an algorithm for constructing a triangle with three sides of given lengths that satisfy the Triangle Inequality.

Example 1   Construct a triangle given sides of lengths 2, 4, and 5.

2

4

5

Step 1.   Construct any line. Choose point X on the line.
Step 2.   Construct $\odot X_1$ with radius $XY = 5$.
Step 3.   Construct $\odot X_2$ with radius 4.
Step 4.   Construct $\odot Y$ with radius 2.
Step 5. $\odot X_2 \cap \odot Y = \{Z, W\}$. (The circles will not intersect if the Triangle Inequality is violated.)
Step 6.   Both $\triangle XYZ$ and $\triangle XYW$ are triangles with sides 2, 4, and 5.

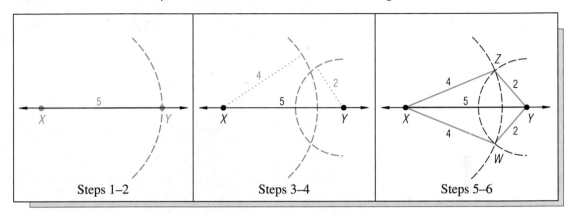

Steps 1–2   Steps 3–4   Steps 5–6

Check   Measure to see if the sides of the constructed triangle have the required lengths.

Now consider a situation where you are asked to draw a triangle given measures of its three angles. First, check that the angle measures add to 180°. If they do, you can draw an appropriate triangle.

Example 2   Draw a triangle ABC in which $m\angle A = 80$, $m\angle B = 45$, and $m\angle C = 55$.

Solution   First, check that $m\angle A + m\angle B + m\angle C = 180$. Then, to start, draw a line containing one of the sides. We draw $\overleftrightarrow{AB}$. Now draw a 45° angle at B open to the right and an 80° angle at A open to the left. The result is the desired triangle.

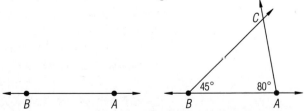

Check   Does $m\angle C = 55$? It does, so the triangle satisfies the given conditions.

Notice that only two angles were needed in Example 2. The third angle is the check. This is because all triangles with two given angles have congruent third angles.

Theorem:

If two triangles have two pairs of angles congruent, then their third pair of angles is congruent.

Proof

Draw a picture and restate the given in terms of the picture.

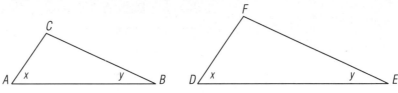

Given: $\angle A \cong \angle D$, $\angle B \cong \angle E$.
Prove: $\angle C \cong \angle F$.

The proof uses algebra. Since the pairs of angles are congruent, they have the same measures.
Let $m\angle A = m\angle D = x$, and let $m\angle B = m\angle E = y$.
Now, because of the Triangle-Sum Theorem in $\triangle ABC$,
$$x + y + m\angle C = 180,$$
so $$m\angle C = 180 - x - y.$$
Similarly, in $\triangle DEF$,
$$x + y + m\angle F = 180$$
$$m\angle F = 180 - x - y.$$
Using the Transitive Property of Equality, $m\angle C = m\angle F$.
So they are congruent.

In the following situation, you are asked to draw a triangle given some angles and some sides.

■ ■ ■ ■ ■ ■ ■ ■ ■

Example 3   In a triangular sail ABC, $m\angle A = 70$, $AB = 5$ meters, and $AC = 3.5$ meters. Make a scale drawing using centimeters instead of meters as the unit.

Solution   First draw the 70° angle. Call it $\angle A$. Let 1 cm in the drawing equal 1 meter of the actual sail. Then, mark off 5 cm on one side and 3.5 cm on the other. Connect the points.

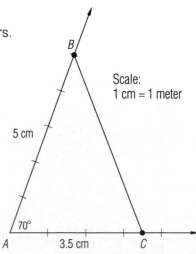

Examples 1–3 in this lesson showed how to draw a triangle given measures of some of its sides or angles.

Example	Given	Name for given condition
1	three sides	SSS
2	three angles	AAA
3	two sides and included angle	SAS

In Questions 11–19, you are asked to draw triangles given AA, SSA, SA, SS, ASA, and AAS. Part **b** of these questions introduces an important idea: will everyone else's drawings be congruent to yours? In other words, is enough given to determine the size and shape of the triangle?

Questions

Covering the Reading

1. What is a lean-to roof?

2. State the Triangle Inequality.

3. Construct a triangle with sides of the lengths given here.

3 cm

4 cm

5 cm

4. Construct a triangle with sides having the lengths given at the left.

5. If two angles of a triangle have measures $x°$ and $y°$, what is the measure of the third angle?

6. In quadrilateral $ABCD$, $\overline{AC}$ bisects $\angle DAB$ and $\angle DCB$. Why are angles B and D congruent?

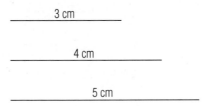

7. Draw a triangle with angles of measures 110° and 30°.

8. Suppose in a triangular sail ABC, m$\angle A = 80$, $AB = 4.5$ meters, and $AC = 2$ meters. Make a scale drawing using centimeters instead of meters as the unit.

9. A triangular plot of land is bounded by side lengths $AB = 250$ feet, $BC = 200$ feet, and $AC = 300$ feet. A surveyor has found that m$\angle A \approx 41$, m$\angle B \approx 83$, and m$\angle C \approx 56$. Draw an accurate picture of this plot of land with 1 inch = 100 feet.

10. Try the construction of Example 1 with these segments. Explain what happens.

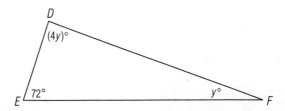

In 11–19, you may use an automatic drawer or any other drawing tools.
   a. Accurately draw a triangle ABC with the given information.
   b. Conjecture whether all other accurately drawn triangles will be congruent to yours.

11. SS condition: $AB = 2''$, $BC = 1\frac{3}{4}''$.

12. AA condition: m$\angle A = 70$, m$\angle B = 38$.

13. SA condition: $AB = 4$ cm, m$\angle A = 60$.

14. SSS condition: $AB = 4$ cm, $BC = 5$ cm, $AC = 6$ cm.

15. AAA condition: m$\angle A = 41$, m$\angle B = 100$, m$\angle C = 39$.

16. SSA condition: $AB = 2''$, $BC = 1''$, m$\angle A = 20$.

17. SAS condition: $AB = 2''$, $BC = 1''$, m$\angle B = 20$.

18. ASA condition: m$\angle A = 55$, $AB = 3''$, m$\angle B = 90$.

19. AAS condition: m$\angle A = 40$, m$\angle B = 60$, $BC = 3$ cm.

20. $\triangle QZP \cong \triangle KRA$. List six pairs of corresponding parts. *(Lesson 6-7)*

21. The composite of two reflections over parallel lines is a(n) __?__ . *(Lesson 6-2)*

22. Find the measures of angles D and F in $\triangle DEF$. *(Lesson 5-7)*

```
        D
       /(4y)°
      /      \
     /        \
    /          \
   / 72°      y° \
  E ──────────────── F
```

23. State the Kite Symmetry Theorem. *(Lesson 5-4)*

24. The measure of an angle is greater than the measure of a complement to it. What can be deduced about this measure? *(Lesson 3-2)*

25. Two sides of a triangle are 91 cm and 38 cm. Give the possible lengths of the third side. *(Lesson 1-9)*

26. Find the congruent copy of each figure at the left in the picture at the right.

book

telephone receiver

car

parrot

roller skate

bell

airplane

bugle

mouse

rooster's head

wool cap

bathrobe

yo-yo

Puritan's hat

"Hidden Pictures" puzzle by Christopher Wray from *Highlights for Children*, July-August, 1986.

LESSON

7-2

Triangle Congruence Theorems

In Lesson 7-1, you drew or constructed a triangle given some lengths of sides or measures of angles. After drawing each triangle, you were asked if everyone else's triangle would be congruent to yours. This is an important question. Stated differently, it is: What is enough about the measures of a triangle's sides and angles so that all triangles drawn with those measures are congruent?

Consider the SSS condition. This means two triangles have three pairs of congruent sides. It can be proved that these triangles are congruent.

SSS Congruence Theorem:

If, in two triangles, three sides of one are congruent to three sides of the other, then the triangles are congruent.

Proof

Given $\overline{AB} \cong \overline{DE}$, $\overline{BC} \cong \overline{EF}$, and $\overline{AC} \cong \overline{DF}$. Here is a possible figure.

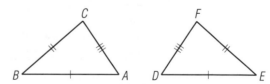

The proof uses the idea of transitivity of congruence. That is, to prove $\triangle ABC \cong \triangle DEF$, we prove that each triangle is congruent to a third triangle. An appropriate third triangle for this task is a nicely located image of $\triangle ABC$ under an isometry.

Since $\overline{AB} \cong \overline{DE}$, there is an isometry which maps $\overline{AB}$ onto $\overline{DE}$. So there is a congruent image $\triangle A'B'C'$ of $\triangle ABC$ which shares a side with $\triangle DEF$. Now $\overline{AC} \cong \overline{A'C'}$ and $\overline{BC} \cong \overline{B'C'}$, so by the Transitive Property of Congruence $\overline{A'C'} \cong \overline{DF}$ and $\overline{B'C'} \cong \overline{EF}$. Thus $\triangle A'B'C'$ and $\triangle DEF$ form a kite. The common side $\overline{DE}$ is the symmetry diagonal of that kite.

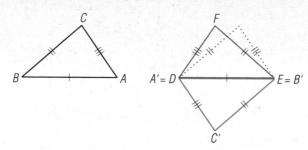

Since this kite is reflection-symmetric to $\overleftrightarrow{DE}$, $\triangle DEF$ is a reflection image of $\triangle A'B'C'$. So, if all three pairs of sides of $\triangle ABC$ and $\triangle DEF$ are congruent, then $\triangle ABC$ can be mapped onto $\triangle DEF$ by an isometry. (First map $\overline{AB}$ onto $\overline{DE}$ as we did, then reflect $\triangle A'B'C'$, the image of $\triangle ABC$, over $\overleftrightarrow{DE}$.) So, by the definition of congruence, $\triangle ABC \cong \triangle DEF$.

For instance, if two triangles have sides with lengths 6.5, 2.8, and 7.0, the triangles are congruent.

Now consider the SAS condition. This refers to two sides and the angle they include (the **included angle**). This information also is enough to make triangles congruent.

SAS Congruence Theorem:

> If, in two triangles, two sides and the included angle of one are congruent to two sides and the included angle of the other, then the triangles are congruent.

Proof

The given here is that $\overline{AB} \cong \overline{DE}$, $\overline{AC} \cong \overline{DF}$, and $\angle A \cong \angle FDE$. (Look carefully at the tick and angle marks. They are the only things making this drawing different from the previous drawing.)

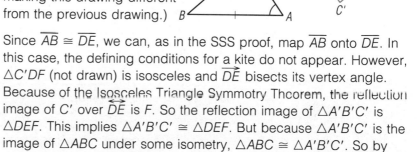

Since $\overline{AB} \cong \overline{DE}$, we can, as in the SSS proof, map $\overline{AB}$ onto $\overline{DE}$. In this case, the defining conditions for a kite do not appear. However, $\triangle C'DF$ (not drawn) is isosceles and $\overrightarrow{DE}$ bisects its vertex angle. Because of the Isosceles Triangle Symmetry Theorem, the reflection image of C' over $\overleftrightarrow{DE}$ is F. So the reflection image of $\triangle A'B'C'$ is $\triangle DEF$. This implies $\triangle A'B'C' \cong \triangle DEF$. But because $\triangle A'B'C'$ is the image of $\triangle ABC$ under some isometry, $\triangle ABC \cong \triangle A'B'C'$. So by the transitivity of congruence, $\triangle ABC \cong \triangle DEF$. This proves that the SAS condition guarantees congruence.

For instance, if two triangles have sides of lengths 4″ and 6″ including an angle of 50°, then the triangles are congruent.

The ASA condition refers to two angles and the side which they include (called the **included side**). This condition also yields congruent triangles.

ASA Congruence Theorem:

If, in two triangles, two angles and the included side of one are congruent to two angles and the included side of the other, then the triangles are congruent.

Proof

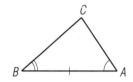

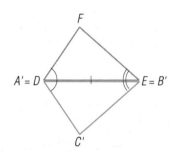

Given $\overline{AB} \cong \overline{DE}$, $\angle A \cong \angle FDE$, and $\angle B \cong \angle FED$, as shown at the left. Again consider the image $\triangle A'B'C'$ of $\triangle ABC$ under an isometry mapping $\overline{AB}$ onto $\overline{DE}$. $\triangle A'B'C'$ and $\triangle DEF$ form a figure much like that in the other two congruence theorems, but with two pairs of congruent angles.

Again, think of reflecting $\triangle A'B'C'$ over line $\overleftrightarrow{DE}$. Applying the Side-Switching Theorem to $\angle C'DF$, the image of $\overrightarrow{A'C'}$ is $\overrightarrow{DF}$. Applying the Side-Switching Theorem to $\angle C'EF$, the image of $\overrightarrow{B'C'}$ is $\overrightarrow{EF}$. This forces the image of C' to be on both $\overrightarrow{DF}$ and $\overrightarrow{EF}$, and so the image of C' is F. Therefore the image of $\triangle A'B'C'$ is $\triangle DEF$.

So if originally two angles and the included side are congruent ($\overline{AB} \cong \overline{DE}$, $\angle A \cong \angle D$, $\angle B \cong \angle E$) then $\triangle ABC$ can be mapped onto $\triangle DEF$ by an isometry exactly as before. (First map $\overline{AB}$ onto $\overline{DE}$ as we did, then reflect the image of $\triangle ABC$ over the line $\overleftrightarrow{DE}$.) Thus, by the definition of congruence, $\triangle ABC \cong \triangle DEF$.

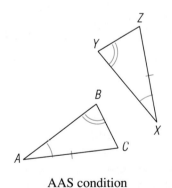

AAS condition

There is another condition to consider: AAS. This means two angles and one pair of *corresponding non-included* sides of two triangles are congruent. The AAS condition leads to congruent triangles because if two pairs of angles are congruent, the third pair is also congruent. For instance, in the diagram at the left, $\angle C \cong \angle Z$. So ASA can be applied to make them congruent. This can always be done.

AAS Congruence Theorem:

If, in two triangles, two angles and a non-included side of one are congruent respectively to two angles and the corresponding non-included side of the other, then the triangles are congruent.

The situation below is not AAS because the congruent sides are not corresponding sides. They are not opposite corresponding angles. Even though the third pair of angles are congruent, you can see that the triangles are not congruent.

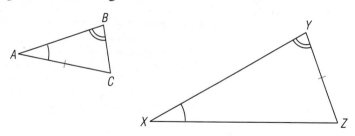

This is not the AAS condition.
(In △ABC and △XYZ, side $\overline{AC}$ does not correspond to side $\overline{YZ}$.)

Example Using only the information marked, is the pair of triangles congruent? Justify each pair of congruent triangles with a triangle congruence theorem.

a. **b.**

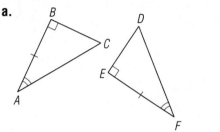

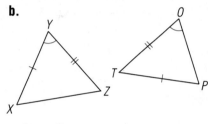

c. **d.**

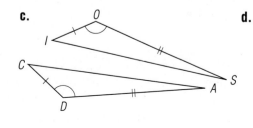

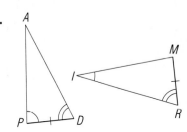

Solution

a. △ABC ≅ △FED by the ASA Congruence Theorem.
b. You cannot conclude that the triangles are congruent. The congruent angles are not included by the corresponding sides in both triangles.
c. △CAD ≅ △ISO by the SAS Congruence Theorem.
d. You cannot conclude that the triangles are congruent. The congruent angles are not in the same relative positions in the triangles.

1. List four conditions that lead to triangle congruence.

2. **a.** *Multiple choice.* The triangle congruence theorems have the same
   (a) antecedent   (b) consequent
   (c) proof   (d) conditional
   b. What words are the same in all the triangle congruence theorems?

3. $\triangle ABC$ has sides of 2, 8, and 7 centimeters. $\triangle DOT$ has sides of 7, 2, and 8 centimeters. What can you conclude about the triangles?

4. In the proof of the SSS Congruence Theorem, the symmetry of what figure is used?

5. In the proof of the SAS Congruence Theorem, the symmetry of what figure is used?

6. *Multiple choice.* What additional information is needed to have the SAS condition in the triangles below?
   (a) $\overline{BC} \cong \overline{DE}$ (b) $\overline{AC} \cong \overline{DE}$
   (c) $\overline{BC} \cong \overline{EF}$ (d) $\overline{AC} \cong \overline{EF}$

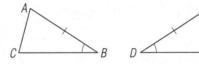

7. State the ASA Congruence Theorem.

8. Use the figure below. In $\triangle ACD$, what side is included by $\angle A$ and $\angle ADC$?

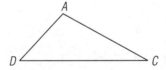

9. Give reasons as found in the proof of the ASA Congruence Theorem. In quadrilateral *EFGH* below, $\overleftrightarrow{FH}$ bisects angles *F* and *H*. Consider $\overleftrightarrow{FH}$ as the reflecting line.

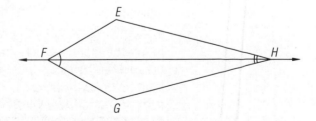

   a. Why is the image of *E* on $\overrightarrow{HG}$?
   b. Why is the image of *E* on $\overrightarrow{FG}$?
   c. Because of the definition of congruence, $\triangle EFH \cong$ ___?___ .

In 10–15, if the given triangles are congruent, explain why they are congruent, and indicate corresponding vertices.

10.

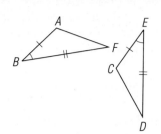

11.

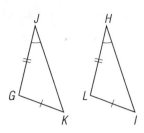

12.

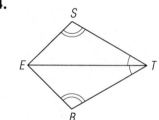

13.

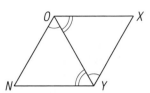

14.

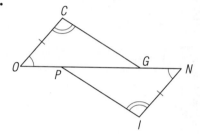

15.

16. Given $\overline{DP} \cong \overline{JK}$, $\overline{DO} \cong \overline{JL}$, $\overline{OP} \cong \overline{LK}$.
   a. $\triangle DPO \cong$ ___?___
   b. If $OD = 5$ yards, then ___?___ is 5 yards.
   c. $\angle O \cong \angle$ ___?___
   d. If $m\angle P = 73$, then ___?___ = 73.

17. a. Construct a triangle DEF with $DE = 6$ cm, $EF = 8$ cm, and $DF = 10$ cm.
   b. Will everyone else's correct drawings be congruent to yours?

18. a. Draw a triangle satisfying the following information. One side has length 2.5″. Two angles have measures 37° and 105°.
   b. Will everyone else's triangles (if correctly drawn) look congruent to yours? Why or why not?

19. a. Draw a triangle with $AB = 3″$, $CA = 2.75″$, and $m\angle CAB = 80$.
   b. Will everyone else's correctly done drawings be congruent to yours? Why or why not?

20. In this sail for a hang glider, seam $\overline{BD}$ bisects $\angle ABC$, and $\angle A \cong \angle C$. Why can you be sure that the cloth used for the left side can be cut from the same pattern outline as the right side?

21. Sally attached three sticks together as shown. She rotated stick A until it made an angle of 23° with the meter stick, and stick B so that it made an angle of 49° with the meter stick. She secured where A and B crossed to make a triangle. Why will anyone get a triangle congruent to hers if they repeat the procedure?

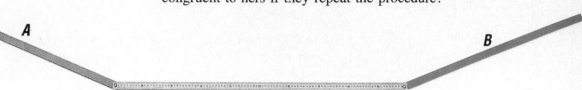

A   B

Review

22. $\triangle ABC \cong \triangle DEF$. If m$\angle A$ = 32 and m$\angle B$ = 64, what is m$\angle F$? *(Lessons 7-1, 6-7)*

23. Arrange in order from most general to most specific: rhombus, figure, square, quadrilateral, kite. *(Lesson 5-2)*

24. Suppose x is the measure of an angle and $360 - 3x < 90$. Is the angle acute, obtuse, or right? *(Lesson 3-2, Previous course)*

Exploration

25. Below, $\triangle ABC \cong \triangle DEF$. Trace this figure. Locate lines ℓ, m, and n so that $r_n \circ r_m \circ r_\ell(\triangle ABC) = \triangle DEF$.

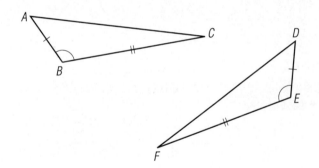

Triangle Congruence Proofs

To use any triangle congruence theorem, you need to know that three parts (SSS, SAS, ASA, or AAS) of one triangle are congruent to the corresponding three parts of another. The particular theorem then enables you to conclude that the triangles are congruent. Because the triangles are congruent, all their corresponding parts are congruent due to the CPCF Theorem. Thus the SSS, SAS, ASA, and AAS theorems enable you to get six pairs of parts congruent where you only had three. That makes them quite powerful.

Example 1   **Given:** $\angle EBA \cong \angle CBD$
$\overline{AB} \cong \overline{BC}$
$\angle A \cong \angle C$.

Prove: $\overline{EB} \cong \overline{DB}$.

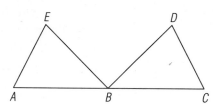

Draw   Copy the figure and mark it with the given information.

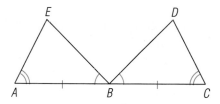

Analyze   Two pairs of angles and their included sides are congruent. This is the ASA condition. To get corresponding parts, the correct order for the vertices of the triangles must be used.

Write   **Given:** $\overline{AB} \cong \overline{BC}$, $\angle EBA \cong \angle CBD$, $\angle A \cong \angle C$.

Conclusions	Justifications
1. $\triangle ABE \cong \triangle CBD$	**ASA Congruence Theorem** (from the given)
2. $\overline{EB} \cong \overline{DB}$	**CPCF Theorem**

Often information is not given in as nice a way as in Example 1. Even so, from given information you can deduce enough to get congruent triangles.

Example 2   **Given:**   *M* is the midpoint of $\overline{CD}$ and $\overline{EF}$.
            Prove: △*CME* ≅ △*DMF*.

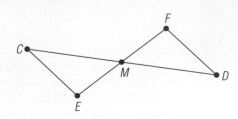

Draw and Analyze   Because *M* is a midpoint of two segments, there are two pairs of equal sides. The intersecting lines form vertical angles which are congruent. Marked in the figure below are two sides and the included angle of each triangle. This is the SAS condition.

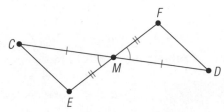

Write   **Given:**   **M is the midpoint of $\overline{CD}$.**
                M is the midpoint of $\overline{EF}$.

Conclusions	Justifications
1. $MC = MD, ME = MF$	definition of midpoint (meaning)
2. ∠*CME* ≅ ∠*DMF*	Vertical Angle Theorem
3. △*CME* ≅ △*DMF*	SAS Congruence Theorem (steps 1 and 2)

There are two things to notice in this proof. First, we use equality of length (or measures) and congruence interchangeably. Second, in the justification for step 3, the part in parentheses refers to the steps in which the corresponding parts were explicitly stated as congruent. You must state these parts either in the given or in the proof before applying a triangle congruence theorem.

In Example 2, you could conclude ∠*E* ≅ ∠*F* by the CPCF Theorem. This in turn enables you to conclude that lines $\overleftrightarrow{EC}$ and $\overleftrightarrow{FD}$ are parallel by the AIA = ⇒ // Lines Theorem. Angles often lead to deductions about parallel lines. This is one of the important features of congruent triangles; they allow deductions to be made about angles and lines.

Example 3   **Given:** $AB = CD$
$BC = AD.$

Prove: $\overline{AB} \parallel \overline{CD}.$

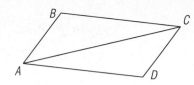

Draw   Copy the figure and mark it with the given information. Label the angles which might help get parallel lines for convenience.

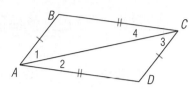

Analyze   The triangles have the side $\overline{AC}$ in common. With the given, this is enough for SSS.

Write   **Given:** $AB = CD, BC = AD.$

Conclusions	Justifications
1. $\overline{AC} \cong \overline{AC}$	Reflexive Property of Congruence
2. $\triangle ABC \cong \triangle CDA$	SSS Congruence Theorem (step 1 and given)
3. $\angle 1 \cong \angle 3$	CPCF Theorem
4. $\overline{AB} \parallel \overline{CD}$	AIA = ⇒ ∥ Lines Theorem

Important theorems can be proved using the triangle congruence theorems. The AAS Congruence Theorem helps to prove the converse of the Isosceles Triangle Theorem.

Theorem:

If two angles of a triangle are congruent, then the sides opposite them are congruent.

Proof

Draw a figure and write the given and prove in terms of that figure.

Given: $\angle B \cong \angle C.$
Prove: $\overline{AB} \cong \overline{AC}.$

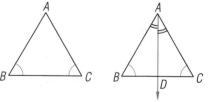

Triangles are needed. By drawing $\overrightarrow{AD}$, the bisector of $\angle A$, there is enough to deduce $\triangle ABD \cong \triangle ACD$.

Conclusions	Justifications
1. $\angle BAD \cong CAD$	def. of angle bisector (meaning)
2. $\overline{AD} \cong \overline{AD}$	?
3. $\triangle ABD \cong \triangle ACD$	AAS Congruence Theorem (steps 1, 2, and given)
4. $\overline{AB} \cong \overline{AC}$	?

You are asked to fill in the missing justifications as Question 5.

These kinds of proofs are helpful in deducing properties of many figures, as you will see. Writing triangle congruence proofs takes some practice; it often takes a while to become proficient.

Questions

Covering the Reading

1. Given: $\angle 1 \cong \angle 2$
   $\overline{AC} \cong \overline{AE}$
   $\overline{AB} \cong \overline{AD}$.
   a. Copy the figure and mark the given on it.
   b. What theorem justifies the congruence of the triangles?
   c. Prove: $\angle B \cong \angle D$.

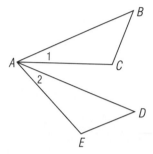

2. Using the figure and given of Example 2, complete this proof that $\overline{EC} \cong \overline{FD}$.

Conclusions	Justifications
1. $MC = MD$, $ME = MF$	a. ?
2. $\angle CME \cong \angle DMF$	b. ?
3. $\triangle CME \cong \triangle DMF$	c. ?
4. $\overline{EC} \cong \overline{FD}$	d. ?

3. Using the figure and given of Example 3, prove $\overleftrightarrow{BC} \parallel \overleftrightarrow{AD}$.

4. Finish this statement of the converse of the Isosceles Triangle Theorem: If two angles of a triangle are congruent, then ? .

5. In the proof of the converse of the Isosceles Triangle Theorem, give a justification for
   a. conclusion 2;   b. conclusion 4.

Applying the Mathematics

6. a. With angle measures as given below, which sides of $\triangle ABC$ are congruent?
   b. What is the justification for your answer to **a**?

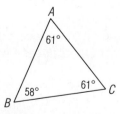

7. Given: $AB = CD$
   $BC = AD$.
   Prove: $\triangle ABC \cong \triangle CDA$.

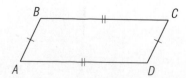

8. Use the figure at the right. Supply the missing justifications.

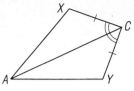

Given: $\overrightarrow{CA}$ bisects $\angle XCY$.
 $XC = YC$.
Prove: $\angle X \cong \angle Y$.

Conclusions	Justifications
1. $\overline{AC} \cong \overline{AC}$	a. <u> ? </u>
2. $\angle XCA \cong \angle YCA$	b. <u> ? </u>
3. $\triangle ACX \cong \triangle ACY$	c. <u> ? </u>
4. $\angle X \cong \angle Y$	d. <u> ? </u>

9. Use the figure at the right.

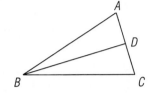

Given: $\triangle ABC$ is isosceles with vertex angle B. D is the midpoint of $\overline{AC}$.
Prove: $\triangle ABD \cong \triangle CBD$.

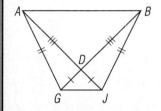

10. a. List all eight triangles in the figure at the left.
 b. From the marked information, there are three pairs of triangles which can be proved congruent. Name them, with vertices in corresponding order.

Review

11. Tony and Trisha each made a triangle out of straws with lengths 3 cm, 4 cm, and 6 cm. *True* or *false*?
 a. The two triangles must be congruent.
 b. The two triangles must have the same orientation.
 (Lessons 7-2, 7-1)

12. Explain why the SAS Congruence Theorem cannot be used to prove $\triangle ADC$ congruent to $\triangle ABC$ in the figure below. *(Lesson 7-2)*

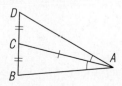

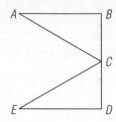

13. Given: *C* is the midpoint of $\overline{BD}$. *AC = EC*.
∠*ACB* ≅ ∠*DCE*.
Why are the triangles congruent? *(Lesson 7-2)*

14. Electric wires run from post to post over the buildings shown below. We can't measure the length of wire needed because the buildings are in the way. Place a stake at *H*. Then mark off *J* on $\overleftrightarrow{FH}$ so that *FH = HJ*. Now mark off *I* on $\overleftrightarrow{GH}$ so that *GH = HI*. What triangle congruence theorem indicates that △*FGH* ≅ △*JIH* so that the distance from *I* to *J* is equal to the distance between the posts? *(Lessons 7-2, 6-7)*

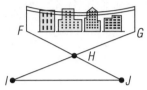

15. Draw a triangle with sides 3 cm, 11 cm, and 6 cm. *(Lesson 7-1)*

In 16 and 17, all five segments in the figure below are congruent.

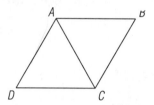

16. Make and justify at least two conclusions from this given information. *(Lessons 5-4, 5-3, 4-2)*

17. If the perimeter of *ABCD* is *x*, what is the length of $\overline{AC}$? *(Previous course)*

18. The sum of the measures of the acute angles in a right triangle is __?__. *(Lesson 5-7)*

19. a. Draw a figure to test this conjecture: If the midpoints of the sides of a rhombus are connected in order, the resulting figure is a square.
b. Do you think the conjecture is true? *(Lesson 5-3)*

Exploration

20. a. What would be an SSSS condition for two quadrilaterals to be congruent?
b. Show by drawing a counterexample that there is no SSSS Congruence Theorem for quadrilaterals.

7-4

Overlapping Triangles

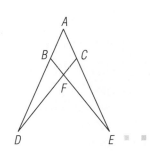

How many triangles do you see in the figure at the left? At first, many people see only the small triangles *BFD* and *CFE*. But there are **overlapping triangles** *ACD* and *ABE*. Given appropriate information, these triangles can be proved congruent just as other triangles can.

Example 1 In the figure at the left above, if *AC* = *AB* and *AD* = *AE*, prove ∠*D* ≅ ∠*E*.

Analyze It may seem that the triangles to use are the small triangles *BFD* and *CFE*. But no sides or angles of these triangles are given as congruent. So try the overlapping triangles, △*ACD* and △*ABE*. At the beginning you may have to draw the figure twice to see the triangles. Mark the figure with the given information.

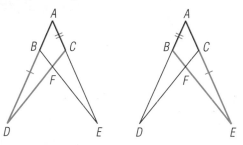

Notice that although only two sides are given congruent, there is a common angle, ∠*A*.

Write Given: *AC* = *AB* and *AD* = *AE*.

Conclusions	Justifications
1. ∠*A* ≅ ∠*A*	**Reflexive Property of Congruence**
2. △*ADC* ≅ △*AEB*	**SAS Congruence Theorem (step 1 and given)**
3. ∠*D* ≅ ∠*E*	**CPCF Theorem**

With overlapping triangles, keeping track of corresponding vertices can be tricky. As you deduce congruent sides or angles, mark the figure.

Example 2 **Given:** $\overline{GH} \cong \overline{GK}$
$\overline{GJ} \cong \overline{GI}.$
Prove: $\overline{HJ} \cong \overline{KI}.$

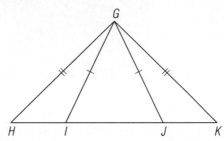

Analyze $\overline{HJ}$ and $\overline{KI}$ are sides of the overlapping triangles *GHJ* and *GKI*. So it is natural to try to prove these triangles congruent. Also, the marked congruent sides mean that $\triangle GIJ$ and $\triangle GHK$ are isosceles, so their base angles are congruent. This is enough.

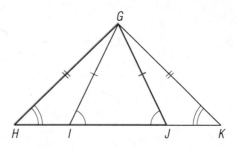

Write

Conclusions	Justifications
1. $\angle H \cong \angle K$	**Isosceles Triangle Thoerem (with $\triangle GHK$)**
2. $\angle GJI \cong \angle GIJ$	**Isosceles Triangle Theorem (with $\triangle GIJ$)**
3. $\triangle GHJ \cong \triangle GKI$	**AAS Congruence Theorem (steps 1, 2, and given)**
4. $\overline{HJ} \cong \overline{KI}$	**CPCF Theorem**

Notice that the proof in Example 2 uses the AAS Congruence Theorem, not SAS or SSS, even though two pairs of congruent segments are given. When you analyze a problem, don't be limited by the most obvious clues. Also notice that in Step 3, it does not matter whether the proof used $\overline{GH} \cong \overline{GK}$ or $\overline{GJ} \cong \overline{GI}$.

1. Use the figure below.
   a. How many triangles are in the figure?
   b. It looks like △*QUA* is congruent to what other triangle?
   c. Find a second pair of overlapping triangles that seem congruent.

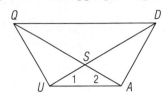

2. Using the diagram and given of Example 1, fill in justifications in the proof that ∠*DCA* ≅ ∠*EBA*.

Conclusions	Justifications
1. ∠*A* ≅ ∠*A*	a. ___?___
2. △*ADC* ≅ △*AEB*	b. ___?___
3. ∠*DCA* ≅ ∠*EBA*	c. ___?___

3. Using the figure and given of Example 2, prove that
   ∠*HGJ* ≅ ∠*KGI*.

4. In the figure of Question 1, suppose $\overline{QU} \cong \overline{AD}$ and $\overline{QA} \cong \overline{UD}$.
   Prove: ∠1 ≅ ∠2.

5. Given: *AD* = *AE*
              m∠*D* = m∠*E*.
   Prove: *EB* = *CD*.

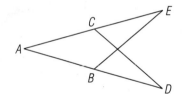

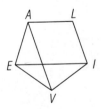

6. In pentagon *ALIVE* at the left, $\overline{AE} \cong \overline{IV}$ and ∠*AEV* ≅ ∠*EVI*.
   Prove that $\overline{AV} \cong \overline{IE}$.

7. Given: *PR* = *QS*
              PS = *QR*.
   Prove: m∠*P* = m∠*Q*.

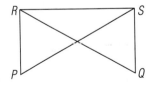

8. Given: *G, J, K,* and *H* are collinear.
              $\overline{GJ} \cong \overline{HK}$ and $\overline{GI} \cong \overline{HI}$.
   Prove: $\overline{JI} \cong \overline{KI}$. *(Lesson 7-3)*

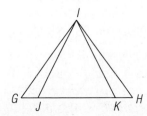

9. Given that $\overline{DF}$ and $\overline{AG}$ intersect at E with segments equal as marked, justify each conclusion in this proof that $\angle FGE \cong \angle DBC$. *(Lessons 7-3, 6-7, 4-4)*

Given: $AE = EF$; $EG = EB$.

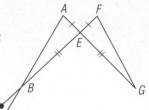

Conclusions	Justifications
1. $\angle AEB \cong \angle FEG$	**a.** ?
2. $\triangle ABE \cong \triangle FGE$	**b.** ?
3. $\angle FGE \cong \angle ABE$	**c.** ?
4. $\angle ABE \cong \angle DBC$	**d.** ?
5. $\angle FGE \cong \angle DBC$	**e.** ?

10. Given: $\overline{QR} \parallel \overline{TU}$
S is the midpoint of $\overline{QU}$.

Prove: S is the midpoint of $\overline{RT}$. *(Lesson 7-3)*

11. $\overline{PC}$ is a vertical radio tower supported by the taut guy wires $\overline{PA}$ and $\overline{PB}$. Explain why the guy wires will have the same length if they are attached to level ground at the same distance from C. *(Lessons 7-3, 7-2)*

12. a. Draw a triangle with $AB = 6.5$ cm, $BC = 4$ cm, and $m\angle A = 32$.
b. Will everyone else's correct drawing be congruent to yours? *(Lessons 7-2, 7-1)*

In 13 and 14, *QRST* at the right is the translation image of *MNOP*.
True or *false*? *(Lessons 6-7, 6-6)*

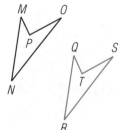

13. $MNOP \cong QRST$

14. $MQ = OS$

15. If y is the measure of an angle and $0 < 180 - 2y$, is the angle acute, obtuse, or right? *(Lesson 3-2)*

16. Below, $WY = 13$, $WZ = 25$, and $XZ = 17$. Find WX. *(Lesson 10-8)*

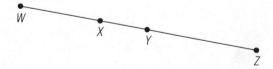

17. Is there an SSASS Congruence Theorem for quadrilaterals?

LESSON 7-5

The SSA Condition and HL Congruence

The distance of the children from the maypole is determined by the height of the pole and the length of the streamer. See Question 13.

Since there are AAS and ASA Congruence Theorems and there is a congruence theorem with 2 sides and an included angle (SAS), it is natural to ask what happens if the angle is not included. We call this the **SSA condition.**

Examine $\triangle ABC$ and $\triangle XYZ$ below. There are two pairs of congruent sides, $\overline{AB} \cong \overline{XY}$ and $\overline{BC} \cong \overline{YZ}$. Also, there is a pair of corresponding non-included angles, $\angle A \cong \angle X$.

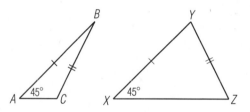

But clearly the triangles are not congruent. In fact, a translation image of $\triangle ABC$ fits nicely into $\triangle XYZ$.

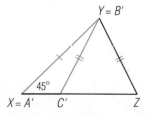

Thus, in general, the SSA condition does not guarantee the congruence of triangles. However, when the corresponding non-included angles are right angles, the situation is different. Recall that in a right triangle, the **legs** are the sides that include the right angle while the **hypotenuse** is the side opposite the right angle. Suppose

$BC = YZ$, $AB = XY$, and $\angle C$ and $\angle Z$ are right angles as shown in the triangles below. This is the **hypotenuse-leg** or **HL condition.** This is enough to guarantee congruence.

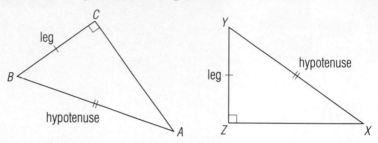

HL Congruence Theorem:

If, in two right triangles, the hypotenuse and a leg of one are congruent to the hypotenuse and a leg of the other, then the two triangles are congruent.

Proof

Given: $\overline{BC} \cong \overline{YZ}$; $\overline{AB} \cong \overline{XY}$.
$\angle C$ and $\angle Z$ are both right angles.
Prove: $\triangle ABC \cong \triangle XYZ$.

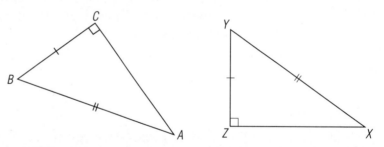

Since $\overline{BC} \cong \overline{YZ}$, there is a composite of reflections that maps $\overline{BC}$ onto $\overline{YZ}$, with the image of A on the other side of $\overline{YZ}$ from X. This gives the figure below, in which $\triangle ABC \cong \triangle A'B'C'$.

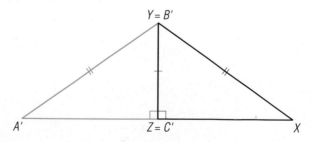

By Angle Addition, $m\angle A'ZX = 180$, so A', Z, and X are collinear. Since $\overline{AB} \cong \overline{XY}$ and $\overline{AB} \cong \overline{A'B'}$, by the Transitive Property of Congruence, $\overline{A'B'} \cong \overline{XY}$. This makes $\triangle A'YX$ a big isosceles triangle. Applying the Isosceles Triangle Theorem, $\angle A' \cong \angle X$. Thus by the AAS Congruence Theorem, $\triangle A'B'C' \cong \triangle XYZ$, making $\triangle ABC \cong \triangle XYZ$, again by the Transitive Property of Congruence.

Example 1 The triangles in the figure below are congruent. For each pair of triangles, indicate the corresponding vertices and the theorem that justifies the congruence.

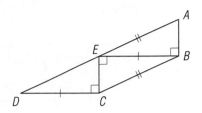

Solution
1. △*ABE* ≅ △*CEB* by HL Congruence.
2. △*CEB* ≅ △*ECD* by SAS Congruence.
3. △*ABE* ≅ △*ECD* by the Transitive of Property of Congruence.

Example 2 Given △*ABC* and △*POT* with the congruent parts marked, make and justify at least three conclusions.

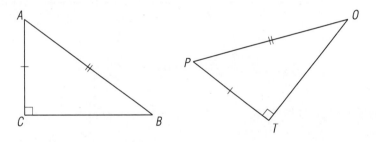

Solution Here are two conclusions you could have made before studying this chapter.

Conclusion	Justification
1. △*ABC* is a right triangle.	definition of right △ (suff. cond.)
2. m∠*B* + m∠*A* = 90	Triangle-Sum Theorem

Here are four conclusions possible because of triangle congruence ideas.

3. △*ABC* ≅ △*POT*	HL Congruence Theorem (step 1 and given)
4. ∠*A* ≅ ∠*P*	CPCF Theorem
5. $\overline{BC}$ ≅ $\overline{OT}$	CPCF Theorem
6. ∠*O* ≅ ∠*B*	CPCF Theorem

The HL condition is the special case of SSA when the congruent angles are right angles. Because we could deduce an HL Congruence Theorem, the SSA condition works sometimes. A natural question is: Does the SSA condition give congruent triangles at any other time? The answer is "Yes." It is written as the *SsA Congruence Theorem* since, for it to work, the sides opposite the congruent angles in each triangle must be longer than the other congruent sides. It is presented here without a proof because the proof is quite difficult.

SsA Congruence Theorem:

If, in two triangles, two sides and the angle opposite the longer of the two sides in one are congruent respectively to two sides and the angle opposite the corresponding side in the other, then the triangles are congruent.

If $\overline{AB} \cong \overline{XY}$, $\overline{AC} \cong \overline{XZ}$, $\angle C \cong \angle Z$, and $AB > AC$ (so $XY > XZ$ by substitution), then $\triangle ABC \cong \triangle XYZ$.

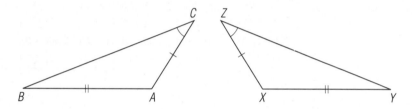

Questions

Covering the Reading

1. Draw two noncongruent triangles satisfying the SSA condition.

2. **a.** What kind of triangle has sides represented by H and L?
   b. What does H stand for? What does L stand for?

3. *Multiple choice.* Which of these justifications is not used in the proof of the HL Congruence Theorem?
   (a) AAS Congruence Theorem   (b) Isosceles Triangle Theorem
   (c) Triangle-Sum Theorem   (d) Angle Addition Property

4. When does the SSA condition lead to congruence?

In 5–7, use the information given in the figure. **a.** What triangle congruence theorem tells you that the pair of triangles is congruent? **b.** Write the congruent triangles with vertices correctly corresponding.

5.   **6.**   **7.**

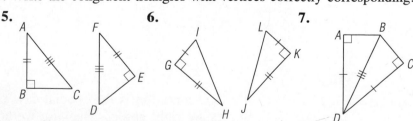

8. Follow the steps to make a single drawing of a triangle given the SSA condition.
  a. Draw a ray $\overrightarrow{XY}$.
  b. Draw an $\angle ZXY$ with measure 50° and with $XZ = 11$ cm.
  c. Draw circle Z with radius 9 cm. Let W be a point of intersection of $\odot Z$ and $\overrightarrow{XY}$.
  d. Consider $\triangle XZW$. Will everyone else who does this correctly have a triangle XZW congruent to yours?

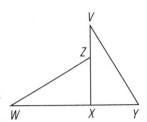

9. Use the figure at the left.
  Given: $\overline{VX} \perp \overline{WY}$
  $WZ = VY$
  $XZ = XY$.
  Prove: $\angle W \cong \angle V$.

10. Use the figure at the right.
  Given: $AP = AR$,
  $\angle P$ and $\angle R$ are right angles.
  Prove: **a.** $\triangle PBA \cong \triangle RBA$
  b. $PBRA$ is a kite.
  c. a different conclusion of your own choosing

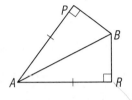

11. Two circles are **concentric** if they have the same center. The concentric circles below have center O, with $OQ > OP$. If $\angle OAB \cong \angle OPQ$, complete the proof that $\triangle ABO \cong \triangle PQO$.

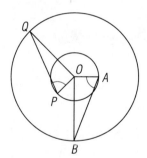

Given: $OQ > OP$, $\angle OAB \cong \angle OPQ$

Conclusions	Justifications
1. $OP = OA$	**a.** ?
2. $OQ = OB$	**b.** ?
3. $\triangle ABO \cong \triangle PQO$	**c.** ?

12. Use the figure at the right.
  Given: $\overline{BD} \perp \overline{AC}$
  $AB = BC$.
  Prove: $\triangle ABD \cong \triangle CBD$.

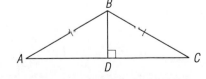

13. June and April are dancing around the maypole. The streamers they are holding are the same length. If June's and April's hands are the same height, explain why their hands are also the same distance from the maypole.

Review

14. Fill in the justifications in this proof that the diagonals of an isosceles trapezoid are congruent. *(Lessons 7-4, 5-5)*

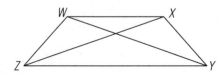

Given: *WXYZ* is an isosceles trapezoid with bases $\overline{WX}$ and $\overline{ZY}$.
Prove: $\overline{XZ} \cong \overline{WY}$.

Conclusions		Justifications
1. $\angle WZY \cong \angle XYZ$	**a.**	?
2. $\overline{WZ} \cong \overline{XY}$	**b.**	?
3. $\overline{ZY} \cong \overline{ZY}$	**c.**	?
4. $\triangle WZY \cong \triangle XYZ$	**d.**	?
5. $\overline{XZ} \cong \overline{WY}$	**e.**	?

15. Use the figure at the right.
Given: $AB = AC$, $BD = CE$.
Prove:
a. $\angle ADE \cong \angle AED$
b. $\triangle ADE$ is isosceles. *(Lessons 7-4, 7-3)*

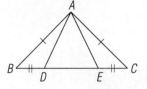

16. Find all triangles congruent to $\triangle AGX$, given $\overline{AB} \perp \overline{XY}$ and the figure at the left as marked. *(Lesson 7-2)*

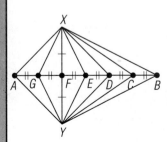

17. **a.** Draw $\triangle QRS$ with m$\angle Q$ = 45, m$\angle R$ = 80, and $RS = 2''$.
    b. Will everyone else's correct drawing be congruent to yours? Explain why or why not. *(Lessons 7-2, 7-1)*

18. Suppose r($\triangle ABC$) = $\triangle DEF$. State a conclusion which follows due to each justification. *(Lessons 6-5, 4-5, 4-2)*
    a. definition of congruence
    b. Flip-Flop Theorem
    c. Figure Reflection Theorem

Exploration

19. Explore this conjecture. If, in quadrilaterals *ABCD* and *EFGH*, angles *A, C, E,* and *G* are right angles, $AB = EF$, and $BC = FG$, then the quadrilaterals are congruent.

7-6

Properties of Special Figures

Soccer balls are constructed from regular pentagons and regular hexagons.

An important use of the triangle congruence theorems is to deduce properties of special figures. *PARL* below is a parallelogram. Its diagonals, $\overline{PR}$ and $\overline{AL}$, form 4 nonoverlapping triangles and four overlapping triangles. (Do you see these eight triangles?) Pairs of these triangles can be proved congruent and, from the congruences, many properties of *PARL* can be deduced. Because *PARL* is not otherwise special in any way, these properties are true in any parallelogram.

Example   **Given:**   Parallelogram *PARL*.

Prove:
1. $\triangle RPL \cong \triangle PRA$
2. $\overline{PA} \cong \overline{RL}, \overline{PL} \cong \overline{RA}$
3. $EP = ER$.

Draw   The figure is marked. Some of the angles which may be used are numbered.

Analyze
1. There is a common side to $\triangle RPL$ and $\triangle PRA$. Each pair of parallel sides makes a pair of congruent alternate interior angles. This is sufficient for congruence of the triangles.
2. These are corresponding parts of $\triangle RPL$ and $\triangle PRA$.
3. Show $\triangle ERL \cong \triangle EPA$ to get $EP = ER$ by corresponding parts.

Write

Conclusions	Justifications
1. $\overline{PA} \parallel \overline{LR}$	def. of parallelogram (meaning)
2. $\angle 1 \cong \angle 2$	// Lines $\Rightarrow$ AIA = Theorem
3. $\overline{PL} \parallel \overline{AR}$	___?___
4. $\angle 5 \cong \angle 6$	___?___
5. $\overline{PR} \cong \overline{RP}$	___?___
6. $\triangle RPL \cong \triangle PRA$	___?___ (This proves 1.)
7. $\overline{PA} \cong \overline{RL}, \overline{PL} = \overline{RA}$	CPCF Theorem (This proves 2.)
8. $\angle 3 \cong \angle 4$	Vertical Angle Theorem
9. $\triangle ERL \cong \triangle EPA$	AAS Congruence Theorem (Steps 2, 7, 8)
10. $EP = ER$	CPCF Theorem (This proves 3.)

You are asked to fill in the missing justifications in Question 1.

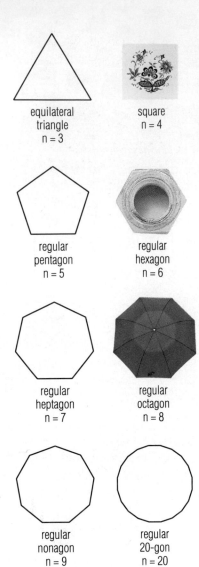

equilateral triangle
n = 3

square
n = 4

regular pentagon
n = 5

regular hexagon
n = 6

regular heptagon
n = 7

regular octagon
n = 8

regular nonagon
n = 9

regular 20-gon
n = 20

Regular *n*-gons

Another type of figure which lends itself to congruent triangles is the *regular polygon*.

Definition:

A **regular polygon** is a convex polygon whose angles are all congruent and whose sides are all congruent.

The regular polygons with 3 sides are the equilateral triangles. Those with 4 sides are squares. Otherwise they are simply called regular pentagons, regular hexagons, and so on.

In the Example, the given was simply a parallelogram, yet many properties were deduced. The final conclusion $EP = ER$ implies E is the midpoint of $\overline{PR}$. Since we could have substituted diagonal $\overline{LA}$ for $\overline{PR}$, E is also the midpoint of $\overline{LA}$. Thus, this one proof has proved the following properties of parallelograms.

Properties of a Parallelogram Theorem:

In any parallelogram:
a. each diagonal forms two congruent triangles;
b. opposite sides are congruent;
c. the diagonals intersect at their midpoints.

Because of the Quadrilateral Hierarchy Theorem, you can further conclude that the properties of parallelograms apply to all rhombuses, rectangles, and squares.

A corollary of the Properties of a Parallelogram Theorem involves the distance between parallel lines. This result is important for deducing area formulas, as you will see in the next chapter.

Theorem:

The distance between parallel lines is constant.

Proof

Given: $\ell \parallel m$, $\overline{AB} \perp \ell$, $\overline{XY} \perp \ell$.
Prove: $\overline{AB} \cong \overline{XY}$.

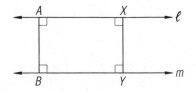

We know that $\overline{AB} \perp m$ and $\overline{XY} \perp m$ by the Perpendicular to Parallels Theorem. So AB and XY are distances between ℓ and m.

Also, *ABYX* satisfies the sufficient condition for a rectangle. Since opposite sides of any parallelogram are congruent, opposite sides of this rectangle are congruent. So $\overline{AB} \cong \overline{XY}$.

In Lesson 4-5, you learned how to construct the circle through three non-collinear points. Thus there is a circle which contains all the vertices of an equilateral triangle. Now think of squares. Because the diagonals of a square bisect each other (part **c** of the Properties of a Parallelogram Theorem) and because the diagonals have equal length (a square is a rectangle), the intersection of the diagonals of a square is the center of a circle which contains all the vertices of the square.

Using congruent triangles, this result can be extended to apply to all regular polygons.

Center of a Regular Polygon Theorem:

> In any regular polygon there is a point (its center) which is equidistant from all its vertices.

Proof

Analyze Since the theorem is known to be true for regular polygons of 3 and 4 sides, the cases that need to be dealt with have 5 or more sides. What is done is to show that the circle through three consecutive vertices of the regular polygon contains the next vertex. Then that fourth vertex can be used with two others to obtain the fifth, and so on, as many times as needed.

Given: regular polygon *ABCD*...
Prove: There is a point *O* equidistant from *A, B, C, D*, ...

Draw *ABCD*... at the left.

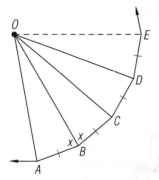

Write Let *O* be the center of the circle containing *A, B*, and *C*. Then *OA = OB = OC*. Since *AB = BC* by the definition of regular polygon, *OABC* is a kite with symmetry diagonal $\overline{OB}$. Thus $\overrightarrow{BO}$ bisects ∠*ABC*. Let *x* = m∠*ABO* = m∠*OBC*. Since △*OBC* is isosceles, m∠*OBC* = m∠*OCB* = *x*. Now the measures of the angles of the regular polygon are equal to 2*x*, so m∠*OCD* = *x* also. Then △*OCB* ≅ △*OCD* by the SAS Congruence Theorem, and so by the CPCT Theorem, *OC* = *OD*.

The Center of a Regular Polygon Theorem implies that there is a circle which contains all the vertices of a regular polygon. This enables regular polygons to be drawn quite easily. Draw the circle first and equally space the vertices of the polygon around the circle.

Questions

Covering the Reading

1. Fill in the missing justifications in the proof in the Example.

2. Consider parallelogram *ABDC*.
   a. Which sides are congruent?
   b. Which angles are congruent?
   c. The midpoints of __?__ and __?__ are the same.

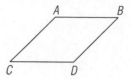

3. Repeat Question 2, but suppose *ABDC* is a rhombus.

4. *ZQID* below is a trapezoid with bases $\overline{ZO}$ and $\overline{ID}$. $\overleftrightarrow{ZO} \perp \overline{DR}$. $\overleftrightarrow{ID} \perp \overline{PO}$.
   a. Which two segments are congruent?
   b. What theorem justifies your answer to part **a**?

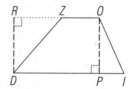

5. A regular polygon with four sides is usually called a(n) __?__ .

6. a. Draw a regular hexagon.
   b. Draw a regular heptagon.

Applying the Mathematics

7. Prove: If *ABCDE* is a regular pentagon, then $\overline{AC} \cong \overline{AD}$.

8. a. In rectangle *RIGH* with diagonals intersecting at *T*, how many triangles are formed?
   b. Arrange them in sets of congruent triangles.

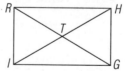

In 9 and 10, *OPQR* at the left is a parallelogram.

9. If *OQ = PR = x*, find as many lengths in terms of *x* as you can.

10. If m∠*POR* = 102, find as many other angle measures as you can.

11. a. Draw a regular decagon.
    b. What is the sum of the measures of the angles of a regular decagon?
    c. What is the measure of each angle of a regular decagon?

12. Construct equilateral triangles *AOB, BOC, COD, DOE, EOF*, and *FOA* where points *A, B, C, D, E*, and *F* are distinct, coplanar points.
    a. What kind of figure is *ABCDEF*?
    b. Justify your answer to part **a**.

336

13. In quadrilateral *ABCF* below, $\overline{AE} \perp \overline{CF}$ and $\overline{BD} \perp \overline{CF}$. Also, $AE = BD$ and $AF = BC$. Prove that $\angle F \cong \angle C$. *(Lesson 7-5)*

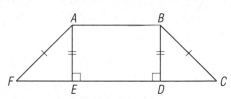

14. In right triangles *ABC* and *XYZ* below, two sides and an angle of one are congruent to two sides and an angle of the other. Why aren't the triangles congruent? *(Lesson 7-5)*

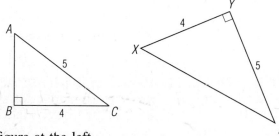

15. Use the figure at the left.
Given: *X* is the midpoint of $\overline{MN}$.
$\angle M \cong \angle N$
$\angle MXZ \cong \angle NXY$.
Prove: $\angle Y \cong \angle Z$. *(Lesson 7-4)*

16. Use the figure below.
Given: $\triangle PTS$ is isosceles with vertex angle *T*, and
$m\angle PTQ = m\angle STR$.
Prove: **a.** $\triangle TPQ \cong \triangle TSR$; **b.** $\triangle TQR$ is isosceles. *(Lesson 7-3)*

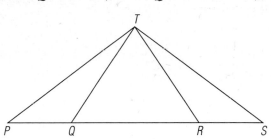

17. a. Draw a triangle with sides of length 2″, 3.5″, and a 90° angle included by them.
b. Will everyone's correct drawing of this triangle be congruent to yours? Explain your answer. *(Lessons 7-2, 7-1)*

18. Justify the conclusion. *(Lessons 3-5, 3-3)*
Given: $\overline{AB} \perp m$, $\overline{CD} \perp m$.
Conclusion: $\overline{AB} \parallel \overline{CD}$.

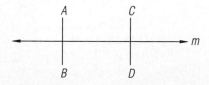

19. Below, $\overline{AB} \cong \overline{XY}$ and $\angle A \cong \angle Y$. Name three additional pieces of information each of which is enough to guarantee congruence of the triangles and name the appropriate congruence theorem to justify. *(Lesson 7-2)*

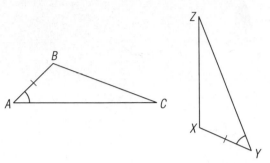

20. Write a true if-then statement whose converse is false. *(Lesson 2-4)*

Exploration

21. Regular pentagon *ABCDE* and its diagonals are drawn.
  a. How many triangles are in the drawing?
  b. Sort the triangles into sets of congruent triangles.

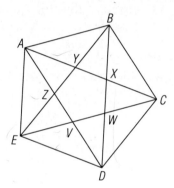

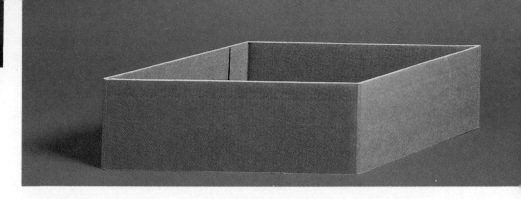

7-7

Sufficient Conditions for Parallelograms

Pictured above is a rectangular box with its top and bottom re-moved, so it is no longer rigid. If you are careful not to bend the sides, then the colored edge always seems to be a parallelogram. This can be proved with the help of the triangle congruence theorems.

To determine what is given in this proof, note that the box once was rectangular, so opposite sides are known to be of the same length. But the angles can now change; they no longer must be right angles. Using only the fact that opposite sides have the same length, you can prove that the quadrilateral is a parallelogram. This is done in Example 1.

■ ■ ■ ■ ■ ■ ■ ■ ■ ■

Example 1   **Prove:**   If both pairs of opposite sides of a quadrilateral are congruent, the quadrilateral is a parallelogram.

Draw   Use a representative figure and restate the theorem in terms of the figure.

Given: Quadrilateral $ABCD$.
         $\overline{AB} \cong \overline{CD}$; $\overline{AD} \cong \overline{BC}$.

Prove: $ABCD$ is a parallelogram.

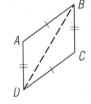

Analyze   If a diagonal is drawn, then the triangles formed are congruent. This gives enough to deduce that opposite sides are parallel.

Write

Conclusions	Justifications
1. Draw $\overline{BD}$.	Two points determine a line. (Point-Line Postulate)
2. $\overline{BD} \cong \overline{DB}$	Reflexive Property of $\cong$
3. $\triangle ABD \cong \triangle CDB$	SSS Congruence Theorem (Step 2 and given)
4. $\angle ABD \cong \angle CDB$	CPCF Theorem
5. $\overline{AB} \parallel \overline{CD}$	AIA $= \Rightarrow \parallel$ Lines Theorem
6. $\angle ADB \cong \angle CBD$	___?___
7. $\overline{AD} \parallel \overline{BC}$	___?___
8. $ABCD$ is a parallelogram.	definition of parallelogram (sufficient condition)

Question 5 asks you to fill in the missing justifications.

You should verify the result of Example 1 by trying to draw a plane figure with opposite sides congruent that is not a parallelogram. It can't be done.

Example 1 shows that both pairs of opposite sides being congruent is a *sufficient condition* for a quadrilateral to be a parallelogram. In general, *p* is a **sufficient condition** for *q* means *if p, then q* or *p implies q*. Sufficient conditions for parallelograms are any conditions that imply a figure is a parallelogram.

Pictured below are three quadrilaterals having *one pair of sides both parallel and congruent*. In each, $\overline{WX} \parallel \overline{YZ}$ and $WX = YZ$.

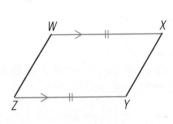 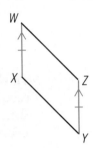 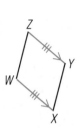

These quadrilaterals appear to be parallelograms. Thus this condition *may* be a sufficient condition. In Example 2, it is proved to be so.

Example 2 **Prove:** If a quadrilateral has a pair of sides both parallel and congruent, the quadrilateral is a parallelogram.

Draw Draw a figure and restate the given in terms of the figure.

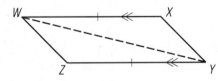

Given: WXYZ is a quadrilateral with $\overline{WX} \parallel \overline{YZ}$ and $WX = YZ$.
Prove: WXYZ is a parallelogram.
Analyze Again, a diagonal forms triangles that are congruent. The proof is similar to that in Example 1 and you are asked to fill in the justifications in Question 7.

Write

Conclusions	Justifications
1. Draw $\overline{WY}$.	?
2. $WY = WY$	?
3. $m\angle XWY = m\angle ZYW$	?
4. $\triangle WZY \cong \triangle YXW$	?
5. $m\angle ZWY = m\angle XYW$	?
6. $\overline{WZ} \parallel \overline{XY}$	?
7. WXYZ is a parallelogram.	?

Examples 1 and 2 have proved parts **(a)** and **(d)** of the following theorem. Parts **(b)** and **(c)** are left for you to do in Questions 10 and 11.

Sufficient Conditions for a Parallelogram Theorem:

If, in a quadrilateral,

    (a) both pairs of opposite sides are congruent, or
    (b) both pairs of opposite angles are congruent, or
    (c) the diagonals bisect each other, or
    (d) one pair of sides is parallel and congruent,

then the quadrilateral is a parallelogram.

Notice that all four parts **(a)–(d)** are converses of properties of parallelograms. But beware. Not all converses of properties are true. Consider this property of rectangles.

If a quadrilateral is a rectangle, its diagonals are congruent.

The converse of this theorem is

If the diagonals of a quadrilateral are congruent, then it is a rectangle.

To prove this converse is *not* true, a counterexample is all that is needed. Recall that a counterexample to an if-then statement is a situation in which the antecedent is true and the consequent is false. Here are two counterexamples to the above converse.

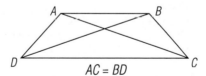
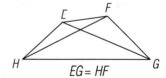

quadrilaterals with congruent diagonals that are not rectangles

Questions

Covering the Reading

1. Give three properties of parallelograms.

2. According to its definition, what is a sufficient condition for a figure to be a parallelogram?

3. Give four sufficient conditions for parallelograms.

4. Name a property of a rectangle whose converse is not a sufficient condition for a rectangle.

In 5 and 6, consider the proof of Example 1.

5. Write the justifications for Steps 6 and 7.

6. Suppose auxiliary segment $\overline{AC}$ was drawn instead of $\overline{BD}$. Prove the theorem using $\overline{AC}$ instead of $\overline{BD}$.

7. Finish the proof of Example 2.

Applying the Mathematics

8. Prove or disprove: If quadrilateral $ABCD$ has $\overline{AB} \parallel \overline{CD}$ and $\angle A \cong \angle C$, then $ABCD$ is a parallelogram.

9. Two yardsticks and two meter sticks are joined end to end to form a quadrilateral. What possible quadrilaterals can be formed?

10. Finish the proof of part (b) of the Sufficient Conditions for a Parallelogram Theorem.

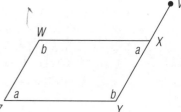

Part (b): If opposite angles of a quadrilateral are congruent, then the quadrilateral is a parallelogram.
Given: Quadrilateral $WXYZ$
  $m\angle W = m\angle Y$
  $m\angle WXY = m\angle Z$.
Prove: $WXYZ$ is a parallelogram.

Let $m\angle WXY = m\angle Z = a$ and $m\angle Y = m\angle W = b$.
Now $a + b + a + b = 360$ so $2a + 2b = 360$
or $a + b = 180$. Thus $b = 180 - a$. The rest of the proof is in column format.

Conclusions	Justifications
1. $m\angle W = m\angle Y = 180 - a$	Substitution
2. $m\angle WXV + a = 180$	**a.** ?
3. $m\angle WXV = 180 - a$	Addition Property of Equality
4. $m\angle WXV = m\angle W$	Substitution (Step 1 into 3)
5. $\overline{WZ} \parallel \overline{XY}$	**b.** ?
6. $m\angle WXV = m\angle Y$	Substitution (Step 1 into 3)
7. $\overline{WX} \parallel \overline{ZY}$	**c.** ?
8. $WXYZ$ is a parallelogram.	**d.** ?

11. The quadrilaterals V, W, X, and Y which form the sides of this hatbox are parallelograms. Why must the quadrilateral Z also be a parallelogram?

12. If the diagonals of a quadrilateral bisect each other, then the quadrilateral is a parallelogram.

Given: Quadrilateral *ABCD*.
        O is the midpoint of $\overline{AC}$ and $\overline{BD}$.
Prove: *ABCD* is a parallelogram.

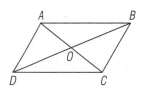

Conclusions	Justifications
1. $\overline{AO} \cong \overline{OC}$; $\overline{DO} \cong \overline{OB}$	**a.** __?__
2. $\angle AOD \cong \angle COB$	**b.** __?__
3. $\triangle AOD \cong \triangle COB$	**c.** __?__
4. $\overline{AD} \cong \overline{BC}$	**d.** __?__
5. $\angle ADO \cong \angle CBO$	**e.** __?__
6. $\overline{AD} \parallel \overline{BC}$	**f.** __?__
7. *ABCD* is a parallelogram.	Sufficient Conditions of a Parallelogram Theorem, part (d)

13. Prove in two steps without drawing a figure: If both pairs of opposite sides of a quadrilateral are congruent, then both pairs of opposite angles are congruent. (Hint: Use logical principles.)

Review

14. a. What is the sum of the measures of the angles of an octagon?
b. What is the sum of the measures of the angles of a regular octagon?
c. What is the measure of each interior angle of a regular octagon? *(Lessons 7-6, 5-7)*

15. Prove that the diagonals of a rectangle are congruent.
(Lesson 7-6)

16. State the HL Congruence Theorem. *(Lesson 7-5)*

In 17–19, **a.** draw the triangle. **b.** Will everyone else's correct drawings be congruent to yours? **c.** Explain why or why not. *(Lessons 7-2, 7-1)*

17. triangle *ABC* where *AB* = 5 cm, *BC* = 7 cm, and m∠*B* = 110

18. triangle *DEF* where *DE* = 2″, m∠*E* = 90, and m∠*F* = 60

19. triangle *GHI* where m∠*G* = 60, m∠*H* = 35, and m∠*I* = 85

Exploration

20. Given: Quadrilateral *ABCD* with *AB* = *CD* and ∠*A* ≅ ∠*C*. Is *ABCD* a parallelogram or not? Prove it or produce a counterexample.

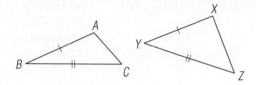

The SAS Inequality

The SAS Congruence Theorem states that when two sides and the included angle of a triangle are congruent to corresponding parts of a second triangle, the triangles will be congruent. But what happens if the included angles are not congruent?

Percy, a sleepy Persian cat, is having a big yawn as shown below. As he starts his yawn, his mouth is not opened wide, but in the second picture his mouth is opened very wide. A geometric view of this everyday occurrence is as follows. The top and bottom of his jaw are the same in both pictures; thus $AB = XY$ and $BC = YZ$. But since m$\angle XYZ$ is greater than m$\angle ABC$, $XZ > AC$. This result generalizes as the *SAS Inequality*.

SAS Inequality Theorem:

If two sides of a triangle are congruent to two sides of a second triangle, and the measure of the included angle of the first triangle is less than the measure of the included angle of the second, then the third side of the first triangle is shorter than the third side of the second.

Proof

A figure is drawn. Below it is stated the given and what is to prove in terms of the figure.

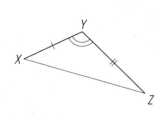
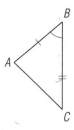

Given: $AB = XY$, $BC = YZ$, and $m\angle B < m\angle Y$.
Prove: $AC < XZ$.

The method to use is not obvious. Since $AB = XY$, there is an isometry T with $T(\overline{AB}) = \overline{XY}$. $\triangle A'B'C'$ (in blue) is $T(\triangle ABC)$. T is chosen so that C', the image of C, is on the same side of $\overline{XY}$ as Z. The result is shown below. Note that $\triangle C'YZ$ (not drawn) is isosceles since $C'Y = ZY$.

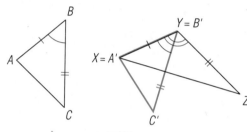

Since $m\angle A'B'C' < m\angle XYZ$, $\overrightarrow{YC}$ lies in the interior of $\angle XYZ$. Below, the symmetry line m of isosceles $\triangle C'YZ$ is drawn, intersecting $\overline{XZ}$ at Q. m is the $\perp$ bisector of $\overline{C'Z}$, so Q is equidistant from C' and Z, making $QC' = QZ$.

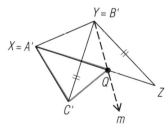

Now focus on $\triangle A'C'Q$ (in orange). From the Triangle Inequality,
$$A'C' < A'Q + QC'.$$
But $A'C' = AC$, $A'Q$ is XQ, and $QC' = QZ$. Substituting,
$$AC < XQ + QZ.$$
$XQ + QZ = XZ$ by the Betweenness Theorem.
So $AC < XZ$ by substitution.

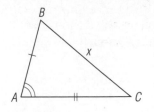

You now know many things about triangles and SAS. From the lengths *AB* and *AC* of two sides of a triangle, you can compute a range of possible lengths for the third side $\overline{BC}$ using the Triangle Inequality. The larger m∠*A* is, the larger *BC* is. If you know m∠*A*, the length of the third side is determined. This length can be found using trigonometry, a branch of mathematics that we introduce later in this course.

Questions

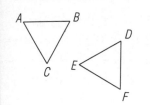

1. If *AB* = *DF*, *AC* = *DE*, and m∠*A* > m∠*D* in the figure at the left, then *BC* is (greater than, less than, equal to) *EF*.

2. State an application of the SAS Inequality Theorem.

3. *Multiple choice.* Which of the following is *not* used in the proof of the SAS Inequality?
   (a) Betweenness Theorem
   (b) Isosceles Triangle Symmetry Theorem
   (c) Isosceles Triangle Theorem

4. The Triangle Inequality is applied to which triangle in the proof of the SAS Inequality Theorem?

5. Suppose in △*ABC* that *AB* = 6″, *BC* = 3″, and m∠*B* = 62.
   a. Is *AC* uniquely determined?
   b. What branch of mathematics studies the calculation of *AC* from this given information?

6. a. Draw △*ABC* with *AB* = 9 cm, *BC* = 6 cm, and m∠*B* = 40.
   b. Draw △*DEF* with *DE* = 9 cm, *EF* = 6 cm, and m∠*E* = 80.
   c. Measure *AC* and *DF*.
   d. Which is longer?
   e. Why?

7. Use the figure at the right as marked. Explain why *RS* > *QR*.

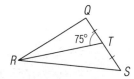

In 8 and 9, suppose Percy the cat's jaws $\overline{BA}$ and $\overline{BC}$ are the same length, 5 cm.

8. What are the largest and smallest possible lengths for $\overline{AC}$, the opening of his mouth?

9. What will be the length of $\overline{AC}$ when m∠*ABC* = 60?

10. What theorem explains the fact that as a lunchbox is opened, the distance between the front of the top and the handle increases?

11. Prove or produce a counterexample: If one angle of a quadrilateral is bisected by a diagonal and the angles not cut by the diagonal are congruent, then the quadrilateral is a kite. *(Lesson 7-7)*

12. Use the figure at the right.
Given: $QT = RS$
         $TS = QR$.
Prove: **a.** $\triangle QTS \cong \triangle SRQ$
         b. $\overline{QT} \parallel \overline{RS}$ *(Lesson 7-6)*

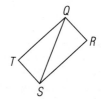

In 13 and 14, tell whether the triangles as marked are congruent. If so, what triangle congruence theorem justifies the congruence? *(Lesson 7-2)*

13.

14.

15. **a.** Draw a triangle with sides of length 3, 7, and 8 cm.
b. Draw a triangle with sides of length 3, 5, and 7 cm.
c. Measure the angles of these triangles to verify that two of the angles are congruent and two are supplementary. *(Lesson 7-1)*

In 16 and 17, $\triangle GHI$ has been reflected over line ℓ, and then its image has been reflected over line m.

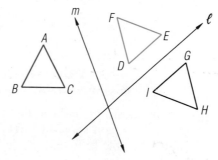

16. $\triangle GHI \cong$ __?__ $\cong$ __?__ *(Lesson 6-5)*

17. $\triangle BAC$ is a (reflection, rotation, translation) image of $\triangle GHI$. *(Lesson 6-3)*

18. One side of a triangle is double the length of a second side. The third side is triple the length of the second side. Explain why this is impossible. *(Lesson 1-9)*

19. The SAS Inequality Theorem is sometimes called the Hinge Theorem. Explain the reasoning behind this nickname.

Summary

In this and previous chapters, you have learned many ways of deducing that segments are congruent. Segments are congruent in situations involving regular polygons, midpoints, radii of the same circle, isosceles triangles, and kites, because of the definitions of these terms. And segments are also congruent when they are corresponding parts of congruent figures.

You have also learned many ways of deducing that angles are congruent. Angles are congruent when there are angle bisectors, isosceles trapezoids, or regular polygons, because of the definitions of those terms. When parallel lines are cut by transversals, corresponding angles and alternate interior angles are congruent. Two intersecting lines form congruent vertical angles, and base angles of isosceles triangles are congruent. Angles are congruent also when they are corresponding parts of congruent figures.

Using properties of isometries, we deduced five conditions that force triangles to be congruent. Four sets of conditions always work: SSS, SAS, ASA, and AAS. A fifth condition we call SsA works when the pair of congruent sides opposite the congruent angles is known to be longer than the other pair. A special case of SsA for right triangles is called HL.

From congruent segments and angles, you can get congruent triangles. Congruent triangles enable many properties of figures to be deduced. Some properties of parallelograms, isosceles trapezoids, rectangles, and regular polygons were deduced, as were some sufficient conditions for parallelograms.

Vocabulary

Below are the most important terms and phrases for this chapter.
For the starred(*) terms you should be able to give a definition of the term.
For the other terms you should be able to give a general description and a specific example of each.
You should be able to state any theorem in if-then form and draw a picture.

Lesson 7-2
SSS Congruence Theorem
included angle
SAS Congruence Theorem
included side; non-included side
ASA Congruence Theorem
AAS Congruence Theorem

Lesson 7-3
converse of the Isosceles
   Triangle Theorem

Lesson 7-4
overlapping triangles

Lesson 7-5
legs, hypotenuse of a right
   triangle
concentric circles
HL Congruence Theorem
SsA Congruence Theorem

Lesson 7-6
Properties of a Parallelogram
   Theorem
* regular polygon
Center of a Regular Polygon
   Theorem

Lesson 7-7
sufficient condition
Sufficient Conditions for a
   Parallelogram Theorem

Lesson 7-8
SAS Inequality Theorem

Progress Self-Test

Directions: Take this test as you would take a test in class. You will need a ruler, compass, and protractor. Then check your work with the solutions in the Selected Answers section in the back of the book.

1. Use the figure below. $\angle 1 \cong \angle 3$ and $\angle 2 \cong \angle 4$.
  a. Name the congruent triangles with vertices in correct order.
  b. What theorem guarantees that the triangles are congruent?

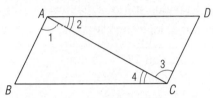

2. $\overleftrightarrow{AC}$ and $\overleftrightarrow{BD}$ below intersect at M. M is the midpoint of $\overline{AC}$ and $\overleftrightarrow{AB} \parallel \overleftrightarrow{CD}$. Justify each conclusion.
  a. $\overline{AM} \cong \overline{MC}$
  b. $\angle AMB \cong \angle CMD$
  c. $\angle MBA \cong \angle MDC$
  d. $\triangle MBA \cong \triangle MDC$

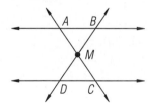

3. a. Draw a triangle LMN with $LM = 10$ cm, $MN = 8$ cm, and m$\angle L = 30$.
  b. Will everyone else's correct drawing be congruent to yours?
  c. Explain why or why not.

4. a. Draw a triangle ABC with $AB = 2.5''$, $BC = 4.5''$ and $AC = 3.5''$.
  b. Will everyone else's correct drawing be congruent to yours?
  c. Explain why or why not.

5. State three sufficient conditions for a quadrilateral to be a parallelogram.

6. State the SAS Inequality Theorem in your own words.

7. Use the figure below.
  Given: $PS = PT$
  Angles S and T are right angles.
  Prove: **a.** $QS = QT$
  b. $\overleftrightarrow{QP}$ is the angle bisector of $\angle SQT$.

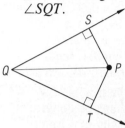

8. Walt bought Kelly a pogo stick for her birthday. The handle $\overline{AB}$ is parallel to and congruent to the foothold $\overline{CD}$. Prove that $ABDC$ is a parallelogram.

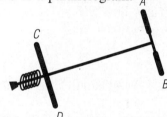

9. Given: $ABCDEFGHIJ$ is a regular decagon.
  Prove: $AC = FH$.

10. Use the figure at the right.
  Given: $WX = WY$;
  $\angle WUY \cong \angle WVX$.
  Prove: $\triangle WUV$ is isosceles.

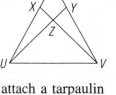

11. $\overline{AB}$ and $\overline{AC}$ are ropes that attach a tarpaulin over a picnic table. $\overline{AD}$ is perpendicular to the ground, which is level. If B and C are each the same distance from D, explain why the ropes have the same length.

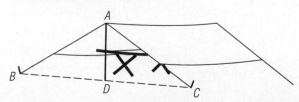

Chapter Review

Questions on **SPUR** Objectives

SPUR stands for **S**kills, **P**roperties, **U**ses, and **R**epresentations. The Chapter Review questions are grouped according to the SPUR Objectives for this chapter.

SKILLS deal with the procedures used to get answers.

■ **Objective A:** *Draw triangles satisfying given conditions and determine whether all such triangles are congruent. (Lessons 7-1, 7-2, 7-5)*

In 1–9, **a.** draw the triangle. **b.** Will everyone else's correct drawings be congruent to yours? **c.** Explain why or why not.

1. triangle *ABC* in which *AB* = 5 cm, *BC* = 6 cm, and *AC* = 8 cm

2. triangle *DEF* in which *DE* = 3″, *EF* = 2″, and *DF* = 2.5″

3. triangle *GHI* in which *GH* = 6 cm, m∠*G* = 60, and m∠*H* = 70

4. triangle *JKL* in which *JK* = 2.75″, m∠*K* = 40, and m∠*L* = 100

5. right triangle *MNO* with hypotenuse *MN* = 7.5 cm and leg *MO* = 4.5 cm

6. a right triangle with legs having lengths 1″ and 1.25″

7. triangle *STU* with m∠*S* = 30, *ST* = 6 cm, and *TU* = 4 cm

8. triangle *VWX* with *VW* = 4″, m∠*W* = 55, and *WX* = 2″

9. triangle *YZA* with m∠*Y* = 60, *YZ* = 2 cm, and *ZA* = 5 cm

PROPERTIES deal with the principles behind the mathematics.

■ **Objective B:** *Determine whether figures are congruent from information given in drawings.* *(Lesson 7-2)*

10. **a.** The triangles at the right are congruent by what theorem?
    b. $\overline{AB} \cong$ _?_
    c. ∠*A* ≅ _?_
    d. ∠*B* ≅ _?_

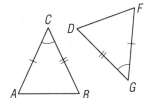

11. Refer to the figure below.
    a. Which triangle congruence theorem guarantees that the two triangles are congruent?
    b. Name the congruent triangles with vertices in correct order.

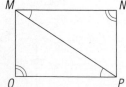

In 12–15, **a.** explain why the given triangles are congruent and **b.** indicate corresponding vertices.

12.

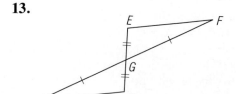

13.

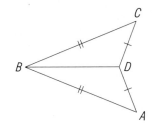

14.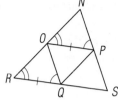

15.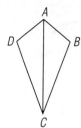

■ **Objective C:** *Write proofs that triangles are congruent.* (Lessons 7-3, 7-4, 7-5)

16. Fill in the blanks to complete this proof.
Given: $\angle DAC \cong \angle BAC$
$\angle DCA \cong \angle BCA$.
Prove: $\triangle ADC \cong \triangle ABC$.

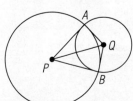

Conclusions	Justifications
1. $\overline{AC} \cong \overline{AC}$	**a.** ?
2. $\triangle ADC \cong \triangle ABC$	**b.** ?

17. Use the figure of Question 16.
Given: $\overline{AD} \perp \overline{DC}$, $\overline{AB} \perp \overline{BC}$,
$AD = AB$.
Prove: $\triangle ADC \cong \triangle ABC$.

18. Circles P and Q intersect
at A and B.
Prove: $\triangle APQ \cong \triangle BPQ$.

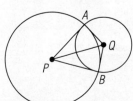

19. Refer to the figure below.
Given: $\overrightarrow{UW}$ bisects $\angle YUV$.
$\overline{UW} \cong \overline{UY}$; $\angle V \cong \angle UXY$.
Prove: $\triangle UVW \cong \triangle UXY$.

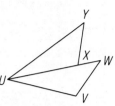

20. Refer to the figure below.
Given: $\overline{AB} \cong \overline{DC}$; $\angle ABC \cong \angle DCB$.
Prove: $\triangle ACB \cong \triangle DBC$.

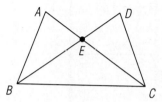

■ **Objective D:** *Apply the triangle congruence and CPCF theorems to prove that segments or angles are congruent.* (Lessons 7-3, 7-4, 7-5, 7-6)

21. Refer to the figure below. Fill in the blanks to complete this proof.
Given: $\overline{AB} \cong \overline{AC}$
$\overline{BD} \cong \overline{DC}$.
Prove: $\angle BAD \cong \angle CAD$.

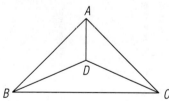

Conclusions	Justifications
1. $\overline{AD} \cong \overline{AD}$	**a.** ?
2. $\triangle ABD \cong \triangle ACD$	**b.** ?
3. $\angle BAD \cong \angle CAD$	**c.** ?

22. Refer to the figure at the right.
Given: *ABCDEFGH*
is a regular
octagon.
Prove: $\overline{AC} \cong \overline{BD}$.

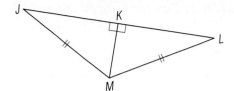

23. Refer to the figure below.
Given: $\overleftrightarrow{JK}$ bisects $\angle MJL$.
$\overline{MJ} \cong \overline{LJ}$
Prove: $\angle M \cong \angle L$.

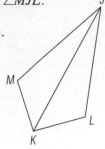

24. Refer to the figure below.
Given: N is the midpoint of $\overline{OE}$.
$\ell \parallel m$.
Prove: $\overline{AE} \cong \overline{UO}$.

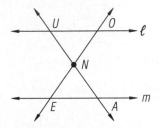

25. Refer to the figure below.
Given: $\angle ABC \cong \angle DCB$
$\angle A \cong \angle D$.
Prove: $\overline{AC} \cong \overline{DB}$.

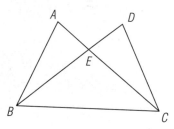

■ **Objective E:** *Determine whether conditions are properties of or sufficient conditions for parallelograms. (Lessons 7-6, 7-7)*

In 26–30, complete each statement with the most specific correct answer.

26. The diagonals of a parallelogram __?__.

27. Opposite angles of a parallelogram are __?__.

28. If all pairs of consecutive angles in a trapezoid are supplementary, then the trapezoid is a(n) __?__.

29. A quadrilateral is a parallelogram if its diagonals __?__.

30. A quadrilateral is a parallelogram if one pair of opposite sides is both __?__ and __?__.

31. Complete the proof of this statement: If one pair of opposite angles of a trapezoid is congruent, then the trapezoid is a parallelogram.
Given: $ABCD$ below is a trapezoid with bases $\overline{AB}$ and $\overline{DC}$.
$\angle A \cong \angle C$.
Prove: $ABCD$ is a parallelogram.

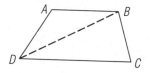

USES deal with applications of mathematics in real situations.

■ **Objective F:** *Use theorems about triangles and parallelograms to explain real situations.*
(Lessons 7-2, 7-7, 7-8)

32. $\overline{RA}$ and $\overline{AB}$ are beams of the same length at the end of a roof. $\overline{AP}$ is perpendicular to $\overline{RB}$. Explain why $\overline{RP}$ and $\overline{PB}$ have the same length.

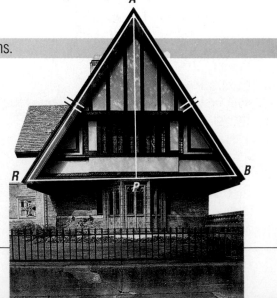

33. A radio tower is supported by guy wires that hit the level ground at points *A, C,* and *D*. Explain why, if the angles at *A, C,* and *D* have the same measure, then these points are the same distance from *B*, the bottom of the tower. (Assume the tower is perpendicular to the ground.)

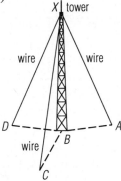

34. Tony and Maria each made pieces of triangular jewelry with sides 21 mm, 18 mm, and 26 mm. Explain why the pieces must have the same shape.

35. What theorem explains this fact: the more you open a door, the wider the opening is.

36. A scout used the following process to estimate the width of a river. Standing directly across from the tree at point *P*, the scout walked 10 paces to *X*, placed a stick at *X*, then continued on $\overrightarrow{PX}$ 10 paces to *Q*. The scout then turned 90° and walked until point *R*, where the scout, stick, and tree were lined up.
  a. Which line segments have lengths equal to the width of the river?
  b. Why does this method work?

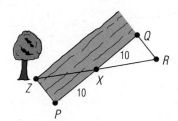

37. The sides of a corral *ABCD* are measured. *AB* is found to be 123′ 4″ long, *BC* = 73′ 6″, *CD* = 124′ 1″, and *AD* = 73′ 11″. Then *ABCD* is approximately in the shape of a(n) __?__ .

38. See the figure below. You have two equally long diagonal supports, $\overline{MN}$ and $\overline{PQ}$, for a bed. How should they be attached so that you can be certain *MPNQ* is a parallelogram?

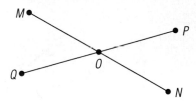

REPRESENTATIONS deal with pictures, graphs, or objects that illustrate concepts.

There are no objectives for Representations in this chapter.

Measurement Formulas

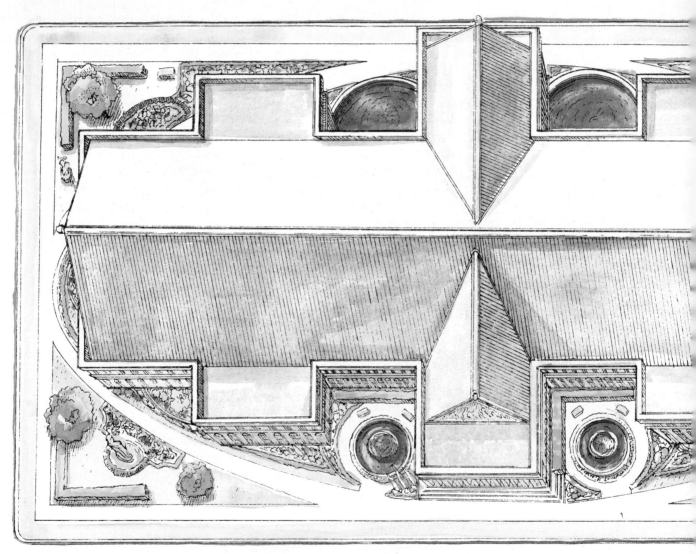

Diagramed below is a museum surrounded by an elliptical walkway. The museum and walkway both lie inside a large rectangle that is 2 blocks long and 1 block wide.

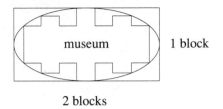

1 block

2 blocks

Area measures the space occupied by a two-dimensional region. The area of the rectangle is clearly 2 square blocks. The museum occupies a space inside that. So the area of the museum is less than 2 square blocks. The area of the elliptical region is larger than the area of the museum but smaller than the area of the rectangle. All of this can be seen by separating out the three regions.

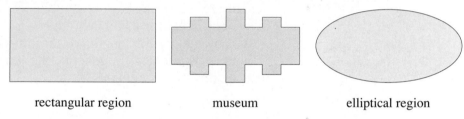

rectangular region   museum   elliptical region

Perimeter is different. The **perimeter** of a region is the length of its boundary. It tells you how far it would be to walk around it. The perimeter of the rectangle above is 6 blocks. It is harder to calculate the perimeter of the museum because the museum is a nonconvex 28-gon. But you can see that it would take longer to walk around all the walls of the museum than to walk around either the rectangle or the ellipse. The perimeter of the museum is longer than the perimeter of either the rectangle or the ellipse.

Thus the museum has the smallest area but the longest perimeter. So, though area and perimeter both measure how big something is, they are quite different.

You probably already know how to calculate the area and perimeter of squares, rectangles, and circles. In this chapter, you will learn formulas for the areas of many of the figures you have studied so far in this book. You will learn how these formulas are related to each other, so that if you forget one of them, you may be able to derive it.

Formulas for perimeter are the simplest, so this chapter begins with them.

Perimeter Formulas

Reproduced below is a portion of a United States mileage and driving-time map from the *1989 Rand McNally Road Atlas*. It is a network whose nodes are towns or cities. The lengths of arcs in this network are given in miles and in minutes. For instance, the length of the arc from Hannibal to Jefferson City is 108 miles or 2 hours, 23 minutes.

There are many paths on this network. For instance, there is a path from Springfield to Dallas through Atoka. The length of that path is found by adding the lengths of the individual arcs. It is 424 miles or 7 hours, 58 minutes. In general, the length of a path is the sum of the lengths of its segments.

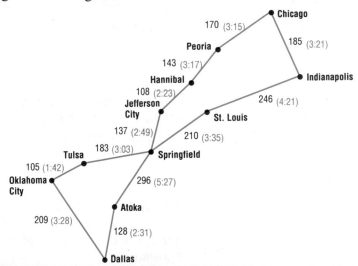

Definition:

The **perimeter of a polygon** is the sum of the lengths of its sides.

There are two polygons in this network. There is a heptagon *CPHJSStI* and a pentagon *STODA*. Think of traveling along the sides of one of these polygons, say *STODA*. You will have taken a tour through five cities (the vertices), ending where you started. According to this map, you will have traveled about 921 miles and it would take you a little over 16 hours. In calculating these totals, you have calculated the *perimeter* of *STODA*.

The above situation illustrates that the length of a side of a polygon may be measured in various units. Usually the units are those of length in the metric system (meters, centimeters, etc.) or in the customary system (inches, miles, etc.). To help you convert from one unit to another in either system or between systems, use the conversion formulas at the back of this book. When calculating perimeter, the important thing is that the units for all sides be the same.

If all the sides of a polygon have different lengths, there is no special formula for its perimeter. A formula for the perimeter p of a triangle with sides x, y, and z is just $p = x + y + z$.

$$p = x + y + z$$

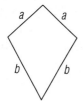

But if a polygon has some sides equal, then the calculations of the perimeter can be shortened. For instance, we know that a kite has two pairs of equal sides. If the lengths of these sides are a and b, then its perimeter p can be given by the formula

$$p = a + a + b + b$$

or, using simple algebra, $p = 2a + 2b$

or, factoring, $p = 2(a + b)$.

■ ■ ■ ■ ■ ■ ■ ■ ■ ■

Example 1   Kite *ABCD* with ends *B* and *D* has side lengths as shown. Find its perimeter.

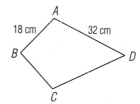

Solution 1   Use the definition of perimeter.

Perimeter of *ABCD* = *AB* + *BC* + *CD* + *AD*

Since *B* and *D* are ends of the kite, *AB* = *BC* and *CD* = *AD*. Substituting,

perimeter of *ABCD* = 18 cm + 18 cm + 32 cm + 32 cm
= 100 cm.

Solution 2   Use a formula. If *a* and *b* are the lengths of the sides, then the perimeter

$$p = 2(a + b)$$
$$= 2(18 \text{ cm} + 32 \text{ cm})$$
$$= 2(50 \text{ cm})$$
$$= 100 \text{ cm}.$$

Recall that the opposite sides of a rectangle are congruent. So the perimeter of the rectangle in Example 2 below is $\ell + w + \ell + w$, or $2\ell + 2w$, or $2(\ell + w)$. In general, the formulas at the back of the book have an advantage in that they allow you to apply what you know about algebra to geometry, and thus shorten calculations.

Example 2   Most flags are rectangles about 1.6 times as long as they are wide. If you have 10 meters of material for the edges, about how big a flag can you make?

Solution   First draw a picture. The edges are the length ℓ and width w of the rectangle. The perimeter
$$p = 2(\ell + w).$$
Here, $\ell = 1.6w$ and $p = 10$.
Substitute for p and ℓ.
$$10 = 2(1.6w + w)$$
$$10 = 2(2.6w)$$
$$10 = 5.2w$$

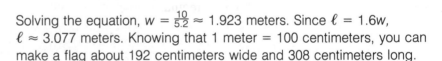

The Gadsden Flag of South Carolina, which was used around 1776, was one of many flags used by the American colonies to rally public support against the British.

Solving the equation, $w = \frac{10}{5.2} \approx 1.923$ meters. Since $\ell = 1.6w$, $\ell \approx 3.077$ meters. Knowing that 1 meter = 100 centimeters, you can make a flag about 192 centimeters wide and 308 centimeters long.

If all sides of a polygon have the same length, the polygon is called **equilateral.** Rhombuses and squares are equilateral quadrilaterals. There are equilateral polygons with any number of sides. A formula for the perimeter of an equilateral polygon follows directly from the definition of perimeter.

equilateral pentagon

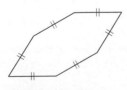

equilateral hexagon

Equilateral Polygon Perimeter Formula:

In an equilateral polygon with n sides of length s, the perimeter $p = ns$.

Since all regular polygons are equilateral, this formula applies to regular polygons. For instance, in an equilateral triangle, $p = 3s$. In a square, $p = 4s$. In a regular octagon, $p = 8s$.

Questions

In 1–3, use the map pictured in this lesson.

Covering the Reading

1. What does the number 3:28 on the segment from Oklahoma City to Dallas mean?

2. A trucker with a perishable load should choose which route from Chicago to Dallas?

3. Give the perimeter of the polygon *StICPHJS:*
   a. in miles;
   b. in hours.

4. Give three different expressions for the perimeter of the polygon pictured below.

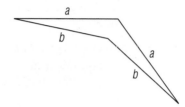

In 5–9, give the perimeter of each figure.

5. A rectangular shaped piece of land $3\frac{1}{2}$ miles long and $\frac{1}{2}$ mile wide

6. an equilateral hexagon with one side of length 14 mm

7. a square with side t

8. an equilateral triangle with side s

9. a regular heptagon with side $(x + 1)$

10. The perimeter of a rectangle is 70. One side of the rectangle is 3 times the length of the other. What are the lengths of the sides?

11. A poster is to be 1.5 times as wide as it is high. If its edges total 3 meters in length, how wide will the poster be?

Applying the Mathematics

12. The perimeter of a rhombus is 12 feet.
    a. Is this enough information to find the length of a side of the rhombus?
    b. If so, find that length. If not, why not?

13. A stop sign is a regular octagon. If its edges total 10′ in length, what is the length of each side?

14. The perimeter of an equilateral triangle is p. What is the length of each side?

15. The boundary of the museum on the first page of the chapter has sides of three different lengths. Let the smallest sides have length *s,* the middle sides have length *m,* and the largest sides have length ℓ.
a. What is the perimeter of the museum?
b. If *s* = 25 meters, *m* = 50 meters, and ℓ = 100 meters, what is the perimeter of the museum?
c. If *s* = 25 meters, *m* = 50 meters, and ℓ = 100 meters, estimate the perimeter of the surrounding rectangle.

16. a. On the map drawn in this lesson, distance is measured in hours and minutes. Name some place whose distance from where you live you know in minutes, but not in miles or kilometers.

b. Give an example of a situation in which the time to get from *A* to *B* is more important than is the distance in miles or kilometers.

17. A rectangle has perimeter 16. Suppose the sides are integers. Graph all pairs of possible lengths ℓ and widths *w*.

18. If all angles of a polygon have the same measure, the polygon is **equiangular.**
a. What is the sum of the measures of the angles in an equiangular decagon?
b. What is the measure of each angle in an equiangular decagon?
c. What is the measure of each angle in an equilateral decagon?

Review

19. *Multiple choice.* The measure of each angle of a regular *n*-gon is
(a) $\dfrac{360}{n}$

(b) $\dfrac{n(n-3)}{2}$

(c) $(n-2) \cdot 180$

(d) $\dfrac{(n-2) \cdot 180}{n}$. *(Lesson 7-6)*

20. In the figure below, find m∠*BDC*. *(Lesson 3-1)*

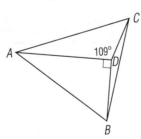

21. Is the network shown in this lesson traversable? *(Lesson 1-4)*

22. Fill in the blanks of these conversion formulas. *(Previous course)*
a. 1 yard = __?__ feet
b. 1 kilometer = __?__ meters
c. 1 mile = __?__ feet

23. One inch is about 2.54 centimeters. About what part of an inch is two centimeters? *(Previous course)*

24. Do these calculations, which are like those often found when adding lengths. *(Previous course)*
   a. 3 feet 6 inches + 8 feet 11 inches
   b. 8 · (2 feet, 3 inches)
   c. 2.4 meters + 62 centimeters

25. If $p = 2\ell + 2w$, $\ell = 11$, and $p = 25$, find w. *(Previous course)*

26. **a.** Multiply 5 by $3 + 2y$.
   b. How can you check your answer to part **a**? *(Previous course)*

27. Show that $(x + 1)(2x - 3)$ is not equal to $2x^2 - 3$. *(Previous course)*

28. *Multiple choice.* $(r + s)^2 =$
   (a) $r^2 + s^2$
   (b) $r^2 + rs + r^2$
   (c) $r^2 + 2rs + s^2$
   (d) none of these. *(Previous course)*

29. Refer to the map in this lesson.
   a. What average speed did the map makers assume in a trip from Dallas to Oklahoma City?
   b. What average speed is assumed in a trip from Dallas to Atoka?
   c. What conditions could account for the different rates?
   (Previous course)

Exploration

30. In the *1973 Rand McNally Road Atlas,* the path from Springfield to Atoka was labeled 289 (5:15). In the *1988 Rand McNally Road Atlas,* the same path was labeled 294 (6:45). What might account for the difference between these numbers and those given in the *1989 Rand McNally Road Atlas?*

LESSON

8-2

Tiling the Plane

Floors and walls are often covered with copies of the same polygon. A rectangular tile pattern may cover a floor, as pictured above. Square glass blocks in outside walls are often used.

Other regions can be used to cover the plane. Here are two tiling patterns using copies of $\triangle ABC$. Notice that the patterns are different. Pattern II contains kites whereas Pattern I does not.

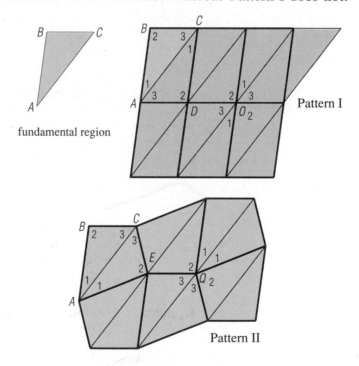

fundamental region

Pattern I

Pattern II

A covering of a plane with congruent copies of the same region, with no holes and no overlaps, is called a **tessellation.** The region is called a **fundamental region** for the tiling. $\triangle ABC$ is a fundamental region for each tessellation shown above. We say that $\triangle ABC$ **tessellates** the plane.

Look at the points O and Q in the patterns above. Six regions meet at these points. Each angle in the fundamental region is represented twice at O. Thus the 360° around a point is completely accounted for by the six angles—twice the sum of the angles of the fundamental region. In general, in any tessellation of a region, where the regions meet at a point, the sum of the angle measures must be 360. If this does not occur, a tessellation is not possible.

The idea of a tessellation is an old one. The word "tessellate" comes from a Latin word meaning "small stone." Small stones, put together into mosaics, covered the floors of many Roman buildings. The Moors, whose religion (Islam) still does not allow any pictures in their places of worship, used all kinds of tessellations in decorating their mosques. Below is a photograph of tessellations in the Alhambra, a museum in Grenada, Spain, that was built in the 1300s as a mosque.

In studying tessellations one key question is whether a given shape can cover the plane. It is easy to see that any triangular region can tessellate the plane.

Algorithm for tessellating part of a plane with any triangular region *ABC*:

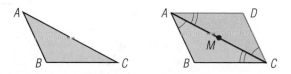

Step 1. Rotate $\triangle ABC$ 180° about *M*, the midpoint of $\overline{AC}$. The image of $\triangle ABC$ is the congruent triangle *CDA*. Since the triangles are congruent, $\angle BAC \cong \angle ACD$ and $\angle DAC \cong \angle ACB$. Because of the AIA = $\Rightarrow$ // Lines Theorem, $\overleftrightarrow{CD}$ // $\overleftrightarrow{AB}$ and $\overleftrightarrow{AD}$ // $\overleftrightarrow{BC}$. So *ABCD* is a parallelogram.

Step 2. Repeatedly translate the region $ABCD$ (and $\overline{AC}$) along $\overleftrightarrow{BC}$ in both directions with magnitude BC.

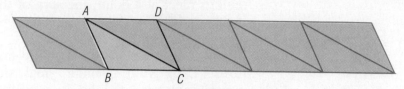

Step 3. Translate the entire figure along $\overleftrightarrow{AB}$ in both directions with magnitude AB. The result covers the plane.

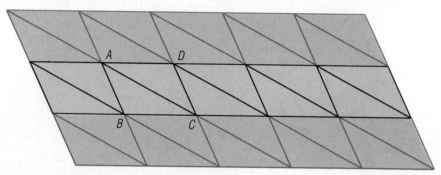

It is not as easy to see that any quadrilateral region will tessellate. (You are asked to explore this in the Questions.) Beyond this there are still unsolved problems. In 1975, Marjorie Rice, a homemaker from California, discovered a new type of pentagon that tessellates the plane. As recently as 1985, Rolf Stein of the University of Dortmund in West Germany found still another new type of tessellating pentagon. So an old application of geometry is still yielding new mathematics.

Questions

Covering the Reading

1. What is a tessellation?

In 2–4, trace the figure repeatedly to show a tessellation using the figure as a fundamental region.

2. 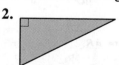 **3.** 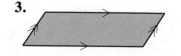 **4.**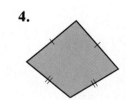

5. A museum where many tessellations can be found is the __?__.

6. What is the key question concerning tessellation mentioned in this lesson?

7. A new type of tessellating pentagon was discovered as recently as __?__.

8. Give two examples of tessellations seen where you live.

B

A C

In 9 and 10, use △*ABC* at the left as the fundamental region.

9. Make a tessellation in which kites occur.

10. Make a tessellation in which no kites occur.

11. The tessellation below is from the work of the artist Maurits Escher. Trace a possible fundamental region.

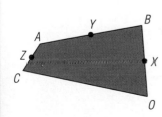

12. At the left is an octagon made of 5 squares. Trace it and show that it will tessellate the plane.

13. *Multiple choice.* Pictured here are regular polygons with 3, 4, 5, and 6 sides. Three of these polygons can be fundamental regions for a tessellation. Which one cannot?

(a)   (b) (c)   (d)

equilateral triangle   square   regular pentagon   regular hexagon

14. a. Follow this algorithm to tessellate with quadrilateral *ABOC* at the left, where *X*, *Y*, and *Z* are the midpoints of $\overline{BO}$, $\overline{AB}$, and $\overline{AC}$.

Y
A   B
Z
C   X

O

Step 1. Trace quadrilateral *ABOC*.
Step 2. Rotate *ABOC* 180° about *X*. (image *A'OBC'*).
Step 3. Rotate *A'OBC'* 180° about *Y'*, the image of *Y* (image *OA'B*C**).
Step 4. Rotate *OA'B*C** 180° about *Z**, the image of *Z'* (image *C*A"CO*).

b. There are now 4 angles with vertex *O*. How do you know that these angles fit around *O* exactly?

c. What needs to be done to complete the tessellation?

15. A regular pentagon has perimeter 13. What is the length of a side? *(Lesson 8-1)*

16. A parallelogram has perimeter 462 cm. One side is 185 cm. Find the lengths of the other three sides. *(Lessons 8-1, 7-7)*

17. What is the measure of each angle of a regular pentagon? *(Lesson 5-7)*

18. A rectangle has vertices at $(-2, 5)$, $(-2, -1)$, $(3, -1)$, and $(3, 5)$. Find its perimeter. (Hint: A drawing may help.) *(Lessons 8-1, 1-3)*

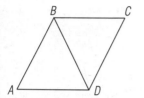

19. Refer to the figure at the left.
Given: $m\angle ABD = m\angle BDC$
$m\angle ADB = m\angle DBC$.
Prove: $AB = CD$. *(Lessons 7-4, 6-7)*

20. Expand: $(a + 5)^2$. *(Previous course)*

21. Solve: $2x^2 = 54$. *(Previous course)*

22. *Multiple choice.* $\sqrt{27} =$
(a) $9\sqrt{3}$ (b) $3\sqrt{9}$ (c) $9\sqrt{9}$ (d) $3\sqrt{3}$. *(Previous course)*

23. a. Who were the Moors?
b. What happened to them?

24. The artist Maurits Escher was famous for his tessellations.
a. When did he live?
b. Look in a library for books containing pictures of his work.

25. Below is part of a tessellation using the pentagon discovered by Rolf Stein. Trace the part below and continue it to fill a sheet of paper.

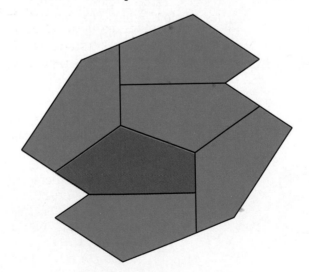

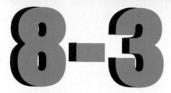

Fundamental Properties of Area

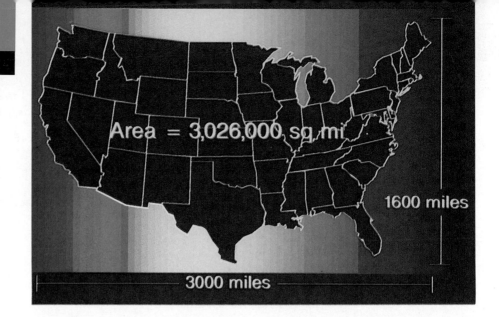

Area = 3,026,000 sq. mi.

1600 miles

3000 miles

An almanac gives the area of the 48 contiguous United States as about 3,026,000 square miles. (The other two states, Alaska and Hawaii, add about 593,000 square miles to the area.) The contiguous United States is about 3000 miles from east to west and 1600 miles from north to south. In this and the next lesson, you will see how this area can be calculated.

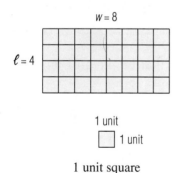

$w = 8$

$\ell = 4$

1 unit

1 unit

1 unit square

To find the area of a region, cover it with congruent copies of a fundamental region. The area is the number of copies that are needed. For instance, the rectangle with length $\ell = 4$ and width $w = 8$ can be covered with 32 unit squares. So we say that the area is 32 square units or 32 units^2. There are 4 rows and 8 columns. These numbers are the **dimensions** of the rectangle. The number of squares in the rectangle is the product of its dimensions.

Whenever the dimensions of the rectangle are integers, the unit squares will fit exactly. But suppose a farm is shaped like a rectangle, 1.5 kilometers by 2.5 kilometers, as shown here.

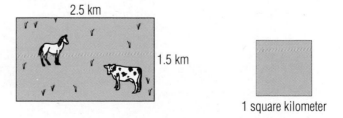

2.5 km

1.5 km

1 square kilometer

One way to find the farm's area is shown by the figures on the next page. First a unit is picked. Here the natural unit is 1 square kilometer. Then the farm region is split into square kilometers.

There are two whole-square kilometers, three half-square kilometers, and one quarter-square kilometer. Think of putting them end to end. The result is 3.75 square kilometers. This is exactly what you could get by multiplying 1.5 kilometers by 2.5 kilometers.

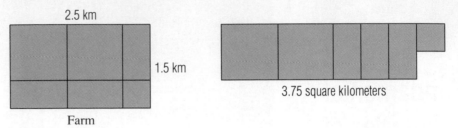

2.5 km

1.5 km

Farm

3.75 square kilometers

This one situation illustrates the four fundamental properties of area which we assume.

Area Postulate:

    a. Uniqueness Property Given a unit region, every polygonal region has a unique area.

    b. Rectangle Formula The area of a rectangle with dimensions ℓ and w is ℓw.

    c. Congruence Property Congruent figures have the same area.

    d. Additive Property The area of the union of two nonoverlapping regions is the sum of the areas of the regions.

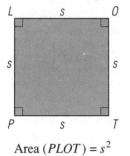

$L \quad s \quad O$

$s \qquad s$

$P \quad s \quad T$

Area $(PLOT) = s^2$

A special case of the Rectangle Formula is that the area of any square with side s is s^2. This is pictured at the left.

Sometimes we write **Area(F)** for the *area of a figure F*. With this notation, the Congruence Property of Area becomes: If $F \cong G$, then Area(F) = Area(G). **Nonoverlapping** regions means regions that do not share interior points. They may share boundaries, as in the drawing below. The Additive Property of Area becomes:
If F and G do not overlap, the Area(F $\cup$ G) = Area(F) + Area(G).

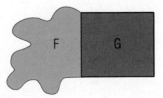

Area (F $\cup$ G) = Area (F) + Area (G)

Notice that the perimeter of F $\cup$ G does not equal the sum of the perimeters of F and G. (The common border is counted twice.)

All of the fundamental properties of area are used in Example 1.

■ ■ ■ ■ ■ ■ ■ ■ ■

Example 1   The floor plan of a ranch house is drawn on a coordinate system.

a. Find the dimensions of rooms I, II, and III if the unit is 1 foot.

b. Find the floor area of the house.

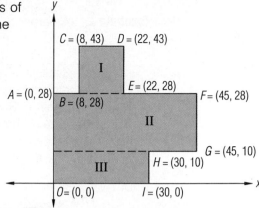

Solution

a. I, II, and III are rectangles. The horizontal dimensions are found by subtracting an appropriate pair of x-coordinates of the vertices. For example, $CD = |22 - 8| = 14$. Similarly, the vertical dimensions are found by subtracting the y-coordinates of the vertices. For example, $BC = |28 - 43| = 15$.

Dimensions of room I: $CD = 14$ and $BC = 15$
Dimensions of room II: $AF = 45$ and $FG = 18$
Dimensions of room III: $IO = 30$ and $HI = 10$

b. By the Additive Property of Area, the area of the house is the sum of the areas of I, II, and III. By the Rectangle Formula:

Area(I) = 15 ft · 14 ft = 210 sq ft
Area (II) = 18 ft · 45 ft = 810 sq ft
Area (III) = 10 ft · 30 ft = 300 sq ft.

Now apply the Additive Property of Area.

Area(floor plan) = 210 + 810 + 300
= 1320 sq ft

Check   One way to check is to consider the rectangle with vertices (0, 0), (45, 0), (45, 43), and (0, 43). This rectangle has area 43 · 45, or 1935 sq ft. It includes the entire floor plan plus rectangles in three corners. The sum of the areas of those corner rectangles, added to the floor plan's area, should be 1935 sq ft. You are asked to verify this in the Questions.

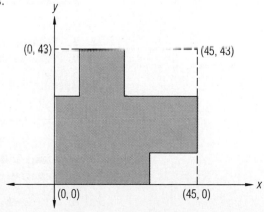

Example 2 provides a common use of area.

▪ ▪ ▪ ▪ ▪ ▪ ▪▪

Example 2   A carpet dealer advertises a particular carpet for $18.95 a square yard. How much will it cost to carpet a room that is 9 feet by 12 feet?

Solution   Since the price of carpeting is in square yards, the dimensions of the room must be converted from feet to yards: 9 feet = 3 yards and 12 feet = 4 yards. Thus, in square yards, the area of the room is 3 yards · 4 yards = 12 yards². The cost of the carpeting is 12 · $18.95 = $227.40. This is before tax and any other charges such as installation or padding.

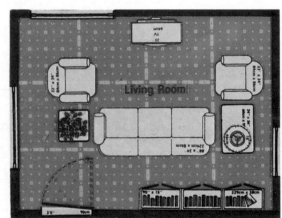

9 feet = 3 yards

12 feet = 4 yards

Questions

Covering the Reading

1. Below, two different unit squares are used to determine the area of the large congruent rectangles.

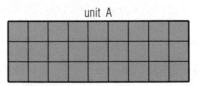

unit A

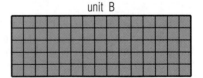

unit B

   a. What is the area using unit A?
   b. What is the area using unit B?

2. Rectangle *ABCD* has dimensions 8.3 cm and 11.4 cm.
   a. What is an appropriate unit of area in this situation?
   b. Find Area (*ABCD*).

3. Suppose the United States were a rectangle 3000 miles from east to west and 1600 miles from north to south.
   a. What would be the perimeter of the United States?
   b. What would be its area?

4. Find the area of each polygonal region.
  a. *ABFG*
  b. *CDEF*
  c. *ABCDEG*

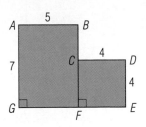

5. What properties of area are used in answering Question 4?

6. A floor plan of a house is given below. Each unit of length is one meter. Find the area of the floor.

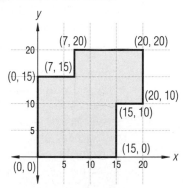

7. Verify the check in Example 1 in this lesson.

8. A carpet dealer advertises a particular carpet for \$11.95 a square yard. How much will it cost to carpet a room that is 15 feet by 12 feet (before tax or any other charges)?

Applying the Mathematics

9. Find the area of the polygon whose vertices are given.
  a. (0, 0), (0, 10), (10, 10), (10, 0)
  b. (0, 0), (0, *k*), (*k*, *k*), (*k*, 0)

10. At the left, *ABCD* and *AMEN* are squares, *M* is the midpoint of $\overline{AB}$, and *BC* = 16. Find Area(*BCDNEM*).

11. The area of a rectangle is 50 square yards. The length of the rectangle is 100 yards. What is the width of the rectangle?

12. To the nearest whole unit, find the side of a square with the given area.
  a. 49 square units
  b. $\frac{3}{4}$ square unit
  c. 200 square units
  d. 3141 square units

13. a. A desk is 24″ by 12″. What is its area in square inches?
  b. The same desk is 2′ by 1′. What is its area in square feet?
  c. How many square inches are in a square foot?

14. At the left, all the angles are right angles.
  a. *MO* = __?__
  b. *MR* = __?__
  c. Area ($\overline{MOQR}$) = __?__

15. The length of a rectangle is 3 times its width *w*. Find its area in terms of *w*.

16. Find the number of 3 ft by 1 ft pieces of sod needed to cover a normal 120 yd by 160 ft football field (end zones are included in these dimensions).

17. Using a tracing of kite *ABCD* below as a fundamental region, draw a part of a tessellation of a plane. *(Lesson 8-2)*

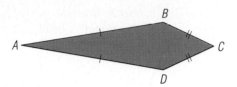

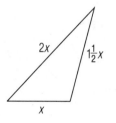

18. A pool is 50 m long and 25 m wide.
  a. A fence around the pool is built parallel to the sides of the pool and 10 m from each side. What is the perimeter of the fenced region?
  b. If a park district has money for 200 meters of fencing, how far from the pool (equally on all sides) can they put the fence? *(Lesson 8-1)*

In 19 and 20, find all solutions. *(Previous course)*

19. $x^2 = 16$

20. $5y^2 = 240$

21. *Multiple choice.* Which is equal to $\sqrt{75}$? *(Previous course)*
  (a) $3\sqrt{5}$ (b) $5\sqrt{3}$ (c) $5\sqrt{15}$ (d) $25\sqrt{3}$

22. Calculate to the nearest hundredth. *(Previous course)*
  a. $\sqrt{2}$ **b.** $\sqrt{3}$ **c.** $\sqrt{4^2 + 3^2}$ **d.** $\sqrt{\frac{25}{4}}$

23. The longest side of the triangle at the left is twice as long as the shortest side. The third side is $1\frac{1}{2}$ times as long as the shortest side. If the perimeter of the triangle is 45, how long are its three sides? *(Lesson 8-1)*

24. Factor: $\frac{1}{2}ha + \frac{1}{2}hb$. *(Previous course)*

25. Draw a hierarchy for quadrilaterals. *(Lesson 5-6)*

26. Find a rectangular room where you live. Calculate its area **a.** to the nearest square foot; **b.** to the nearest square meter.

27. In 1860, the area of the United States was 3,021,295 square miles. By 1870, the area had become 3,612,299 square miles. What caused such a large change?

8-4

Areas of Irregular Regions

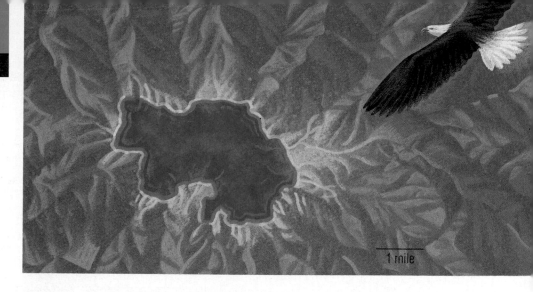

1 mile

Here is a picture of a lake.

Like many shapes, its boundary is not the union of circular arcs or segments. The shape is *irregular*. Still it has an area; it takes up space. For all sorts of reasons, such as zoning or for planning to stock the lake with fish, people might want to know its area.

To get a first approximation, you can draw a rectangle around the lake.

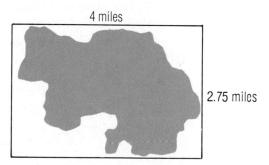

4 miles

2.75 miles

The area of the lake is less than the area of the rectangle, which is 4 miles · 2.75 miles. That is, the area of the lake is less than 11 square miles.

To get a better estimate, you might cover the lake with part of a tessellation of congruent squares. Here the squares are 1 mile on a side.

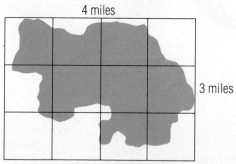

4 miles

3 miles

The squares above are too big to accurately estimate the lake's area. Within every square you would have to estimate how much of the square is covered by the lake. Smaller squares are needed. Below, the squares are $\frac{1}{2}$ mile on a side.

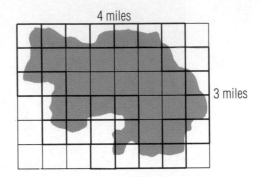

4 miles

3 miles

The idea now is to count the number of small squares entirely inside the lake. (There are 13.) Then count the number of squares partially covering the lake. (These are the boundary squares. You should get 28. They are drawn with bold edges.) A useful approximation is that, on average, each boundary square is half covered. So add the first number to *half* the second: $13 + \frac{28}{2} = 13 + 14 = 27$. An estimate for the area is 27 of these squares. Since each small square is $\frac{1}{2}$ mile on a side, the area of each small square is $\frac{1}{4}$ square mile, so an estimated area of the lake is $27 \cdot \frac{1}{4}$ square mile, or 6.75 square miles.

In general, if I is the number of inside squares, B is the number of boundary squares, and U is the area of a single square, then an estimate for the total area is $(I + \frac{1}{2}B) \cdot U$.

To get still a better estimate, use a grid with smaller squares. Below, the sides of the squares are $\frac{1}{4}$ mile, so $U = \frac{1}{16}$ square mile. We have identified those squares that lie on the boundary. In Question 4, you are asked to use this grid to estimate the area of the lake.

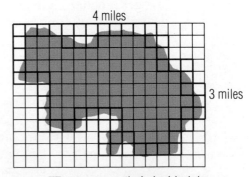

4 miles

3 miles

77 squares entirely inside lake
59 squares on boundary
56 squares entirely outside lake

When calculating area this way, do not spend too much time deciding whether a square is entirely inside or on the boundary. You only get an estimate anyway, so do not search for an exact answer.

The above procedure can be continued using finer and finer grids. The estimates can be made to differ from the actual area by no more than .1 square mile, or .01 square mile, or even closer. When smaller and smaller squares are used, we say that the estimates approach the actual area as a *limit*.

The biggest advantage of this method is that it works for any reasonably smooth curve. This same idea is used in calculus to calculate areas bounded by curves. Although it takes a long time to figure out areas in this way by hand, the method can be programmed to be done by a computer, and, when the curve can be described by an equation, there may exist a simple formula for its area.

Questions

Covering the Reading

1. Three tessellations of squares are used in this lesson to estimate the area of a lake. What is the area of a square: **a.** in the first grid; **b.** in the second grid; **c.** in the finest grid?

2. Give two reasons people might have for estimating the area of a lake.

3. *Multiple choice.* Using a grid, suppose E is the number of squares entirely inside a region and P is the number of squares partially inside the region. If each square has area Q square units, which is an estimate for the region's area (in square units)?

   (a) $(E + 2P) \cdot Q$

   (b) $\left(E + \dfrac{P}{2}\right) \cdot Q$

   (c) $(2E + P) \cdot Q$

   (d) $\left(\dfrac{E}{2} + P\right) \cdot Q$

4. Using the finest grid, estimate the area of the lake in this lesson.

5. **a.** What is an advantage of the method of using grids to estimate area?
   b. What is a disadvantage?

6. The area of a region is the __?__ of the estimates made using finer and finer grids.

Applying the Mathematics

7. Recall that the resolution of TV screens or computer monitors of different sizes can be compared by calculating the number of dots (pixels) per square inch. A Macintosh computer screen is about 5.5" by 7.5". There are 512 rows and 342 columns of dots. About how many dots per square inch is this?

8. Estimate the area of the triangle below **a.** using the grid at the left, then **b.** using the grid at the right. The small squares at the left are $\frac{1}{4}''$ on a side.

a.

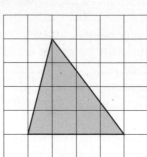

b.

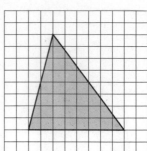

9. At the left is a scale drawing of a lake covered with a grid of squares each 0.5 km on a side. Estimate the area of the lake.

In 10–12, use this information. An *acre* is a unit of area often used to measure plots of land. Originally an acre was about the amount of land a farmer could plow in a day. Today an acre has an exact measure: 640 acres = 1 square mile.

10. There are 5280 feet in a mile. **a.** How many square feet are in a square mile? **b.** How many square feet are in an acre?

11. Lake Dumont in the state of Michigan has an area of 215 acres. About what part of a square mile is this?

12. A house is built on a rectangular half-acre lot. What might be the dimensions (in feet) of the lot?

13. A farm in Europe has an area of 30 square kilometers. A farm in the United States has an area of 20 square miles. Using 1 mile ≈ 1.6 km, which farm is bigger?

Review

14. A tilted square of side y is placed inside a square with side x. What is the area of the shaded region? *(Lesson 8-3)*

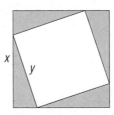

15. Factor: $x^2 - y^2$. *(Previous course)*

16. A person wishes to tile the kitchen floor with square tiles 8 inches on a side. If the kitchen measures 10 feet by 12 feet, how many tiles are needed? *(Lesson 8-3)*

17. A rectangle has an area of 96 square units. If its width is 4 units, what is its perimeter? *(Lessons 8-3, 8-1)*

18. If the unit of area of a figure is square kilometers, what is the natural unit for the perimeter of the figure? *(Lesson 8-1)*

In 19 and 20, use the figure at the right.

19. Given: $\angle PAQ \cong \angle DAR$
$\angle PQA \cong \angle DRA$
$PQ = RD$.
Prove: $\triangle PAD$ is isosceles.
(Lessons 7-4, 5-1)

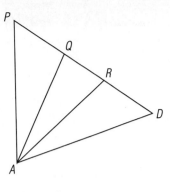

20. Accurately draw or construct
the line perpendicular to $\overline{AD}$
containing P. *(Lesson 3-6)*

In 21 and 22, solve. *(Previous course)*

21. $x^2 + 9 = 25$

22. $y^2 + 10 = 90$

23. *Multiple choice.* If $\sqrt{48} = k\sqrt{3}$, what is k? *(Previous course)*
(a) 4
(b) 16
(c) $\sqrt{45}$
(d) cannot be determined

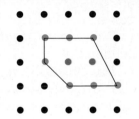

24. *Multiple choice.* When the vertices of a polygon are on a lattice,
there is a formula for its area. The formula is known as Pick's
Theorem. Use the polygon at the left and test with other polygons, to
answer this question. Let P be the number of lattice points *on* the
polygon. Let I be the number of lattice points *inside* the polygon.
Which is the polygon's area (in square units)?
(a) $\frac{1}{2}P + I - 1$
(b) $\frac{1}{2}P + I$
(c) $\frac{1}{2}P + I + 1$
(d) $\frac{1}{2}(P + I)$

25. Below is a pentagon that tessellates, of a type discovered by Marjorie
Rice in 1975. Draw enough of a tessellation to show the pattern.

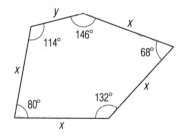

This photograph of a diamond shows triangular pock marks left in the outermost layers when crystal growth stopped.

Most of the shapes you have studied so far have not been irregular, but are special types of polygons. These shapes are so common that formulas have been developed to give their areas in terms of lengths of segments. One such formula is assumed in the Area Postulate: The area of a rectangle equals the product of its dimensions.

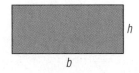

Area = hb

All of the other area formulas for polygons can be derived from that postulate. To start, it is easy to find the area of any right triangle ABC. Just rotate $\triangle ABC$ 180° about M, the midpoint of $\overline{AC}$, as you did in making a tessellation. The image is $\triangle CDA$. Quadrilateral $ABCD$ is a parallelogram with a right angle, so $ABCD$ is a rectangle. By the Congruence and Additive Properties of the Area Postulate, the area of each triangle is half the rectangle.

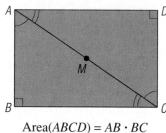

Area($ABCD$) = $AB \cdot BC$
So Area($\triangle ABC$) = $\frac{1}{2}(AB \cdot BC)$.

This argument shows:

Right Triangle Area Formula:

The area of a right triangle is half the product of the lengths of its legs.

$A = \frac{1}{2}hb$

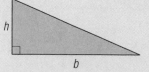

From the area of a right triangle, a formula for the area of *any* triangle can be derived. The idea of *altitude* is needed. In a triangle, an **altitude** is the perpendicular segment from a vertex to the line containing the opposite side. In each drawing below, $\overline{AD}$ is the altitude to side $\overline{BC}$ of $\triangle ABC$.

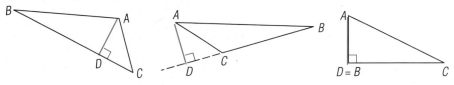

altitude $\overline{AD}$ inside $\triangle ABC$ altitude $\overline{AD}$ outside $\triangle ABC$ altitude $\overline{AD}$ on $\triangle ABC$
D between B and C   D not between B and C   D = B

Suppose $\triangle ABC$ is given and you don't know its shape. As shown above, there are only three possibilities for the altitude from A to side $\overline{BC}$. Either the altitude is inside the triangle, outside the triangle, or is a side of the triangle. In all cases, the same simple formula for the area of the triangle can be deduced.

Triangle Area Formula:

The area of a triangle is half the product of a side and the altitude to that side.

$A = \frac{1}{2} hb$

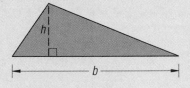

Proof

We want the area of $\triangle ABC$, which could be any triangle. In each case below, b is a side of the triangle and h is an altitude to that side. We want to show in all cases that
Area($\triangle ABC$) $= \frac{1}{2} hb$.

Case I: The altitude is inside the triangle. The altitude splits $\triangle ABC$ into two right triangles. Let $BD = x$ and $DC = y$. Then $x + y = b$.

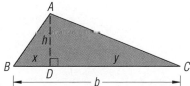

Area($\triangle ABC$) = Area($\triangle ABD$) + Area($\triangle ADC$)	Additive Property of Area
$= \frac{1}{2} hx + \frac{1}{2} hy$	Right Triangle Area Formula
$= \frac{1}{2} h(x + y)$	Distributive Property
$= \frac{1}{2} hb$	Substitution

Case II: The altitude is outside the triangle. The area of △ABC is found by subtracting.

Area(△ABC) = Area(△ADC) − Area(△ADB)

$$= \frac{1}{2}h(x + b) - \frac{1}{2}hx$$
$$= \frac{1}{2}hx + \frac{1}{2}hb - \frac{1}{2}hx$$
$$= \frac{1}{2}hb$$

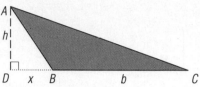

Case III: The altitude is a side of the triangle. In this case, the triangle is a right triangle, so the formula works.

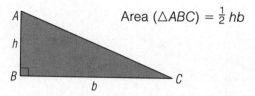

Area (△ABC) = $\frac{1}{2}hb$

In the Example, the unit is not given; therefore, the answer is given using a general term of square units, or units^2.

■ ■ ■ ■ ■ ■ ■ ■

Example Given coordinates as shown, find the area of:

a. △ABC
b. △ADE
c. △ACE.

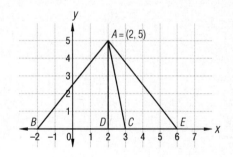

Solution $\overline{AD}$ is the altitude of each triangle and $AD = 5$ units.

a. Area(△ABC) = $\frac{1}{2} \cdot BC \cdot AD$
$$= \frac{1}{2} \cdot |3 - \text{-}2| \cdot 5$$
$$= \frac{1}{2} \cdot 5 \text{ units} \cdot 5 \text{ units}$$
$$= 12.5 \text{ units}^2$$

b. Area(△ADE) = $\frac{1}{2} \cdot DE \cdot AD$
$$= \frac{1}{2} \cdot |6 - 2| \cdot 5$$
$$= \frac{1}{2} \cdot 4 \text{ units} \cdot 5 \text{ units}$$
$$= 10 \text{ units}^2$$

c. Area(△ACE) = $\frac{1}{2} \cdot CE \cdot AD$
$$= \frac{1}{2} \cdot |6 - 3| \cdot 5$$
$$= \frac{1}{2} \cdot 3 \text{ units} \cdot 5 \text{ units}$$
$$= 7.5 \text{ units}^2$$

1. Define: altitude of a triangle.

2. Sketch a triangle and an altitude:
  a. with the altitude outside the triangle;
  b. with the altitude coinciding with a side;
  c. with the altitude interior to the triangle.

In 3–5, give an area formula for the figure.

3. rectangle   **4.** right triangle   **5.** triangle

6. a. How is Area($\triangle ABC$) related to the area of the two right triangles in the figure below?

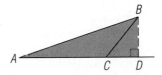

  b. If $BD = 7$ mm, $AC = 15$ mm, and $CD = 5$ mm, what is Area($\triangle ABC$)?

7. Give the area of
  a. $\triangle EFH$;
  b. $\triangle FGH$;
  c. $\triangle EGH$.

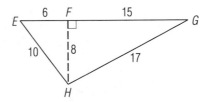

In 8–10, find the area of the triangle.

8.

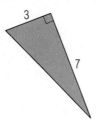

9.

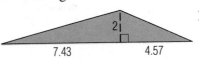

10.

11. Find the area of: **a.** $\triangle PQR$; **b.** $\triangle PRS$; **c.** $\triangle PQS$.

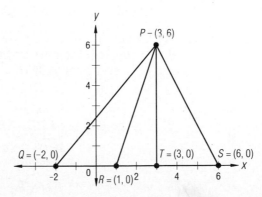

12. Main, First, and Elm streets border the triangular lot with dimensions (in feet) as given below. If Main is an east-west street and First a north-south street, what is the area of the lot?

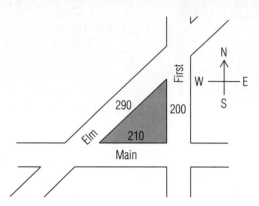

13. Trace △*XYZ* at the left.
   a. Construct one of its altitudes.
   b. Estimate its area in square centimeters by measuring an altitude and appropriate side and using the Triangle Area Formula.

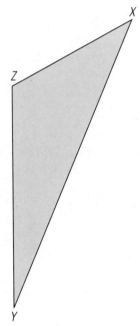

14. Approximate dimensions (in meters) of *ABC*, a part of a roof, are given at the right. $\overline{AC} \cong \overline{BC}$.
   a. What is the perimeter of this part of the roof?
   b. What is its area?

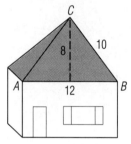

15. Given △*ABC* with altitudes $\overline{AW}$ and $\overline{CF}$. If *AB* = 8, *CF* = 6, and *AW* = 7, find *CB*.

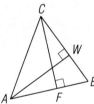

16. Find the length of a side of a triangle whose area is 18 square inches and altitude is 1 foot in length.

17. The grid at the right is a tessellation of unit squares. Find the exact area of quadrilateral *ABCD*.

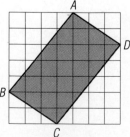

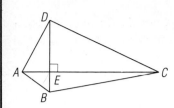

18. A quadrilateral with perpendicular diagonals is drawn at the left.
   a. Prove that the area of this quadrilateral is $\frac{1}{2} AC \cdot BD$, half the product of the lengths of its diagonals.
   b. To which of the following types of quadrilaterals does the result of part **a** apply: isosceles trapezoids, kites, parallelograms, rectangles, rhombuses, squares, or trapezoids?

Review

19. Estimate the area of Texas **a.** first using the grid below at the left, then **b.** using the grid at the right. Each little square at the left is 96 miles on a side. *(Lesson 8-4)*

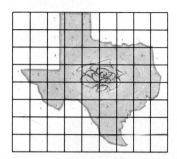
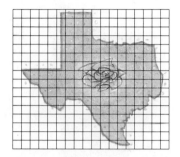

20. At the left, *PRVW* is a square. *Q* and *T* are midpoints. $RT = x$. Find the area of the green section. *(Lesson 8-3)*

21. Hexagon *ABCDEF* has vertices at points $A = (0,12)$, $B = (11, 12)$, $C = (11, 4)$, $D = (9, 4)$, $E = (9, 0)$, and $F = (0, 0)$. Find Area(*ABCDEF*). *(Lesson 8-3)*

In 22 and 23, rewrite with a smaller integer under the radical sign. *(Previous course)*

22. $\sqrt{18}$.

23. $\sqrt{45}$

Exploration

24. Below, the named points are equally spaced along the path *AEHLA*. Each point *A, B, C, D, E* is connected to each point *H, I, J, K, L*. How many triangles in the drawing have the same area as $\triangle CLH$?

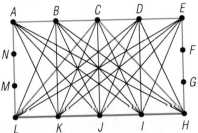

25. Use a ruler, compass, or automatic drawer.
   a. Draw a triangle $\triangle ABC$, the altitudes to $\overline{AB}$, $\overline{BC}$, and $\overline{AC}$, and extend the altitudes so they intersect.
   b. Repeat part **a** with triangles of various shapes.
   c. Conjecture when the altitudes intersect inside a triangle, when outside the triangle, and when at a point on the triangle.

Areas of Trapezoids

Knowing a formula for the area of a triangle is useful because any polygon can be split into triangles. When this occurs, it is said that the polygon has been **triangulated.** Below, pentagon *ABCDE* at the left has been copied and triangulated at the right.

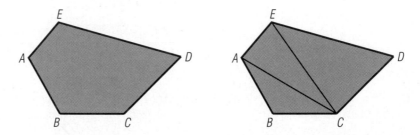

This idea provides an algorithm for getting the area of *any* polygon. Step 1: Triangulate the polygon. Step 2: Get the area of each triangle (by measuring lengths of sides and altitudes). Step 3: Add the areas to get the area of the polygon.

But an algorithm is not the same as a formula. There is no known general formula for the area of a polygon even if you know all the lengths of its sides and the measures of its angles. But if a polygon can be split into triangles with altitudes or sides of the same length, then there can be a formula. One kind of polygon that can be split in this way is the trapezoid. A bonus is that a trapezoid area formula will apply to all of the special kinds of quadrilaterals which are below the trapezoid in the hierarchy of quadrilaterals.

Here is an example of how to get the area of a trapezoid. In trapezoid *CDEF* below, given are the lengths of the bases (10 and 5) and its *altitude* $\overline{CP}$ (14). The **altitude of a trapezoid** is the distance between its bases. This is enough to find the area.

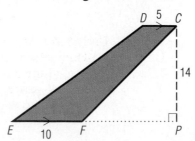

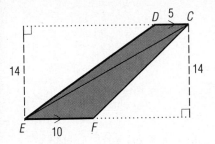

First, split the trapezoid into triangles *CDE* and *CEF*. Do you see that in each triangle, one side and the altitude to that side is known? Furthermore, in each case the altitude is 14. So the area can be found.

$$\text{Area}(CDEF) = \text{Area}(\triangle CDE) + \text{Area}(\triangle CEF)$$
$$= \tfrac{1}{2}(14 \cdot 5) + \tfrac{1}{2}(14 \cdot 10)$$
$$= 35 + 70$$
$$= 105 \text{ square units}$$

The idea of this example can be used to deduce a formula for the area of a trapezoid.

Trapezoid Area Formula:

The area of a trapezoid equals half the product of its altitude and the sum of the lengths of its bases.

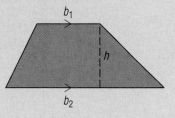

$$A = \tfrac{1}{2}h(b_1 + b_2)$$

Proof

Draw a figure. *CPIO* is a trapezoid with altitude h and bases b_1 and b_2. The proof is just a generalization of the example that preceded the theorem.

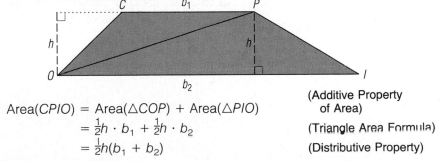

$$\text{Area}(CPIO) = \text{Area}(\triangle COP) + \text{Area}(\triangle PIO) \qquad \text{(Additive Property of Area)}$$
$$= \tfrac{1}{2}h \cdot b_1 + \tfrac{1}{2}h \cdot b_2 \qquad \text{(Triangle Area Formula)}$$
$$= \tfrac{1}{2}h(b_1 + b_2) \qquad \text{(Distributive Property)}$$

In symbols, if A is the area of a trapezoid with bases b_1 and b_2 and altitude h, then $A = \tfrac{1}{2}h(b_1 + b_2)$. Because of the Commutative Property of Multiplication, $\tfrac{1}{2}h(b_1 + b_2) = h \cdot \tfrac{1}{2}(b_1 + b_2)$. Remember that $\tfrac{1}{2}(b_1 + b_2)$ is the mean or average of b_1 and b_2. So the area of a trapezoid equals the product of its altitude and the average of its bases.

Example 1   Compute the area of polygon *ABCD* below.

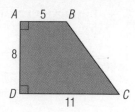

Solution   From the markings, you can deduce that $\overline{AB} \parallel \overline{CD}$, making *ABCD* a trapezoid with $b_1 = 5$, $b_2 = 11$, and $h = 8$. Apply the Trapezoid Area Formula.

$$
\begin{aligned}
\text{Area}(ABCD) &= \tfrac{1}{2}h(b_1 + b_2) \\
&= \tfrac{1}{2} \cdot 8(5 + 11) \\
&= 4 \cdot 16 \\
&= 64 \text{ units}^2
\end{aligned}
$$

Since a parallelogram is a special trapezoid, the trapezoid formula applies to parallelograms as well. For example, *SPOT* is a parallelogram with altitude *h*. In a parallelogram, opposite sides are equal, so $b_1 = b_2 = b$.

$$
\begin{aligned}
\text{Area}(SPOT) &= \tfrac{1}{2}h(b_1 + b_2) \\
&= \tfrac{1}{2}h(b + b) \\
&= \tfrac{1}{2}h(2b) \\
&= hb
\end{aligned}
$$

Since either pair of parallel sides can be considered as its bases, a parallelogram has two altitudes.

Parallelogram Area Formula:

The area of a parallelogram is the product of one of its bases and the altitude for that base.

$A = hb$

In Example 2, lengths of sides and altitudes are given. You must be careful to sort out which lengths to use.

Example 2 Find the area of the parallelogram *ABCD* at the right.

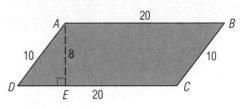

Solution

$$Area = hb$$
$$= 8 \cdot 20$$
$$= 160 \text{ units}^2$$

(Notice that the side with length 10 is not used.)

Another way of justifying the Parallelogram Area Formula is as follows. In Example 2, think of translating $\triangle ADE$ to the right of the parallelogram. A rectangle *ABFE* is formed. Its area is the same as that of the parallelogram. So the area of the parallelogram is 160 units^2.

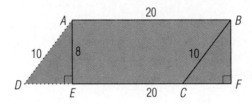

Questions

Covering the Reading

1. Trace trapezoid *ABCD* below and triangulate it.

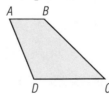

2. Describe an algorithm for obtaining the area of any polygon.

In 3 and 4, use the figure at the right.

3. **a.** Name the bases and altitude of trapezoid *EFGH*.
   b. Find Area(*EFGH*).

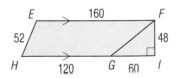

4. Find Area(*EFIH*).

5. Give the area formula for any trapezoid.

6. *Multiple choice.* To find the area of a trapezoid,
   (a) you must triangulate;
   (b) you must use the Trapezoid Area Formula;
   (c) you can either triangulate or use the Trapezoid Area Formula.

7. $\frac{1}{2}(b_1 + b_2)$ is the __?__ or __?__ of b_1 and b_2.

In 8–10, find the area of the largest trapezoid in the drawing.

8.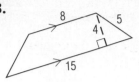

9.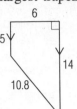

10.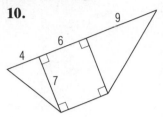

11. Give an area formula for any parallelogram.

In 12 and 13, find the area of the parallelogram.

12.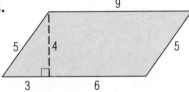

13.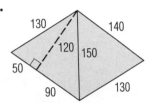

Applying the Mathematics

In 14 and 15, find the area of the trapezoid with the given vertices.

14.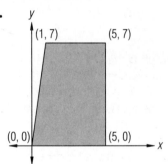

15.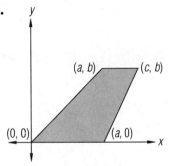

16. A trapezoid has one base 20, a second base 15, and an area of 60. What is the altitude of the trapezoid?

Review

In 17 and 18, use the figure below. *(Lesson 8-5)*

17. *Multiple choice.*
    The area of △*ABC* is
    (a) $h + x + g$ units^2
    (b) hx units^2
    (c) $\frac{1}{2}hxg$ units^2
    (d) $\frac{1}{2}hx$ units^2.

18. *Multiple choice.*
    The area of △*ABE* is
    (a) $h(x + y + z)$ units^2
    (b) $\frac{1}{2}h(x + y + z)$ units^2
    (c) $g + x + y + z + j$ units^2
    (d) $\frac{1}{2}(g + j)(x + y + z)$ units^2

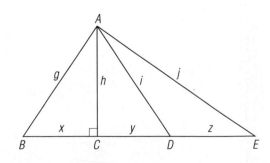

19. A piece of fabric is made in the shape at the left. Explain how the amount of fabric needed for that piece could be estimated. *(Lesson 8-4)*

20. Draw a rectangle with perimeter 100 mm and area less than 50 square mm. *(Lessons 8-3, 8-1)*

21. If the length of a radius of $\odot O$ is $6x$, what is the length of a diameter? *(Lesson 2-5)*

22. Find the area of $\triangle KLM$ below. *(Lesson 8-5)*

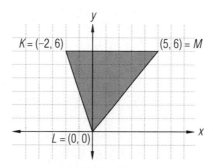

In 23 and 24, expand. *(Previous course)*

23. $(a + b)(c + d)$ **24.** $(e + f)^2$

Exploration

Hoover Dam in Lake Mead, Nevada

25. The state of Nevada is roughly shaped like a trapezoid.
  a. Use the dimensions given below to estimate the area of the trapezoid that includes Nevada.
  b. The Colorado River cuts a region off southeast Nevada that is almost a trapezoid with north-south bases 80 and 120 miles long and an east-west length of 30 miles. Approximate the area of this region, shaded in the drawing.
  c. From your calculations in **a** and **b,** estimate the area of Nevada.
  d. From a map or almanac, find the area of Nevada in square miles. How close is your estimate from part **c**?

8-7

The Pythagorean Theorem

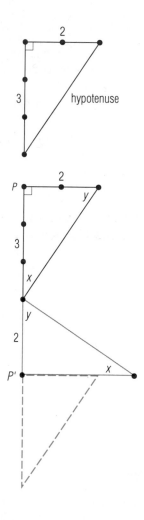

area = A | side = $\sqrt{A}$

From the area of a square you can determine the length of any of its sides. If the area is A, the length of the side is $\sqrt{A}$. That is why $\sqrt{A}$ is called the **square root** of A. Just as a plant rests on its roots, a square can rest on its (positive) square root.

Thus if the area of a square is 400 square centimeters, its side has length 20 cm. If the area is 13 square feet, its side has length $\sqrt{13}$ feet. You can verify the latter of these with a calculator: $\sqrt{13} \cdot \sqrt{13} \approx 3.6055513 \cdot 3.6055513 \approx 13$.

This idea, that area can tell you something about length, was used by the Greek mathematician Pythagoras in the 6th century B.C. to obtain the theorem that is named after him. The *Pythagorean Theorem* enables you to find the length of the hypotenuse of a right triangle if you know the lengths of its legs. It is a famous theorem and most students have seen it before taking a geometry course.

But first imagine that you do not know this theorem. (This will be easy if in fact you don't!) Suppose you were given a right triangle with legs of 2 and 3 units. There are a couple of ways you could find the length of the hypotenuse. You could draw the right triangle and estimate the hypotenuse by measuring. At the left is a right triangle with legs of length 2 cm and 3 cm. You can measure the hypotenuse. You should get about 3.6 cm.

An exact answer can be found by the procedure illustrated at the left. Translate the triangle 5 cm along its 3 cm side. Under this translation, the image of P is P'. Then rotate the image triangle 90° about P'. Do this process twice more and you get a figure like that below. The angle measures x and y add to 90°, so the angles of the middle figure (shaded) are right angles. All sides of the shaded region are congruent, so they have the same length. So the shaded region is a square.

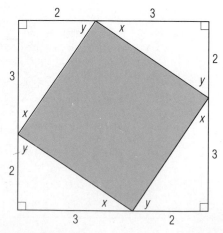

Of course, the large, outlining figure is also a square. Its area is 5 · 5 or 25. Each corner triangle has area $\frac{1}{2}$ · 2 · 3, or 3, so the four corners have a total area of 12. This leaves 13 for the area of the shaded square. So its side is $\sqrt{13}$. This agrees with the estimate found by measuring.

The sides of the right triangle are thus 2, 3, and $\sqrt{13}$. Notice that $2^2 + 3^2 = (\sqrt{13})^2$. The general relationship is the Pythagorean Theorem, and its proof involves the same procedure as above, except with a and b instead of 2 and 3.

Pythagoras (6th century B.C.) imagined to have the appearance and stature of a Biblical figure, by an unknown artist in an 18th century copper engraving book (no drawing of the actual Pythagoras exists)

Pythagorean Theorem:

In any right triangle with legs a and b and hypotenuse c,
$$a^2 + b^2 = c^2.$$

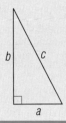

Proof

The original triangle with its translation and rotation images is below. Its legs are a and b and the hypotenuse is c. The area of the shaded square is thus c^2. Now we find the shaded area in a second way.

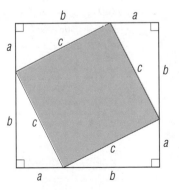

Side of big square = $a + b$.
Area of big square = $(a + b)^2$.
Each of the four corner right triangles has area $\frac{1}{2} ab$.
So the shaded square has area
$(a + b)^2 - 4 \cdot \frac{1}{2} ab = a^2 + 2ab + b^2 - 2ab$
$\qquad\qquad\qquad = a^2 + b^2.$
But the area of the shaded square is c^2. So $c^2 = a^2 + b^2$.

The Pythagorean Theorem is useful in many kinds of problems.

Example 1 Find YZ in the picture below.

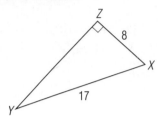

Solution From the Pythagorean Theorem,
$$XZ^2 + YZ^2 = XY^2.$$
So
$$8^2 + YZ^2 = 17^2$$
$$64 + YZ^2 = 289$$
$$YZ^2 = 225$$
$$YZ = 15 \text{ units.}$$

Check Does $8^2 + 15^2 = 17^2$? Yes, $64 + 225 = 289$.

Materials tend to expand when heated. Roads and railroad tracks must be built with some "give" to allow for expansion in hot weather. The expansion is more than most people think, as the Pythagorean Theorem can show.

Example 2 Suppose a 200-foot long rail ($\overline{AB}$ in the drawing) is solidly anchored at both ends. On a hot day, such a rail could expand 1 inch in length, causing it to buckle. Though it might curve, as shown below in an exaggerated picture, use a right triangle ($\triangle AMC$) to estimate the distance h it curves out from the straight track.

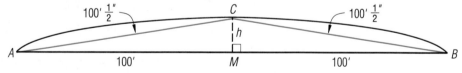

Solution First make the units consistent. Inches are easier. $100' = 1200''$ and so $100'\frac{1}{2}'' = 1200.5''$. Using the Pythagorean Theorem in $\triangle AMC$,
$$AM^2 + MC^2 = AC^2$$
$$1200^2 + h^2 = 1200.5^2$$
$$1,440,000 + h^2 = 1,441,200.25$$
$$h^2 \approx 1200.25$$
$$h \approx \sqrt{1200.25} \text{ or about 35 inches.}$$
The track will buckle almost 3 feet! For this reason, expansion joints are put on tracks. They give room for the rail to expand.

To make a right triangle, the ancient Egyptians took a rope with 12 equally spaced knots in it, and then bent it in two places to form a triangle with sides of lengths 3, 4, and 5.

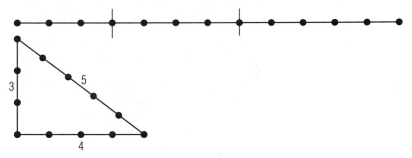

Does this work, or is it just close? Here we know $3^2 + 4^2 = 5^2$, and wonder if the triangle is a right triangle. This is an instance of the converse of the Pythagorean Theorem. Since the converse of a theorem is not necessarily true, its truth needs to be checked. As it happens, this converse is true. The proof is subtle; it uses the Pythagorean Theorem itself and the SSS Congruence Theorem.

Pythagorean Converse Theorem:

If a triangle has sides of lengths a, b, and c, and $a^2 + b^2 = c^2$, then the triangle is a right triangle.

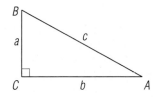

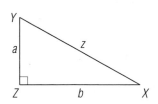

Proof

At the left is the given triangle ABC with sides of length a, b, and c and with $c^2 = a^2 + b^2$. The goal is to prove that $\triangle ABC$ is a right triangle. Consider right $\triangle XYZ$ with legs of lengths a and b.

By the Pythagorean Theorem, in $\triangle XYZ$, $\qquad\qquad a^2 + b^2 = z^2.$
But it is given that $\qquad\qquad\qquad\qquad\qquad\quad a^2 + b^2 = c^2.$
By substitution, $\qquad\qquad\qquad\qquad\qquad\qquad\quad z^2 = c^2.$
Taking positive square roots of each side, $\qquad\quad z = c.$

Thus, by SSS Congruence, $\triangle ABC \cong \triangle XYZ$. So, by the CPCF Theorem, $\angle C$ is a right angle and thus $\triangle ABC$ is a right triangle.

Questions

Covering the Reading

1. Babylonian manuscripts indicate knowledge of the Pythagorean Theorem a thousand years before Pythagoras. About how many years ago were the Babylonian manuscripts created?

2. If a square has area 225 square meters, how long is a side?

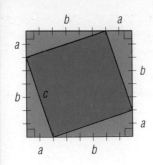

3. Use the figure at the left.
   a. What is the area of each corner triangle?
   b. What is the area of the large square?
   c. What is the area of the tilted square in terms of a and b?
   d. What is c in terms of a and b?

4. To find the length of the hypotenuse of a right triangle, which is shorter, the method of Question 3 or the Pythagorean Theorem?

5. *Multiple choice.* In this lesson, the Pythagorean Theorem is proved by   (a) triangulation
   (b) estimating square roots
   (c) the method of Question 3.

6. State the Pythagorean Theorem.

In 7 and 8, find the length of the hypotenuse in each right triangle.

7.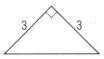

8.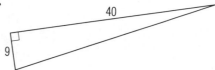

In 9 and 10, find the length of the third side of each right triangle.

9.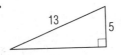

10.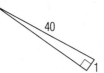

11. Suppose that the track in Example 2 expanded only 1/2″ instead of 1″. To the nearest inch, by how much would the track buckle?

In 12–20, a set of three numbers that can be sides of a right triangle is called a **Pythagorean Triple.** Determine if the set is a Pythagorean Triple.

12. 3, 4, 5

13. 70, 24, 74

14. 10, 24, 26

15. 14, 8, 17

16. 25, 24, 7

17. 40, 9, 41

18. 1.67, 2.67, 3.33

19. 1.5, 3.6, 3.9

20. 2, $2\frac{2}{3}$, $3\frac{1}{3}$

Applying the Mathematics

21. If a square room has an area of 20 square feet, to the nearest inch what is the length of a wall of the room?

In 22–24, it helps to draw a picture.

22. Felice walked from her home due north 10 miles, then due east 3 miles. How far, to the nearest tenth of a mile, is she from home?

23. Find the length of a diagonal of a rectangular field with sides 24 meters and 70 meters.

24. The base of a 10-foot ladder is placed 2 feet away from a wall. How high up the wall will the ladder reach?

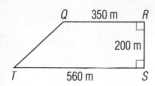

Q — 350 m — R
200 m
T — 560 m — S

25. How long would it take a person to walk around the trapezoidal field pictured here, at a rate of 90 meters per minute? (Hint: Find QT by drawing a perpendicular from Q to $\overline{TS}$.)

26. One leg of a right triangle is twice the length of the other. How many times larger than the smaller leg is the hypotenuse? (That is, find the value of k in the drawing below.)

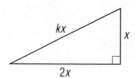

27. Surveyors were hired to find the area of the empty lot $\triangle DNF$. First, they laid off an east-west line $\overleftrightarrow{EW}$. Then they measured segments and recorded distances.

segment	$\overline{DC}$	$\overline{NB}$	$\overline{FG}$	$\overline{CB}$	$\overline{BG}$
distance (in feet)	80	200	160	66	250

What is the area of the lot? (Hint: Find the area of $FNDCG$ and subtract the area of $FDCG$.) *(Lesson 8-6)*

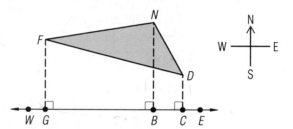

28. Explain how the area formula for a parallelogram is deduced from the formula for the area of a trapezoid. *(Lesson 8-6)*

29. Find the area of the triangle of Question 7. *(Lesson 8-5)*

30. Drawn at the left is a pond in Wilson Park. If 1 cm on this drawing corresponds to 100 m on the pond, estimate the area of the pond by tracing it on a grid. A good estimate here is within 10,000 square meters of the actual area. *(Lesson 8-4)*

31. A rectangle has area 12 and perimeter 26. By trial and error, find the dimensions of the rectangle. *(Lessons 8-3, 8-1)*

32. For any positive numbers x and y with $x > y$, the three numbers
$$x^2 - y^2, \quad 2xy, \quad x^2 + y^2$$
will be a Pythagorean triple. For instance, if $x = 3$ and $y = 2$, then $x^2 - y^2 = 5$, $2xy = 12$, and $x^2 + y^2 = 13$. Since $5^2 + 12^2 = 13^2$, the set $\{5, 12, 13\}$ is a Pythagorean triple. Some Pythagorean triples are the correct answers in Questions 12–20. By substitution, find some other Pythagorean triples not listed there.

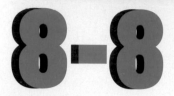

Arc Measure and Arc Length

Arcs of circles are formed by the streets in a planned community in Sun City, Arizona.

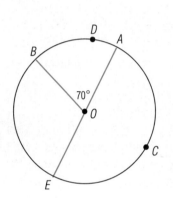

A circle with center *O* is drawn at the left. Suppose you walk along the circle counterclockwise from *A* to *B*. The part of the circle you have walked is **arc AB**, written $\overset{\frown}{AB}$.

The measure of arc $\overset{\frown}{AB}$ is given in degrees, and is the same as the measure of the *central angle AOB*. Thus, the *measure of the arc AB* is 70°. That is, from *A* to *B* you have walked 70° around the circle. This tells how much you have turned and what part of the 360° circle you have traversed. If you walked the other way (clockwise) from *A* to *C* to *B*, you would have gone 290° around the circle.

Now we define these terms more precisely. A **central angle of a circle** is an angle whose vertex is the center of the circle. So, when *A* and *B* are points on a circle *O*, then ∠*AOB* is a central angle. When ∠*AOB* is not a straight angle, the points of ⊙*O* that are on or interior to ∠*AOB* constitute the **minor arc** $\overset{\frown}{AB}$. The points *A* and *B* are the **endpoints** of the arc.

The points of ⊙*O* which are on or exterior to ∠*AOB* constitute a **major arc** of circle *O*. Above at the left, this arc is named $\overset{\frown}{ACB}$. The third point *C* is included to distinguish the major arc ($\overset{\frown}{ACB}$) from the minor arc ($\overset{\frown}{AB}$). For extra clarity, the minor arc above can also be described as $\overset{\frown}{ADB}$.

When a central angle is a straight angle, then the arcs are called **semicircles**. Above, ∠*AOE* is a straight angle, and both $\overset{\frown}{ACE}$ and $\overset{\frown}{ABE}$ are semicircles.

Definitions:

The **degree measure of a minor arc** or **semicircle** $\overset{\frown}{AB}$ of circle *O*, written **m$\overset{\frown}{AB}$,** is the measure of central angle *AOB*.
The **degree measure of a major arc** $\overset{\frown}{ACB}$ of circle *O*, written **m$\overset{\frown}{ACB}$,** is 360° − m$\overset{\frown}{AB}$.

Example 1   In ⊙O at the right, find **a.** m$\widehat{RS}$;   **b.** m$\widehat{RTS}$.

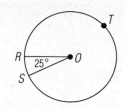

Solution

a. m$\widehat{RS}$ = m∠ROS = 25°

b. m$\widehat{RTS}$ = 360° − m$\widehat{RS}$ = 360° − 25° = 335°

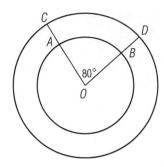

At the left, in the two concentric circles with center O, arcs $\widehat{AB}$ and $\widehat{CD}$ have the same degree measure as m∠O: m$\widehat{AB}$ = m$\widehat{CD}$ = 80°. Yet if you walked from C to D, you would walk a longer distance than if you walked from A to B. The arcs $\widehat{AB}$ and $\widehat{CD}$ have different lengths. **Arc length** *is not the same* as arc measure. Arc length indicates a distance; arc measure indicates an amount of a turn.

In the larger circle at the left, the length of $\widehat{CD}$ is a distance measured in linear units such as centimeters or inches, but m$\widehat{CD}$ is measured in degrees. The units of measure are different. To avoid confusion, in this book we always put the degree ° sign by an arc measure.

The *length* of an arc can be estimated by drawing chords. A **chord** is a segment whose endpoints are on a given circle. Below, the length of $\widehat{MN}$ is approximated by MP + PQ + QR + RN. By drawing more and more chords, their total length approaches the length of the arc as a limit. If this is done with an entire circle, the limit is the **circumference of a circle.** The term *circumference* is a synonym for perimeter. It is how far you would go if you walked around the circle. The ratio of the circumference C to the diameter d is equal in all circles. It is denoted by the famous number π, the Greek letter *pi*.

Definition:

$π = \dfrac{C}{d}$, where C is the circumference and d the diameter of a circle.

The number π is irrational; π cannot be written either as a finite or repeating decimal or as a simple fraction. The decimal for π is infinite. Here are the first 50 decimal places.

3.14159 26535 89793 23846 26433 83279 50288 41971 69399 37510

Most scientific calculators have a key for π which gives the first 6 or 8 places in its decimal approximation. π is about 3.14159 or about $\frac{22}{7}$.

Solving the defining equation $\pi = \frac{C}{d}$ for C gives a formula for the circumference of any circle.

Circle Circumference Formula:

If a circle has circumference C and diameter d, then $C = \pi d$.

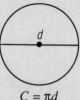

$C = \pi d$

Substituting $2r$ for d in the formula gives another version of it.
$$C = 2\pi r$$

Substituting 3.14 for π in the circumference formula gives an estimate for C.
$$C \approx 3.14d$$

In real situations, the estimate you use for π depends on the accuracy of the data. In Example 2, the given information does not warrant a closer approximation than 3.14.

Example 2 A mountain bicycle wheel has a diameter of 22 inches. If a rider can get it to go 300 revolutions in a minute, how far will the bike have traveled?

Solution One revolution moves the bike the length of the circumference.
$$C \approx 3.14 \cdot 22$$
$$= 69.08 \text{ inches each revolution}$$
In 300 revolutions, the distance traveled is
$$300 \cdot 69.08 = 20{,}724 \text{ inches.}$$
Dividing by 12 gives the answer in feet, about 1727 feet.

Check Is 1727 feet about what should be expected? 22″ is a little less than 2 feet. π is a little more than 3. So the circumference of the wheel is about 6 feet. In 300 revolutions, the bike should go about 1800 feet. The answer seems reasonable.

You can compute the length of an arc if you know its radius and the degree measure of the arc.

Example 3 In ⊙O, OB = 1.3 cm and m∠AOB = 80. Find the length of $\overset{\frown}{AB}$.

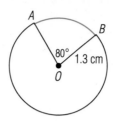

Solution m∠AOB = 80, so m$\overset{\frown}{AB}$ = 80°. Thus $\overset{\frown}{AB}$ covers $\frac{80}{360}$ of the entire circumference of ⊙O. So:

$$AB = \frac{80}{360} \cdot C$$
$$= \frac{80}{360} \cdot (2\pi r)$$
$$= \frac{80}{360} \cdot 2 \cdot \pi \cdot 1.3$$
$$= \frac{208\pi}{360} \text{ cm}$$
$$\approx 1.8 \text{ cm}.$$

Questions

Covering the Reading

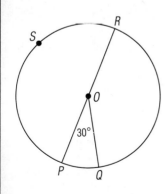

In 1–6, $\overline{PR}$ is a diameter of ⊙O at the left below.

1. Name the minor arcs in the drawing.

2. a. m$\overset{\frown}{PQ}$ = __?__
   b. m$\overset{\frown}{PSQ}$ = __?__

3. a. m$\overset{\frown}{PSR}$ = __?__
   b. m$\overset{\frown}{PQR}$ = __?__
   c. m$\overset{\frown}{QR}$ = __?__

4. P and Q are the __?__ of $\overset{\frown}{PQ}$.

5. ∠ROQ is a(n) __?__ angle of ⊙O.

6. $\overset{\frown}{PSR}$ is a(n) __?__.

7. What is the difference between arc length and arc measure?

8. Circumference is a synonym for __?__.

9. Is circumference an arc length or an arc measure?

10. Define: π.

11. π is often approximated by the fraction __?__ or the decimal __?__.

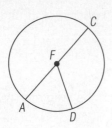

In 12 and 13, use ⊙F at the left.

12. a. Name all radii shown.
 b. Name all diameters shown.
 c. If $CF = 7$, then $FD = \underline{\ \ ?\ \ }$.
 d. If $CA = 28$, then $FD = \underline{\ \ ?\ \ }$.
 e. If $CA = 6x$, then $FC = \underline{\ \ ?\ \ }$.

13. If $CA = 8$, find the circumference of the circle: **a.** exactly; **b.** to the nearest tenth.

14. In Example 2 of this lesson, how far will the bike travel in five minutes if the wheel turns 210 revolutions per minute?

15. In ⊙O below, m$\widehat{AB} = 30°$. Find the length of $\widehat{AB}$:
 a. exactly;
 b. to the nearest hundredth.

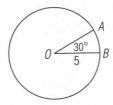

Applying the Mathematics

16. A square wall ten meters on a side contains a circular pond. How long is it around the pond?

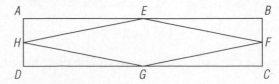

10 m

17. On the Allen-Bradley Company building in Milwaukee, Wisconsin, are four clocks facing in four different directions. The minute hand on each clock is 20′ long. How far does the tip of the minute hand travel in a day
 a. measured in degrees;
 b. measured in feet?

Allen-Bradley clock, Milwaukee, Wisconsin

18. Suppose it takes you 110 seconds to walk around a circular garden. At this rate, about how long would it take you to walk straight through the garden along a diameter?

Review

19. *E, F, G,* and *H* are midpoints of the sides of rectangle *ABCD*. If $AB = 8$ and $BC = 6$, find the perimeter of *EFGH*. *(Lessons 8-7, 8-1)*

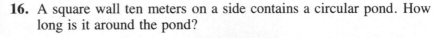

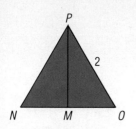

20. △*PON* is equilateral. *M* is the midpoint of $\overline{NO}$.
  a. Give the length of $\overline{PM}$.
  b. Give the area of △*PON*. *(Lessons 8-7, 8-5)*

In 21–26, give a formula for the indicated quantity.
(Lessons 8-6, 8-5, 8-3, 8-1)

21. area of a trapezoid

22. area of a rectangle

23. perimeter of a square

24. perimeter of a kite

25. the measure of an angle in a regular *n*-gon

26. area of a triangle

In 27 and 28, $\ell \parallel m$, $\overline{XZ} \parallel \overline{YW}$, and ∠ *ZXY* is acute.

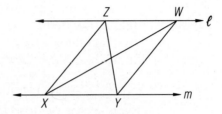

27. *Multiple choice.* *(Lesson 8-5)*
  (a) Area(△*XYZ*) > Area(△*XYW*)
  (b) Area(△*XYZ*) = Area(△*XYW*)
  (c) Area(△*XYZ*) < Area(△*XYW*)

28. *Multiple choice.*
  If *q* is the perimeter of △*XYZ* and *r* is the perimeter of △*XYW*, then
  (a) *q* > *r*   (b) *q* = *r*   (c) *q* < *r*. *(Lesson 8-1)*

29. Refer to Example 2. How fast is the rider going in miles per hour?
  (Previous course)

30. a. Measure the circumference of your neck with a tape measure to the nearest half inch or centimeter.
  b. Assuming your neck is circular, use your measurement to estimate your neck's radius.
  c. What would be another way to get its radius? (Cutting is not allowed, of course!)

The Area of a Circle

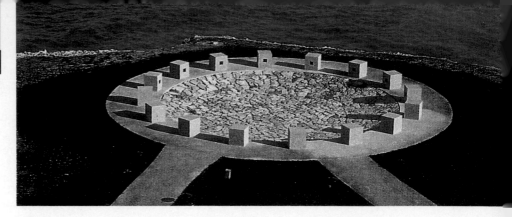

These rocks, grouped to form a circle, can be found at a lookout point where the Gulf of Mexico and the Carribean Sea meet. The design is based on an old Mayan style.

A circle is not a polygon. But it can be approximated as closely as you want by a polygon. We could try to get its area by finer and finer grids, using the method in Lesson 8-4. However, it is easier to use three-sided *wedges* (or *sectors*) and put them together to form a figure like a parallelogram.

Circle *A* at the left below has radius *r*. It is split into 16 sectors. Each sector is close to a triangle with altitude *r* and a curved base. At the right the sectors are rearranged to form something like a parallelogram. The height of the "parallelogram" is *r*. Each base is a union of 8 arcs. So each base is half the circumference.

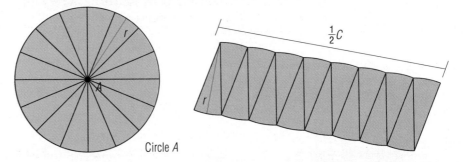

Circle *A*

As the number of wedges increases, the wedges more closely form a parallelogram, and the area of the parallelogram becomes a better approximation to the area of the circle. We say that the limit of the area of the parallelogram is the area of the circle. This argument yields a famous formula.

Circle Area Formula:

The area A of a circle with radius r is $A = \pi r^2$.

$A = \pi r^2$

Proof

Use the drawing on page 402 of a circle split into wedges and reformed to approximate a parallelogram.

Conclusions	Justifications
Area(circle A) = limit of Area(parallelogram)	Congruence and Additive Properties of Area
$= h \cdot b$	Parallelogram Area Formula
$= r \cdot \frac{1}{2}C$	Substitution
$= r \cdot \frac{1}{2} \cdot 2\pi r$	definition of circumference
$= r \cdot \pi r$	Assoc. Prop. of Multiplication
$= \pi r^2$	definition of exponent

Example 1 Find the area of the top of a manhole cover with diameter 22″.

Solution Since $d = 22″$, $r = 11″$.
$$\text{Area(circle)} = \pi r^2$$
$$= 121\pi$$
$$\approx 121 \cdot 3.14$$
$$\approx 380 \text{ square inches}$$

Recall that the probability of an event is the ratio
$$\frac{\text{measure of event}}{\text{measure of all possibilities}}.$$

Example 2 A circle is drawn through the four vertices of a square with side 7 cm.
a. If a dart is thrown at random into the circle, what is the probability that it lands in the square?
b. Approximate the area of the shaded region between the square and the circle.

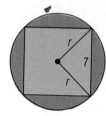

Solution **a.** The event is landing in the square. The probability equals
$$\frac{\text{area of square}}{\text{area of circle}}.$$
The area of the square is 7^2 cm², or 49 cm². For the area of the circle, find its radius first. $r^2 + r^2 = 7^2$, so $2r^2 = 49$, so $r^2 = \frac{49}{2}$ cm. The area of the circle is πr^2, or $\frac{49\pi}{2}$ cm². Thus the probability is

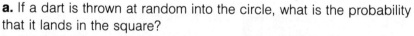

$$\frac{49 \text{ cm}^2}{\frac{49\pi}{2} \text{ cm}^2} = \frac{1}{\frac{\pi}{2}} = \frac{2}{\pi}.$$

With a calculator, $\frac{2}{\pi} \approx 0.64$, so the probability is about 64%. About 64% of the area of the circle is within the square.
b. Area(shaded region) = Area(circle) − Area(square)
$$= \frac{49\pi}{2} - 49$$
$$\approx 77 - 49$$
$$\approx 28 \text{ cm}^2$$

Covering the Reading

1. A circle with radius 10 below is split into 16 sectors. The 16 sectors can be put together (as in the lesson) into a "parallelogram."
   a. What is the height of the parallelogram?
   b. What is the base of the parallelogram?
   c. What is the area of the parallelogram?

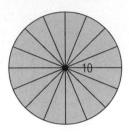

In 2–4, give the exact area.

2. a circle with radius r

3. a circle with radius 70″

4. a circle with diameter 10 inches

5. Estimate the area of the circle in Question 3 to the nearest square inch.

6. In Example 2, suppose that the side of the square was 9 cm.
   a. If a dart is thrown at random into the circle, what is the probability that it lands in the square?
   b. Approximate the area of the shaded region between the square and the circle (to the nearest tenth of a cm²).

Applying the Mathematics

7. a. Give the area of a field that can be irrigated by a circular sprinkler 60 meters long rotating around a fixed point.
   b. Give the circumference of this field, to the nearest meter.

8. A circle has area 144π. Find:
   a. its radius;   **b.** its diameter;   **c.** its circumference.

9. *ABCD* below is a square with side 8 and $\overline{AB}$ is a diameter of the circle.
   a. Find the area of the shaded region.
   b. Find the perimeter of the shaded region.

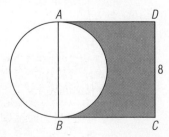

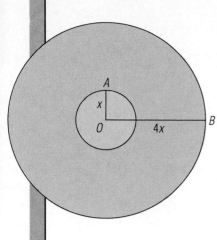

10. **a.** On a 10″ pizza, what measures 10″: the radius, diameter, or circumference?
    b. How many times more ingredients are in an 18″ pizza than in a 10″ pizza with the same thickness?

11. Use the concentric circles at the left. $OA = x$, $OB = 4x$. The small circle is a bull's eye on a dart board. If a dart lands randomly in the large circle, what is the probability it will land: **a.** in the bull's eye; **b.** outside the bull's eye?

12. Eight circular metal disks are to be cut out of a 12 cm by 24 cm piece of metal. The rest is wasted.
    a. How much of the metal is wasted?
    b. What percent of the metal is wasted?

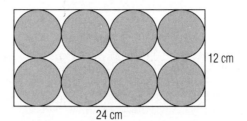

12 cm

24 cm

Review

13. In ⊙O below, $OA = 15$ and m∠$AOB = 72$.
    a. Find m$\overarc{AB}$.
    b. Find the length of $\overarc{AB}$. *(Lesson 8-8)*

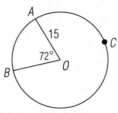

14. A windmill is turning in the wind. If the length of a blade is 12 meters and it makes 15 revolutions in a minute, how far will a point on its tip have traveled in an hour? *(Lesson 8-8)*

15. ⊙C below is contained by a square with sides of length 90. What is the circumference of ⊙C? *(Lesson 8-8)*

windmill in Consuegra, Spain

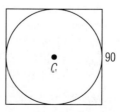

90

16. A rectangle has dimensions 16″ by 22″.
    a. Find the lengths of its diagonals. *(Lesson 8-7)*
    b. Find its perimeter. *(Lessons 8-7, 8-1)*

17. The two legs of a right triangle have lengths $4x$ and $9x$.
    a. What is the area of the triangle?
    b. What is the perimeter of the triangle? *(Lesson 8-7, 8-5, 8-1)*

18. Can 13, 84, and 85 be the lengths of sides of a right triangle? *(Lesson 8-7)*

19. Estimate the area of Lake Michigan **a.** using the grid at the left, then **b.** using the grid at the right. *(Lesson 8-4)*

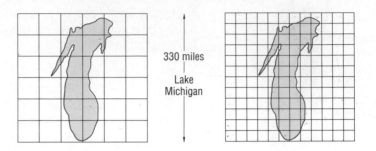

20. Find the area of the polygon with vertices (4, 3), (4, -3), (-4, -3), and (-4, 3). *(Lesson 8-3)*

In 21 and 22, use parallelogram *DEFG* below.

21. Find the measures of angles *D*, *E*, and *F*. *(Lesson 5-5)*

22. Trace and draw a part of a tessellation with *DEFG* as the fundamental region. *(Lesson 8-2)*

23. Fill in the blanks in these conversion formulas. *(Previous course)*
   a. 1 centimeter = __?__ meter
   b. 1 yard = __?__ inches
   c. 1 mile = __?__ yards

Exploration

24. Find a soft drink or other can with a circular base.
   a. Measure the diameter *d* with a ruler as accurately as you can.
   b. Measure the circumference *C* by rolling it, again as accurately as you can.
   c. Calculate $\frac{C}{d}$ to the nearest hundredth.
   d. What number should $\frac{C}{d}$ approximate?
   e. Why isn't $\frac{C}{d}$ exactly that number?

Summary

This chapter is devoted to deriving and applying formulas for area, perimeter, and circumference. Perimeter measures the boundary of a figure. An equilateral n-gon with sides of length s has perimeter ns. A circle with diameter d has circumference πd. The length of an arc is a fraction of that circumference.

In contrast to perimeter, area measures the space enclosed by a figure. This space can be estimated by using congruent squares. With finer and finer grids, even the areas of irregular shapes can be estimated. Grids are examples of tessellations, patterns in which congruent copies of a single region cover the plane. Tessellations are based on rotation, translation, and reflection images of a fundamental region.

Mathematics captivates the imagination of many people because so many things can be derived from just a few simple statements. In this chapter, that idea is exemplified by the derivation of many area formulas from just a few basic properties.

A rectangle with dimensions h and b has area hb. Splitting it with a diagonal, two congruent right triangles are formed. Each has area $\frac{1}{2}hb$. By splitting into right triangles, the area of any triangle can be shown to be $\frac{1}{2}hb$. Putting two triangles together, the area of any trapezoid is $\frac{1}{2}h(b_1 + b_2)$. A special case of a trapezoid is a parallelogram, whose area is hb. (See the List of Formulas at the back of the book for a summary of these and other formulas.)

This chapter contains some of the most important formulas in all geometry. Areas of right triangles and squares help to develop the Pythagorean Theorem: In a right triangle with legs a and b and hypotenuse c, $c^2 = a^2 + b^2$. The area of triangles can be put together to derive the formula $A = \pi r^2$ for the area of a circle.

Vocabulary

Below are the most important terms and phrases for this chapter.
For the starred (*) terms you should be able to give a definition of the term. For the other terms you should be able to give a general description and a specific example of each.

Lesson 8-1
*perimeter
equilateral polygon
equiangular polygon
Equilateral Polygon Perimeter
 Formula: $p = ns$

Lesson 8-2
tessellation, tessellate
fundamental region

Lesson 8-3
dimensions
Area Postulate:
 Uniqueness Property of Area
 Rectangle Formula: $A = \ell w$
 Congruence Property of Area
 Additive Property of Area
Area(F)
nonoverlapping regions

Lesson 8-4
irregular region
grid, limit

Lesson 8-5
*altitude of a triangle
Right Triangle Area Formula:
 $A = \frac{1}{2}hb$
Triangle Area Formula:
 $A = \frac{1}{2}hb$

Lesson 8-6
triangulate
*altitude of a trapezoid
Trapezoid Area Formula:
 $A = \frac{1}{2}h(b_1 + b_2)$
Parallelogram Area Formula:
 $A = hb$

Lesson 8-7
square root
Pythagorean Theorem:
 $c^2 = a^2 + b^2$
Pythagorean Converse Theorem
Pythagorean triple

Lesson 8-8
*central angle of a circle
arc, minor arc, $\overset{\frown}{AB}$,
major arc, $\overset{\frown}{ADB}$
semicircle, endpoints of an arc
*degree measure of an arc
circumference, arc length,
chord, *π (pi)
Circle Circumference Formula:
 $C = \pi d$

Lesson 8-9
wedge, sector
Circle Area Formula: $A = \pi r^2$

Progress Self-Test

Directions: Take this test as you would take a test in class. Then check your work with the solutions in the Selected Answers section in the back of this book. You will need graph paper and a calculator in addition to pencil and paper.

1. Draw part of a tessellation with trapezoid *PQRS* as a fundamental region.

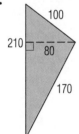

2. A rectangle has area 200 m² and length 25 m. What is its width?

3. The perimeter of a regular hexagon is *q*. What is the length of a side?

In 4–6, give the area of the figure.

4.

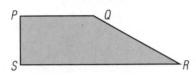

5.

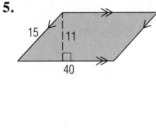

6.

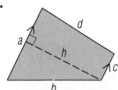

7. The two legs of a right triangle have lengths 11 and 60. What is the perimeter of the triangle?

8. A frame 2″ wide is put around a rectangular painting that is 12″ by 17″. What is the outside perimeter of the frame?

In 9 and 10, Circle *A* with radius 5 is contained in square *WXYZ*.

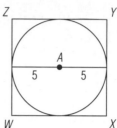

9. How much longer is it to go around the square than to go around the circle?

10. If a point is chosen at random inside the square, what is the probability that it is in the circle?

In 11 and 12, $\overrightarrow{OC}$ bisects right angle *DOB* in ⊙*O* below. *OB* = 20.

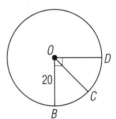

11. What is the length of arc $\overparen{CD}$?

12. What is m$\overparen{CBD}$?

13. In the map and grid shown below, each small square of the grid has side length 10 miles. Use the method of this chapter to determine the area of Hawaii.

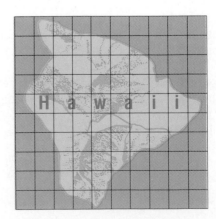

14. A 5-meter ladder is resting against a wall. Its base is 1.8 meters away from the wall. How high up the wall will it reach? Answer to the nearest tenth of a meter.

15. In October, 1989, an earthquake measuring 7.1 on the Richter scale caused substantial damage in San Francisco, 80 miles from the epicenter in Santa Cruz, California. To the nearest hundred square miles, how much area was within 80 miles of the epicenter?

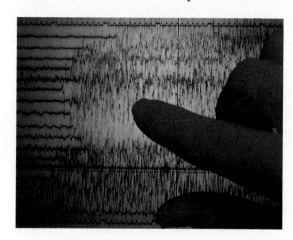

16. A room measures 9 ft by 15 ft. How many square yards of carpeting arc needed to cover the floor?

17. A park is shaped like a square and has a perimeter of 2640 ft. What is its area?

18. Explain how the area formula for a right triangle is deduced from the formula for the area of a rectangle.

19. a. Could 11, 60, and 61 be lengths of sides of a right triangle?
   b. Why or why not?

20. A triangle has vertices (8, 0), (-1, 0), and (0, 1). Find its area.

21. Find the area of the octagon below.

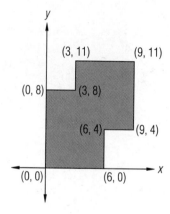

Chapter Review

Questions on **SPUR** Objectives

SPUR stands for **S**kills, **P**roperties, **U**ses, and **R**epresentations.
These Chapter Review questions are grouped according to the
SPUR Objectives for this chapter.

SKILLS deal with the procedures used to get answers.

▣ **Objective A:** *Draw a tessellation using a given figure as a fundamental region.* (*Lesson 8-2*)

In 1–3, trace the figure and draw part of a tessellation using the figure as a fundamental region.

1.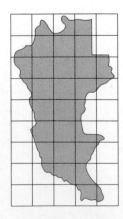

2.

3.

▣ **Objective B:** *Describe or apply a method for determining the area of an irregular-shaped region.* (*Lesson 8-4*)

In 4 and 5, two grids cover the same island. Each small square at the left below is 100 feet on a side. Estimate the area of the island (in square feet).

4.

5.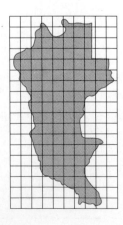

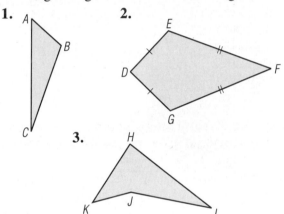

6. A metal piece is to be made in the shape shown below. Explain how the amount of metal needed for that piece could be estimated.

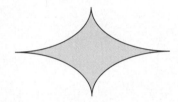

▣ **Objective C:** *Calculate perimeters of parallelograms, kites, and equilateral polygons from lengths of sides, and vice-versa.* (*Lesson 8-1*)

In 7–10, give the perimeter of the figure.

7. a kite in which one side has length 10 and another side has length 6

8. a rhombus in which one side has length t

9. a regular pentagon in which one side has length 47 meters

10. a square whose area is 324 square feet

11. The perimeter of a rectangle is 28 cm. One side has length 4 cm. What is the length of the other side?

12. If the perimeter of an equilateral triangle is P, what is the length of a side of the triangle?

13. *ABCD* is a parallelogram pictured below. If its perimeter is 75, what are the lengths of its sides?

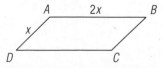

14. An equilateral hexagon has perimeter 1. What is the length of each side?

■ Objective D: *Calculate areas of squares, rectangles, parallelograms, trapezoids, and triangles from relevant lengths.* (*Lessons 8-3, 8-5, 8-6*)

In 15–19, calculate the area of the figure.

15. a square whose perimeter is 100 feet

16. the rectangle *MOST* drawn below

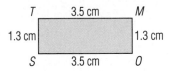

17. △*EFG* at the right in which *GE* = 36*x*

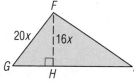

18. a trapezoid with bases 11 and 13 and altitude 6

19. the triangle with sides of lengths 13, 14, and 15 drawn here

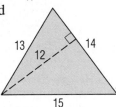

20. Find the area of the isosceles trapezoid below.

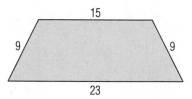

■ Objective E: *Given areas of figures, determine relevant lengths.* (*Lessons 8-3, 8-5, 8-6*)

21. A right triangle has area 60 square millimeters and one leg has length 6 millimeters. What is the length of the other leg?

22. The bases of a trapezoid have lengths 20 feet and 30 feet and the trapezoid has area 800 square feet. What is the length of the altitude of the trapezoid?

23. A square has area $12.25s^2$. What is the length of a side of this square?

24. Can a rectangle with area 20 have one side of length 21? If so, draw such a rectangle. If not, tell why not.

■ Objective F: *Calculate lengths and measures of arcs, the circumference, and the area of a circle from relevant lengths, and vice-versa.* (*Lesson 8-8, 8-9*)

25. Give the circumference and area of a circle with radius 10: **a.** exactly; **b.** estimated to the nearest hundredth.

26. Give the circumference and area of a circle with diameter 6 cm: **a.** exactly; **b.** estimated to the nearest cm or sq cm.

27. A circle has area 144π. What is its diameter?

28. A circle has circumference 40*x* meters. What is its radius?

29. $\overline{BD}$ is a diameter of ⊙*O*. m∠*AOD* = 20.
  a. Find m$\widehat{AD}$.
  b. Find m$\widehat{AB}$.
  c. Find m$\widehat{ADB}$.

30. What is the length of a 60° arc of a circle with radius 9?

■ Objective G: *Apply the Pythagorean Theorem to calculate lengths of sides in right triangles and other figures.* (*Lesson 8-7*)

In 31 and 32, find the length of the missing side.

31. 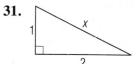   **32.**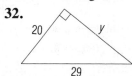

33. The two legs of a right triangle have lengths 6*x* and 7*x*. What is the perimeter of the triangle?

34. The hypotenuse of a right triangle is 50 and one leg is 40. What is the area of the triangle?

35. A rectangle has dimensions 60 cm by 45 cm. What is the length of a diagonal?

■ Objective H: *Apply the Pythagorean Converse.* (*Lesson 8-7*)

In 36–39, could the numbers be lengths of sides of a right triangle?

36. 8, 31, 32   **37.** 16, 30, 34

38. 1, 2, √3   **39.** 2, 4, 20

PROPERTIES deal with the principles behind the mathematics.

■ **Objective I:** *Tell how to derive formulas for area.*
(Lessons 8-3, 8-5, 8-6, 8-9)

40. Explain how the area formula for a trapezoid is derived from the formula for the area of a triangle.

41. Explain how the area formula for a parallelogram is derived from the formula for the area of a trapezoid.

42. Give dimensions of a rectangle with perimeter 200 ft and area less than 100 ft^2.

43. In the figure below, $\ell \parallel m$.
Multiple choice.
  (a) Area ($\triangle ABC$) < Area ($\triangle ABD$)
  (b) Area ($\triangle ABC$) = Area ($\triangle ABD$)
  (c) Area ($\triangle ABC$) > Area ($\triangle ABD$)

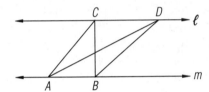

44. $\overline{AB}$ is a diameter of $\odot O$, $\overline{AO}$ is a diameter of $\odot P$. $AP = x$. Find the area of the shaded region.

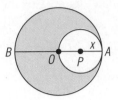

45. *WXYZ* is a square, with segments as marked. Find the area of the shaded region.

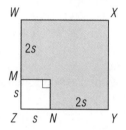

46. If the unit of the perimeter of a figure is millimeters, what is a natural unit for the area of the figure?

USES deal with applications of mathematics in real situations.

■ **Objective J:** *Apply perimeter formulas for parallelograms, kites, and regular polygons to real situations. (Lessons 8-1, 8-7)*

47. A frame 3 cm wide is put around a rectangular-shaped painting that is 8 cm by 20 cm. What is the outside perimeter of the frame?

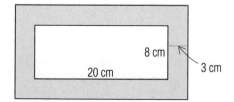

48. A stop sign is a regular octagon. Since it is metal, it could be sharp. Consequently, the manufacturer of the sign wishes to dull its edges by wrapping them with tape. If one edge of the sign has length *k,* what is the total length of tape needed?

49. A rectangular room is 9′ by 11′. Baseboard is to be put around the room in all places except the 3′ wide door. How many feet of baseboard are needed?

50. How long would it take for a person to walk around the trapezoidal field pictured here at a rate of 300 feet per minute?

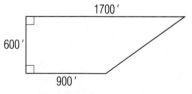

■ **Objective K:** *Apply the Pythagorean Theorem in real situations. (Lesson 8-7)*

51. If a 20-foot ladder reaches 18 feet high on a wall, how far away from the wall is the bottom of the ladder?

52. A rectangular field is 100 meters by 200 meters. To the nearest meter, how long is it diagonally across the field?

■ **Objective L:** *Apply formulas for areas of squares, rectangles, parallelograms, trapezoids, and triangles to real situations. (Lessons 8-3, 8-5, 8-6)*

53. What is the area of a square park that is 210 meters on a side?

54. A person wishes to tile a bathroom floor with 1″ square tiles. How many tiles will be needed if the floor is 6′ long and 4′ wide?

55. What is the area of the field pictured in Question 50?

56. A triangular piece of fabric is needed for a sail. If the sail is to be 14′ high and is 15′ long at the base, about how much fabric will be used?

57. The larger square in Question 45 represents a farm, and the smaller square has been planted with corn. If a skydiver falls onto the farm, what is the probability he will fall on the part planted with corn?

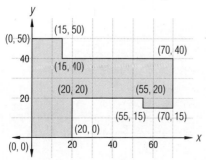

■ **Objective M:** *Apply formulas for the area and circumference of a circle to real situations. (Lessons 8-8, 8-9)*

58. Due to a chemical spill, the authorities had to evacuate all people within 3 km of the spill. To the nearest tenth of a square kilometer, how much area had to be evacuated?

59. A park 600 feet square contains a circular path, as pictured at the right. To the nearest foot, how long is it once around the path?

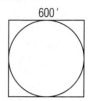

600′

60. A car's tire has a radius of 1 foot. How many revolutions does the tire make while the car goes 1 mile? (1 mile = 5280 feet)

61. For her dog, Betsy wants to make a circular play area surrounded by a fence. She has 100 feet of fence. What is the diameter of the largest play area she can make?

62. Use the figure for Question 44. If a dart lands at random in the larger circle, what is the probability that it will land in the smaller circle?

REPRESENTATIONS deal with pictures, graphs, or objects that illustrate concepts.

■ **Objective N:** *Determine the areas of polygons on a coordinate plane. (Lessons 8-3, 8-5, 8-6)*

63. Find the area of the decagon below.

64. A triangle has vertices (7, -4), (-3, -4), and (-1, 11). Find its area.

65. The grid is in unit squares. Find the area of quadrilateral *ABCD*.

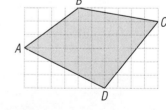

66. Find the area of the quadrilateral with the given vertices. Assume *a, b,* and *c* are positive, with *b* > *c*.

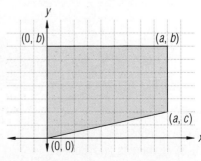

CHAPTER 8   Chapter Review   **413**

Three-Dimensional Figures

The world is not flat. Everything you touch or see, from paper to pencil, from house to car, from city to planet, is not in a single plane. The world is three-dimensional. This is why it was necessary for artists, if they wanted to convey reality, to develop the techniques of perspective.

Every figure has counterparts in a higher dimension.

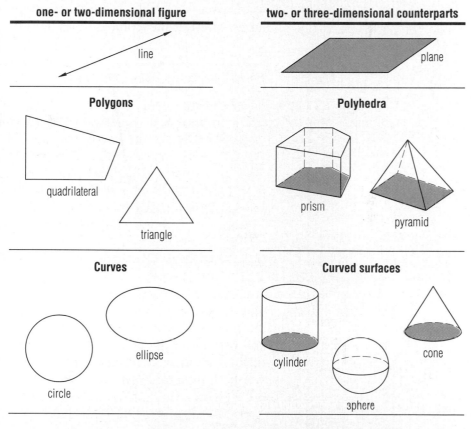

one- or two-dimensional figure	two- or three-dimensional counterparts
line	plane
Polygons	**Polyhedra**
quadrilateral	prism
triangle	pyramid
Curves	**Curved surfaces**
ellipse	cylinder
circle	cone
	3phere

In this chapter, you will learn the important properties of the above basic three-dimensional shapes, how to draw them, and how they are used. You will also see how they are related to the two-dimensional figures you already know.

9-1

Points, Lines, and Planes in Space

Recall from Chapter 1 that the three terms "point," "line," and "plane" are undefined because we cannnot define every word and because, in different situations, they may have different meanings. A point could be an ordered pair, a location, a node of a network, or a dot. A line might be an arc connecting two nodes in a network, a set of ordered pairs described by an equation like $y = 2x + 5$, or a line of sight. In order to reason precisely with points and lines, it is necessary to make assumptions about them. Our assumptions were summarized in the Point-Line-Plane Postulate, repeated here.

Point-Line-Plane Postulate (Lesson 1-7):

a. Given a line in a plane, there exists a point in the plane not on the line. Given a plane in space, there exists a point in space not on the plane.

b. Every line is a set of points that can be put into a one-to-one correspondence with the real numbers, with any point on it corresponding to 0 and any other point corresponding to 1.

c. Through any two points, there is exactly one line.

d. On a number line, there is a unique distance between two points.

Just as you have an idea about what points and lines should be, you may have ideas about planes. Most of the figures you have seen in the previous chapters are coplanar. Think of a plane as being flat and having no thickness, like a tabletop that goes on forever. In fact, mathematicians draw a plane in three dimensions like they would draw a tabletop.

table

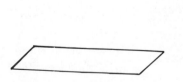

plane (as seen slightly
from above)

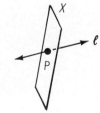

line ℓ intersecting plane X
at point P

To convey these ideas precisely, three new parts—**e**, **f**, and **g**—are added to the Point-Line-Plane Postulate. The remainder of this lesson discusses these three new parts and presents other information about planes.

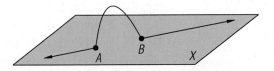

e. If two points lie in a plane, the line containing them lies in the plane.

This guarantees that segments connecting points do not jump out of planes. It implies that planes are flat and go on forever.

impossible because of **e**

f. Through three noncollinear points, there is exactly one plane.

Part **f** is sometimes restated: Three noncollinear points determine a plane.

A tripod works on the principle of part **f**. It balances on the plane containing the tips of its three legs even when on the side of a hill (as long as its center of gravity is above the triangular region determined by the points). But a chair with four legs will not balance on a floor unless the tips of the legs are coplanar.

The tripod balances on the plane containing A, B, and C.

The chair is sturdy only if E, F, G, and H lie in the same plane.

Three noncollinear points A, B, and C also determine other figures. They can determine a triangle ABC or $\angle ABC$; a line $\overleftrightarrow{AB}$ and a point C not on it; two intersecting lines $\overleftrightarrow{AC}$ and $\overleftrightarrow{BC}$; and so on. Through any of these there is exactly one plane.

However, there are many planes through a single line. Think of an open door in various positions. At each position a broad side of the door determines a plane through an imaginary line determined by the hinges. The planes are called **intersecting planes.**

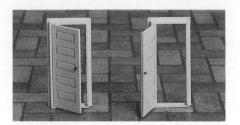

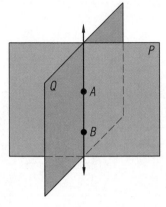

Intersecting planes P and Q
$P \cap Q = \overleftrightarrow{AB}$

g. If two different planes have a point in common, then their intersection is a line.

Part **g** implies that planes, like lines, have no thickness. This part also implies that it is impossible for two different planes to intersect in just a single point. Even though planes cannot be drawn as if they go on forever, they do.

A sewing needle piercing fabric is like a line intersecting a plane.

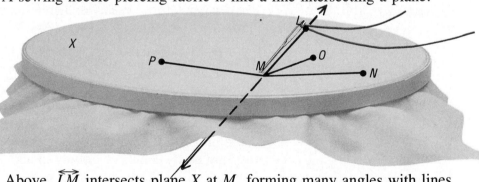

Above, $\overleftrightarrow{LM}$ intersects plane X at M, forming many angles with lines in the plane through M. Three of the angles are $\angle LMO$, $\angle LMN$, and $\angle LMP$. The measure of the smallest of all the possible angles defines the angle measure between the line and the plane. This cannot be greater than 90°. In a three-dimensional drawing like the one above, it is difficult to tell if the smallest angle has been drawn.

If the measure of an angle between a line and a plane is 90°, then the line is *perpendicular* to the plane. Think of a flagpole. The pole is perpendicular to any line on the ground through the pole. This makes the pole perpendicular to the ground.

Definition:

A **line ℓ is perpendicular to a plane X** if and only if it is perpendicular to every line in X through their intersection.

The ideas of parallel and perpendicular lines have counterparts with planes. Two planes are **parallel planes** if and only if they have no points in common, or they are identical. As with parallel lines, the distance between parallel planes is measured along any perpendicular segment connecting the planes. The distance to a plane from a point not on it is measured along the perpendicular segment to the plane from the point.

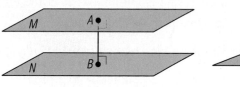

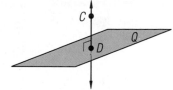

parallel planes M and N
distance AB between them

$\overleftrightarrow{CD}$ perpendicular to plane Q
distance CD from point C to plane Q

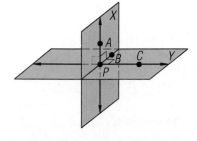

Suppose planes X and Y intersect in $\overleftrightarrow{PB}$, as shown at the left. Then the planes are **perpendicular planes** if and only if, when $\overline{PA} \perp \overline{PB}$ in X and $\overline{PC} \perp \overline{PB}$ in Y, then $\overline{PA} \perp \overline{PC}$ in the plane determined by A, P, and C.

Questions

Covering the Reading

In 1–6, name a higher dimensional counterpart for the one- or two-dimensional idea.

1. line

2. polygons

3. circle

4. collinear

5. perpendicular lines

6. If two lines in a plane are perpendicular to the same line, then they are parallel.

In 7–10, draw the figure.

7. two parallel planes

8. a plane as seen slightly from above

9. two intersecting planes

10. a line perpendicular to a plane

11. a. When will a three-legged stool rest solidly on rough ground?
b. When will a four-legged stool rest solidly?
c. To what part of the Point-Line-Plane Postulate are the answers to **a** and **b** related?

12. Can the figure be contained by exactly one plane?
a. a line and a point not on the line
b. two intersecting lines
c. three non-collinear points
d. a triangle

13. The front and back walls of most classrooms are like parts of parallel planes. How is the distance between them measured?

14. How would you measure the distance from the upper right hand corner of this page to the floor?

Applying the Mathematics

In 15–17, think of a classroom having west, east, north, and south walls, a floor, and a ceiling. What in the classroom illustrates each idea?

15. two perpendicular planes

16. three planes each perpendicular to the other two

17. a line perpendicular to a plane

18. Draw a plane intersecting two parallel planes.

19. Draw a line that intersects a plane at a 30° angle.

20. A 180-foot tall pine tree is chopped down in a forest. When "timber" is yelled, what is the approximate measure of the angle through which the tree falls?

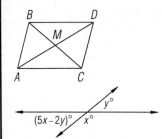

21. The *angle of inclination* of an object S in the sky is the measure of the angle formed by S, the observer, and the plane of the earth. For instance, a star halfway up to overhead has an angle of inclination of 45°.
   a. What is the largest possible angle of inclination?
   b. What is the angle of inclination of a star that is $\frac{1}{3}$ the way from the horizon to directly overhead?

Review

In 22–25, give a precise definition.

22. segment *(Lesson 1-8)*

23. polygon *(Lesson 2-7)*

24. quadrilateral *(Lesson 2-7)*

25. rectangle *(Lesson 5-2)*

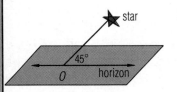

26. Given: M is the midpoint of $\overline{BC}$ and $\overline{AD}$ in the figure at the left.
   Prove: $ABDC$ is a parallelogram. *(Lesson 7-7)*

27. Two lines intersect with angle measures as pictured at the left. Find x and y. *(Lesson 3-2)*

28. Three identical cubes are pictured below. What symbol is on the face opposite the black disc? *(Lesson 1-5)*

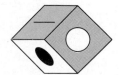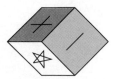

Exploration

29. Examine the legs of a chair at home or in school.
   a. Measure the angle between each leg and the plane of the floor.
   b. Are most of the chair legs you see perpendicular to the floor?

9-2

A carton is a surface.   A brick is a solid.

Prisms and Cylinders

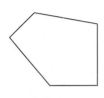

polygon

polygonal region

Recall that polygons and polygonal regions are different. A polygon refers to the boundary, whereas a polygonal region is the union of the boundary and the interior.

Similarly, a distinction is made with three-dimensional figures. A **surface** is the boundary of the three-dimensional figure. A **solid** is the union of the boundary and the region of space enclosed by the surface. The earth is a solid; a soap bubble is not, it is a surface. A brick is a solid; a carton is a surface. A solid is distinguished from a surface by shading and showing none of the hidden edges.

The carton pictured below exemplifies a surface called a **box.** The union of a box and its interior is called a **rectangular solid.** Boxes are as important in three dimensions as rectangles are in two, so it is useful to have names for their parts. In the next two paragraphs, we refer to the box drawn below.

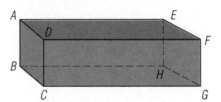

A box has six **faces.** Each face is a rectangular region. The faces are drawn as parallelograms to give the appearance of three dimensions. When two of the faces are horizontal, all faces can be identified by their locations: top *(AEFD)*, bottom *(BHGC)*, right *(EFGH)*, left *(ADCB)*, front *(DFGC)*, and back *(AEHB)*. The **opposite faces** lie in parallel planes. The plane of the front face is perpendicular to the planes of the top, bottom, and sides. At each corner of the box, three planes meet and each of these planes is perpendicular to the other two.

The 12 segments, $\overline{AB}$, $\overline{AE}$, $\overline{AD}$, $\overline{BH}$, etc., are the **edges** of the box. Each edge is perpendicular to two faces. For example, edge $\overline{CG}$ is perpendicular to the left face *ABCD* and the right face *EFGH*. The endpoints of the edges are the 8 **vertices** of the box, *A*, *B*, *C*, *D*, *E*, *F*, *G*, and *H*. Consider the lines $\overleftrightarrow{AD}$ and $\overleftrightarrow{CG}$. These lines are not coplanar. They are called **skew lines.**

Most classrooms are very much like big boxes. The floor and two adjacent walls meet in a bottom corner of the room just as the bottom, front, and left side of the box on the previous page meet. The plane of the floor is perpendicular to the plane of each wall.

Classrooms and cartons exemplify the same kind of geometric figure. Even a piece of notebook paper can be thought of as a three-dimensional figure, for it has thickness (about 0.002 inch or 0.05 mm). Thus, the geometric figure that best describes the *surface* of a piece of notebook paper is a box. Part of the power of geometry is that the same ideas may apply to things as small as parts of atoms or as large as galaxies, as wide as classrooms or as thin as paper.

A rectangular solid is a special type of *cylindric solid*. In general, to form a cylindric solid, begin with a two-dimensional region. Think of translating the region out of its plane into space in a fixed direction. Below, a circular region and a pentagonal region have been translated in the direction indicated by the arrow. Their translation images lie in a plane parallel to the original plane. Note that circles are represented by ovals to appear three-dimensional.

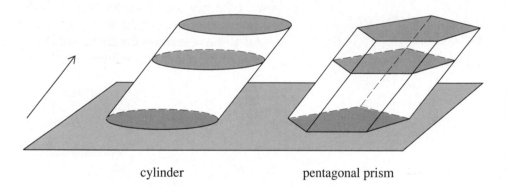

cylinder   pentagonal prism

Definition:

A **cylindric solid** is the set of points between a region and its translation image in space, including the region and its image.

The original region and its translation image are the **bases** of the cylindric solid. Bases are always congruent and always in parallel planes. The **height** or **altitude** of the solid is the distance between the planes of the bases. The rest of the surface of the solid is the **lateral surface.** The union of the bases and the lateral surface is the **cylindric surface.**

Two cylindric surfaces have special names.

When the direction of sliding is perpendicular to the plane of a base, a **right prism** or **right cylinder** is formed. A non-right prism or cylinder is called **oblique.** The cylinder drawn on the previous page is oblique; a can is a right cylinder.

Prisms are named by their bases. On page 422 a pentagonal prism is shown. A triangular prism has a triangle for its bases; a regular hexagonal prism has bases that are regular hexagons; and so on. The faces of the lateral surface of a prism are called **lateral faces** and are always parallelograms.

Tin cans, rolls of paper as shown in the adjacent photograph, rolls of steel, and new pencils (without erasers) are a few of the physical objects that illustrate cylindric solids or surfaces. You should be able to sketch any type of cylindric surface.

Example Sketch a right hexagonal prism.

Solution

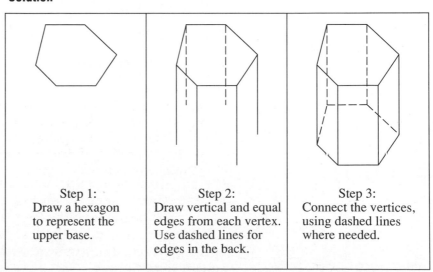

| Step 1: Draw a hexagon to represent the upper base. | Step 2: Draw vertical and equal edges from each vertex. Use dashed lines for edges in the back. | Step 3: Connect the vertices, using dashed lines where needed. |

To sketch an oblique prism, in Step 2 you would draw parallel, nonvertical, and equal edges.

If the base of a prism is a parallelogram, then the prism is a **parallelepiped.** All the faces of a parallelepiped are parallelograms, and opposite faces are congruent.

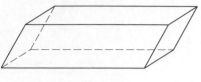

parallelepiped

A box is a right parallelepiped whose base is a rectangle. Thus its fancy name is **rectangular parallelepiped.** In this book the simpler name, *box,* is usually used.

From their definitions, the various types of cylindric surfaces fit nicely into a hierarchy.

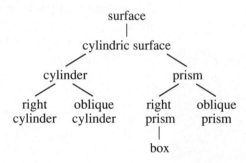

Questions

Covering the Reading

1. What is the difference between a solid and a surface?

2. Sketch: **a.** the surface of a brick; **b.** a solid brick.

3. Use the box drawn below.
   a. A segment connecting two vertices is a(n) __?__ .
   b. How many faces does the box have?
   c. Name faces in two parallel planes.
   d. How many edges does the box have?
   e. Name two parallel edges not on the same face.

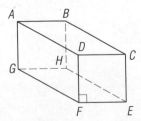

4. Give the special name for the surface of a cylindric solid:
   a. if its base is a hexagon;
   b. if its base is a circle.

In 5–8, sketch a figure of the given type.

5. triangular right prism

6. oblique regular octagonal prism

7. right cylinder

8. an oblique cylindrical solid

9. Another name for *rectangular parallelepiped* is __?__ .

In 10 and 11, tell which three-dimensional figure most resembles the real world object. Give as specific a name as you can, distinguishing solids from surfaces.

10. phonograph record (ignoring the hole in the middle)

11. unsharpened pencil without an eraser

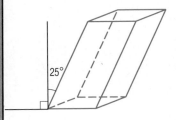

In 12 and 13, use the fact that the edges of an oblique prism are not perpendicular to the plane of the base. Such prisms seem to lean as does the famous Leaning Tower of Pisa. The amount of lean is measured from the perpendicular as shown at the left.

12. Sketch a triangular prism with a 30° lean.

13. Sketch a pentagonal prism with a 60° lean.

In 14 and 15, apply what you know about two-dimensional figures.

14. A box is drawn below. $BC = 4$, $HG = 12$, and $CG = 3$.
   a. Find the length of $\overline{FH}$.
   b. Find the length of $\overline{BH}$. (Hint: There are right triangles in this drawing.)
   c. Find the area of $\triangle BFH$.

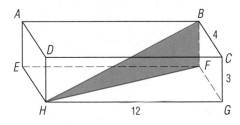

15. Refer to the oblique cylinder below.
   a. What is the height of the cylinder?
   b. What is the area of the lower base?

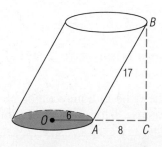

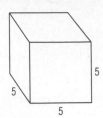

16. A cube is made of sticks, so it is hollow and you can stick a hand through it.
   a. If one edge has length 5, what is the total length of the sticks needed to make the cube?
   b. Generalize part **a** for edges of any length.

17. By changing the dotting of segments, a surface can be made to appear to be viewed from a different direction. Change the dashed lines in Figure 3 of the Example to cause the surface to appear to be viewed from underneath.

18. A computer artist wants to show a box on a computer screen. For this the artist has to think of the drawing as two-dimensional, even though it looks three-dimensional. Given the coordinates of *A*, *B*, *C*, and *D* as shown below, what are the coordinates of *E*, *F*, *G*, and *H*?

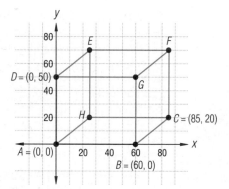

Review

19. Name a three-dimensional counterpart of intersecting lines. *(Lesson 9-1)*

20. Draw two perpendicular planes. *(Lesson 9-1)*

21. How many planes contain two given points *A* and *B*? *(Lesson 9-1)*

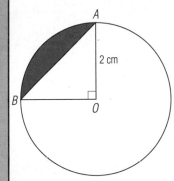

22. Circle *O* has radius 2 cm. What is the area of the shaded region between the circle and the hypotenuse of right triangle *AOB*? *(Lessons 8-9, 8-5)*

23. Draw a tessellation of the plane using equilateral triangles. *(Lesson 8-2)*

24. Define: **a.** coplanar; **b.** collinear. *(Lessons 1-2, 1-1)*

In 25–27, factor. *(Previous course)*

25. $2\ell w + 2wh$ **26.** $\pi r^2 + \pi h^2$ **27.** $\pi r^2 + 2\pi rh$

Exploration

28. Some prisms have a special property relative to light. What is this property?

29. The cells in honeycombs of bees are in the shapes of hexagonal prisms. Why do bees use this shape?

9-3

Pyramids and Cones

The pyramids of Giza, Egypt: Mycerinus, Chephren, and Cheops

Transamerica Building, San Francisco, California

One of the wonders of the world is the collection of pyramids of the ancient Egyptians. The first Egyptian pyramid built seems to have been designed by Imhotep for the pharaoh Zoser around 2600 or 2800 B.C. Pyramids were built in many places in the ancient world for temples and burial sites. The Transamerica building in San Francisco is a recent building shaped like a pyramid.

A *solid pyramid* is a set of points on and between a polygonal region (its *base*) and a point (its *vertex*) not in the plane of the region. Like prisms, pyramids are classified by the shape of the base. The Egyptian pyramids are square. Pictured below is a pentagonal pyramid.

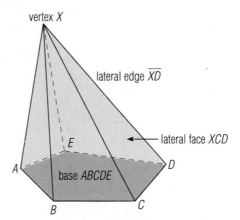

The parts of a pyramid are named in the figure. Segments connecting the vertex of the pyramid to the vertices of the base are **lateral edges.** The sides of the base are edges but not lateral edges. The polygonal regions formed by the edges are the **faces** of the pyramid. All faces, other than the base, are triangular regions, and are the **lateral faces** of the pyramid.

In a **regular pyramid,** the base must be a regular polygon and the segment connecting the vertex to the center of this polygon must be perpendicular to the plane of the base.

Example 1   Sketch a regular square pyramid.

Solution

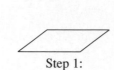

Step 1:
Use a parallelogram to represent a
square not in the plane of the paper,
and put a point above its center.

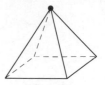

Step 2:
Sketch the lateral edges, using
dashed lines for the unseen edges.

A *cone* is like a pyramid in that it has one base and a vertex. But
the base of a cone is a circle. The line through the vertex and the
center of the circle is the **axis** of the cone. When the axis is perpendicular to the plane of the circle, the cone is called a **right cone.**
The surface of a cone other than the base is the **lateral surface** of
the cone. A **lateral edge** of a cone is any segment connecting its
vertex to a point on the circle.

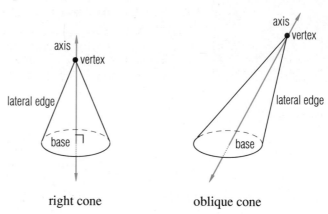

right cone   oblique cone

Pyramids and cones are two types of **conic surfaces.**

Definitions:

Given a region (the **base**) and a point (the **vertex**) not in the
plane of the region, a **conic solid** is the set of points between
the vertex and all points of the base, together with the vertex
and the base.

A **cone** is the surface of a conic solid whose base
is a circle.

A **pyramid** is the surface of a conic solid whose base
is a polygon.

The **height** or **altitude** of a pyramid or cone is the length of a segment from the vertex perpendicular to the plane of the base. In a regular pyramid or right cone, that segment contains the center of the base.

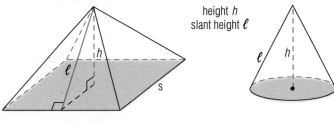

height h
slant height ℓ

regular pyramid   right cone

Each lateral face of a regular pyramid is an isosceles triangle congruent to all the other lateral faces. The altitude from the vertex on any one of the lateral faces of a regular pyramid (ℓ in the drawing above at the left) is called the **slant height** of the pyramid. The slant height is greater than the height but less than the length of a lateral edge. In a right cone, the slant height equals the length of a lateral edge.

■ ■ ■ ■ ■ ■ ■ ■■

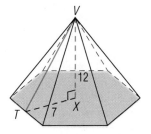

Example 2 Find the slant height VT of the regular hexagonal pyramid shown at the left below.

Solution   To find VT, create the right triangle VXT, where VX is the height. By the Pythagorean Theorem,

$$VT^2 = TX^2 + VX^2$$
$$= 7^2 + 12^2$$
$$= 193.$$
$$VT = \sqrt{193} \approx 14 \text{ units}$$

Notice the similarities between the definitions of cones and pyramids, and how they are related to cylinders and prisms. In the next chapter, you will see similarities in the formulas for the volumes and surface areas of these figures.

Below is a hierarchy of conic surfaces. Compare this hierarchy with the hierarchy of cylindric surfaces. They are very much alike.

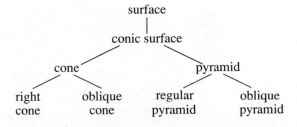

surface
|
conic surface

cone   pyramid

right   oblique   regular   oblique
cone   cone   pyramid   pyramid

1. A square pyramid is sketched below. Name:
   a. its base; **b.** its vertex;
   c. a lateral edge; **d.** a lateral face.

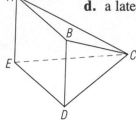

2. Draw a triangular pyramid.

3. O is the center of the circle drawn at the left, and $\overline{MO}$ is perpendicular to the plane of the circle.
   a. What is the name of the surface?
   b. Name its axis.
   c. Name a lateral edge.
   d. Name its vertex
   e. Name the base.
   f. What is its height?
   g. What is its slant height?

In 4–6, name each three-dimensional surface.

4.

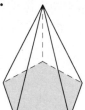

5.

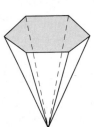

6.

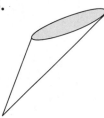

7. Sketch a cone with a base having radius 2 cm.

8. a. Sketch a regular octagonal pyramid.
   b. On your sketch, identify the height and the slant height.

9. In the regular pentagonal pyramid below, $RQ = 4$ and $PQ = 10$.
   a. Find the height.
   b. Find the slant height.

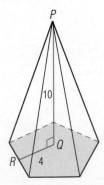

10. Suppose the base of a pyramid is an *n*-gon.
   a. How many faces has the pyramid?
   b. How many edges has the pyramid?

11. The base of a right cone has radius 3 cm. The height of the cone is 11 cm.
   a. Make a sketch of this cone.
   b. Find the slant height.
   c. Find the area of its base.

In 12 and 13, when a conic surface is cut by a plane parallel to its base, the part of the conic surface between and including the two parallel planes is called a **truncated cone** or **truncated pyramid.**

truncated
cone

truncated
pentagonal
pyramid

12. Where in a circus might you find a truncated cone?

13. Draw a truncated hexagonal pyramid. (Hint: Think of the original vertex as a vanishing point.)

14. Cut a quarter of a disk out of a piece of paper with dimensions as shown. Bend the paper so that $\overline{AB}$ and $\overline{AC}$ coincide and a cone is formed.
   a. What is the circumference of the base of this cone?
   b. What is the radius of the base of the cone (to the nearest tenth of an inch)?

15. Suppose you can only see the edges of a regular square pyramid and they glow in the dark. From where are you looking if you see it as shown?

   a.   **b.**   **c.**

   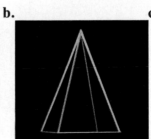   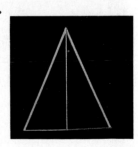

16. Define: cylindric solid. *(Lesson 9-2)*

17. What is the difference between a right cylinder and an oblique cylinder? *(Lesson 9-2)*

18. Tell how many different planes contain:
   a. three given noncollinear points;
   b. a given △*ABC*;
   c. a given line. *(Lesson 9-1)*

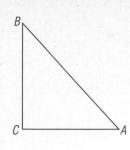

19. Given $\triangle ABC$ with m$\angle A = 50$, m$\angle B = 40$. What definition or theorem justifies each statement?
    a. m$\angle C = 90$
    b. $\overline{BC} \perp \overline{CA}$
    c. $\triangle ABC$ is a right triangle.
    d. $AC^2 + BC^2 = AB^2$ *(Lessons 8-7, 3-5, 3-2)*

20. Refer to the cube drawn below, in which $AT = 5$. Find:
    a. AB; b. EA; c. ET. *(Lessons 5-2, 8-7)*

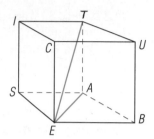

21. Of two rectangles, one has double the length and triple the width of the other. How do their areas compare? *(Lesson 8-3)*

In 22 and 23, factor. *(Previous course)*

22. $\pi r \ell + 2\pi r$ 23. $\ell h + wh$

Exploration

24. The pyramids of Egypt have been called one of the seven "wonders of the ancient world."
    a. Name one of the other wonders of the ancient world.
    b. Look in an almanac to find the name of a structure that has been called one of the wonders of today's world.

432

Plane Sections

A 3-dimensional counterpart of the circle is the *sphere*.

Definition:

A **sphere** is the set of points in space at a fixed distance (its radius) from a point (its center).

To draw a solid sphere (such as an orange or a baseball), shade the drawing as below at the left. To draw the surface (a basketball or a tennis ball), normally only an outline is drawn. Then arcs are added to give the illusion of depth.

solid sphere

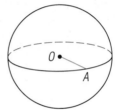

sphere

The terminology of a circle extends to spheres. Above at the right is a sphere with center O and radius OA. We also call the segment $\overline{OA}$ a **radius.** Similarly, the **diameter** of a sphere is a number that is twice the radius, while any segment connecting two points of the sphere and containing the center of the sphere is *a* diameter.

Think of slicing a melon. The boundary of the slice is like the intersection of a plane and a sphere. The intersection is a point if the plane just touches the sphere, and a circle otherwise. (This can be proved; see Question 20.) If the plane contains the center of the sphere, the intersection is called a **great circle** of the sphere. A great circle (shown in orange below) splits the sphere into two **hemispheres.** Otherwise the intersection is called a **small circle** (in blue below).

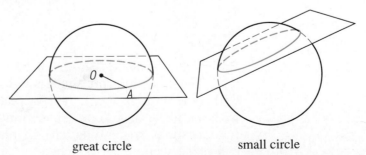

great circle   small circle

The earth is almost a solid sphere. One of its great circles is the equator. Points on the equator are about 6378 km (or 3963 miles) from the center of the earth. However, the earth has been slightly flattened by its rotation. The North and South poles are about 6357 km (or 3950 miles) from the center of the earth.

Below are two sketches of the earth. The sketch at the left is of the earth as seen from slightly north of the equator, so the equator is tilted. Notice how the oval representing the circle of the equator is widened to give the illusion of looking at it from above. Then the South Pole cannot be seen. The sketch at the right is as seen from the plane of the equator.

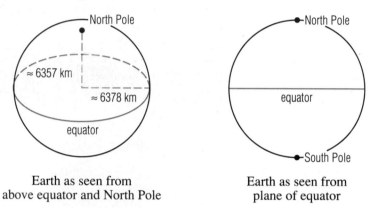

Earth as seen from
above equator and North Pole

Earth as seen from
plane of equator

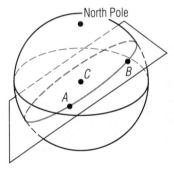

There are many planes through two points. So if points *A* and *B* are on a sphere, there are many planes that contain them. However, in Lesson 9-1, you learned there is only one plane that contains three noncollinear points. So if *A* and *B* are not endpoints of a diameter, there is only one plane containing *A*, *B*, and the sphere's center *C*. The intersection of that plane with the sphere is a great circle. To get from point *A* to point *B* on the earth, aircraft and ocean liners often travel along an arc of that great circle because it is the shortest way to get from *A* to *B*. The path they take is called a **great circle route.** Both great circles and small circles are examples of *plane sections* of a sphere.

Definition:

A **plane section** of a three-dimensional figure is the intersection of that figure with a plane.

Biologists use plane sections of tissue to study a tissue's cell structure. These sections are thin enough so that light from a microscope will shine through them. A floor plan is an intersection of a building with the plane of a floor. Concerning these and other plane sections, two questions arise. What are the plane sections of a figure? How can plane sections be sketched?

Prisms and cylinders: If the intersecting plane is parallel to the bases, then the section is a region congruent to the bases. Sketch it by drawing edges parallel to the edges of the bases. This is pictured below.

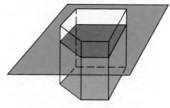

plane section // to bases

Suppose the intersecting plane is not parallel to the bases and does not intersect them. For a prism, the section is a polygon with the same number of sides but not congruent to the bases. Sketch it by identifying the intersections of the plane and the lateral edges and joining the appropriate vertices (as shown below, at the left). For a cylinder, the plane section is an ellipse (as shown below, at the right).

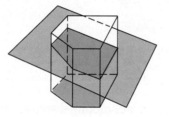

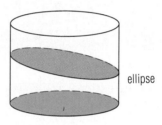

ellipse

plane section not // to bases   plane section not // to bases

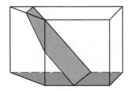

Plane sections may have quite different shapes if the plane intersects a base as well as lateral faces. An example of a plane intersecting a solid quadrangular prism is shown at the left; the plane section is a pentagonal region.

Pyramids and cones: Sections parallel to the base have shapes similar to the base, but they are smaller. Sketch them by drawing segments or arcs parallel to the base.

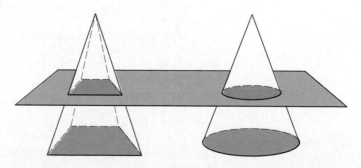

Below at the far left are two right conical surfaces with the same axis, formed by rotating a line intersecting the axis about that axis. The plane sections formed are called the **conic sections.** The conic sections describe orbits of planets and paths of balls and rockets. They are used in radar, telescopes, headlights, and TV receivers, and you are certain to study them in other mathematics courses.

The thrown basketball follows the path of a parabola.

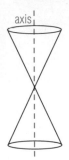    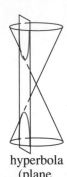

| circle | ellipse | parabola | hyperbola |
| (plane ⊥ to axis) | (plane not ⊥ to axis, intersecting only one cone) | (plane // to edge) | (plane intersecting both cones) |

Questions

1. Define: sphere.

2. How does the definition of *sphere* differ from the definition of *circle*?

3. The intersection of a plane and a sphere is either a single point or a(n) __?__ .

4. Define: great circle.

5. Define: small circle.

6. What is a plane section?

7. **a.** Draw a cylinder and a plane section parallel to its bases.
   b. How do the section and the bases compare?

8. **a.** Draw a right square pyramid and a plane section parallel to its base.
   b. How do the section and the base compare?

9. What are the conic sections?

10. *Multiple choice.* Thinking of the earth as a sphere, the equator is
    (a) a diameter
    (b) a small circle
    (c) a great circle
    (d) a chord.

11. Name two fields in which you would often see plane sections of objects.

12. What is the length of a diameter of the earth: **a.** at the equator; **b.** connecting the poles?

In 13–15, copy the figure shown.

    a. Sketch a plane section parallel to the base.
    b. Sketch a plane section not parallel to and not intersecting the base(s).
    c. Name the shape of each section.

13.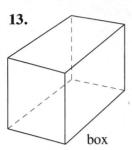
box

14.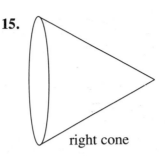
regular hexagonal pyramid

15. right cone

In 16 and 17, plane sections of an object are shown, as seen in a microscope focused at different levels of the object. Scientists use these plane sections to approximate its shape. Sketch a shape that yields the given sequence of plane sections.

16.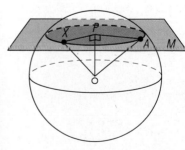

17.

In 18 and 19, tell which three-dimensional figure most resembles the real world object. Distinguish solids from surfaces.

18. blown-up balloon

19. golf ball

20. Here is a proof that the intersection of a sphere and a plane not through its center is a circle. Given is sphere O and plane M, intersecting in the curve as shown at the left. Fill in the justifications.

Proof

Let P be the foot of the $\perp$ from point O to plane M. Let A be a fixed point and X be any other point on the intersection. Then $\overline{OP} \perp \overline{PA}$ and $\overline{OP} \perp \overline{PX}$, because **a.** _?_. $\overline{OP} \cong \overline{OP}$, because of the **b.** _?_ and $\overline{OA} \cong \overline{OX}$ because **c.** _?_. So $\triangle OPX \cong \triangle OPA$ by **d.** _?_. Thus, due to **e.** _?_, $PX = PA$. Thus any point X on the intersection lies at the same distance from P as A does. So by the definition of circle (sufficient condition), the intersection of sphere O and plane M is the circle with center P and radius PA.

21. A *quadrangular pyramid* has a quadrilateral as its base. Draw a quadrangular pyramid. *(Lesson 9-3)*

22. Draw a right cylinder whose lateral edges are congruent to a diameter of the base. *(Lesson 9-2)*

23. In the box below, $AB = 10$, $AE = 6$, and $AD = 8$. Find each length. (Some segments are not drawn.) *(Lesson 9-2)*
   a. *CD*   **b.** *DE*   **c.** *CE*

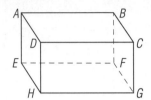

24. Using the information in this lesson, give the circumference of the equator: **a.** to the nearest 100 miles; **b.** to the nearest 100 km. *(Lesson 8-8)*

25. Give the definition. *(Lessons 4-7, 4-1)*
   a. reflection image of a point P over a line ℓ when P is not on ℓ
   b. reflection-symmetric figure

26. From the information in this lesson, about how many km are in 1 mile? *(Previous course)*

27. On the earth, the union of the prime meridian and international date line approximates a great circle containing the North and South poles.
   a. Name a country through which the prime meridian goes.
   b. Name the ocean that contains the international date line.
   c. What is the purpose of this circle?

28. a. It is possible for a plane section of a cube to be a hexagon. Draw a cube or make a model to demonstrate how this happens.
   b. Is it possible for a plane section of a cube to be a pentagon?
   c. Is it possible for a plane section of a cube to be a triangle?
   d. Is it possible for a plane section of a cube to be a quadrilateral that is not a parallelogram?

438

9-5

Reflections in Space

Many of the properties of reflections in two dimensions carry over to three dimensions. For example, when you look in a mirror, the mirror appears to lie halfway between you and your image. It contains the midpoint of the segment connecting a point to its image. That is, the mirror *bisects* the segment. Also, an imaginary line from the tip of your nose to its image will always be perpendicular to the mirror.

In general, a plane M is the **perpendicular bisector** of a segment $\overline{AB}$ if and only if $M \perp \overline{AB}$ and M contains the midpoint of $\overline{AB}$. This enables three-dimensional reflections (over planes) to have the same defining condition as their two-dimensional counterparts (over lines).

> **Definition:**
>
> For a point A which is not on a plane M, the **reflection image of A over M** is the point B if and only if M is the perpendicular bisector of $\overline{AB}$. For a point A on a plane M, the **reflection image of A over M** is A itself.

reflecting plane M

B is the reflection image of A over M.

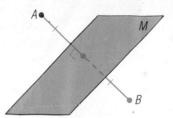

Reflections over planes preserve the same properties as their two-dimensional counterparts. That is, reflections in space preserve angle measure, betweenness, collinearity, and distance. So the definition of congruence in the plane can be extended to three dimensions.

> **Definition:**
>
> Two figures F and G in space are **congruent figures** if and only if G is the image of F under a reflection or composite of reflections.

You are congruent to your mirror image.

A two-dimensional figure has been defined to be reflection-symmetric if and only if it coincides with its image under some reflection. There is a corresponding definition for three dimensions.

Definition:

A space figure F is a **reflection-symmetric figure** if and only if there is a plane M such that $r_M(F) = F$.

The plane M is called a **symmetry plane.** The presence or absence of symmetry planes is used to help rock collectors, chemists, and geologists identify types of crystals. In some applications, reflection symmetry is called **bilateral symmetry.** Many animals have bilateral symmetry.

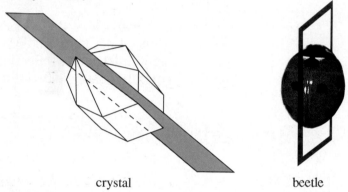

crystal   beetle

The body surfaces of most people have approximate bilateral symmetry. The right side and left side are reflection images of each other over the plane that goes through the middle of the body from head to toe. Note that you cannot slide or turn a right hand onto a left hand, because they have different orientation. Like reflections over a line, reflections over a plane reverse orientation.

Space figures may have any number of symmetry planes, from zero to infinitely many. The right cylinder below at the left has infinitely many vertical symmetry planes (any plane through $\overline{PQ}$) and one horizontal symmetry plane. The regular triangular pyramid at the right has exactly 3 symmetry planes, one of which is drawn.

right cylinder

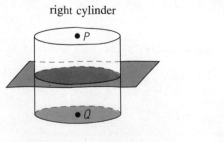

One symmetry plane is
the ⊥ bisector of $\overline{PQ}$.

triangular pyramid
(△ABC equilateral)

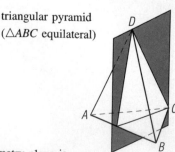

One symmetry plane is
the ⊥ bisector of $\overline{AB}$.

Example Determine the number of symmetry planes for a common cardboard box, like that shown here. Sketch each symmetry plane.

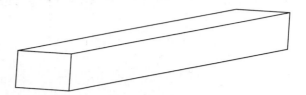

Solution A box is a right rectangular prism. Planes parallel to the opposite faces which intersect four edges at their midpoints are symmetry planes. There are thus three symmetry planes. The sketch below shows these planes, one parallel to each pair of parallel faces.

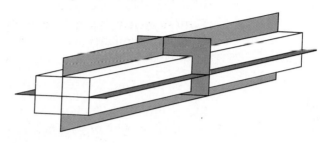

Questions

Covering the Reading

In 1–6, **a.** tell if the figure has bilateral symmetry; **b.** give the number of symmetry planes.

1.

right circular
cylinder

2.

regular square
pyramid

3.

top

4.

parallelepiped

5.

right cone

6.

oblique circular
cylinder

7. How many symmetry planes does a box have?

8. *Multiple choice.* If a human stands upright, the symmetry plane is:
   (a) Parallel to the ground about waist high.
   (b) ⊥ to the ground, halfway between the front and back.
   (c) ⊥ to the ground, halfway between right and left sides.

9. Name a property of a figure not preserved by reflections in space.

10. Trace the diagram below and sketch the reflection image of the surface over the shaded plane.

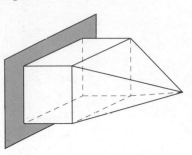

11. How many symmetry planes does a cube have?

12. A symmetry plane of a triangular pyramid is drawn in this lesson. Draw and label the plane section of the pyramid formed by the symmetry plane.

13. Repeat Question 12 for the beetle in this lesson.

14. Is it possible for a prism to have only one plane of symmetry? Explain why or why not, and sketch one if it is possible.

In 15 and 16, copy the figure shown.
  a. Sketch a plane section parallel to the bases.
  b. Sketch a plane section not parallel to and not intersecting the bases.
  c. Name the shape of each section. *(Lesson 9-4)*

15.

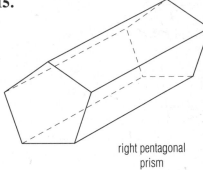

right pentagonal prism

16.

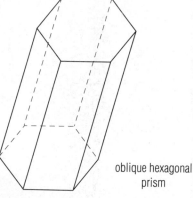

oblique hexagonal prism

In 17 and 18, tell which figure most resembles the real world object. Give as specific a name as you can, distinguishing solids from surfaces. *(Lessons 9-4, 9-2)*

17. a penny

18. a desk drawer

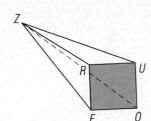

19. In the figure at the left, *FOUR* is a square.
Z is not in the plane of *FOUR*.
 a. Identify the figure.
 b. Name its base.
 c. Name its vertex.
 d. Name all the lateral edges.
 e. Name all faces. *(Lesson 9-3)*

20. Refer to the parallelepiped with bases *DEFG* and *HIJK*
pictured below.
 a. What is the area of a base?
 b. What is the perimeter of a base?
 c. What is the height of the parallelepiped? *(Lessons 9-2, 8-6, 8-1)*

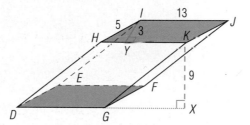

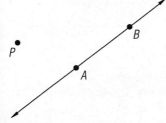

21. Suppose *P* is not on $\overleftrightarrow{AB}$ at the left.
 a. Draw $r_{\overleftrightarrow{AB}}(P)$. Call this point *P'*. *(Lesson 4-1)*
 b. What kind of figure is *PBP'A*? *(Lesson 5-2)*

22. Fill in the blanks. *(Previous course)*
 a. 1 square yard = __?__ square feet
 b. 1 square mile = __?__ square yards
 c. 1 square mile = __?__ acres

In 23 and 24, factor. *(Previous course)*

23. $x^2y - 4x$ **24.** $2\ell h + 2\ell w + 2wh$

Exploration

25. Standing upright and still, you want to see your entire body, head to
toe, in a mirror. How far up and down the wall does the mirror have
to go? (Hint: try with an actual mirror. Block out parts of the mirror
that are not needed.)

26. Find a picture of your face, taken from the front. Except for scars, is
the surface of your face *exactly* symmetric to a vertical plane down
the middle?

9-6

Views of Solids and Surfaces

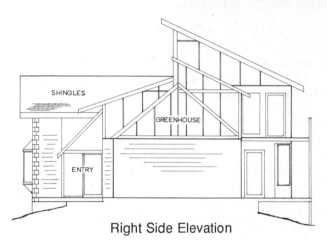

Right Side Elevation

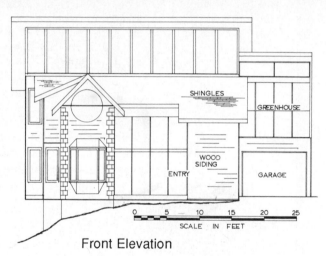

Front Elevation

The house pictured above was built in Ames, Iowa . Like most houses today, it was designed by an architect. Underneath the picture of the house are **views** from the front and right sides. These views are called **elevations.** Architects draw views of a planned building from the top, bottom, and sides to give a client a picture of the finished product. These elevations give accurate scale-model measurements, while most photographs and perspective-type drawings do not.

In geometry, views of three-dimensional figures are drawn without perspective as if the figures are solid but with all visible edges shown. (You were shown two views of the earth in Lesson 9-4.) From the views you can determine a possible shape of the original figure. The abbreviations L (left), R (right), F (front), and B (back) give guidance.

Example 1 Given the rectangular pyramid at the right, draw views from the front, right side, and top.

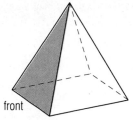

front

Solution The bottoms of the front and side views are the width and length of the base. The views are triangles, the same height as the pyramid. The top view shows the vertex with edges going towards the vertices of the base.

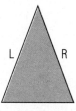
L   R

front view

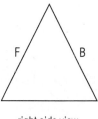
F   B

right side view

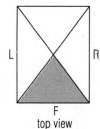
L   R

F

top view

Few people can determine shapes just from views without experience. In this book, unless told otherwise, assume that the solids and surfaces viewed are those we have already discussed—prisms, cylinders, pyramids, or cones—or combinations of them, as in Example 2.

Example 2 Here are three views of a prefabricated building made up of sections in the shape of congruent boxes.

a. How tall in stories is the building?
b. How long in sections is the building from front to back?
c. Where is the tallest part of the building located?

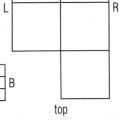
L   R

top

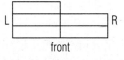
L   R

front

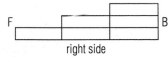
F   B

right side

Solution

a. The top view tells you nothing about the height of the building. The front view tells you it is 3 stories high on the left. The right side view confirms that the height, in the back, is 3 stories.
b. The top view tells you it is 3 sections long, the right side view confirms this.
c. The front view tells you that the tallest point is somewhere on the left side. The right side view tells you that the tallest point is at the back. Combining this, you can conclude that the tallest point of the building is at the back left corner.

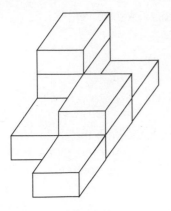

Here is a drawing of a possible shape for the building whose views are given in Example 2. There are other possible shapes. In the middle row either the left or the right side or both sides could be two stories high.

It helps to make sketches to understand views. In making your sketches, you may want to put the hidden lines in at first and erase them as the shape nears completion. Sometimes, in picturing these solids and surfaces, the hidden lines are omitted so that the final shape is more easily viewed.

Questions

Covering the Reading

1. To an architect, what are elevations?

2. A building is pictured at the right.
   a. Draw a top view.
   b. Draw a view from the right side.
   c. Draw a front view.

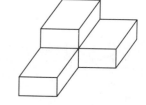

In 3–7, sketch the **a.** top, **b.** front, and **c.** right side views of each shape.

3. a cube

4. a sphere

5. a triangular prism

6.

7.

8. A building has the views shown below.
   a. How tall in stories is the building?
   b. How long in sections is the building from front to back?
   c. Where is the tallest part of the building located?

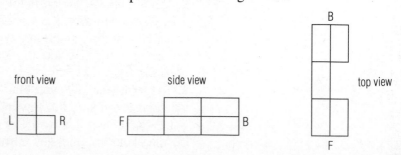

9. Sketch a possible shape, different from the solution given, for the building with the views given in Example 2.

In 10 and 11, refer to the elevations at the beginning of this lesson.

10. How wide (in feet) is the house? (Include the garage.)

11. How high is it (in feet) from the ground to the top of the upper roof?

12. Which solid studied in this chapter has these views?

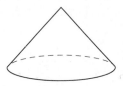

top view   front view   side view

13. Give the number of symmetry planes of the cube in Question 3. *(Lesson 9-5)*

In 14 and 15, use the right circular cone shown below.

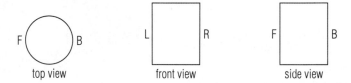

14. **a.** How many symmetry planes are there?
    b. Sketch a plane section parallel to the base.
    c. Sketch a plane section parallel to an edge.
    d. Name the sections in parts **b** and **c**. *(Lessons 9-5, 9-4)*

15. If the base of the cone has radius 8 and its slant height is 10, what is its height? *(Lessons 9-3, 8-7)*

16. How many great circles on the earth contain a given point in New York and a given point in Tokyo? *(Lesson 9-4)*

Akihabara District in Tokyo, Japan

17. A regular heptagonal region is translated into a congruent region in a parallel plane. What solid figure is formed by connecting all points of the original region and its image? *(Lesson 9-2)*

18. Here is a view of the moon and its equator as seen from the earth. The distance from L to R (through the center of the moon) is approximately 2160 miles.
   a. What is the approximate radius of the moon?
   b. How far is it from L to R along the surface of the moon?
   (Lesson 8-8)

19. The area of a square is 11 square units.
   a. What is the length of a side?
   b. What is the length of a diagonal? *(Lesson 8-7)*

20. Given: $\overline{AD}$ is an altitude in $\triangle ABC$.
   a. Find Area($\triangle ABC$).
   b. Find AC. *(Lessons 8-7, 8-5)*

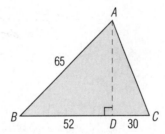

21. Given: $ABCD$ is a parallelogram with diagonals $\overline{AC}$ and $\overline{BD}$.
   Prove: $\triangle AQB \cong \triangle CQD$. *(Lesson 7-7)*

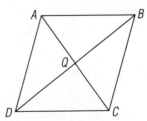

In 22 and 23, factor. *(Previous course)*

22. $x^2y^2 + 4x^2y + 6xy$

23. $\pi r^2 + 2\pi rh - \pi h$

24. Draw a front, side, and top elevation of the building in which you live.

Making Surfaces

A 3-dimensional surface which is the union of polygonal regions and which has no holes is called a **polyhedron**. The plural of polyhedron is either **polyhedrons** or **polyhedra.** Prisms and pyramids are special kinds of polyhedra. Each polygonal region is a **face** of the polyhedron. Each vertex of the region is a **vertex** of the polyhedron. Each side of the region is an **edge** of the polyhedron. Polyhedra can be classified by the number of faces. Below are pictured a tetrahedron (4 faces) and a hexahedron (6 faces). The tetrahedron has 4 vertices and 6 edges. A cube and a box are both special types of hexahedra.

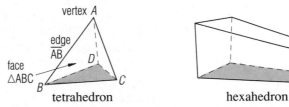

tetrahedron   hexahedron

In previous lessons you have used perspective and nonperspective drawings, plane sections, and views to describe 3-dimensional figures in 2-dimensional drawings. You can also go the other way and use 2-dimensional drawings that can make polyhedra and other 3-dimensional surfaces.

A **net** is a 2-dimensional figure that can be folded on its segments or curved on its boundaries into a 3-dimensional surface. To find the net for a particular surface, you can cut along the edges of the surface until it is flat. Suppose cuts are made along some of the edges of a cube. Then the cube can be flattened out.

Below is drawn a net for a cube. The six faces are identified by the first letters of the words up, down, left, right, back, and front. If you cut around the outside boundary and then fold these squares along their common edges so as to make perpendicular faces, a cube will be formed.

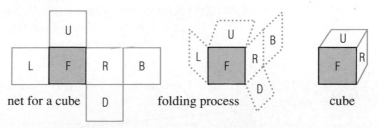

net for a cube   folding process   cube

Not all networks of six squares fold to make a cube. The 2 by 3 network drawn below at the left is not a net for a cube. It can be folded into a prism with no bases, as shown below at the right, but this is not a polyhedron.

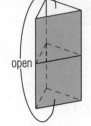

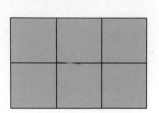

open

Prisms and pyramids often have relatively simple nets.

Example 1   Draw a net for a regular square pyramid like the one shown here.

Solution   The base is a square, and the faces are triangles with one side on the square. It is easiest to draw the square base first, and then make all the faces congruent and attached to a side of the square. The altitude of each triangular face must be greater than one half that side. Do you see why? The finished net is shown below at the right.

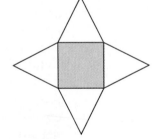

Example 2   Draw a net for the right triangular prism shown here.

Solution   The bases are congruent triangles. The other faces are rectangles with one pair of sides the same length as the corresponding sides of the base. A net is shown here.

450

In both Examples 1 and 2, the nets were drawn. You may be able to improve accuracy by constructing the bases and faces using a straightedge and compass, or by very careful tracing and measuring with ruler and protractor. Printout from an automatic drawer can also be useful.

Cones and cylinders have simple nets.

Example 3   Draw a net for a right cylinder *h* units high with base diameter *d*.

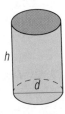

Solution   First draw the circle that will be one base. The lateral surface of a cylinder is a rectangle. Since the diameter of the circle is *d*, the rectangle will have one side of length π*d*, to match the circumference of the base. The other side is the height *h* of the cylinder.

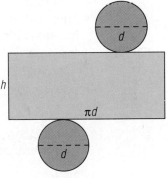

A net for a cone is given in Question 9.

Questions

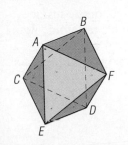

1. Define: polyhedron.

2. Is the surface a polyhedron?
   a. cone   **b.** cube
   c. cylinder   **d.** prism
   e. pyramid   **f.** sphere

3. Pictured at the left is an octahedron.
   a. Name its vertices.
   b. Name its edges.
   c. Name its faces.

4. A hexahedron is pictured in this lesson. Give the number of:
a. vertices; **b.** edges; and **c.** faces.

5. Here is a net for a cube. Identified are the locations of three faces. Where will the other squares of the net wind up on the cube?

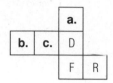

6. Draw a net for a pyramid whose base is a pentagon. Make each side of the pentagon 2 inches or 5 cm. Cut out the net and fold it to make a pyramid.

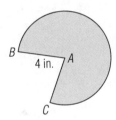

3 cm

4 cm

7. Suppose you wanted to make the cylinder pictured at the left out of cardboard. Draw a net you could use. Make the net actual size. Cut it out to make the cylinder.

8. Draw a net for a regular triangular prism with a height of 2″. Make the net actual size.

9. a. If the partial disk below is cut out of cardboard and $\overline{AB}$ is moved to coincide with $\overline{AC}$, what 3-dimensional figure will be formed?

B
4 in.
A

C

b. Let $AB = 4$ in. and $m\angle BAC = 100$. Cut out the shape and make the surface.

Applying the Mathematics

10. *Multiple choice.* Which is not a net for a cube?

(a)   (b)   (c)   (d)

11. A polyhedron is **convex** if the segment connecting any two points of it is contained within the corresponding solid. Draw a nonconvex polyhedron.

12. Order from most general to most specific: polyhedron, surface, pentagonal pyramid, regular pentagonal pyramid, pyramid, figure.

In 13 and 14, give the number of: **a.** vertices; **b.** edges; and **c.** faces.

13. a pyramid whose base is an octagon

14. a prism whose base is an *n*-gon

15. Draw a net for a cereal box.

16. *Multiple choice.* Descartes discovered and Euler proved a simple relationship between the numbers of vertices V, edges E, and faces F of any polyhedron. By examining polyhedra, determine which of the following is the relationship.
(a) $V + E - F = 2$
(b) $F + E - V = 2$
(c) $F + V - E = 2$
(d) $E + F - V = 2$

Review

17. Here are three views of a building. *(Lesson 9-6)*
a. How tall in stories is the building?
b. How long in sections is the building from front to back?
c. Where is the tallest part of the building located?

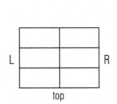
top

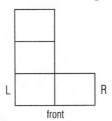
front

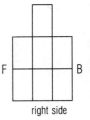
right side

18. Draw top, front, and side views of the chair pictured at the left. (Assume the seat is horizontal.) *(Lesson 9-6)*

19. Refer to the right triangular prism of Example 2 in this lesson.
a. Is the figure reflection-symmetric?
b. If so, give the number of symmetry planes. *(Lesson 9-5)*

20. *Multiple choice.* A bass drum is best described as
(a) a cylindric solid
(b) a cylindric surface
(c) a spherical solid
(d) a spherical surface.
(Lessons 9-4, 9-2)

21. Use the figure below. R is the midpoint of $\overline{QS}$. The figure is not drawn to scale.

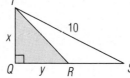

a. If $x = 6$, find y.
b. If $x = 8$, find y.
c. If $x = 8$, find Area($\triangle TQR$). *(Lessons 8-7, 8-5)*

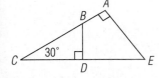

22. $\triangle CAE$ and $\triangle CDB$ are right triangles, as pictured at the left. *True* or *false*? $m\angle CBD - m\angle E = 0$ *(Lesson 5-7)*

23. Suppose, in a quadrilateral $ABCD$, that $AB = BC = CD = DA$. Why can you conclude that $ABCD$ is a rhombus? *(Lessons 5-2, 3-3)*

24. $m\angle 1 = t$ and $m\angle 2 = t - 10$. Find t if angles 1 and 2 are supplementary. *(Lesson 3-2)*

25. A **regular polyhedron** is a convex polyhedron in which all faces are congruent regular polygons and the same number of edges intersect at each of its vertices. There are only five regular polyhedra; they are pictured here.

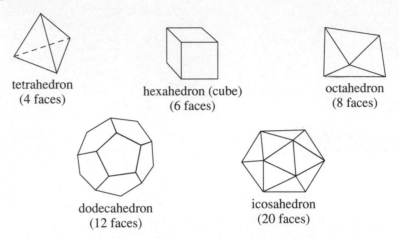

tetrahedron
(4 faces)

hexahedron (cube)
(6 faces)

octahedron
(8 faces)

dodecahedron
(12 faces)

icosahedron
(20 faces)

a. Determine the number of vertices of each regular polyhedron.
b. Determine the number of edges of each regular polyhedron.

In 26–30, use cardboard and tape to construct a model of the regular polyhedron from the net provided. The patterns shown below should be enlarged. Cut on solid lines, fold on dotted lines.

26. tetrahedron

27. cube

28. octahedron

29. dodecahedron

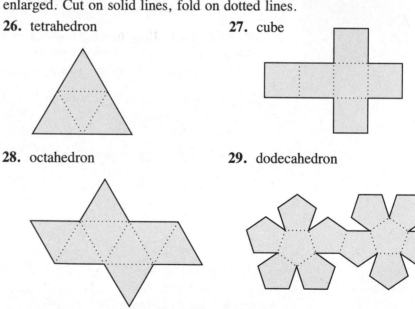

30. icosahedron

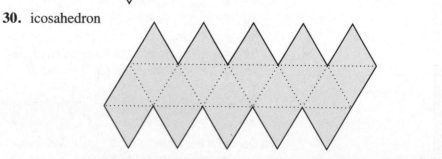

9-8

The Four-Color Problem

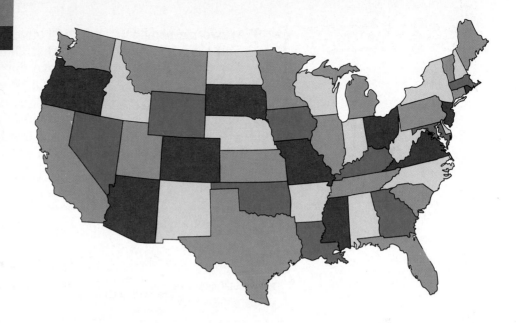

Here is a map of the 48 states of the continental United States. To distinguish the states, each state has been colored differently than any of its neighbors. If two states only share a corner, as is the case with Colorado and Arizona, then they can have the same color. Notice that only four colors are needed for this map.

In 1852, after studying many maps, Thomas Guthrie, a British mathematician, conjectured that *any* regions of a map on a sphere or a plane could be so distinguished if four colors were used. For Guthrie, regions could have any shape as long as they were connected. (The two unconnected parts of the state of Michigan could have different colors.)

The Four-Color Conjecture (1852-1976):

Suppose regions which share a border of some length must have different colors. Then any map of regions on a plane or a sphere can be colored in such a way that only four colors are needed.

Guthrie was not able to prove his conjecture. In fact, many mathematicians tried to prove the conjecture but failed. For almost 125 years, this conjecture, the "four-color problem," was one of the most famous undecided questions in mathematics. By 1975, mathematicians had proved that any map with fewer than 40 states could be colored with four colors or less, but they had not proved that *any* map could be so colored.

By working on this problem, mathematicians discovered much new mathematics. Much of the mathematics of complicated networks, called *graph theory*, was discovered in the search for a proof to the Four-Color Conjecture.

In 1976, two mathematicians at the University of Illinois, Wolfgang Haken and Kenneth Appel, *proved* that Guthrie's Four-Color conjecture was correct. They could not prove this just by drawing maps and coloring, for there are infinitely many maps. First they showed that any map they needed to consider was one of 1,952 types of maps. Then they used a computer to help prove that for each type, no more than four colors would be needed to color it. Because of their proof, the Four-Color Conjecture became the Four-Color *Theorem*.

The Four-Color Theorem (1976):

Suppose regions which share a border of some length must have different colors. Then any map of regions on a plane or a sphere can be colored in such a way that only four colors are needed.

While working on the four-color problem, mathematicians examined many other surfaces, particularly surfaces with holes. One of these surfaces is called a **torus.** A torus is formed by bending a cylinder until its bases coincide. The result looks like a doughnut. It has been proved that no more than seven colors are needed to color any map drawn on a torus. Below is a way to make a torus with a map needing seven colors.

To make a torus:
1. Begin with a rectangle.

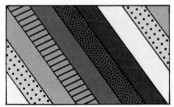

2. Roll it into a cylinder.

3. Bend the cylinder until the bases coincide.

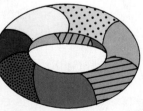

Work is still being done on this topic. In 1987, Elizabeth Wilmer, a student at Stuyvesant High School in New York City, won second prize in the nation in the Westinghouse Science Talent Search for her work on a *three*-color problem. She analyzed maps which could be colored with three colors. Here is an example of such a map with 19 regions.

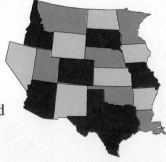

456

1. Who first stated the Four-Color Conjecture, and when?

2. **a.** State the Four-Color Theorem.
   b. Who proved this theorem, and when?

3. How many years elapsed between the statement and proof of the Four-Color Conjecture?

4. Trace the map at the left. Show that it can be colored with no more than four colors.

5. Draw a map with 15 states or regions that can be colored with three colors. (Do not use part of the U.S. map).

6. Who is Elizabeth Wilmer?

7. Any map on a torus can be colored with no more than __?__ colors.

8. Make a torus.

9. Below is a map of Europe. Trace the map and color it using the least number of colors. (Hint: Start where the countries are most densely packed, and end up on the outside countries.)

10. In the map below, the borders of states are circular arcs. What is the least number of colors needed to color this map?

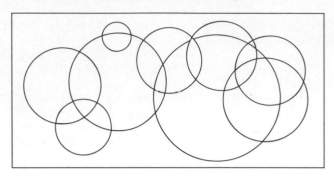

11. Draw a map with only four regions that needs four colors to color it.

Review

12. Draw a net for a pentagonal pyramid. *(Lesson 9-7)*

13. Order from most general to most specific: box, surface, polyhedron, prism, right prism. *(Lesson 9-7)*

14. Give a view of the triangular right prism below as seen from
   a. the top   b. the front   c. the right side. *(Lesson 9-6)*

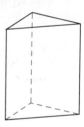

In 15–18, draw the figure. *(Lessons 9-4, 9-3, 9-2, 9-1)*

15. an oblique cone

16. a right prism with a nonconvex kite as a base

17. a solid sphere

18. two intersecting planes

19. *A-BCDE* below is a regular pyramid. *AO* is the height.
Let *DE* = 12 and *AO* = 10.
   a. Find the slant height.
   b. Find the area of △*AOD*. *(Lessons 9-3, 8-7)*

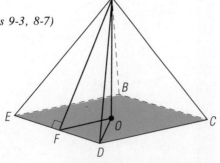

20. Consider $\odot Q$ below with sector RSQ. Suppose $QR = 30$ cm.
  a. Find the length of $\overset{\frown}{RTS}$.
  b. Find the area of the circle.
  c. What percent of the interior of the circle lies in the sector? (Answer to the nearest percent.) *(Lesson 8-8)*

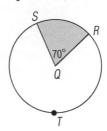

21. If $x = 4$, what is the value of $2x^3 - 7x^2 - x + 11$? *(Previous course)*

Exploration

22. Name all the countries in the map of Question 9.

23. Name all the states in the United States map at the beginning of this lesson that are:
  a. colored in red
  b. colored in blue
  c. colored in yellow
  d. colored in green
  e. missing.

24. Find a globe in a library, study, or store.
  a. How many colors are used to color the countries and the oceans?
  b. What conventions are used in coloring the regions?

Summary

The purpose of this chapter is to familiarize you with the common three-dimensional figures, the figures of solid geometry. To accomplish this, you should know their definitions and how they are related, be able to sketch them, identify plane sections, draw views from different positions, and be able to make some of them from two-dimensional nets. Below is a hierarchy relating many of these surfaces.

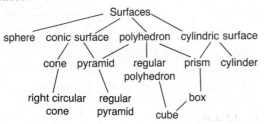

Many ideas from two dimensions extend to three. The basic properties of planes are given in the Point-Line-Plane Postulate. Like lines, planes may be perpendicular or parallel. Circles and spheres have the same defining property except spheres are in 3 dimensions. Reflections and reflection-symmetry are defined the same way in 2 and 3 dimensions except that the reflecting line is replaced by a reflecting plane.

The Four-Color Theorem deals with maps drawn on planes and spheres. In the 124 years it took to discover a proof, much new mathematics about surfaces and networks was discovered.

Vocabulary

Below are the most important terms and phrases for this chapter.
For the starred (*) terms you should be able to give a definition of the term.
For the other terms you should be able to give a general description and a specific example of each.

Lesson 9-1
Point-Line-Plane Postulate,
  parts **e**, **f**, and **g**
intersecting planes
angle measure between
  a line and a plane
*line perpendicular to a plane,
  parallel planes
distance between parallel planes
distance to a plane from a point

Lesson 9-2
surface, solid
box, rectangular solid
faces, edges, vertices of a box
skew lines
*cylindric solid, cylindric surface
*cylinder,
*prism
bases, height, altitude
lateral surface of a cylindric
  surface, lateral face
right prism, oblique prism
right cylinder, oblique cylinder
parallelepiped,
  rectangular parallelepiped

Lesson 9-3
*conic solid, conic surface
*cone, *pyramid
base, vertex, lateral edge,
  lateral face of a conic surface
regular pyramid
axis of a cone, lateral edge of a cone
right cone, oblique cone
right pyramid, oblique pyramid
height, altitude, slant height
truncated cone, truncated pyramid

Lesson 9-4
*sphere, *center of sphere
*the radius of a sphere,
  a radius of a sphere
the diameter of a sphere,
  a diameter of a sphere
*great circle of sphere
*small circle of sphere
hemisphere
*plane section, conic section

Lesson 9-5
perpendicular bisector of a segment
  (in space)
*reflection image of a point
  over a plane
reflecting plane
congruence (in space)
*reflection-symmetric space figure
bilateral symmetry
symmetry (in space)
symmetry plane

Lesson 9-6
view, elevation

Lesson 9-7
*polyhedron, polyhedra, polyhedrons
face, vertex, edge of polyhedron
tetrahedron, hexahedron, octahedron
net, regular polyhedron

Lesson 9-8
The Four-Color Theorem
torus

Progress Self-Test

Directions: Take this test as you would take a test in class. Then check your work with the solutions in the Selected Answers section in the back of the book. You will need graph paper and a calculator.

In 1–4, use this figure.

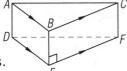

1. Name the figure. Be as specific as possible.
2. Give the number of edges.
3. Give the number of faces.
4. Give the number of vertices.

5. What is the difference between a solid and a surface?

In 6–8, draw each figure.

6. two intersecting planes
7. oblique square prism
8. oblique cylinder

In 9 and 10, use the truncated regular square pyramid drawn here.

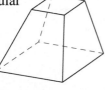

9. Sketch a plane section parallel to the base.
10. How many symmetry planes does this figure have?

In 11–14, use the regular square pyramid pictured here.

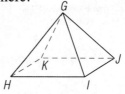

11. a. Name a lateral edge.
    b. Name the vertex.
12. Copy the drawing and identify the height and slant height of the pyramid.
13. Draw a net to make this pyramid.
14. Draw top, front, and right side views of this pyramid.
15. The intersection of the surface of the earth with a plane containing the center of the earth is called a(n) __?__ .

16. Draw six squares that are adjacent to each other but do not form a net for a cube.

17. Refer to the oblique cone at the right. Let $OB = 10$ cm, $AD = 30$ cm, and $BD = 6$ cm.

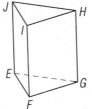

   a. What segment has length equal to the height of the cone?
   b. Find the area of the base of the cone.

18. In the right triangular prism below, $\overline{EF} \perp \overline{FG}$, $EF = 4''$, and $EG = 9''$. If the height of the pyramid is $22''$,

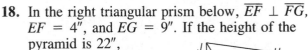

   a. find Area($FIHG$);
   b. find Area($\triangle EFG$).

19. *Multiple choice.* A box is *not* a special type of: (a) hexahedron
       (b) pyramid
       (c) prism
       (d) polyhedron.

20. Name the three-dimensional figure which most resembles a slice of American cheese. Give as specific a name as you can, distinguishing whether it is a solid or a surface.

21. Factor: $\pi r^2 + 2\pi rh$.

22. Here are front, side, and top views of a building.
   a. How tall in stories is the building?
   b. How long in sections is the building from front to back?
   c. Where is the tallest part of the building located?

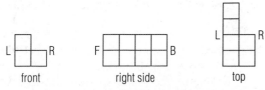

front   right side   top

23. Draw a map with five regions that requires four colors to be colored.

Chapter Review

Questions on **SPUR** Objectives

SPUR stands for **S**kills, **P**roperties, **U**ses, and **R**epresentations.
The Chapter Review questions are grouped according to the
SPUR Objectives for this chapter.

SKILLS deal with the procedures used to get answers.

■ **Objective A:** *Draw common 3-dimensional shapes. (Lessons 9-1, 9-2, 9-3, 9-4)*

In 1–6, draw each figure.

1. two perpendicular planes
2. an oblique cylinder
3. a regular hexagonal prism
4. a sphere
5. a square pyramid
6. a right cone

■ **Objective B:** *Draw plane sections of common 3-dimensional shapes. (Lesson 9-4)*

In 7–9, copy the figure shown.
  a. Sketch a plane section parallel to the base.
  b. Sketch a plane section not parallel to and not intersecting the base(s).
  c. Name the shape of each section.

7.   8.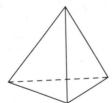

9.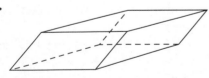

10. a. Draw a sphere and a plane section not containing the center.
    b. Name the plane section. Be as specific as possible.

■ **Objective C:** *Give views of a figure from the top, sides, or bottom. (Lesson 9-6)*

11. Give a view of this oblique circular cylinder as seen from
    a. the top;
    b. the front;
    c. the right side.

In 12 and 13, sketch the **a.** top, **b.** front, and **c.** right side view of the object.

12.

front

13.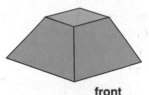

front

14. Draw a picture of the earth with its equator as seen from directly above the North Pole.

■ **Objective D:** *From a net, make a surface, and vice-versa. (Lesson 9-7)*

15. Which are nets for cubes?

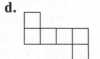

a.   b.

c.   d.

16. Draw a net for a square pyramid.
17. Draw a net for a rectangular parallelepiped.
18. Draw a net for a cylinder.

Objective E: *Given appropriate lengths, calculate areas and lengths in three-dimensional figures.*
(Lessons 9-2, 9-3, 9-4)

19. In the regular triangular pyramid shown, $AC = 12$ and $AD = 10$.
    a. Find the area of the base.
    b. Find the slant height.

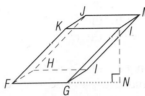

20. In the oblique square prism below, $GN = 15$ and $LN = 40$.
    a. What segment's length equals the height of the prism?
    b. What is the length of $\overline{LG}$?

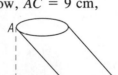

    c. If the perimeter of the base is 52, what is the area of *KLGF*?

21. In the oblique cylinder below, $AC = 9$ cm, $BD = 10$ cm, and $CD = 3$ cm.
    a. Find the area of the base of the cylinder.
    b. Find the height of the cylinder.

22. A sphere has radius of 12″. What is the area of a great circle of that sphere?

23. A right circular cone has a height of 24 mm and a slant height of 25 mm.
    a. Draw such a cone.
    b. Find the area of the base.

Objective F: *From 2-dimensional views of a figure, determine properties of the 3-dimensional figure. (Lesson 9-6)*

In 24 and 25, use the given views of buildings.
    a. How tall in stories is the building?
    b. How long in sections is the building from front to back?
    c. Where is the tallest part of the building located?

24.

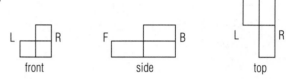

25.

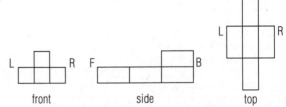

26. Which solid studied in this chapter has these views?

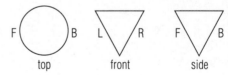

PROPERTIES deal with the principles behind the mathematics.

Objective G: *Identify parts of common three-dimensional figures. (Lessons 9-2, 9-3, 9-7)*

27. Use the figure at the right. In this figure, all opposite faces are parallel, and all adjacent faces are perpendicular.
    a. Give two different names for this figure.
    b. How many edges does the figure have?
    c. Name two edges that are not coplanar.

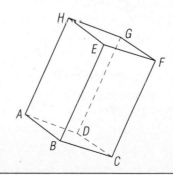

28. *P* is the center of the circle at the right below. *Q* is not in the plane of circle *P*.

   a. Name the figure drawn. Be as specific as possible.

   b. Name a lateral edge.

   c. Name the vertex.

   d. Name the base.

   e. Name the axis.

29. Use the figure at the right.

   a. How many vertices does this figure have?

   b. How many edges does this figure have?

   c. How many faces of this figure are quadrilaterals?

   d. Give a technical name for this figure.

■ **Objective H:** *Distinguish three-dimensional figures by their defining properties.* (Lessons 9-2, 9-3, 9-7)

30. What is the difference between a right cylinder and an oblique cylinder?

31. A pyramid has a triangular base. Could any other face of this pyramid be its base?

32. Order from most general to most specific: prism, cube, square prism, polyhedron.

33. A pentagonal region is translated into a congruent region in a parallel plane. What solid figure is formed by connecting all points of the original region and its image?

USES deal with applications of mathematics in real situations.

■ **Objective I:** *Recognize three-dimensional figures in the real world.* (Lessons 9-2, 9-4)

In 34–37, tell which three-dimensional figure most resembles the real world object. Give as specific a name as you can, distinguishing solids from surfaces.

34. a phonograph record with the middle hole filled in

35. a bubble

36. the moon

37. a sheet of notebook paper

■ **Objective J:** *Determine and draw symmetry planes in 3-dimensional figures.* (Lesson 9-5)

In 38 and 39,

a. tell if the figure has bilateral symmetry;

b. give the number of symmetry planes.

38.

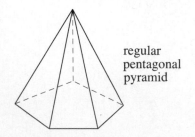

regular pentagonal pyramid

39.

40. How many symmetry planes does a box have?

41. Sketch the reflection image of the comb over the shaded reflection mirror below.

■ **Objective K:** *Factor algebraic expressions using common monomial factoring.* *(Previous course)*

In 42–45, factor.

42. $ph - \frac{1}{2}\ell p$ **43.** $\ell wh + 2\ell w$ **44.** $x^2 y + 2xy + xy^2$ **45.** $4\pi r^2 + \pi r^3$

HISTORY deals with the development of mathematics.

■ **Objective L:** *Relate the history of the Four-Color Problem.* *(Lesson 9-8)*

46. Who stated the Four-Color Conjecture?

47. The Four-Color Conjecture dealt with maps on what surfaces?

48. When was a proof found for the Four-Color Theorem?

49. Draw a map with nine regions that needs four colors in order to be colored.

50. Trace this map of the continent of Africa and color it with at most four colors.

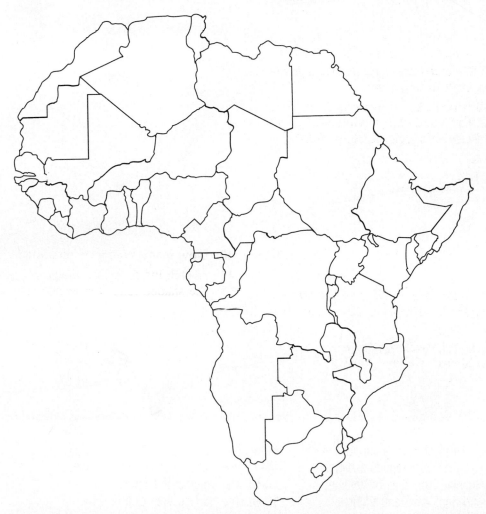

Surface Areas and Volumes

The two most important measures of 3-dimensional figures are **surface area** and **volume.** They are the counterparts of perimeter and area in 2-dimensional figures. Like perimeter, surface area measures a boundary, the surface of a 3-dimensional figure. Volume, like area, measures the space enclosed by the figure.

Surface Area	**Volume**
helps in determining:	helps in determining:
how much paper is needed to make the bag	how much the bag can hold
how much land there is to explore	how much material makes up the moon
how much heat a bird loses through its skin	how much the bird weighs
how much fabric is needed to cover the toy.	how much stuffing is needed to make the toy.

Surface area and volume are quite different, as the above examples show. In this chapter, you will learn how to calculate the surface area and volume of the 3-dimensional figures introduced in the last chapter. You will also learn how these measures are related to each other, and the general properties underlying them.

10-1

Surface Areas of Prisms and Cylinders

The cost of any container, from a suitcase to a new house, from a paper bag to an open air balloon, depends on the amount of material used to make it. The amount of material on the outside of the container is its **surface area (S.A.)**.

Consider a paper bag. It is approximately a box, a type of prism, with the top base missing. Since each face of a box is a rectangular region, the surface area of the bag is the sum of the areas of 5 rectangles. The areas are easily seen by examining the net for the bag.

- - - - - - - ■ ■ ■

Example 1 A paper grocery bag has a base 7″ by 12″ and a height of 17″. At least how much paper is needed to make it?

Solution Draw the bag and a net for it.

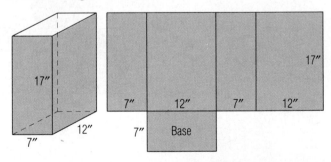

Surface area = area of base + sum of areas of lateral faces
$$= 7 \cdot 12 + (17 \cdot 7 + 17 \cdot 12 + 17 \cdot 7 + 17 \cdot 12)$$
Use the Distributive Property for the lateral surface.
$$= 7 \cdot 12 + 17(7 + 12 + 7 + 12)$$
$$= 84 + 17 \cdot 38$$
$$= 730 \text{ square inches}$$

So at least 730 sq in. of paper is needed. Overlapping parts at the bottom (for strength) and by the seams increase this amount somewhat.

468

The area of the lateral surface of a solid is its **lateral area (L.A.)**. In Example 1, the lateral area was calculated by finding the sum of the areas of the four lateral faces. Since the base rectangle had perimeter 7″ + 12″ + 7″ + 12″ = 38″ and the height of the bag was 17″, the calculation could be reduced to

L.A. = 38 · 17 = perimeter of base · height of prism.

This idea works with any right prism (or cylinder) because the length of any lateral edge equals the height of the prism (or cylinder).

Right Prism-Cylinder Lateral Area Formula:

The lateral area L.A. of a right prism (or cylinder) is the product of its height h and the perimeter (circumference) p of its base.

$$L.A. = ph$$

Proof

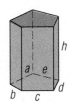
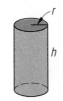

Here are a representative right prism and right cylinder, each with height h. For the prism, the perimeter of a base is $a + b + c + d + e$. For the cylinder, the perimeter of a base is $2\pi r$.

$$p = a + b + c + d + e \qquad\qquad p = 2\pi r$$

Here are their nets.

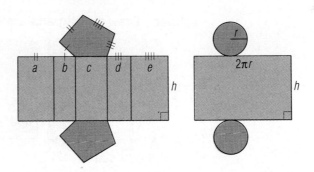

Now we obtain the lateral areas. That is the area of everything but the bases.

For the prism,
L.A. = $(a + b + c + d + e)h$
　　 = ph.

For the cylinder,
L.A. = $2\pi r \cdot h$
　　 = ph.

Every prism or cylinder has two congruent bases. The bases have the same area. So the next theorem holds even for oblique prisms and cylinders.

Prism-Cylinder Surface Area Formula:

The total surface area S.A. of any prism or cylinder is the sum of its lateral area L.A. and twice the area B of a base.
$$S.A. = L.A. + 2B$$

Notice that the formulas for the lateral and surface areas of right prisms are identical to those for cylinders. But the formulas for cylinders can be rewritten in terms of h and r by applying the formulas for the area and circumference (perimeter) of a circle.

In a right cylinder,

$$\begin{aligned} L.A. &= ph & S.A. &= 2B + ph \\ &= (2\pi r)h & &= 2 \cdot \pi r^2 + 2\pi r \cdot h \quad \text{(substituting the formulas)} \\ &= 2\pi rh & &= 2\pi r(r + h) \quad \text{(factoring out } 2\pi r\text{)}. \end{aligned}$$

Some people like to memorize many formulas. We advise you to learn at least those formulas highlighted in boxes. Of course, you must know what each letter in the formula represents. As shown in Example 2, always begin a problem by writing an appropriate formula. Substitute for the area and perimeter only when needed.

Example 2   For the right cylinder shown, find
a. the lateral area and
b. the surface area.

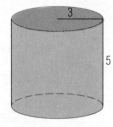

Solution

a. Begin by writing a formula for the lateral area of a right cylinder.
$$L.A. = ph$$
For a cylinder, if r is the radius of the base, $p = 2\pi r$. Here $r = 3$, so $p = 6\pi$.

Substituting,   L.A. $= 6\pi h$.
Since $h = 5$,   L.A. $= 30\pi$ square units.

b. In any cylinder, S.A. = L.A. + 2B.
Since the base is a circle, $B = \pi r^2$, and here $r = 3$.
From part **a**, L.A. $= 30\pi$.

Substituting, $\begin{aligned} S.A. &= 30\pi + 2 \cdot (\pi \cdot 3^2) \\ &= 30\pi + 18\pi \\ &= 48\pi \text{ square units.} \end{aligned}$

Notice that, since lateral area and surface area are areas, they are measured in square units.

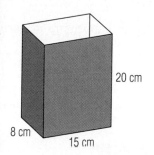

8 cm
20 cm
15 cm

1. Which measures the boundary of a three-dimensional figure, surface area or volume?

2. **a.** Define: lateral area.
   b. What is a formula for the lateral area of a right prism?

3. A small bag has dimensions as pictured at the left. What is its surface area?

4. In a prism or cylinder, S.A. = ___?___ + ___?___ .

In 5–7, a net for a surface is given.
   a. What is the surface?
   b. Calculate its lateral area.
   c. Calculate its surface area.

5.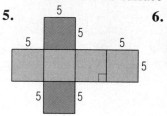

5
5
5
5
5
5
5
5

6.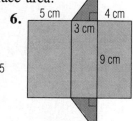

5 cm   4 cm
3 cm
9 cm

7.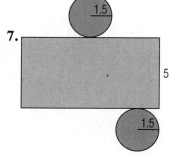

1.5
5
1.5

8. The lateral area of a right cylinder is the ___?___ multiplied by the ___?___ of the base.

9. A right cylinder has height h and base with radius r. Write each formula in terms of r and h.
   a. area of either base   **b.** lateral area   **c.** surface area

In 10 and 11, find the lateral area and surface area of each surface.

10.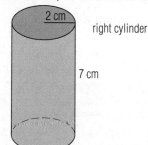

2 cm   right cylinder
7 cm

11.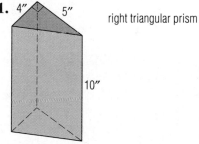

4″   5″   right triangular prism
10″

In 12–15, is the quantity related more to surface area or to volume?

12. how much a railroad box car will hold

13. how much metal is needed to build a box car

14. how much you weigh

15. how much you sweat due to exercise

16. How many square centimeters of sheet metal are needed to make a closed cylindric can with height 20 cm and base radius 9 cm?

In 17–19, find the surface area of the given solid.

17. a box with dimensions 9 cm, 10 cm, and 11 cm

18. a box with dimensions ℓ, w, and h

19. a cube with an edge of length s

20. The edges of a box are doubled in length. What happens to its surface area? (Hint: Try a few special cases.)

21. A fuel storage tank has a diameter of 50 meters and a height of 75 meters. If a gallon of paint can cover about 45 square meters and 2 coats of paint are required, about how many gallons are needed to paint the exterior sides and top of the tank?

22. Draw a net for a square pyramid and shade in the lateral surface. *(Lessons 9-7, 9-3)*

23. What is the center of a regular polygon? *(Lesson 7-6)*

24. Name the postulate applied here: $(2\ell + 2w)h = 2\ell h + 2wh$. *(Lesson 1-7)*

25. What is the cube of $\frac{2}{3}$? *(Previous course)*

26. Find a paper bag in your house.
  a. What are its dimensions?
  b. What is its surface area?
  c. To make the bag, some of the paper has to overlap for gluing. Carefully undo the bag to make it lie flat. Draw its net.
  d. How much paper is used to make the bag?

27. Suppose you wish to make a box with no top and you have 100 square inches of cardboard, as well as scissors and tape. What might be its dimensions?

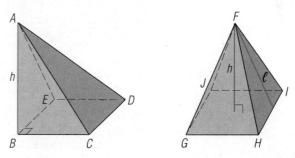

Foam pyramids embedded with carbon line the steel walls of an anechoic chamber.

Surface Areas of Pyramids and Cones

Recall that the *height* of a pyramid or cone is the length of the perpendicular segment from its vertex to the plane of its base. The height also refers to that segment. Below are two square pyramids *A-BCDE* and *F-GHIJ* with the same height h. (Notice how the pyramids are named, with the vertex followed by a dash, followed by a name for the base.) The pyramid *F-GHIJ* is a regular pyramid, since the foot of the perpendicular from *F* to the plane of *GHIJ* is at the center of *GHIJ*.

The lateral area of each of these pyramids is the sum of the areas of the four triangles that are its lateral faces.

L.A. of $A\text{-}BCDE$ = Area($\triangle ABC$) + Area($\triangle ACD$) + Area($\triangle ADE$) + Area($\triangle AEB$)
L.A. of $F\text{-}GHIJ$ = Area($\triangle FGH$) + Area($\triangle FHI$) + Area($\triangle FIJ$) + Area($\triangle FJG$)

Engineers place aircraft in a chamber built of steel walls with an echo-free interior to eliminate outside electronic signals and assure more accurate test results.

There is no simpler formula for the lateral area of *A-BCDE*. If you have enough information, you just calculate each of the four areas and add.

However, the lateral area of the regular pyramid *F-GHIJ* is easier to calculate, because the triangles are congruent isosceles triangles. Remember that the altitude of each of these triangles from the vertex *F* is the *slant height* of the pyramid. (Think of the slant height as the distance you would have to climb if you were trying to climb the pyramid starting at the midpoint of a base and proceeding straight toward its top.) The usual letter for slant height is ℓ, so

$$\begin{aligned} \text{L.A. of } F\text{-}GHIJ &= \tfrac{1}{2}\ell(GH) + \tfrac{1}{2}\ell(HI) + \tfrac{1}{2}\ell(IJ) + \tfrac{1}{2}\ell(JG) \\ &= \tfrac{1}{2}\ell(GH + HI + IJ + JG) \\ &= \tfrac{1}{2}\ell p, \end{aligned}$$

where p is the perimeter of the base.

The formula L.A. = $\frac{1}{2}\ell p$ holds for any regular pyramid. Here is a proof.

Let s be a side of the base of a regular pyramid and ℓ be its slant height. Since the lateral faces are congruent, the area of each lateral face is $\frac{1}{2}\ell s$. Since there are n lateral faces,

$$L.A. = n \cdot \frac{1}{2}\ell s$$
$$= \frac{1}{2}\ell \cdot ns.$$

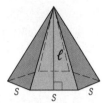

But ns is the perimeter of the base. Substituting p for ns,

$$L.A. = \frac{1}{2}\ell p.$$

Example 1 The pyramid of Khufu, a regular square pyramid 147 m tall and 231 m on a side, is the largest of the Egyptian pyramids.

a. What is the approximate slant height of this pyramid?
b. What is its lateral area?

Solution

a. Draw a picture.

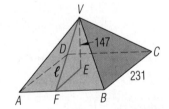

To compute the slant height ℓ, focus on right triangle *VEF. E* is the center of the square, so $EF = \frac{1}{2} \cdot 231 = 115.5$ meters. *VE* is the height, 147 meters. By the Pythagorean Theorem,
$$\ell^2 = EF^2 + VE^2$$
$$= 115.5^2 + 147^2$$
$$\approx 34,950.$$
So $\ell \approx 187$ meters

b. To find the lateral area, use the formula L.A. = $\frac{1}{2}\ell p$.
p is the perimeter of the base, so $p = 4 \cdot 231$ or 924.
$$L.A. = \frac{1}{2}\ell p$$
$$\approx \frac{1}{2} \cdot 187 \cdot 924$$
$$\approx 86,400 \text{ square meters}$$

Question 10 asks you to compare the answer in Example 1 with the area of a football field which, including the end zones, is less than 5400 square meters.

The formula L.A. $= \frac{1}{2}\ell p$ also applies to right cones. Imagine increasing n, the number of sides of the base of the regular pyramid. A cone is the limit of regular pyramids as n increases without bound. The slant height of the pyramids becomes the length of any lateral edge of the cone. The perimeter of the n-gon becomes the circumference of the circular base of the cone.

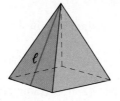  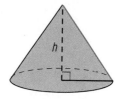

Regular Pyramid-Right Cone Lateral Area Formula:

The lateral area L.A. of a regular pyramid (or right cone) is half the product of the slant height ℓ and the perimeter (circumference) p of its base.
$$\text{L.A.} = \frac{1}{2}\ell p$$

All pyramids and cones have one base. So to calculate surface area, add the area of the base to the lateral area.

Pyramid-Cone Surface Area Formula:

The total surface area S.A. of any pyramid or cone is the sum of its lateral area L.A. and the area B of its base.
$$\text{S.A.} = \text{L.A.} + B$$

Example 2 Find the total surface area of a right cone with slant height 13 and radius of base 10.

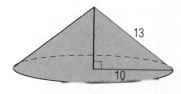

Solution Draw a picture, as at the left. Use the formula S.A. = L.A. + B. The lateral area can be found using the formula
$$\text{L.A.} = \frac{1}{2}\ell p.$$
Here, ℓ is 13. Now p is the perimeter of the base, that is, the circumference $2\pi r$. Thus, $p = 2\pi \cdot 10 = 20\pi$.
So
$$\begin{aligned}\text{L.A.} &= \tfrac{1}{2}\ell p \\ &= \tfrac{1}{2} \cdot 13 \cdot 20\pi \\ &= 130\pi.\end{aligned}$$
The base is a circle. So $\quad \begin{aligned}B &= \pi r^2 \\ &= 100\pi.\end{aligned}$
The total surface area is L.A. + B, or 230π.

Check L.A. should be greater than B. (Do you see why?) $130\pi > 100\pi$, a rough check.

In 1–3, draw a picture.

1. a non-regular pyramid *W-XYZT*

2. a regular pentagonal pyramid *A-BCDEF* with slant height 5, height 4

3. a right cone with slant height ℓ, height h, and radius of base r

4. Each lateral face of a regular pyramid is a(n) __?__ .

In 5 and 6, what does each variable represent? Be as specific as you can.

5. In a pyramid, L.A. $= \frac{1}{2}\ell p$.

6. In a cone, L.A. $= \frac{1}{2}\ell p$.

7. A right cone is the limit of regular pyramids as the number of __?__ increases without bound.

8. At the left, a regular triangular pyramid is pictured. Its slant height is 10 cm and a side of the base is 12 cm. Find its lateral area.

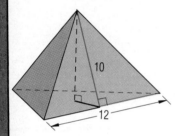

9. The perpendicular from the vertex of a regular pyramid intersects the base at __?__ .

10. About how many times larger is the lateral area of the pyramid of Khufu than the area of a football field?

11. A second Egyptian pyramid is a regular square pyramid 450 ft tall, 755 ft on a side.
a. What is its approximate slant height?
b. What is its approximate lateral area?

12. Use the right cone pictured below.
a. Find its slant height.
b. Find its lateral area.
c. Find its surface area.

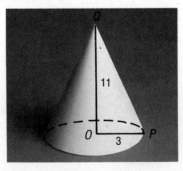

13. *Multiple choice.* For a given cone, which is larger, its lateral area or the area of its base?
(a) lateral area
(b) area of the base
(c) Neither; they are equal.
(d) The answer depends on the cone.

14. a. In a pyramid, which is greater, its height or its slant height?
b. Explain your answer.

In 15–17, **a.** draw the figure; **b.** find its lateral area; **c.** find its surface area.

15. a regular square pyramid with a base perimeter of 40 and a slant height of 50

16. a regular triangular pyramid with slant height 7 and with base of side 6 and area $9\sqrt{3}$

17. a right cone with slant height 17 and base diameter 14

18. Find the surface area of a box with dimensions $1'$, $15''$, and $18''$. *(Lesson 10-1)*

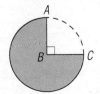

19. Small cans of frozen juice are about 9.5 cm tall and 5.5 cm in diameter. The tops and bottoms are metal; the rest is cardboard.
a. About how much metal is needed?
b. About how much cardboard is needed? *(Lesson 10-1)*

20. Draw a net for a regular square pyramid with dimensions of your choosing. *(Lesson 9-7)*

21. Find the length of each lateral edge in the pyramid of Question 8. *(Lessons 9-3, 8-7)*

22. What are the four assumed properties of area? *(Lesson 8-3)*

23. Line t goes through the points $(6, -4)$ and $(8, 0)$.
a. Graph t.
b. Find the slope of t.
c. Find the slope of a line perpendicular to t. *(Lessons 3-5, 3-4)*

24. Solve in your head. *(Previous course)*
a. $x + 3 = 64$
b. $y \cdot 3 = 64$
c. $z^3 = 64$

25. Cut out a disc with radius $4''$ or 10 cm from a sheet of paper. Then cut out a 90° sector from the disc. This leaves a figure with the shape of the shaded region at the left. Now fold $\overline{AB}$ onto $\overline{BC}$ to form a cone. What is the lateral area of this cone?

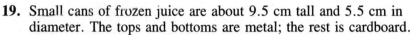

Fundamental Properties of Volume

Each face of the cube below, with sides of length 1, has area 1 square unit. Since there are six faces, the surface area of the cube is 6 square units. But **volume** is quite different from surface area. The volume of this cube is 1 cubic unit or 1 unit^3. For this reason it is called the **unit cube.** Usually volume is measured in cubic units.

1 cubic unit

Volume measures how much a figure will hold, its *capacity*.

Example 1 What is the volume of a paper bag with base 12″ by 7″ and height 17″?

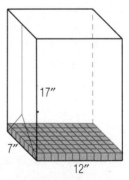

17″

7″

12″

Solution There are 12 · 7 unit cubes in the layer along a base. There are 17 layers. The volume is 12″ · 7″ · 17″, or 1428 cubic inches.

Notice that the volume of this bag is the product of its three dimensions. This is one of the four fundamental properties of volume assumed in the Volume Postulate. Compare these assumptions with the fundamental properties of area assumed in the Area Postulate in Lesson 8-3.

In symbols, if Volume(S) is the volume of a solid S, then the Additive Property of Volume states that if A and B are two nonoverlapping solids, then:

$$\text{Volume}(A \cup B) = \text{Volume}(A) + \text{Volume}(B).$$

Using this property, volumes of more complicated figures can be calculated.

Example 2 Figures I and II are the unions of 5 unit cubes. Give the surface area and volume of each.

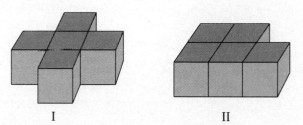

I   II

Solution The volume for each solid is the same, since it is the sum of the volumes of the five cubes.

Volume(I) = Volume(II) = 5 cubic units

In solid I, there are 12 lateral faces (3 on each of the four outside cubes), each with area 1 square unit, and each base has area 5 square units.

$$
\begin{aligned}
\text{S.A.} &= \text{L.A.} + 2 \cdot B \\
&= 12 + 2 \cdot 5 \\
&= 22 \text{ square units}
\end{aligned}
$$

In solid II, there are 10 lateral faces. Each base again has area 5 square units.

$$
\begin{aligned}
\text{S.A.} &= \text{L.A.} + 2 \cdot B \\
&= 10 + 2 \cdot 5 \\
&= 20 \text{ square units}
\end{aligned}
$$

Example 2 illustrates that solids may have equal volumes, but unequal surface areas. However, many people judge the volume of a container by its surface area. They think, "if it looks big, then it holds a lot!"

Pictured at the left are a salad-dressing bottle and a yogurt container. The two containers hold the same amount; they have the same volume. The dressing bottle has greater surface area, giving the false impression that it has greater volume and holds more.

The formula for the volume of a cube is a special case of the formula for the volume of a box where each dimension is the same.

Cube Volume Formula:

The volume of a cube with edge s is s^3.

Proof

For a box,   Volume = ℓwh.
A cube is a box with $\ell = w = h = s$.
Substituting,   Volume = $s \cdot s \cdot s$
                        = s^3.

Because of the Cube Volume Formula, we call s^3 the "cube of s." If a cube has volume 8, its edge will satisfy $s^3 = 8$, and so $s = 2$.

We say that 2 is the *cube root* of 8, and write $2 = \sqrt[3]{8}$. In general, $\sqrt[3]{y}$ is the edge of a cube whose volume is y.

Definition:

x is a **cube root** of y, written $x = \sqrt[3]{y}$, if and only if $x^3 = y$.

Scientific calculators differ in the keys they employ to calculate a cube root. Some have a $\boxed{\sqrt[3]{x}}$ key. On some there is a $\boxed{\sqrt[x]{x}}$ key; on these, to find $\sqrt[3]{n}$, press n $\boxed{\sqrt[x]{x}}$ 3 $\boxed{=}$. On others you can press n $\boxed{\text{INV}}$ $\boxed{x^y}$ 3 $\boxed{=}$.

▪ ▪ ▪ ▪ ▪ ▪ ▪ ▪ ▪

Example 3   A cube has a volume of 50 cubic centimeters. What is the length of an edge?

Solution   Let s be the length of an edge. Since $s^3 = 50$, s is exactly $\sqrt[3]{50}$ cm. To estimate $\sqrt[3]{50}$, use a calculator. 50 $\boxed{\sqrt[x]{x}}$ 3 $\boxed{=}$ displays 3.684... . An edge is approximately 3.7 cm long.

Check   Is $3.7^3 \approx 50$? Yes, $3.7^3 = 50.653$, which is close enough.

Questions

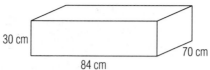

Covering the Reading

1. What is the volume of a box with dimensions 30 cm, 70 cm, and 84 cm?

30 cm   70 cm   84 cm

2. In a sugar cube, each edge has length 1 cm. What is the volume of the cube?

3. Two solids have the same surface area. Must they have the same volume?

4. Two cubes have the same surface area. Must they have the same volume?

5. x is a cube root of y if and only if __?__.

6. **a.** Give the cube of 8.
   b. Give the cube root of 8.

7. Write the exact cube root of 50.

8. With a calculator, estimate the cube root of 100 to the nearest hundredth.

Applying the Mathematics

9. A top is put on the paper bag of Example 1.
   a. By how much does the top change the bag's surface area?
   b. By how much does it change the bag's volume?

10. Some people use the formula $V = Bh$ for the volume of a box.
    a. What is B in this formula?
    b. Why does this formula work?

11. The volume of a bag is 576 in.^{3}. If the base has an area of 48 in.^{2}, what is the height?

12. A cube has volume 29,791 cm^3. What is its surface area?

13. Calculate $\sqrt[3]{25} + \sqrt[3]{100}$ to the nearest hundredth.

14. One cube has edges x centimeters long. Another has edges $3x$ centimeters long. Find the ratio of:
    a. the total surface area of the smaller cube to that of the larger.
    b. the volume of the smaller cube to that of the larger.

x $3x$

LESSON 10-3 Fundamental Properties of Volume   **481**

15. a. 1 yard = __?__ feet
   b. 1 square yard = __?__ square feet
   c. 1 cubic yard = __?__ cubic feet

16. a. Complete this program so that it will print out the correct volume and surface area.

```
10   PRINT "GIVE DIMENSIONS OF BOX"
20   INPUT L, W, H
30   PRINT "THE VOLUME IS " i. _?_ " CUBIC UNITS."
40   PRINT "THE SURFACE AREA IS " ii. _?_ " SQUARE UNITS."
50   END
```

   b. Check your program by letting L = 7, W = 12, and H = 17, and comparing the printout with Example 1 of this lesson and Example 1 of Lesson 10-1.

Review

17. a. Draw a right cone with radius 4 and slant height 12.
   b. Determine its lateral area. *(Lesson 10-2)*

18. Find the surface area of the regular square pyramid pictured at the left. *(Lesson 10-2)*

19. a. In square inches, how much wrapping paper is needed to cover a cylinder 12″ in diameter and 7″ high?
   b. Suppose you can only buy the wrapping paper by the square foot. How many square feet will you need to buy to wrap the cylinder of part **a**? *(Lesson 10-1)*

20. The tent at the right is in the shape of a right prism with isosceles triangle *GHI* as its base.
   a. Find the area of the base of this prism.
   b. If the length of the tent is 7 feet, find the surface area of the tent. (Assume no part of the tent is folded onto the ground.) *(Lessons 10-1, 8-7, 8-5)*

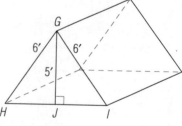

21. Give the singular of each term. *(Lessons 9-7, 2-5, 1-4)*
   a. polyhedra   **b.** radii   **c.** vertices

Exploration

22. Containers holding small amounts can be made to appear to hold more than they do by making them long and thin. Give some examples of these kinds of containers.

23. Two polyhedra made up of 5 unit cubes are shown in Example 2 of this lesson.
   a. Draw some of the other possible polyhedra that are the union of 5 unit cubes.
   b. Which has the most surface area?
   c. Which has the least surface area?

Box cars and other containers are being loaded onto a ship in Hampton, Virginia. Their total volume can be found in a variety of ways.

Multiplication, Area, and Volume

To obtain the area of a rectangle, you merely have to multiply its length by its width. Any positive numbers can be the length and the width. Thus the area of a rectangle is a *model* for the multiplication of two positive numbers. This enables multiplication to be pictured. For instance, the following picture shows that the product of 3.5 and 2.3 is larger than the product of 3 and 2.

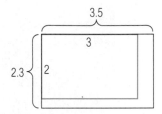

Turning a rectangle on its side does not change its area. But it switches its base and height.

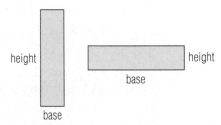

In terms of multiplication this means $hb = bh$, picturing the well-known Commutative Property of Multiplication.

The Box Volume Formula, $V = \ell wh$, models the multiplication of *three* numbers. Any face of a box can be its base, and any sides of the base its length and width, yet the volume will be the same. So not only is commutativity pictured because $V = (\ell w)h = h(\ell w)$, but also associativity because $V = (\ell w)h = \ell(wh)$.

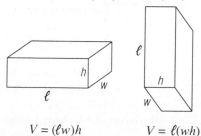

$$V = (\ell w)h \qquad V = \ell(wh)$$

Even the multiplication of polynomials can be pictured by area and volume. For instance, in algebra you probably saw the multiplication of two binomials pictured using areas of rectangles.

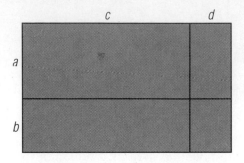

You may have seen the multiplication of two trinomials or other polynomials pictured in this way.

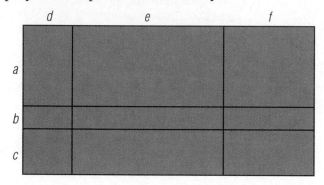

With volume, the multiplication of *three* binomials can be pictured. The big box below has dimensions *a+b, c+d,* and *e+f.* So its volume is the product of those three binomials. But the big box is made up of eight little boxes (parts of seven can be seen), so the volume of the big box is also the sum of the volumes of the eight little boxes.

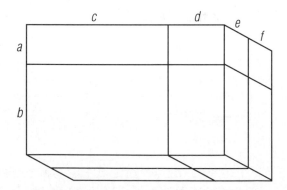

Notice that the product of the three binomials consists of all possible products in which one factor is taken from the first binomial, one from the second, and one from the third.

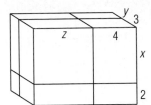

Example 1   Expand $(x + 2)(y + 3)(z + 4)$.

Solution 1   Think of the three factors as the dimensions of a box. The product is the volume of the box. The volume is the sum of the volumes of eight small boxes.

$$V = 3zx + 3\cdot4\cdot x + 3\cdot z\cdot2 + 3\cdot4\cdot2 + yzx + y\cdot4\cdot x + yz\cdot2 + y\cdot4\cdot2$$
$$= 3xz + 12x + 6z + 24 + xyz + 4xy + 2yz + 8y$$

Solution 2   Recall the Distributive Property from your study of algebra.

$$(x + 2)(y + 3)(z + 4)$$
$$= x(y + 3)(z + 4) + 2(y + 3)(z + 4)$$
$$= x(yz + 4y + 3z + 12) + 2(yz + 4y + 3z + 12)$$
$$= xyz + 4xy + 3xz + 12x + 2yz + 8y + 6z + 24$$

Check 1   The two solutions give the same answer, which is a check.

Check 2   Substitute for x, y, and z. Suppose $x = 5$, $y = 10$, and $z = 8$. Then $(x + 2)(y + 3)(z + 4) = 7\cdot13\cdot12 = 1092$. Substituting in the answer yields

$$5\cdot10\cdot8 + 4\cdot5\cdot10 + 3\cdot5\cdot8 + 12\cdot5 + 2\cdot10\cdot8 + 8\cdot10 + 6\cdot8 + 24$$
$$= 400 + 200 + 120 + 60 + 160 + 80 + 48 + 24$$
$$= 1092.$$

Example 1 points out how complicated the change in volume is if you *add* 2 to one edge of a box, 3 to another edge, and 4 to the third edge. The increase in volume is the solution minus xyz, which is the polynomial $4xy + 3xz + 12x + 2yz + 8y + 6z + 24$. But if you *multiply* the edges by 2, 3, and 4, the change in volume is easy to find.

Example 2   A box has dimensions ℓ, w, and h. If the dimensions are multiplied by 2, 3, and 4, respectively, what happens to the volume of the box?

Solution   Draw a picture of the situation.

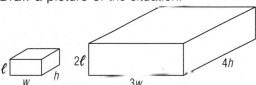

The new volume is $(2\ell)(3w)(4h)$, which is $24\ell wh$, 24 times the old volume.

In general, multiplying any one dimension of a box by a certain number multiplies the volume of the box by that number. In Example 2, if the length were doubled but nothing was done to the other dimensions, the volume would have been doubled. Adding to a dimension of a box does not affect the volume in such a simple way.

1. Use the area model for multiplication to show that $5.6 \cdot 7.8$ is larger than $5 \cdot 7$.

In 2–6, give the algebraic property illustrated.

2. has the same area as

3. has the same volume as

4. At the left, the sum of the areas of the four little rectangles equals the area of the largest rectangle.

5. The sum of the areas of the six little rectangles equals the area of the largest rectangle.

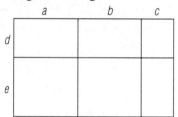

6. The sum of the volumes of the eight little boxes equals the volume of the large box.

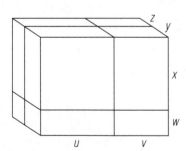

In 7–10, expand.

7. $(x + 9)(2x + 3)$

8. $(3a + 5)(7a + 6)$

9. $(a + 1)(a + 2)(a + 3)$

10. $(a + b + 2)(3a + 8b)$

In 11–13, how is the volume of a box changed if its dimensions are changed in the indicated way?

11. Its length is multiplied by 3 and all other dimensions are kept the same.

12. Its length, width, and height are all multiplied by 3.

13. Six is added to the length and all other dimensions are kept the same.

Applying the Mathematics

Rice harvesting in Indonesia

14. A coating of lead 1 mm thick is put on a steel box safe that has dimensions 28 cm, 20 cm, and 14 cm. What is the amount of lead needed?

15. In a market you see two full bags of rice. Bag *X* is 1.4 times as high as bag *Y*, 1.2 times as wide, and 1.2 times as deep.
a. How do the capacities of these bags compare?
b. How should their prices compare?

In 16–19, expand.

16. $(x - 1)(2x - 5)$

17. $(y - x)(y + x)$

18. $(3a + 2)(b - 6)(a - b)$

19. $(a + b + c)^2$

Review

20. a. 1 meter = __?__ centimeters
b. 1 square meter = __?__ square centimeters
c. 1 cubic meter = __?__ cubic centimeters *(Lesson 10-3, Previous course)*

21. Estimate the cube root of π to the nearest hundredth. *(Lesson 10-3)*

22. A cube has volume 27 in.^{3}. What is its surface area?
(Lessons 10-3, 10-2)

23. A card in the game "Uno" is about 5.6 cm by 8.7 cm. If a stack of 72 cards is about 2.7 cm high, what is the volume of a single card? *(Lesson 10-3)*

24. a. Draw a regular pentagonal pyramid. *(Lesson 9-3)*
b. If each side of the base is 18, and each lateral edge is 41, find its lateral area. *(Lesson 10-2)*

25. Solve: $\pi r^2 = 10$. *(Previous course)*

Exploration

26. Expand $(a + b)^3$ by finding the volume of an appropriate cube in two different ways.

10-5

Volumes of Prisms and Cylinders

Oil, gas, and related products are often stored in huge cylindrical tanks like those pictured above. It is natural to wonder how much gas or oil is stored in each tank. The amount can be calculated if you know the dimensions of the tank and the formula for the volume of a cylinder. This formula and formulas for the volumes of other common three-dimensional figures can be derived from the Area and Volume Postulates you have already studied and from one other postulate to be stated in this lesson.

Consider a region with area B which is the base of a prism or cylinder. Then think of B unit squares covering the region, even if B is not an integer.

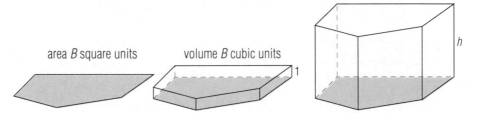

area B square units   volume B cubic units

If a prism with this base has height 1 unit, the prism contains B unit cubes, and so the volume of the prism is B cubic units. This is pictured in the middle figure above. The right figure shows a prism with this base and height h. That prism has h times the volume of the middle prism, and so its volume is Bh. This argument shows that, if a right prism or cylinder has height h and a base with area B, then its volume is Bh.

A cubic foot of liquid contains about 7.48 gallons. This information, which can be found in most almanacs, combined with the volume formula derived above, enables the capacity of an oil storage tank to be found.

Example 1   If a cylindrical storage tank has a diameter of 100 feet and is 70 feet high, how many gallons of oil can it hold? Make a guess before you go on.

Solution   It usually helps to draw a picture, as shown at the left.

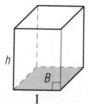

Use the formula $V = Bh$. The radius of the base is 50′, so $B = \pi(50)^2$, or 2500π. (As usual, it is wise not to estimate π until absolutely necessary.) Thus

$$V = Bh$$
$$= 2500\pi \cdot 70$$
$$= 175{,}000\pi \text{ cubic feet}$$
$$\approx 550{,}000 \text{ cubic feet.}$$

Now each cubic foot contains about 7.48 gallons of fuel. So the capacity of the tank is

$$550{,}000 \text{ ft}^3 \cdot 7.48 \frac{\text{gal}}{\text{ft}^3} \approx 4{,}110{,}000 \text{ gallons.}$$

This is more than many people would estimate.

Now suppose you have an oblique prism or cylinder. Recall that in such figures, the lateral edges are not perpendicular to the planes of the bases. Pictured here are a right prism and an oblique prism with congruent bases and equal heights.

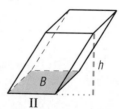

Imagine Prism I to be made up of a stack of thin slices like congruent sheets of paper. Shift the sheets of the first stack until it approximates the form of Prism II.

Note that the height, area of the base, and number of slices are the same in Prism I and Prism II. Consequently,

Volume(Prism II) = Volume(Prism I).

Or, since they have equal heights and bases,

Volume(Prism II) = Bh.

The key ideas of this argument are: (1) the prisms have their bases in the same planes; and (2) the slices in each prism have the same area. Such solids have the same volume. Francesco Bonaventura Cavalieri (1598–1647), an Italian mathematician, first realized the importance of this principle. It is named after him.

Volume Postulate:

e. (Cavalieri's Principle) Let I and II be two solids included between parallel planes. If every plane P parallel to the given planes intersects I and II in sections with the same area, then
$$\text{Volume(I)} = \text{Volume(II)}.$$

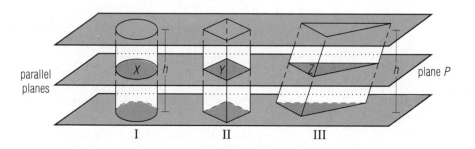

Above, plane P is parallel to the planes containing the bases, and all three solids have bases with area B. Since sections X, Y, and Z are translation images of the bases (this is how prisms and cylinders are defined), they also have area B. Thus the conditions for Cavalieri's Principle are satisfied. These solids have the same volume. But the volume of the box is known.

$$\text{Volume(II)} = \ell \cdot w \cdot h$$
$$= B \cdot h$$

Thus, using Cavalieri's Principle,

$$\text{Volume(I)} = B \cdot h \quad \text{and}$$
$$\text{Volume(II)} = B \cdot h.$$

This proves the following theorem for *all* cylinders and prisms.

Prism-Cylinder Volume Formula:

The volume V of *any* prism or cylinder is the product of its height h and the area B of its base.
$$V = Bh$$

490

For a cylinder, the base is a circle. If the radius is r, then the base has area πr^2. So a special formula for the volume of a cylinder is

$$V = \pi r^2 h,$$

but you should not have to remember it. You can derive it quickly from $V = Bh$.

In an oblique prism or cylinder, the height sometimes must be determined using the Pythagorean Theorem.

Example 2 Find the volume of the parallelepiped pictured below.

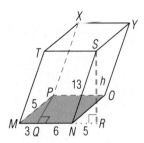

Solution The volume is $B \cdot h$. To find B, the area of the base $MNOP$, its height PQ must be found. Using the Pythagorean Theorem,
$$MQ^2 + PQ^2 = MP^2$$
$$3^2 + PQ^2 = 5^2.$$
So $PQ = 4.$
Thus $B = MN \cdot PQ = 9 \cdot 4 = 36$ square units. The height h of the prism is also found by applying the Pythagorean Theorem.
$$RS^2 + RN^2 = NS^2$$
$$h^2 + 5^2 = 13^2$$
So $h = 12.$
Thus $V = Bh = 432$ square units.

Questions

Covering the Reading

1. A cubic foot of liquid is how many gallons?

2. How many gallons of oil can fill a cylindrical tank with diameter 120 feet and height 60 feet?

3. *Multiple choice.* In this lesson, a stack of paper is used to illustrate all but which of the following?
   (a) Cavalieri's Principle
   (b) that an oblique prism and a right prism can have the same volume
   (c) that the volume of an oblique prism is Bh
   (d) that a cylinder and a prism have the same volume formula

4. Who was Cavalieri and in what century did he live most of his life?

5. State Cavalieri's Principle.

6. Give a formula for the volume of an oblique cylinder.

In 7–12, find the volume of each solid.

7.

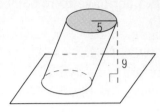

8.

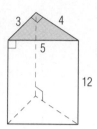

9. a square prism whose base has edge 5 meters, and whose height is 20 meters

10. the parallelepiped drawn below

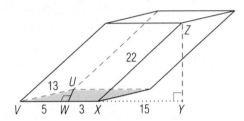

11. a right rectangular prism whose base is 3 feet by 7 feet, and whose height is 10 feet

12. a sewer pipe 200′ long with a radius of 2′

Applying the Mathematics

13. Draw a rectangular prism and a cylinder which, according to Cavalieri, have identical volumes. Include the dimensions of each solid.

14. The volume of an oblique prism is 38 cubic meters. Its height is 4 meters. Find the area of the base.

15. An artist constructed a cylindric solid as shown in the sketch below. What is its volume?

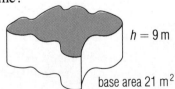

$h = 9\,\text{m}$

base area 21 m²

16. Two cylindric glasses have the same height, but the diameters of the glasses are 2.3″ and 3.3″.
   a. Can the second glass hold twice as much as the first?
   b. Why or why not?

17. A cylinder and cone have bases of the same area and equal heights. Why can't Cavalieri's Principle be applied in this situation?

18. If a cylinder of height h is compared with a cylinder which has the same height, but a radius half that of the first, how do the volumes compare?

19. What does doubling the height of a prism without changing the size of its base do to its volume?

20. A milliliter of water has a mass of 1 gram and occupies 1 cm^3 of space. If a cylindric can is 15 cm high, has radius 3 cm, and is filled with water, what is its mass (to the nearest gram)?

Review

21. Expand $(4x - 5y)(x + 2y + 7)$. *(Lesson 10-4)*

22. The height of a box is multiplied by 4 and the length and width are each multiplied by 5. By how much does this multiply the volume of the box? *(Lesson 10-4)*

23. A closed lead box for vials of plutonium measures 4 cm by 3.5 cm by 2.5 cm on the outside. The inside dimensions are 3 cm by 2.5 cm by 2 cm. How much lead is used to make the box? *(Lesson 10-3)*

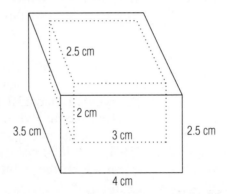

24. Find the surface area of the prism in Question 8. *(Lesson 10-1)*

25. Refer to Example 2 on Page 491. Find the area of *MTSN*. *(Lesson 9-2)*

26. Arrange these quadrilateral area formulas from most general to most specific: $A = s^2$, $A = \frac{1}{2}h(b_1 + b_2)$, $A = \ell w$, $A = hb$. *(Lessons 8-6, 8-4)*

27. Refer to the figure at the right.
Given: $\overline{CD} \cong \overline{EF}$
$\overline{CD} \parallel \overline{EF}$.
Prove: $\angle FCE \cong \angle DEC$.
(Lessons 7-7, 7-3)

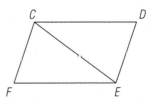

Exploration

28. Find a cylindric juice can in your house. Its volume is probably given in fluid ounces.
a. Calculate its volume in cubic inches.
b. Use this information to determine about how many cubic inches there are to the fluid ounce.

Remembering Formulas

At this point, you have encountered formulas for perimeters and areas of many two-dimensional regions and for lateral areas, surface areas, and volumes of some three-dimensional figures. You will see more formulas in other lessons of this chapter. At this point, you may wonder: Which formulas should I remember? The answer to that question is simple: *Remember formulas which apply to the most figures*.

A hierarchy can help to organize the three-dimensional figures you have seen. First organize by the number of bases, as shown in lines (1) and (2) of the hierarchy below. Prisms and cylinders have two parallel bases. Pyramids and cones have one base. Spheres, which you will encounter later in this chapter, have no base. Some of these figures include special types, shown in line (3). A very special type, from which the volume of all figures is determined, is the one figure in line (4).

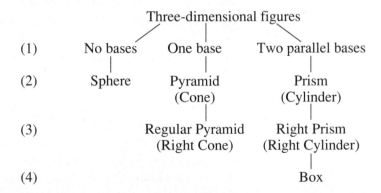

Three-dimensional figures

	No bases	One base	Two parallel bases
(1)	No bases	One base	Two parallel bases
(2)	Sphere	Pyramid (Cone)	Prism (Cylinder)
(3)		Regular Pyramid (Right Cone)	Right Prism (Right Cylinder)
(4)			Box

In this chapter, there are seven—only seven—basic formulas. (Thus far you have seen four of the seven.) Here all seven formulas are superimposed on the hierarchy. No formulas for total surface area are given because all you have to do is add the area of all bases to the lateral area to get a formula. Try to locate the four formulas that have already been discussed.

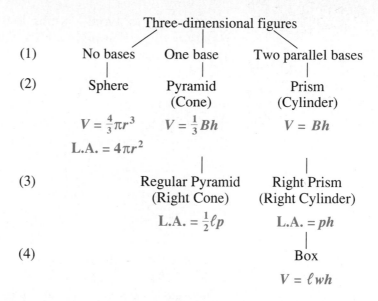

Three-dimensional figures

(1) No bases · One base · Two parallel bases

(2) Sphere · Pyramid (Cone) · Prism (Cylinder)

$V = \frac{4}{3}\pi r^3$ $V = \frac{1}{3}Bh$ $V = Bh$

L.A. $= 4\pi r^2$

(3) Regular Pyramid (Right Cone) · Right Prism (Right Cylinder)

L.A. $= \frac{1}{2}\ell p$ L.A. $= ph$

(4) Box

$V = \ell wh$

One thing is obvious from the list: *To use a formula, you must know what each variable in the formula represents.*

You have seen formulas that are not on the hierarchy. For instance, the formula L.A. $= 2\pi rh$ for the lateral area of a right cylinder is not listed. This is because a few general ideas help reduce the load of formulas to remember. *For special formulas for cones and cylinders, substitute the circle formulas $B = \pi r^2$ and $p = 2\pi r$ in the corresponding formulas for pyramids and prisms.* The idea is simple: cones and cylinders are like pyramids and prisms, but with circular bases.

For example, to obtain a formula for the lateral area of a right cylinder, use the formula **L.A. $= ph$** from the hierarchy. Substitute $2\pi r$ for p to get L.A. $= (2\pi r)h = 2\pi rh$. Practice so that you can do the substitution quickly and thus avoid learning a special formula for the lateral area of a right cone.

In Lesson 10-3, you saw a formula for the volume of a box. You probably had seen this formula before. From this formula alone, all the other volume formulas can be deduced. The process we used— the process of proof—is the most powerful idea of all for remembering formulas. *If you cannot remember a formula, try to derive it from some simpler formulas you know to be true.* That is the way mathematicians recall many of the formulas they have to use. The difficulty with this advice is that it usually takes some time to derive a formula. Often there is not the time. So, if you do not want to spend your time proving or cannot do proofs, you must either learn some formulas by heart or have access to a book containing the formulas.

Another way to avoid learning lots of formulas is to *use general formulas to get formulas for special types of figures*. These ideas are applied in the Example.

Example   Find a formula for the surface area of a box in terms of its height h, length ℓ, and width w.

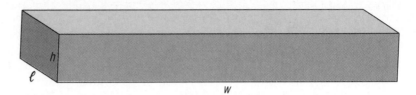

Solution   A box is a prism. Begin with the formula for the lateral area of a prism.
$$\text{L.A.} = ph$$
h is given so it need not be touched. But p is the perimeter of the base. Since the base is a rectangle with length ℓ and width w, its perimeter is $2\ell + 2w$. Substituting,
$$\text{L.A.} = (2\ell + 2w)h.$$
For the surface area, the areas of the two bases must be added.
$$\text{S.A.} = \text{L.A.} + 2B$$
Each base has area ℓw. Thus a formula is
$$\text{S.A.} = (2\ell + 2w)\,h + 2\ell w.$$
Using the Distributive Property, the formula can be rewritten as
$$\text{S.A.} = 2\ell h + 2wh + 2\ell w.$$

Questions

Covering the Reading

1. What are the best formulas to remember?

In 2 and 3, choose from the following:
boxes, cones, cylinders, prisms, pyramids, spheres.

2. In which figures does S.A. = L.A. + $2B$?

3. In which figures does S.A. = L.A. + B?

4. **a.** How many basic formulas are there to learn in this chapter?
   b. Which basic formulas have you seen already?

5. What do the variables represent in the formula L.A. = ph?

6. What is the process for obtaining special formulas for cones and cylinders?

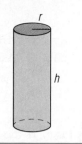

In 7 and 8, consider a right cylinder with height h and base with radius r.

7. Deduce a formula for its lateral area.

8. Deduce a formula for its volume.

9. How do mathematicians recall formulas?

10. Find a formula for the surface area of the right cylinder of Questions 7 and 8 in terms of its height h and the radius r of a base.

11. A right cone has slant height ℓ and its base has radius r.
  a. Find a formula for its L.A. in terms of ℓ and r.
  b. Find a formula for its S.A. in terms of ℓ and r.

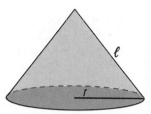

12. **a.** Find the area of an equilateral triangle with one side 400.

  b. Generalize part **a** to find the area of an equilateral triangle with one side s.

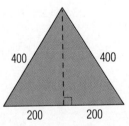

In 13–15, use the formula below for the area of any triangle given the lengths of its sides a, b, and c. It was discovered by Archimedes, but it is known as **Hero's** or **Heron's Formula,** after the Greek mathematician Hero (or Heron) of Alexandria, who lived about 50 A.D. Let s be half the perimeter of the triangle. Then $\text{Area}(\triangle ABC) = \sqrt{s(s-a)(s-b)(s-c)}$.

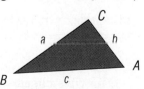

Archimedes (287-212 B.C.)

13. **a.** Use Heron's Formula to find the area of a triangle with sides of lengths 9, 12, and 15.
  b. Use an alternate method to check your work.

14. Find the area of a triangle with sides 10, 17, and 21.

15. Use Heron's Formula to answer Question 12a.

16. Suppose each base of a right prism is an isosceles trapezoid with dimensions as shown. *(Lessons 10-5, 10-1)*

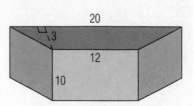

   a. Find its volume.
   b. Find its lateral area.
   c. Find its surface area.

17. The height of a cylinder equals the diameter of its base. If the radius of the base is 27, what is the volume of the cylinder? *(Lesson 10-5)*

18. Expand $(x + y)^2$. *(Lesson 10-4)*

19. By how much is the volume of a cube of side 8 changed if a is added to the length, a is subtracted from the width, and the height remains 8? *(Lesson 10-4)*

20. Pyramids were built throughout the ancient world. Northeast of Mexico City is the regular square pyramid Teotihuacán. This pyramid is 66 m high and 442 m wide at its base. *(Lesson 10-2)*

   a. What is its lateral area?
   b. How does its lateral area compare with that of the pyramid of Khufu (see Lesson 10-2)?

21. a. Draw an oblique cone with base radius 1.5 cm and height 3 cm.
   b. If the lateral area of the cone is 16 cm², what is the surface area of the cone? *(Lesson 10-2)*

22. A ring between two concentric circles is shaded, as at the left. If the radius of the small circle is h and the radius of the large circle is r, what is the area of the ring? *(Lesson 8-9)*

23. Find the slope of line ℓ below. *(Lesson 3-4)*

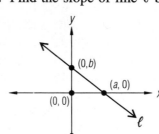

24. Graph: $y = -\frac{1}{2}x + 3$. *(Lesson 1-3)*

25. a. Give dimensions for a cylinder whose surface area is 200π.
   b. Give dimensions for a second cylinder, not congruent to the first, whose surface area is 200π.

Volumes of Pyramids and Cones

In this lesson you will learn a simple formula for the volume of any pyramid or cone. The proof of that formula, however, is not so simple. It will help you to do part **a** of Question 23 before reading on. Use those models and examine the figures drawn as you read.

The cone and triangular pyramid pictured below have their bases in plane P and the bases have the same area B. Planes P, Q, and R are parallel, and the sections formed by plane Q are shaded. Their heights are the same, as both vertices lie in plane R. Under these conditions, the sections have the same area also. Cavalieri's Principle says that the two solids then have the same volume. Thus any cones or pyramids with bases of equal area and with equal heights have identical volumes.

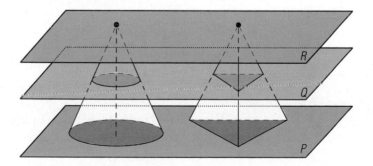

Thus, if the volume of a single pyramid is found, all others with the same height and base area will have the same volume. So pick a simple pyramid.

Consider the triangular pyramid *D-AGC* below in which $\overline{DC}$ is perpendicular to the plane of the base $\triangle AGC$. Let Area($\triangle AGC$) = B and $DC = h$. The volume of *D-AGC* is wanted.

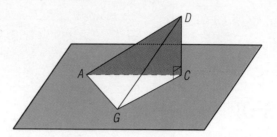

Form a triangular *prism* with congruent bases *AGC* and *FED*, and with edges parallel and equal to $\overline{DC}$. This prism has volume Bh. It will now be shown that this prism has 3 times the volume of the pyramid.

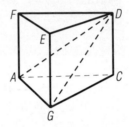

Draw $\overline{FG}$ in the prism above; it is a diagonal of rectangle *AGEF*. Notice that $\triangle AFG \cong \triangle EGF$. Now there are three nonoverlapping pyramids whose union is the prism. Each is outlined below in colored edges, while the rest of the prism is dashed.

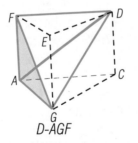

D-AGF

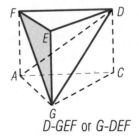

D-GEF or G-DEF

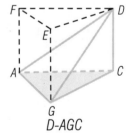

D-AGC

If you have your cutout models from Question 23, try to put the three of them together to form a prism, just as is done here.

The pyramids *D-AGF* and *D-GEF* have the same volume since the height of each is from *D* to the plane of parallelogram *AGEF*, and the bases are congruent. Similarly *G-DEF* and *D-AGC* are equal in volume because they have equal heights ($DC = EG$) and congruent bases. By the Transitive Property of Equality, the three pyramids have the same volume. So each pyramid has a volume that is one-third the volume of the prism. Consequently, the volume of pyramid *D-AGC* is $\frac{1}{3}Bh$.

The next step is to show that this formula works for any pyramid or cone. In general, the triangular base can be made to have *any* given area. By Cavalieri's Principle, the volume of any pyramid or cone can be equated with the volume of a pyramid of the same height and a given triangular base. For instance, if the base of a cone has area 6π units^2, a triangular pyramid of the same height can be constructed with a base of area 6π units^2. This argument proves the following theorem.

Pyramid-Cone Volume Formula:

The volume V of any pyramid or cone equals $\frac{1}{3}$ the product of its height h and its base area B.
$$V = \tfrac{1}{3} Bh$$

Notice that the volume of a pyramid may be easier to calculate than its surface area.

Example 1 Find the volume of the pyramid of Khufu. (Recall that this pyramid is a regular square pyramid 147 m high with each side of the base 231 m.)

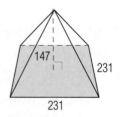

Solution Use the formula
$$V = \tfrac{1}{3} Bh.$$

The base is a square, so $B = (231)^2 = 53{,}361$ square meters. From the given, $h = 147$ meters.

Thus
$$V = \tfrac{1}{3} \cdot 53{,}361 \cdot 147$$
$$\approx 2{,}610{,}000 \text{ cubic meters.}$$

The volume is about 2,610,000 m^3. This is over 2500 times the capacity of a middle-size house with a volume of 1000 m^3!

The formula $V = \frac{1}{3}Bh$ holds for a cone. If the radius of the base of the cone is r, then $B = \pi r^2$. So a formula for the volume of a cone is
$$V = \tfrac{1}{3}\pi r^2 h.$$

This is a formula you should not have to memorize, but be able to derive.

If you know all but one quantity in a formula, you can solve an equation to determine the unknown.

■ ■ ■ ■ ■ ■ ■ ■■

Example 2 If a cone has a height of 6 in. and a volume of 40 in.³, what is the radius of its base?

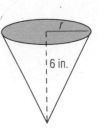

Solution The relevant formula is $V = \frac{1}{3} Bh$.
Here $h = 6$ and $V = 40$.
Substituting, $40 = \frac{1}{3} B \cdot 6$
                              $40 = 2B$.
So $B = 20$.
But $B = \pi r^2$. So $20 = \pi r^2$
                              $r^2 = \frac{20}{\pi}$.

So $r = \sqrt{\frac{20}{\pi}} \approx 2.52$ in.

Questions

Covering the Reading

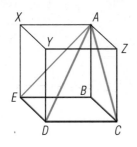

1. Two pyramids with congruent bases and heights have equal __?__ .

2. At the left, how does the volume of pyramid A-$BCDE$ compare with the volume of the box?

3. Find the volume V of a pyramid with height 6 and base area 57.

4. A formula of the volume of a cone is $V =$ __?__ or $V =$ __?__ .

5. Find the volume of a cone with height $8'$ and base of radius $2'$.

In 6–8, find the volume of the solid.

6.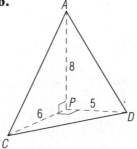

right triangular pyramid with base PCD and height AP

7.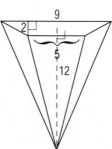

trapezoidal pyramid with height 12

8.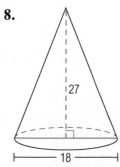

right cone with height 27 and diameter 18

9. A cone has a volume of 40 cm³. Its height is 5 cm. What must be the radius of the base?

10. A cone and a cylinder have identical bases and equal heights. If the volume of the cylinder is *V*, then the volume of the cone is __?__ .

11. The largest monument ever built is the Quetzalcóatl at Cholula de Rivadabia, a pyramid about 60 miles southeast of Mexico City. The Quetzalcóatl is 177 feet tall and its base covers 45 acres. (Recall 1 acre = 43,560 ft^2.) Determine the volume of the Quetzalcóatl to the nearest million cubic feet.

12. Consider the soft drink cup pictured below.
    a. How many cm^3 of liquid will it hold?
    b. How many times will it need to be used in order to fill a liter jug? (Note: 1 liter = 1000 cm^3.)
    c. How much paper is needed to make the cup?

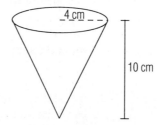

13. What happens to the volume of a cone if the height is kept the same but the radius of the base is multiplied by 7?

14. What happens to the volume of a pyramid if its base is kept the same but its height is multiplied by 31.8?

15. If △*ABC* is spun about $\overleftrightarrow{AB}$, a right cone is formed.
    a. What is the height of the cone?
    b. Find the volume of the cone.

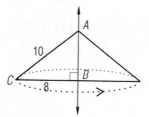

16. How much paper is needed to cover a box that is *ℓ* inches long, *w* inches wide, and *h* inches high? *(Lessons 10-6, 10-1)*

17. Give a formula for the lateral area of the regular square pyramid pictured at the left. *(Lesson 10-6)*

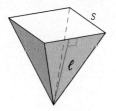

18. Find the volume and surface area of the right triangular prism pictured. *(Lessons 10-5, 10-1)*

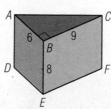

19. Find the area of the large rectangle pictured below. *(Lesson 10-4)*

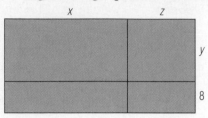

20. A two-by-four is a piece of wood that starts out measuring 2″ by 4″ by k' (it can have any length) but is planed to $1\frac{5}{8}$″ by $3\frac{5}{8}$″ by k'. What percent of the wood is lost in the planing? *(Lesson 10-3)*

21. Bernard bought a 10-gallon fish tank. He was told a tank could support one guppy for every 168 in.^{3} of water. Bernard measured the tank and found it to be 20″ by 1′ by 10.5″. How many guppies can the tank support? *(Lesson 10-3)*

Exploration

22. a. Make a cone using a net like that at the left, but bigger.
   b. After the cone is made, make an open-top cylinder with height and base the same as the cone.
   c. Fill the cone with dirt or sand. How many times must you empty the cone into the cylinder in order to fill up the cylinder?

23. a. Trace two copies of net I and one of net II. Make a pyramid from each tracing. (Fold so the markings are "inside" the pyramids.)
   b. Fit the three pyramids together to form a right triangular prism.
   c. What have you shown?

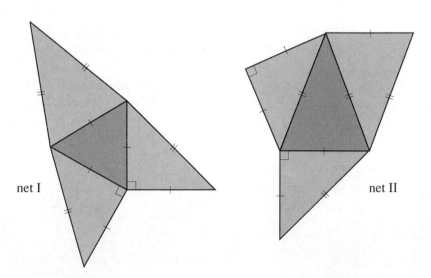

net I   net II

10-8

The Volume of a Sphere

Here is how the volume formulas of this chapter have developed. It began with a postulate in Lesson 10-3.

$$V = \ell wh \qquad \text{(volume of a box)}$$

Cavalieri's Principle was then applied and the following formula was deduced in Lesson 10-5.

$$V = Bh \qquad \text{(volume of a prism or cylinder)}$$

A prism can be split into 3 pyramids with congruent heights and bases. Using Cavalieri's Principle again, a formula was derived in Lesson 10-7.

$$V = \tfrac{1}{3}Bh \qquad \text{(volume of a pyramid or cone)}$$

In this lesson, still another application of Cavalieri's Principle results in a formula for the volume of a sphere.

Both the sphere and cylinder below have a height of $2r$ and each cone in the cylinder has a height of r. An amazing result is that the volume of the sphere equals the volume *between the cylinder and the two cones.*

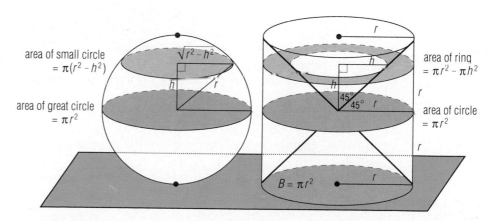

area of small circle
$= \pi(r^2 - h^2)$

area of great circle
$= \pi r^2$

$\sqrt{r^2 - h^2}$

area of ring
$= \pi r^2 - \pi h^2$

area of circle
$= \pi r^2$

$B = \pi r^2$

Here is how that can be shown. On the previous page, the purple sections are the plane sections resulting from a plane slicing these figures in their middles. These purple sections are congruent circles with area πr^2. At h units above each purple section is a section shaded in pink. In the sphere, by the Pythagorean Theorem, the pink section is a small circle with radius $\sqrt{r^2 - h^2}$. The area of this section is found using the familiar formula for the area of a circle.

$$\text{Area(small circle)} = \pi(\sqrt{r^2 - h^2})^2 = \pi(r^2 - h^2)$$

For the region between the cylinder and the cones, the section is the pink ring between circles of radius r and h. (The radius of that section of the cone is h because the acute angle measures $45°$, so an isosceles triangle is formed.)

$$\text{Area(ring)} = \pi r^2 - \pi h^2 = \pi(r^2 - h^2)$$

Thus the pink sections have equal area. Since this works for any height h, Cavalieri's Principle can be applied. This means that the volume of the sphere is the difference in the volume of the cylinder $(B \cdot 2r)$ and the volume of the two cones (each with volume $\frac{1}{3}B \cdot r$).

$$\begin{aligned}
\text{Volume of sphere} &= (B \cdot 2r) - 2 \cdot (\tfrac{1}{3}B \cdot r) \\
&= 2Br - \tfrac{2}{3}Br \\
&= \tfrac{4}{3}Br
\end{aligned}$$

But here the bases of the cones and cylinder are circles with radius r. So $B = \pi r^2$. Substituting,

$$\begin{aligned}
\text{Volume of sphere} &= \tfrac{4}{3} \cdot \pi r^2 \cdot r \\
&= \tfrac{4}{3}\pi r^3.
\end{aligned}$$

Sphere Volume Formula:

The volume V of any sphere is $\frac{4}{3}\pi$ times the cube of its radius r.

$$V = \tfrac{4}{3}\pi r^3$$

To approximate the volume of a sphere, calculators are helpful.

· · · · · · · ■ ■

Example 1 Find the volume of a sphere with radius 12.

Solution Substitute into the volume formula.
$$V = \tfrac{4}{3}\pi r^3$$
$$= \tfrac{4}{3}\pi(12)^3$$
$$= 2304\pi \approx 7238 \text{ units}^3$$

Example 2   A standard bowling ball cannot be more than 27 inches in circumference. What is the maximum volume of such a ball (to the nearest cubic inch) before the holes are drilled?

Solution   First find the radius of the ball. Use the circumference formula.

$$C = 2\pi r$$
$$27 = 2\pi r$$

So
$$r = \frac{27}{2\pi} \approx 4.3''.$$

Now substitute into the volume formula $V = \frac{4}{3}\pi r^3$.

$$V \approx \frac{4}{3} \cdot \pi (4.3)^3$$
$$\approx \frac{4}{3} \cdot \pi \cdot 79.507$$
$$\approx 333 \text{ cubic inches}$$

Even after drilling the holes, there are more than 300 cubic inches of rubber or plastic in a standard bowling ball.

Questions

Covering the Reading

In 1–3, use this drawing of a sphere, cylinder, and two cones. Sections formed by their intersections with a plane four units above and parallel to the horizontal plane through the figures' middles are colored.

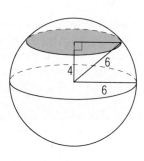
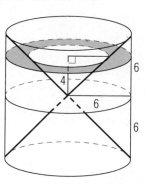

1. Give the area of:
   a. the section of the sphere;
   b. the ring between the cylinder and the cone.

2. Give the volume of:
   a. the cylinder;
   b. the two cones;
   c. the solid region between the cylinder and the two cones;
   d. the sphere.

3. By applying __?__ , the equal answers to parts **a** and **b** of Question 1 lead to equal answers to parts **c** and **d** of Question 2.

4. **a.** Draw a sphere with radius 8 cm.
   b. Find its volume.

5. *Multiple choice.*
   How much material is needed to make a standard bowling ball?
   (a) less than 100 cubic inches
   (b) between 100 and 200 cubic inches
   (c) between 200 and 300 cubic inches
   (d) between 300 and 400 cubic inches

Applying the Mathematics

6. A basketball has a diameter of about 9.5 inches. If it is put into a cube-shaped box for shipping, what percent of the box is filled by the basketball?

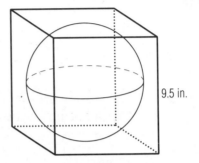

9.5 in.

7. The volume of a sphere is 268 cubic meters. Find its radius to the nearest meter.

8. A filled ice cream cone has the shape of a hemisphere atop a cone. If the cone has height 10 cm, and the hemisphere radius is 3 cm, how much ice cream is there?

9. A spherical water tank with diameter 16 meters supplies water to a small town. The town uses about 500 cubic meters of water per day. How long would a full tank last if:
   a. 300 cubic meters were replaced each day?
   b. no water were replaced due to drought conditions?

10. A sphere has diameter d. Give its volume.

Review

In 11 and 12, find the volume of the solid. *(Lessons 10-7, 10-3)*

11.

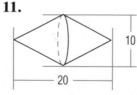

10

20

union of two right cones with same base

12.

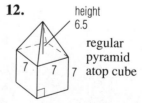

height
6.5

7   7   7

regular pyramid atop cube

13. Which of the fundamental properties of volume is needed in both Questions 11 and 12? *(Lesson 10-3)*

14. **a.** A cube has surface area 96 m². Find its volume.
    b. A cube has surface area x. Find its volume in terms of x.
    (Lessons 10-6, 10-3)

In 15 and 16, choose from the following:
boxes, cones, cylinders, prisms, pyramids, spheres. *(Lesson 10-6)*

15. In which figures does $V = Bh$?

16. In which figures does L.A. $= \frac{1}{2}\ell p$?

17. Two prisms have congruent bases and equal heights. One of the solids is oblique and one is right. *True or false*?
a. The solids have the same volume.
b. The solids have the same surface area. *(Lesson 10-5)*

18. Expand $(x + 3)(2y)(z + 4)$. *(Lesson 10-4)*

19. The dimensions of a box are tripled.
a. What happens to its surface area?
b. What happens to its volume? *(Lesson 10-4)*

20. To the nearest tenth, calculate $\sqrt[3]{85} - \sqrt[3]{5}$. *(Lesson 10-3)*

21. A hole is cut through the $3 \times 3 \times 3$ cube at the left, from top to bottom, as indicated. Then the big cube with the hole is dipped in white paint. *(Lesson 10-1)*
a. What is the surface area of the big cube with the hole?
b. How many of the 24 smaller cubes that are left are painted on exactly three faces?
c. How many of the 24 cubes that are left are painted on exactly two faces?
d. How many of the 24 cubes that are left are painted on exactly one face?
e. How many of the 24 cubes that are left are painted on no faces?

22. Given: $\triangle ABC$ is isosceles with vertex $\angle A$.
$\overleftrightarrow{AD}$ bisects $\angle BAC$.
Prove: $\triangle BCD$ is isosceles. *(Lessons 5-1, 4-4)*

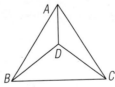

In 23 and 24, multiply. *(Previous course)*

23. $\dfrac{3}{r} \cdot \dfrac{1}{3} \cdot r \cdot x$ **24.** $\dfrac{3}{r} \cdot \dfrac{4}{3}\pi r^3$

Exploration

25. Unlike a cone or cylinder, it is impossible to make an accurate 2-dimensional net for a sphere. For this reason, maps of the earth on a sheet of paper must be distorted. The Mercator projection is one way to show the earth. How is this projection made?

10-9

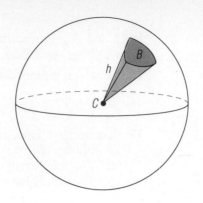

The Surface Area of a Sphere

The only formula left from the hierarchy of Lesson 10-6 is for the surface area of a sphere. Surprisingly, this formula is derived from the volume formula. The idea is to consider a solid sphere as being made up of "almost pyramids" with vertices at the center of the sphere. One such "pyramid" is drawn above. The solid is not exactly a pyramid because its base is not exactly a polygon. Even so, when the base of the "almost pyramid" is small, its volume is close to that of a pyramid, namely $\frac{1}{3}Bh$. Since $h = r$, the radius of the sphere, each "almost pyramid" has volume $\frac{1}{3}Br$.

Now break up the entire sphere into "almost pyramids" with bases having areas B_1, B_2, B_3, and so on.

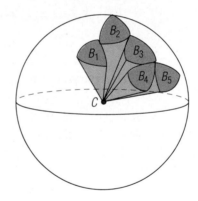

The volume V of the sphere is the sum of the volumes of all the "almost pyramids" with bases B_1, B_2, B_3, … .

$$V = \tfrac{1}{3}B_1r + \tfrac{1}{3}B_2r + \tfrac{1}{3}B_3r + \tfrac{1}{3}B_4r + \ldots$$
$$= \tfrac{1}{3}r(B_1 + B_2 + B_3 + B_4 + \ldots)$$

The sum of the bases is the surface area (S.A.) of the sphere. The volume V is $\frac{4}{3}\pi r^3$. Substituting,

$$\tfrac{4}{3}\pi r^3 = \tfrac{1}{3}r \cdot \text{S.A.}$$

To solve for the surface area, multiply both sides by $\dfrac{3}{r}$.

$$\frac{3}{r} \cdot \frac{4}{3}\pi r^3 = \frac{3}{r} \cdot \frac{1}{3} r \cdot \text{S.A.}$$

Thus $\qquad\qquad 4\pi r^2 = \text{S.A.}$

Surprisingly, this formula indicates that the surface area of a sphere is equal to 4 times the area of a great circle of the sphere.

Example   Find the surface area of a beach ball with radius 50 cm.

Solution   S.A. $= 4\pi r^2 = 4 \cdot \pi \cdot 50^2 = 10,000\pi$ exactly, or approximately 31,416 square centimeters.

In the Example, the surface area measures how much plastic is needed for the surface of the beach ball. To determine how much air is inside the inflated beach ball, volume is needed. The volume of the beach ball above is $\frac{4}{3}\pi r^3 = \frac{4}{3}\pi(50^3) \approx 523,600$ cm^3.

You now have encountered all of the surface area and volume formulas discussed in this book. The hierarchy given in Lesson 10-6 is shown below. These are the key formulas to remember. In all cases r represents radius, h represents height, p represents perimeter, and B represents area of a base. For regular pyramids, ℓ represents slant height, while for a box, ℓ represents length.

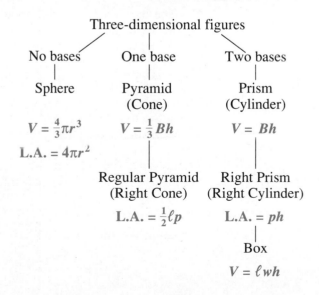

Three-dimensional figures

No bases — One base — Two bases

Sphere   Pyramid (Cone)   Prism (Cylinder)

$V = \frac{4}{3}\pi r^3$ $V = \frac{1}{3}Bh$ $V = Bh$

L.A. $= 4\pi r^2$

Regular Pyramid (Right Cone)   Right Prism (Right Cylinder)

L.A. $= \frac{1}{2}\ell p$ L.A. $= ph$

Box

$V = \ell wh$

Questions

Covering the Reading

1. A sphere can be imagined as the union of __?__ , whose base areas add up to the __?__ of the sphere.

2. State the Sphere Surface Area Formula.

3. The surface area of a spherc is __?__ times the area of a great circle.

In 4 and 5, find the surface area of the sphere: **a.** exactly; **b.** to the nearest square unit.

4. a sphere with radius 6

5. a sphere with diameter 100″

6. Name the no-base, one-base, and two-base figures in the hierarchy of 3-dimensional figures you have studied in this chapter.

Applying the Mathematics

7. The area of the United States is about 3,600,000 square miles. What percent is this of the area of the earth, which is approximately a sphere with radius 3950 miles?

8. A sphere has diameter d. Give its surface area.

9. A pavilion at the 1986 World's Fair in Vancouver, pictured at the left, had a dome with diameter 35 meters. Estimate the cost of covering the dome with gold foil that costs $3.20 per square meter.

10. A baseball is nearly a sphere with a circumference (great circle) of about 9.1 inches.
    a. Estimate the volume of a baseball, to the nearest 0.1 cubic inch.
    b. Estimate the surface area of a baseball, to the nearest 0.1 square inch.

11. The moon has diameter about $\frac{1}{4}$ that of the earth.
    a. How do their surface areas compare?
    b. How do their volumes compare?

12. A sphere has volume 36π cubic meters. What is the surface area?

13. A sphere of radius r fits exactly into a cylinder, touching the cylinder at the top, bottom, and sides. How does the surface area of the sphere compare to the lateral area of the cylinder?

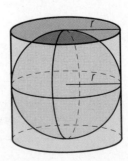

14. Refer to Question 7. Find the volume of the earth. *(Lesson 10-8)*

15. a. Draw a sphere with radius 2.5 cm.
b. Find its volume. *(Lesson 10-8)*

16. A cone has base radius of 15 and a slant height of 17. Picture this cone and find its volume. *(Lesson 10-7)*

17. One jar of jam is twice as tall as another, but only half as wide. Which jar has more jam? *(Lessons 10-5, 10-4)*

18. You can make two different cylinders by rolling an 8.5″ by 11″ piece of notebook paper along its sides.
a. What is the lateral area of each cylinder?
b. Which has the most volume? *(Lessons 10-5, 10-1)*

19. A cube has sides of length 13. A second cube has 5 times the volume of the first cube. To the nearest tenth, what is the length of a side of the second cube? *(Lesson 10-4)*

20. Cheese is aged in large blocks. The block below is to be removed from the aging cellar, wrapped in foil, and shipped. *(Lesson 10-1)*
a. At a minimum, how many square cm of foil are needed?
b. A distributor cuts the block into 15 cm × 7.5 cm × 3 cm slabs to sell to grocery stores. At a minimum, how much foil is needed to wrap all the slabs from the block?

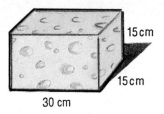

15 cm

15 cm

30 cm

21. A transformation T maps (*x, y*) onto (3*x*, 3*y*). Graph the image of △*ABC* where *A* = (2, 1), *B* = (-1, -1), and *C* = (0, -3). *(Lesson 6-1)*

In 22 and 23, an almanac, atlas, dictionary, or encyclopedia is necessary.

22. What three countries cover more of the surface of the earth than the United States? What percent (to the nearest tenth) of the surface does each cover?

23. What percent (to the nearest tenth) of the surface of the earth is covered by **a.** the Pacific Ocean; **b.** the Atlantic Ocean; **c.** all the oceans together?

Summary

The lateral or surface area of a three-dimensional figure measures its boundary, which is two-dimensional. So these areas, like the areas you studied in Chapter 8, are measured in square units. Volume measures the space enclosed by a three-dimensional figure. Beginning with the formula $V = \ell wh$ for the volume of a box, this chapter developed formulas for the volumes of other figures. Four basic properties of volume and Cavalieri's Principle were employed. The following chart contains a summary of these formulas.

	Volume	Lateral Area Right or Regular	Surface Area
Prism (Cylinder)	Bh	ph	L.A. $+ 2B$
Pyramid (Cone)	$\frac{1}{3}Bh$	$\frac{1}{2}p\ell$	L.A. $+ B$
Sphere	$\frac{4}{3}\pi r^3$		$4\pi r^2$
Cube	s^3		$6s^2$

In these formulas, B is the area of a base, p the perimeter of a base, h the height, ℓ the slant height, L.A. the lateral area, and r the radius. You can obtain special formulas for cones and cylinders by substituting πr^2 for B and $2\pi r$ for p.

Vocabulary

Below are the most important terms and phrases for this chapter.
For the starred (*) term you should be able to give a definition of the term.
For the other terms you should be able to give a general description and specific example of each.

Lesson 10-1
surface area, S.A.
lateral area, L.A.
Right Prism-Cylinder Lateral
 Area Formula
Prism-Cylinder Surface
 Area Formula

Lesson 10-2
regular pyramid
Regular Pyramid-Right Cone
 Lateral Area Formula
Pyramid-Cone Surface Area
 Formula

Lesson 10-3
volume
unit cube
*cube root, $\sqrt[3]{}$
Volume Postulate (parts **a–d**)
Cube Volume Formula

Lesson 10-5
Cavalieri's Principle
 (Volume Postulate **e**)
Prism-Cylinder Volume Formula

Lesson 10-6
Heron's Formula

Lesson 10-7
Pyramid-Cone Volume Formula

Lesson 10-8
Sphere Volume Formula

Lesson 10-9
Sphere Surface Area Formula

Progress Self-Test

Directions: Take this test as you would take a test in class. Use a ruler and calculator. Then check your work with the solutions in the Selected Answers section in the back of the book.

1. An oblique rectangular prism has dimensions 3 cm by 6 cm by 15 cm and height 14 cm.
   a. Draw an appropriate figure and indicate the formula you would use to find its volume.
   b. Find its volume.

2. A regular square pyramid has base edges of length 20 and slant height of length 26.
   a. Draw an appropriate figure and indicate the formula you would use to find its lateral area.
   b. Find its lateral area.

3. The largest asteroid, Ceres, has a diameter of 620 miles. Assuming Ceres is spherical in shape, what is its volume?

4. How much paper is needed for a cone-shaped megaphone with radius 4″ and slant height 18″? (Ignore the small open end.)

5. Find the volume of the inside of a pipe 20″ long and with an inside radius of 3″, as drawn below.

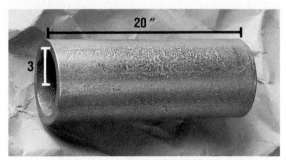

6. Find the volume of this right cone.

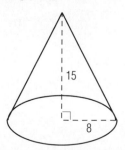

In 7 and 8, the base of a right prism has area 40 and perimeter 32. Its height is 30.

7. What is its lateral area?

8. What is its volume?

In 9 and 10, a box has a volume of 400 cubic cm, a height of 10 cm, and a width of 5 cm.

9. What is its length?

10. What is its surface area?

11. A sphere has a surface area of 100π. What is its radius?

12. Give the cube root of 400 to the nearest whole number.

13. State Cavalieri's Principle.

14. A prism and a pyramid have congruent bases and their heights are equal. How do their volumes compare?

15. Jupiter has 11 times the diameter of the earth. How do their surface areas compare?

In 16 and 17, choose from the following figures: box, cube, regular pyramid, prism, right cylinder, sphere, cone.

16. For which figures does S.A. = L.A. + B?

17. For which figures does L.A. = ph?

18. Find the volume of the box pictured below.

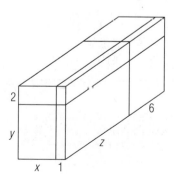

Chapter Review

Questions on **SPUR** Objectives

SPUR stands for **S**kills, **P**roperties, **U**ses, and **R**epresentations.
The Chapter Review questions are grouped according to the
SPUR Objectives for this chapter.

SKILLS deal with the procedures used to get answers.

■ **Objective A:** *Draw 3-dimensional figures, given their dimensions. (Lessons 10-1, 10-2, 10-8)*

In 1–4, show the given information on the figure.

1. Draw a cylinder whose height is twice its diameter.
2. Draw a cone with radius 3 and slant height 5.
3. Draw a sphere with diameter $1\frac{3}{4}''$.
4. Draw a square pyramid with slant height 15 and height 9.

■ **Objective B:** *Calculate surface areas and volumes of cylinders and prisms from appropriate lengths, and vice-versa. (Lessons 10-1, 10-3, 10-5)*

5. Refer to the right cylinder drawn below. Find its **a.** lateral area; **b.** surface area; **c.** volume.

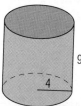

6. Refer to the right square prism drawn below. Find its **a.** volume; **b.** surface area.

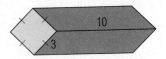

7. The base of the prism drawn below is a right triangle with legs of lengths 5 and 12. The distance between the bases of the prism is 24. Find the volume of the prism.

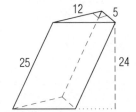

8. If a cylinder is to have a volume of 30π cubic units and a base with radius 3, what must its height be?

9. Find the surface of a cube whose volume is 125 cubic units.

10. Find the volume of a right cylinder whose lateral area is 60π square centimeters and whose base has diameter 12 centimeters.

■ **Objective C:** *Calculate surface areas and volumes of pyramids and cones from appropriate lengths, and vice-versa. (Lessons 10-2, 10-7)*

11. Find the surface area and volume of the right cone drawn below.

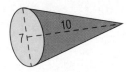

In 12 and 13, refer to the square pyramid drawn below.

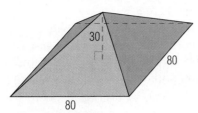

12. Find its volume.
13. Find **a.** the slant height;
    b. its lateral area; **c.** its total surface area.

14. Find the volume of the cone drawn below.

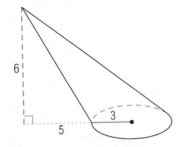

15. The slant height of a regular pentagonal pyramid is 20. The perimeter of the base is also 20. What is the lateral area of the pyramid?

16. If a pyramid has volume 75 cubic centimeters and its base has area 5 square centimeters, what is its height?

■ **Objective D:** *Calculate the surface area and volume of a sphere from appropriate lengths, and vice-versa. (Lessons 10-8, 10-9)*

17. Give the surface area and volume of a sphere with radius 72.
18. Give the surface area and volume of a sphere with diameter 3 mm.
19. A sphere has volume 288π. What is its radius?
20. A sphere has volume 40π cubic units. What is its surface area?

■ **Objective E:** *Calculate cube roots. (Lesson 10-3)*

21. Give the cube root of 27,000.
22. Approximate the cube root of 50 to the nearest tenth.
23. One cube has side length 4. A second cube has twice the volume of the first cube. To the nearest hundredth, what is the length of a side of the second cube?
24. To the nearest hundredth, calculate $\sqrt[3]{15} + \sqrt[3]{21}$.

PROPERTIES deal with the principles behind the mathematics.

■ **Objective F:** *Develop formulas for specific figures from more general formulas.*
   (Lessons 10-2, 10-3, 10-6, 10-7, 10-8)

25. Find a formula for the surface area of a regular square pyramid with edge s and slant height ℓ.

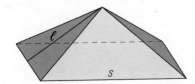

26. A right cone has slant height ℓ and its base has radius r. Find a formula for its volume.

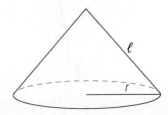

27. All of the dimensions of a box are tripled.
    a. What happens to the surface area?
    b. What happens to the volume?

28. The sides of a cube are multiplied by 9. What happens to its volume?

29. The diameter of a pizza is doubled. If it remains the same thickness, how do the volumes of the new and old pizzas compare?

30. The diameter of the earth is multiplied by 109 to give the diameter of the sun. How do their volumes compare?

31. A prism and pyramid have bases of the same area and equal heights. Why can't Cavalieri's Principle be applied in this situation?

32. In deriving the formula for the volume of a sphere, a plane section of a sphere was shown to be equal in area to what other figure?

33. Two cylindric solids have congruent bases and equal heights. One of the solids is oblique and one is right. *True* or *false*?
    a. The solids have the same volume.
    b. The solids have the same surface area.

USES deal with applications of mathematics in real situations.

34. Venus is almost spherical with a radius of about 6000 km. To survey Venus completely, about how many square kilometers must be covered?

35. To the nearest square foot, how much canvas is needed to cover a beach ball that is about 5 feet around?

36. How much paper is needed to make a cylindrical paper cup with a base diameter of 10 cm and a height of 12 cm?

37. An ancient square pyramid is 100 cubits (an ancient unit) on a side. It is 50 cubits high. Find its lateral area.

Objective J: *Apply formulas for volume to real situations.* *(Lessons 10-3, 10-5, 10-7, 10-8)*

38. A corncrib is a cylinder whose base is a circle with diameter 6 meters and whose height is 10 meters. What is the volume of this corncrib?

39. How much can the paper cup of Question 36 hold?

40. How much wood goes into making a solid cube 2.5″ on a side?

41. Find the volume of the pyramid in Question 37.

42. Can a suitcase 3 feet long, 1 foot wide, and 2 feet high hold one million dollar bills, if a dollar bill is 6.125″ long, 2.562″ wide, and 0.004″ thick?

REPRESENTATIONS deal with pictures, graphs, or objects that illustrate concepts.

Objective K: *Represent products of two (or three) expressions as areas of rectangles (or volumes of boxes), and vice-versa.* *(Lesson 10-4)*

In 43 and 44, expand.

43. $(5x + 2)(4y + 3)$

44. $(a + 6)(2a + 1)(a + 8)$

45. Give two ways to compute the area of the rectangle below.

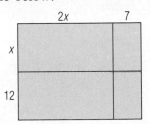

46. Give two ways to compute the volume of the box below.

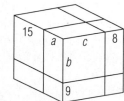

Coordinate Geometry

The use of variables to solve equations as people do today dates only from the work of François Vieté (1540–1603) in the late 1500s. Before that time mathematics was almost entirely arithmetic and geometry. The invention of algebra by Vieté provided people a tool as powerful then as the invention of computers in our century. People wondered what could and could not be done with this new tool. Among the wonderers was René Descartes, who was born in 1596.

You may recall that Descartes, along with Pierre Fermat, invented the idea of geometrically representing ordered pairs of numbers. He was thrilled with his invention, which he called a *method,* for it used algebra to combine arithmetic and geometry, and so unified all the mathematics known up to that time. He used his method, which is now called **coordinate geometry** or **analytic geometry,** to solve many problems which were then very difficult or not able to be solved.

Descartes believed that he had found a method whereby any mathematics problem could be solved or any conjecture proved or disproved. In fact, he thought that mathematics and logic could provide the means whereby any problem in *any* field of endeavor could be solved. Today we know that his belief is not even theoretically possible, but Descartes' dream reflects the power of the coordinate geometry methods he discovered.

In the 20th century, coordinate geometry has found an entirely new area of applications—to computer graphics. By specifying the pixels on a computer screen, computer programmers can generate all sorts of figures and designs. They can show and rotate three-dimensional images, as you have probably seen many times on television. For fun, they can produce animated cartoons and video games. For serious pursuits, they can model the design of anything from atoms to stars, from small animals to large buildings. All of the graphics on the facing page were computer generated using coordinates.

You already know how to graph points and lines and how to determine whether lines are perpendicular or parallel. In this chapter, you will learn how to calculate the distance between points and use that idea to describe circles. You will also learn how to calculate coordinates of midpoints. Many of these ideas can be used the way Descartes used them, to *deduce* properties of figures.

The computer animated figures above were designed using a three-dimensional coordinate system.

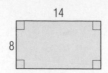

rectangular region with
length 14, width 8

Proofs with Coordinates

Figures can be described with or without coordinates. Above and below are three descriptions of congruent rectangular regions. Two of these descriptions use coordinates.

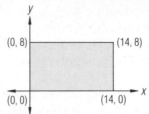

rectangular region with vertices
(0, 0), (14, 0), (14, 8), and (0, 8)

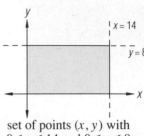

set of points (x, y) with
$0 \le x \le 14$ and $0 \le y \le 8$

Any polygon or polygonal region can be described using a description like the one just above on the left. Just list its vertices in order. Some polygons can be proved to be special.

Example 1 Consider quadrilateral $ABCD$ with vertices $A = (0, 0)$, $B = (8, 0)$, $C = (11, 12)$, and $D = (3, 12)$. Prove that $ABCD$ is a parallelogram.

Solution 1 First draw a picture, as done at the left. In the drawing, it appears that $ABCD$ is a parallelogram. The idea is to use slopes to prove opposite sides parallel. Here is what you might write.

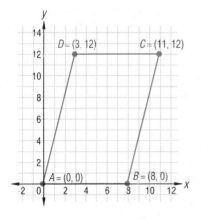

Using the slope formula, $\overline{AD}$ and $\overline{BC}$ have slope 4 and $\overline{DC}$ and $\overline{AB}$ have slope 0. So because of the Parallel Lines and Slopes Theorem, $\overline{AD} \parallel \overline{BC}$ and $\overline{DC} \parallel \overline{AB}$. Thus, by the definition of parallelogram (sufficient condition), $ABCD$ is a parallelogram.

Solution 2 Here is a proof of the same statement, written in two-column form.

Conclusions	Justifications
1. slope of $\overline{AD} = \dfrac{12 - 0}{3 - 0} = 4$	definition of slope (meaning)
$\quad$ slope of $\overline{BC} = \dfrac{12 - 0}{11 - 8} = 4$	
$\quad$ slope of $\overline{DC} = \dfrac{12 - 12}{11 - 3} = \dfrac{0}{8} = 0$	
$\quad$ slope of $\overline{AB} = \dfrac{0 - 0}{8 - 0} = \dfrac{0}{8} = 0$	
2. $\overline{AD} \parallel \overline{BC}$, $\overline{DC} \parallel \overline{AB}$	Parallel Lines and Slopes Theorem
3. $ABCD$ is a parallelogram.	definition of parallelogram (sufficient condition)

David Hilbert

Until the 1800s, it was taken for granted that coordinate methods would lead to the same geometry as the older methods, for there was only one geometry known. The discovery of non-Euclidean geometry brought doubt to this assumption. Only in 1901 did the great German mathematician David Hilbert (1862–1943) prove that analytic and traditional methods could lead to the same conclusions. In the language of this book, the location description and ordered pair description of points are equivalent. They lead to the same properties of figures. That is why you can use them interchangeably.

For example, since *ABCD* (page 522) has been shown to be a parallelogram, you can apply any of the properties of parallelograms to determine more about *ABCD*. For instance, m∠*A* = m∠*C* because they are opposite angles. The area of *ABCD* = *hb*. Here *b* = *AB* = 8, and *h*, the perpendicular from *D* to $\overleftrightarrow{AB}$, is 12. So the area of *ABCD* is 12 · 8 = 96 units^2.

Recall that horizontal and vertical lines are perpendicular; this is how the coordinate plane is defined. Other pairs of lines are perpendicular if the product of their slopes is -1. This enables lines to be proved perpendicular if their slopes are known.

■ ■ ■ ■ ■ ■ ■

Example 2   If *T* = (3, 5), *O* = (-1, -2), and *W* = (-3, 1), prove that △*TOW* is a right triangle.

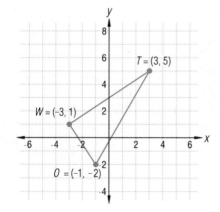

Solution   A drawing shows ∠*W* to be the possible right angle. So try to show $\overline{WO} \perp \overline{WT}$. This can be done by using slope.

Write

Conclusions	Justifications
1. slope of $\overline{WO}$ = $\frac{-2 - 1}{-1 - (-3)}$ = $\frac{-3}{2}$	definition of slope (meaning)
slope of $\overline{WT}$ = $\frac{5 - 1}{3 - (-3)}$ = $\frac{4}{6}$	
2. $\frac{3}{2} \cdot \frac{4}{6}$ = -1	arithmetic
3. $\overline{WO} \perp \overline{WT}$	**Perpendicular Lines and Slopes Theorem**
4. △*TOW* is a right triangle.	**definition of right triangle (sufficient condition)**

Notice how automatic these proofs of parallelism and perpendicularity are. Just calculate and compare slopes! This is why Descartes was so optimistic about his method.

1. Name the mathematician(s) who discovered or invented each field.
   a. algebra   **b.** analytic geometry

2. What was Descartes' dream? .

3. What is another name for analytic geometry?

4. State the Parallel Lines and Slopes Theorem.

5. State the Perpendicular Lines and Slopes Theorem.

6. Given $A = (0, 0)$, $B = (6, 0)$, $C = (9, 1)$, and $D = (3, 1)$. Complete the proof that $ABCD$ is a parallelogram.

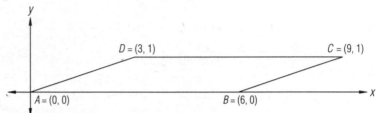

Conclusions	Justifications
1. slope of $\overline{AD}$ = $\frac{1}{3}$	**a.** ?
slope of $\overline{BC}$ = **b.** ?	
slope of $\overline{AB}$ = **c.** ?	
slope of $\overline{DC}$ = **d.** ?	
2. $\overline{AB} \parallel \overline{DC}$ and $\overline{AD} \parallel \overline{BC}$	**e.** ?
3. **f.** ?	Definition of parallelogram (sufficient condition)

7. If $X = (3, 7)$, $Y = (11, 3)$, and $Z = (4, 9)$, prove that $\triangle XYZ$ is a right triangle.

8. Name four areas where figures graphed on coordinate systems are used.

In 9 and 10, use quadrilateral $EFGH$ shown below.

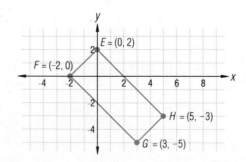

9. Prove: $EFGH$ is a rectangle.

10. Show that $\overline{EG}$ and $\overline{FH}$ are not perpendicular.

11. Given: $W = (0, 0)$, $X = (a, 0)$, $Y = (a + b, c)$, and $Z = (b, c)$.
$a \neq 0$, $c \neq 0$.
Prove: $WXYZ$ is a parallelogram.

12. Given $S = (1, 3)$, $P = (4, 4)$, $A = (3, 1)$, and $T = (0, 0)$.
  a. Draw $SPAT$.
  b. Prove $\overline{SA} \perp \overline{PT}$.

13. Full-grown zebras can range from 46 to 55 inches high at the shoulder and their weights can range from 550 to 650 pounds. Let h be these possible heights and w be these possible weights.
  a. Graph all possible ordered pairs (h, w).
  b. Describe the graph.

Review

In 14–16, find the intersection of the given lines by solving a system. Here is an example. Suppose the lines have equations
$$\begin{cases} 2x + y = 3 \\ x - 3y = 5. \end{cases}$$

Multiply both sides of the top equation by 3 to make the coefficients of y in the equations opposites. (You could also multiply both sides of the bottom equation by -2; this would make the coefficients of x opposites.)
$$\begin{cases} 6x + 3y = 9 \\ x - 3y = 5 \end{cases}$$
Now add, $7x = 14$
so $x = 2.$

This is the x-coordinate of the point of intersection. Substitute into either original equation to find the y-coordinate. We use the first.
$$2(2) + y = 3$$
$$4 + y = 3$$
$$y = -1$$

Thus the point of intersection is $(2, -1)$. *(Previous course)*

14. $\begin{cases} 3x + y = 7 \\ x - y = 1 \end{cases}$ **15.** $\begin{cases} 2x - 5y = 20 \\ 4x + y = 18 \end{cases}$

16. $\begin{cases} y = \frac{1}{2}x \\ y = 2x - 5 \end{cases}$

17. The side of a circular silo 10′ in diameter and 20′ high is to be painted. *(Lessons 10-4, 10-1)*
  a. How large is the area to be painted?
  b. If a bushel is about $1\frac{1}{4}$ cubic feet, about how many bushels of corn could be stored in this silo?

18. The diamond crystal below is in the shape of a regular octahedron. Give the number of vertices, faces, and edges of this crystal. *(Lesson 9-7)*

In 19 and 20, a conclusion is made from the given statement. Name the justification. *(Lessons 8-7, 3-3, 2-5)*

19. Given: ABC is a right triangle with hypotenuse $\overline{AB}$.
  Conclusion: $AB^2 = AC^2 + CB^2$.

20. Given: $\odot P$ contains Q and R.
  Conclusion: $PQ = PR$.

21. **a.** What is the distance between two points on a number line with coordinates 50 and 500?
  b. What is the distance between (50, 100) and (500, 100)?
  (Lesson 1-2)

Exploration

22. Three vertices of a parallelogram are (2, 6), (-1, 5), and (0, -4).
  a. Find at least two possible locations of the fourth vertex.
  b. Are there other possible locations?

11-2

The Distance Formula

The gates on a slalom course are placed at specific distances apart.

In the previous lesson, polygons were described by the coordinates of their vertices. It is possible to calculate the lengths of sides, diagonals, or other segments for such polynomials using a formula to be derived in this lesson.

If two points are on the same horizontal or vertical line, the distance between them can be found by the definition of distance on a number line. Below,

$$PQ = |6 - 2| = 4.$$

(Ignore the second coordinates of P and Q because they are equal.)
Similarly, $\qquad QR = |{-3} - 5| = 8.$
(Ignore the first coordinates of Q and R because they are equal.)

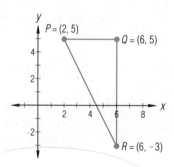

P and R are on an oblique line, but PR can now be found using the Pythagorean Theorem. Because $\overline{PQ} \perp \overline{QR}$, $\triangle PQR$ is a right triangle with hypotenuse $\overline{PR}$. By the Pythagorean Theorem,

$$\begin{aligned} PR^2 &= PQ^2 + QR^2 \\ &= 4^2 + 8^2 \\ &= 16 + 64 \\ &= 80. \end{aligned}$$

So $\qquad PR = \sqrt{80}$, or about 8.94.

You could draw a right triangle every time you had to calculate distances on an oblique line, but it is easier to have a general formula. The desired formula for PR should use only the coordinates of P and R. The idea is to repeat the above process, but use variables.

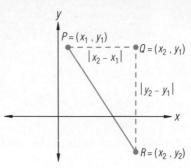

Let $P = (x_1, y_1)$ and $R = (x_2, y_2)$. First find Q so that $\overline{PR}$ is the hypotenuse of a right triangle. Such a point is $Q = (x_2, y_1)$.

$$PR^2 = PQ^2 + QR^2$$
$$= |x_2 - x_1|^2 + |y_2 - y_1|^2$$

Since a number and its absolute value have the same square,

$$|x_2 - x_1|^2 = (x_2 - x_1)^2 \text{ and}$$
$$|y_2 - y_1|^2 = (y_2 - y_1)^2.$$

Thus $\qquad PR^2 = (x_2 - x_1)^2 + (y_2 - y_1)^2.$

Taking square roots, $PR = \sqrt{(x_2 - x_1)^2 + (y_2 - y_1)^2}$.

This gives a formula you should memorize.

Distance Formula:

The distance between two points (x_1, y_1) and (x_2, y_2) in the coordinate plane is
$$\sqrt{(x_2 - x_1)^2 + (y_2 - y_1)^2}.$$

Example 1 Find the distance between (-8, 50) and (30, -11).

Solution Let $(x_1, y_1) = (-8, 50)$ and let $(x_2, y_2) = (30, -11)$. If d is the distance between these points,

$$d = \sqrt{(x_2 - x_1)^2 + (y_2 - y_1)^2}$$
$$= \sqrt{(30 - -8)^2 + (-11 - 50)^2}$$
$$= \sqrt{(38)^2 + (-61)^2}$$
$$= \sqrt{1444 + 3721}$$
$$= \sqrt{5165}$$
$$\approx 71.87.$$

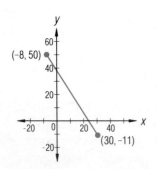

Check Draw a rough picture and mark off units on the line segment, as done at the left. The segment seems to have a length of about 70.

A grid can be put behind any drawing (blueprint, map, picture, etc.) to assign coordinates to points. With the Distance Formula, you can calculate distances between any two points on the drawing without having to measure.

Example 2 Tom bikes from his apartment to Doris' house following the path shown below in black: 3 miles north, then 2 miles east, then $\frac{1}{2}$ mile north, then $\frac{1}{4}$ mile west. By air, how far apart are these places?

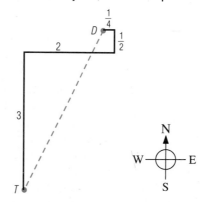

Solution Think of the path as being on a coordinate grid with Tom's place at (0, 0). Doris' house is at the point (1.75, 3.5). The air distance between them is the length of $\overline{TD}$.

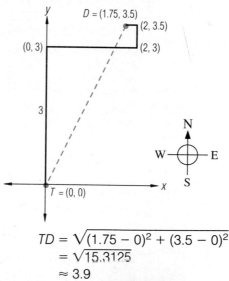

$$TD = \sqrt{(1.75 - 0)^2 + (3.5 - 0)^2}$$
$$= \sqrt{15.3125}$$
$$\approx 3.9$$

They are about 3.9 miles apart.

Questions

Covering the Reading

In 1–6, use the figure below when necessary. Give the distance between the named points.

1. A and B

2. B and C

3. A and C

4. A and the origin

5. B and D

6. (x_1, y_1) and (x_2, y_2)

A graph showing points $C = (6, 7)$, $A = (-5, 2)$, $B = (6, 2)$, and $D = (2, -4)$ on a coordinate plane with x and y axes marked from -6 to 8 and -4 to 6.

7. To get to a hospital from the middle of a nearby town, you can drive 8 miles east, turn and go 4 miles south, and then go 1 mile west. By helicopter, how far is it from the middle of the town to the hospital?

Applying the Mathematics

8. Let $J = (-5, 0)$, $K = (5, 8)$, and $L = (4, -1)$.
   a. Prove that $\triangle JKL$ is isosceles by using the Distance Formula.
   b. Is $\triangle JKL$ equilateral?

9. Given: $A = (4, -7)$, $B = (6, -3)$, $C = (4, 1)$, and $D = (-10, -3)$.
   Prove: $ABCD$ is a kite.

10. On a map, it can be seen that Charles lives 1 mile east and 1.5 miles south of school, while Cynthia lives 2 miles west and 0.8 miles south of school. By air, how far do Charles and Cynthia live from each other?

11. Tell whether the statement is *true* or *false*. If false, give a counterexample.
    a. $|x_2 - x_1| = (x_2 - x_1)$
    b. $|x_2 - x_1|^2 = (x_2 - x_1)^2$
    c. $|x_2 - x_1| = |x_1 - x_2|$
    d. $(x_1 - x_2)^2 = (x_2 - x_1)^2$

12. a. Find the distance between $(1, 2)$ and $(3, 4)$.
    b. Is the answer to part **a** the same as the distance between $(3, 4)$ and $(1, 2)$?
    c. Generalize the result.

13. Let $A = (-1, 3)$ and $B = (11, 2)$. Prove that the point $C = (3, -7)$ is on the circle with center B and radius BA.

14. Prove: $A = (0, 0)$, $B = (4, 0)$, $C = (5, 1)$, and $D = (3, 3)$ are vertices of a trapezoid. *(Lesson 11-1)*

15. Prove that the triangle with vertices $P = (3z, 4z)$, $Q = (7z, 2z)$, and $R = (2z, -8z)$ is a right triangle. *(Lesson 11-1)*

In 16 and 17, find the point of intersection of the lines by solving a system. *(Lesson 11-1, Previous course)*

16. $\begin{cases} -2x + y = 11 \\ x + 2y = 6 \end{cases}$ 　　　　**17.** $\begin{cases} y = 13 \\ 4x - 3y = 10 \end{cases}$

18. a. A square has sides of length 100. What is the length of either diagonal?
b. Generalize part **a.** *(Lesson 8-7)*

19. A parallelogram and triangle have the same base and same altitude. How are their areas related? *(Lessons 8-6, 8-5)*

20. The measure of one acute angle of a right triangle is 45° more than the measure of the other.
a. Is this possible?
b. If so, find the measures. If not, tell why not. *(Lessons 5-7, 3-2)*

21. Lynne has scored 92, 83, and 95 on her three tests so far this grading period. What is her average (or mean) score? *(Previous course)*

22. The distance from point X to (2, 8) is 17.
a. Show that X could be (10, 23).
b. Name five other possible locations of point X. (Hint: Draw a picture.)

11-3

Equations for Circles

You are familiar with equations for lines. There are also equations for circles. Below, a circle is drawn with center (3, 2) and radius 10. By adding or subtracting 10 from either coordinate of (3, 2), four points on the circle can be found. They are (13, 2), (3, 12), (-7, 2), and (3, -8). It would be nice to find an equation satisfied by these four points and all other points on the circle.

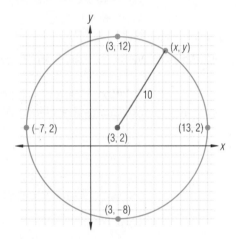

If a point (x, y) is on the circle, then by the Distance Formula,

$$\sqrt{(x - 3)^2 + (y - 2)^2} = 10.$$

This equation is an equation for the circle. However, most people prefer equations without square roots. Squaring both sides gives an equivalent equation.

$$(x - 3)^2 + (y - 2)^2 = 100$$

To check if this is correct, try the point (-7, 2). It should satisfy the equation. Substitute -7 for x and 2 for y.

Does $\quad (-7 - 3)^2 + (2 - 2)^2 = 100?$
Does $\qquad\qquad (-10)^2 + 0^2 = 100?$ Yes.

It is easy to generalize this example.

Theorem (Equation for a Circle):

The circle with center (h, k) and radius r is the set of points (x, y) satisfying

$$(x - h)^2 + (y - k)^2 = r^2.$$

Proof

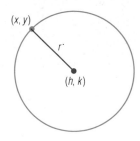

Since r is the radius, by the definition of circle, the distance from (h, k) to any point (x, y) on the circle is r.

That distance is given by the Distance Formula.

$$\sqrt{(x - h)^2 + (y - k)^2} = r$$

Squaring both sides:

$$(x - h)^2 + (y - k)^2 = r^2.$$

- - - - - ▪ ▪ ▪ ▪ ▪

Example 1 Write an equation for the circle with center $(0, -4)$ and radius 7.

Solution Here $r = 7$ and $(h, k) = (0, -4)$. So $h = 0$ and $k = -4$. Substitute the values of $h, k,$ and r into the equation for a circle.

$$(x - 0)^2 + (y - -4)^2 = 7^2$$

Simplify: $x^2 + (y + 4)^2 = 49$ is the desired equation.

Check Draw a picture and find a point on the circle.

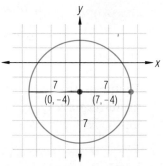

One point on the circle is $(7, -4)$. Does $(7, -4)$ satisfy the equation? Substitute 7 for x and -4 for y.

Does $7^2 + (-4 + 4)^2 = 49$?
Does $7^2 + 0^2 = 49$? Yes.

You could try other points, such as $(0, 3)$, $(-7, -4)$, or $(0, -11)$. Remember that the center is not on the circle, so its coordinates will not satisfy the equation.

From the equation for a circle you can figure out its center and radius.

Example 2 Find the center and radius of the circle with equation
$(x + 1)^2 + (y + 3)^2 = 25$.

Solution Compare the general equation to the given equation.

$$(x - h)^2 + (y - k)^2 = r^2$$
$$(x + 1)^2 + (y + 3)^2 = 25$$

h must be -1 to get $(x + 1)$. k must be -3 to get $(y + 3)$. The center is (h, k), so it is $(-1, -3)$. $r^2 = 25$, so the radius is 5. (r is a length, so r cannot be negative.)

Check Draw a picture of the circle with center $(-1, -3)$ and radius 5.

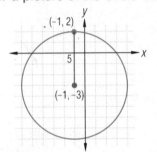

One point on the circle is $(-1, 2)$. Does it satisfy the equation?

Does $\qquad (-1 + 1)^2 + (2 + 3)^2 = 25$?
Does $\qquad\qquad\qquad\quad 0^2 + 5^2 = 25$? Yes.

The circles with the simplest equations are those with center $(0, 0)$, the origin. Then $h = 0$ and $k = 0$, so an equation is

$$(x - 0)^2 + (y - 0)^2 = r^2,$$
or just $\qquad\qquad\qquad\quad x^2 + y^2 = r^2.$

Pictured below is the circle with center $(0, 0)$ and radius 9. Its equation is $x^2 + y^2 = 81$.

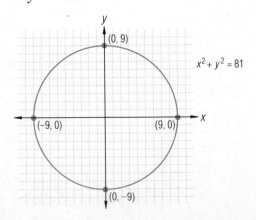

Questions

Covering the Reading

1. Is the point on the circle with center (3, 2) and radius 10?
  a. (13, 2)   **b.** (3, -8)
  c. (8, 7)   **d.** (9, -6)

2. a. What is an equation for the circle with center (-3, 5) and radius 1?
  b. Give the coordinates of four points on the circle.

3. a. What is the distance between (*x*, *y*) and (7, 1)?
  b. Give an equation for the circle with center (7, 1) and radius 5.
  c. Graph this circle.
  d. Give the coordinates of four points on this circle.

4. The circle below has center at the origin and contains (3, 0). What is an equation for it?

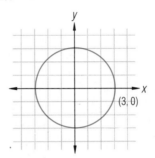

5. The proof of the equation for a circle relies on what formula?

In 6–9, determine **a.** the center, **b.** the radius, and **c.** one point on the circle with the given equation.

6. $(x - 5)^2 + (y - 11)^2 = 81$

7. $(x + 1)^2 + y^2 = 2$

8. $x^2 + y^2 = 25$

9. $(x + 6)^2 + (y + 2)^2 = 1$

Applying the Mathematics

10. A circle has center (2, -1) and touches the *x*-axis at exactly one point. The circle is called **tangent** to the axis.
  a. Draw a picture.
  b. What are the coordinates of the *point of tangency*?
  c. Find an equation for the circle.
  d. Find the area of this circle.

11. Give the coordinates of the 12 lattice points on the circle $x^2 + y^2 = 25$. (Recall that a lattice point is a point with integer coordinates.) Graph the points.

In 12 and 13, graph.

12. $x^2 + y^2 = 16$ **13.** $(x + 5)^2 + (y - 8)^2 = 121$

In 14 and 15, calculate the distance between the points. Assume $x > 0$. *(Lesson 11-2)*

14. (4, -7) and (-1, 5)   **15.** (9x, -40x) and the origin

16. Nancy lives 6 blocks west and 3 blocks north of the park. Domaso lives 5 blocks south of the park. How many blocks by air is it from where Nancy lives to where Domaso lives? *(Lesson 11-2)*

17. Prove that the quadrilateral *QRST* with vertices $Q = (9a, 4b)$, $R = (6a, 2b)$, $S = (a, -7b)$, and $T = (-a, -14b)$ is a trapezoid. *(Lesson 11-1)*

18. Find the intersection of the following lines: *(Lesson 11-1, Previous course)*
$$\begin{cases} x - 7y = 15 \\ 4x + 5y = \text{-}6. \end{cases}$$

19. Suppose $\overleftrightarrow{AB}$ and $\overleftrightarrow{BC}$ have the same slope. What can you conclude about points *A, B,* and *C*? *(Lessons 3-4, 1-7)*

In 20 and 21, draw the diagram. *(Lessons 9-2, 9-1)*

20. two perpendicular planes

21. a parallelepiped

22. Given: $\triangle XYZ$ below is isosceles with vertex angle *X*.
              V is the midpoint of $\overline{XY}$.
              W is the midpoint of $\overline{XZ}$.
    Prove: $\triangle XVW$ is isosceles. *(Lessons 5-1, 4-4)*

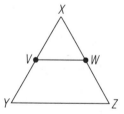

23. Give an equation for a circle on which there are no lattice points and whose interior contains no lattice points. (See Question 11 if you have forgotten the meaning of "lattice point.")

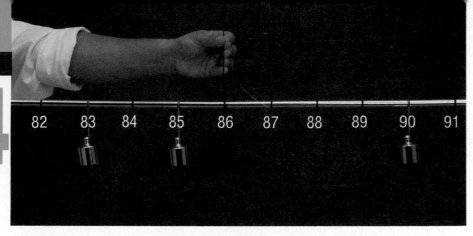

11-4

The Midpoint Formula

Suppose you score 90, 85, and 83 on three tests. Your average or **mean** score is the sum of these numbers divided by 3. It is
$$\frac{90 + 85 + 83}{3} = 86.$$

The mean has a physical interpretation. Think of a weightless ruler with hooks for attaching weights. If equal weights are hung from 90, 85, and 83, the ruler will balance on 86, their mean. The mean is the **center of gravity** of the weighted ruler.

A similar idea is true in two dimensions. Suppose you wish to find the center of gravity of a set of points. The coordinates of the center of gravity are found by computing the mean of the x-coordinates and the mean of the y-coordinates of the points. (The proof of the result depends on laws of physics, and is not presented.)

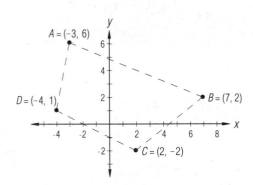

Find the mean of the x-coordinates:
$$\frac{-3 + 7 + 2 + -4}{4} = \frac{2}{4} = 0.5.$$

Find the mean of the y-coordinates:
$$\frac{6 + 2 + -2 + 1}{4} = \frac{7}{4} = 1.75.$$

So the center of gravity is (0.5, 1.75), as shown below.

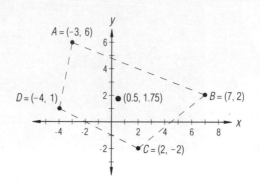

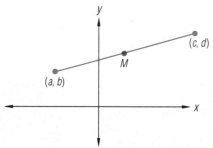

In the simplest case, as shown at the left, there are only two points (or weights) to begin with, and the center of gravity is the midpoint of the segment connecting them.

Coordinates of midpoints are easy to find, though the proof is complicated.

Midpoint Formula:

If a segment has endpoints (a, b) and (c, d), its midpoint is

$$\left(\frac{a + c}{2}, \frac{b + d}{2}\right).$$

Proof

Draw a picture with $P = (a, b)$, $Q = (c, d)$, and $M = \left(\frac{a+c}{2}, \frac{b + d}{2}\right)$.

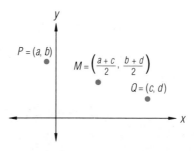

Recall the definition of midpoint. To show that M is the midpoint of $\overline{PQ}$, we need to show that $PM = MQ$ and M is on $\overleftrightarrow{PQ}$.

The algebra that follows is cumbersome, but it works out. To show that $PM = MQ$, we calculate distances using the Distance Formula.

$$PM = \sqrt{\left(\frac{a+c}{2} - a\right)^2 + \left(\frac{b+d}{2} - b\right)^2}$$

$$= \sqrt{\left(\frac{a+c-2a}{2}\right)^2 + \left(\frac{b+d-2b}{2}\right)^2}$$

$$= \sqrt{\left(\frac{c-a}{2}\right)^2 + \left(\frac{d-b}{2}\right)^2}$$

$$MQ = \sqrt{\left(c - \frac{a+c}{2}\right)^2 + \left(d - \frac{b+d}{2}\right)^2}$$

$$= \sqrt{\left(\frac{2c-(a+c)}{2}\right)^2 + \left(\frac{2d-(b+d)}{2}\right)^2}$$

$$= \sqrt{\left(\frac{c-a}{2}\right)^2 + \left(\frac{d-b}{2}\right)^2}$$

Thus $PM = MQ$. To show that M is on $\overline{PQ}$, we calculate the slopes of $\overleftrightarrow{PM}$ and $\overleftrightarrow{MQ}$.

$$\text{slope of } \overleftrightarrow{PM} = \frac{\frac{b+d}{2} - b}{\frac{a+c}{2} - a} = \frac{b+d-2b}{a+c-2a} = \frac{d-b}{c-a}$$

$$\text{slope of } \overleftrightarrow{MQ} = \frac{d - \frac{b+d}{2}}{c - \frac{a+c}{2}} = \frac{2d-(b+d)}{2c-(a+c)} = \frac{d-b}{c-a}$$

The slopes are equal so $\overleftrightarrow{PM} \parallel \overleftrightarrow{MQ}$. Both lines contain point M, so $\overleftrightarrow{PM} = \overleftrightarrow{MQ}$ and M is on $\overleftrightarrow{PQ}$. So M is the midpoint of $\overline{PQ}$.

Fortunately, applying the Midpoint Formula is easier than proving it.

Example 1   If $P = (-10, 6)$ and $Q = (1, 8)$, find the midpoint of $\overline{PQ}$.

Solution   Call the midpoint M. Use the Midpoint Formula.

$$M = \left(\frac{-10 + 1}{2}, \frac{6 + 8}{2}\right)$$
$$= \left(\frac{-9}{2}, \frac{14}{2}\right)$$
$$= (-4.5, 7)$$

Check   Graph the points on a coordinate plane. (-4.5, 7) looks like it is halfway between (-10, 6) and (1, 8). This gives a rough check. You could calculate slopes and lengths of $\overline{PM}$ and $\overline{MQ}$ for an exact check.

The Midpoint Formula is often applied to prove theorems or solve problems. Example 2 is an instance of a theorem proved in the next lesson.

■ ■ ■ ■ ■ ■ ■ ■ ■

Example 2 Let $A = (0, 12)$, $B = (2, -4)$, and $C = (8, 10)$, as shown below. Let M and N be the midpoints of $\overline{AB}$ and $\overline{AC}$.
Prove: $\overline{MN} \parallel \overline{BC}$.

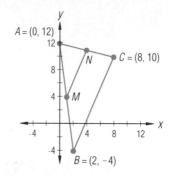

Analyze $\overline{MN}$ and $\overline{BC}$ are parallel if and only if their slopes are equal. So first find the coordinates of M and N.

Write

Conclusions	Justifications
1. $M = \left(\frac{0 + 2}{2}, \frac{12 + -4}{2}\right) = (1, 4)$	Midpoint Formula
$\quad N = \left(\frac{0 + 8}{2}, \frac{12 + 10}{2}\right) = (4, 11)$	
2. The slope of $\overline{MN}$ is $\frac{11 - 4}{4 - 1} = \frac{7}{3}$.	definition of slope (meaning)
$\quad$ The slope of $\overline{BC}$ is $\frac{10 - (-4)}{8 - 2} = \frac{14}{6} = \frac{7}{3}$.	
3. $\overline{MN} \parallel \overline{BC}$	Parallel Lines and Slopes Theorem

You may be surprised to learn another relationship in Example 2 above: $\overline{MN}$ has half the length of $\overline{BC}$. You can verify this result using the Distance Formula. (See Question 10.)

Questions

Covering the Reading

In 1–3, find the mean of the given numbers.

1. 100, 50, 200

2. -1, -3, -5, -7

3. 1492, 1776

4. Equal weights are hung from a (weightless) number line at the points -81 and 47. At what point will the number line balance?

5. Find the center of gravity of the vertices of the figure shown below.

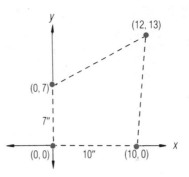

6. Give the coordinates of the midpoint of the segment connecting (x_1, y_1) to (x_2, y_2).

7. a. Give the coordinates of the midpoint of the segment joining (12, -4) and (-2, -8).
   b. Check your answer by using distance and slope.

8. Give the coordinates of the midpoint of the segment with endpoints *(a, b)* and the origin.

9. Use $\triangle DEF$ below. *L, M,* and *N* are midpoints of the sides.
   a. Find the coordinates of *L, M,* and *N*.
   b. Prove $\overline{LM} \parallel \overline{DE}$.
   c. Prove $\overline{MN} \parallel \overline{EF}$.
   d. Prove $MN = \frac{1}{2}EF$.

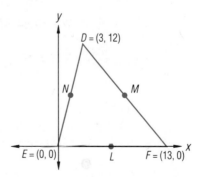

10. In the triangle of Example 2, show that $MN = \frac{1}{2}BC$.

In 11–13, write each expression as a single fraction with no fractions in the numerator or denominator.

11. $\dfrac{a + c}{2} - a$

12. $c - \dfrac{a + c}{2}$

13. $\dfrac{d - \dfrac{b + d}{2}}{c - \dfrac{a + c}{2}}$

14. Below is a graph of the population of non-white families in the United States for two years.

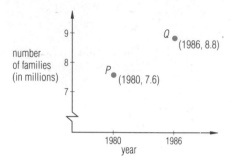

a. Find the midpoint of $\overline{PQ}$.
b. What does each coordinate of the midpoint mean?

15. Give the slope of the segment connecting the origin to the midpoint of the segment with endpoints (14, -11) and (-4, -35).

16. In $\triangle ABC$, $A = (5,7)$, $B = (-2, 0)$, and $C = (-13, 11)$. Find the length of the median from B to $\overline{AC}$.

17. A meter stick is shortened by cutting off 12 centimeters from one end and 20 centimeters from the other. What is the reading at the point on which the new stick balances?

18. M, N, P, and Q are the midpoints of the sides of quadrilateral $ABCD$ below.
a. Prove $MN = PQ$.
b. Prove $\overline{MN} \parallel \overline{PQ}$.
c. What kind of quadrilateral is $MNPQ$?

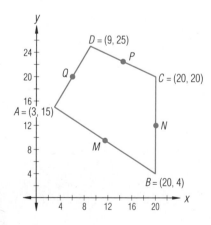

19. The equation of a given circle is $x^2 + y^2 = 75$.
a. Find its center.
b. Find its radius.
c. Find one point on the circle.
d. Find its area. *(Lesson 11-3)*

20. Graph: $(x - 2)^2 + (y - 8)^2 = 4$. *(Lesson 11-3)*

In 21 and 22, solve the system. *(Lesson 11-1)*

21. $\begin{cases} 5x - 2y = 25 \\ 3x + y = 4 \end{cases}$

22. $\begin{cases} x = 14y - 13 \\ 2x + 3y = 36 \end{cases}$

23. The regular square pyramid below has a height of 30 cm. The perimeter of the base is 64 cm.

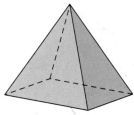

    a. Find its volume.
    b. Find its surface area. *(Lessons 10-6, 10-2)*

24. What is the slope of the line connecting $(a, 0)$ and $(0, -a)$? (Assume $a \neq 0$.) *(Lesson 3-1)*

25. If $x > 0$, simplify: **a.** $\sqrt{x^2}$; **b.** $\sqrt{4x^2}$; **c.** $\sqrt{5x^2}$. *(Previous course)*

Exploration

26. The center of gravity of a polygonal region with more than three sides is not generally the same point as the center of gravity of its vertices. Cut a nonsymmetric convex polygonal region out of cardboard.
    a. By trial and error, find the point where the region will balance on the tip of a pin.
    b. By putting the region on graph paper, find the center of gravity of its vertices and determine how close your point in part **a** is to this point.

The Midpoint Connector Theorem

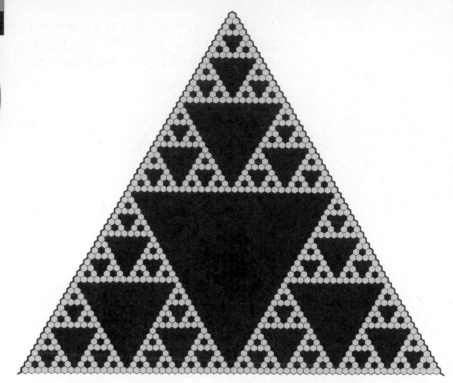

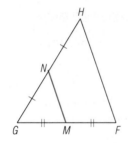

The midpoints of the sides of polygons often determine figures with interesting characteristics. You saw an example in Example 2 of Lesson 11-4. In this lesson, you will see these properties further developed.

A basic property of midpoints is pictured at the left. Segment $\overline{MN}$ joins the midpoints of $\overline{FG}$ and $\overline{GH}$. It is parallel to $\overline{FH}$. It is also half the length of $\overline{FH}$. (Measure to check this.)

These two results can be proved for any triangle. Given any triangle PQR, a coordinate plane can be put on the plane of $\triangle PQR$ so that Q is the origin and $\overline{QR}$ is on the x-axis.

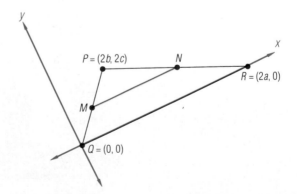

Since R is on the x-axis, its second coordinate is 0. Its first coordinate is not known. You could call it x or any other unknown. Pick $2a$ to more easily calculate midpoints. $R = (2a, 0)$.

Neither coordinate of P is known or determined by R or Q. So call the coordinates $2b$ and $2c$, again to more easily calculate midpoints. $P = (2b, 2c)$. You can use these coordinates to prove the following theorem.

Midpoint Connector Theorem:

The segment connecting the midpoints of two sides of a triangle is parallel to and half the length of the third side.

Proof

Draw: Use $\triangle PQR$ drawn on page 544 with midpoints M and N.

Given: $\triangle PQR$, M the midpoint of $\overline{PQ}$, N the midpoint of $\overline{PR}$.

Prove: a. $\overline{MN} \parallel \overline{QR}$
b. $MN = \frac{1}{2} QR$.

Analyze The coordinates of M and N are needed. For part a, slopes can be used to prove the segments parallel. The Distance Formula can show part b.

Write Place $\triangle PQR$ on a coordinate system with $Q = (0, 0)$, $R = (2a, 0)$, and $P = (2b, 2c)$.

Conclusions	Justifications
1. $M = \left(\dfrac{2b + 0}{2}, \dfrac{2c + 0}{2}\right) = (b, c)$	Midpoint Formula
$\quad N = \left(\dfrac{2b + 2a}{2}, \dfrac{2c + 0}{2}\right) = (b + a, c)$	
2. slope of $\overline{MN} = \dfrac{c - c}{b + a - b} = \dfrac{0}{a} = 0$	definition of slope (meaning)
$\quad$ slope of $\overline{QR} = \dfrac{0 - 0}{2a - 0} = \dfrac{0}{2a} = 0$	
3. $\overline{MN} \parallel \overline{QR}$	Parallel Lines and Slopes Theorem
4. $QR = \sqrt{(2a - 0)^2 + (0 - 0)^2}$ $= \sqrt{4a^2}$ $= 2\sqrt{a^2}$	Distance Formula
5. $MN = \sqrt{((b + a) - b)^2 + (c - c)^2}$ $= \sqrt{a^2 + 0}$ $= \sqrt{a^2}$	Distance Formula
6. $2MN = QR$	Substitution [MN for $\sqrt{a^2}$] (step 5 into step 4)
7. $MN = \frac{1}{2} QR$	Multiplication Property of Equality

The Midpoint Connector Theorem could be proved starting with the most general vertices possible, namely (a, b), (c, d), and (e, f). The proof would be the same, but the algebra would be more complicated. By *conveniently locating* the coordinate plane, the proof is simplified. Convenient locations use the *x*-axis or *y*-axis as symmetry lines, or place one vertex at the origin, or both. Here are convenient locations for some other figures you have studied.

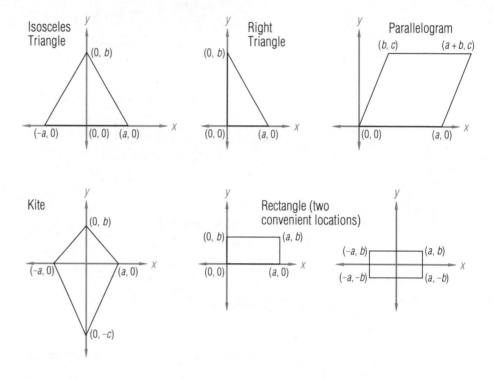

If midpoints will be used, it is better to double the coordinates. In the Example below, this is done to deduce a property of all right triangles.

Example   **Prove:**   In a right triangle, the segment connecting the vertex of the right angle to the midpoint of the hypotenuse has half the length of the hypotenuse.

Draw

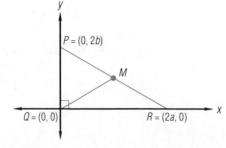

Given: Right $\triangle PQR$ with right angle Q. M is the midpoint of $\overline{PR}$.
Prove: $QM = \frac{1}{2} PR$.

Analyze Place the figure on a coordinate system. Find the coordinates of *M*, then use the Distance Formula to calculate *QM* and *PR*.

Write Place $\triangle PQR$ on a coordinate system with $Q = (0, 0)$, $R = (2a, 0)$, $P = (0, 2b)$.

Conclusions	Justifications
1. $M = \left(\frac{0 + 2a}{2}, \frac{2b + 0}{2}\right) = (a, b)$	**Midpoint Formula**
2. $PR = \sqrt{(2a - 0)^2 + (0 - 2b)^2}$ $= \sqrt{4a^2 + 4b^2}$ $= 2\sqrt{a^2 + b^2}$	**Distance Formula**
3. $QM = \sqrt{(a - 0)^2 + (b - 0)^2}$ $= \sqrt{a^2 + b^2}$	**Distance Formula**
4. $2QM = PR$	**Substitution** **(step 3 into step 2)** **[QM for $\sqrt{a^2 + b^2}$]**
5. $QM = \frac{1}{2} PR$	**Multiplication Property of Equality**

Questions

Covering the Reading

In 1 and 2, *A*, *B*, and *C* are midpoints of the sides of $\triangle LMN$ at the left.

1. If $LN = 12$, what other lengths can be found?

2. If $AB = 5.2$, what other lengths can be found?

3. State the Midpoint Connector Theorem.

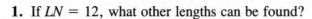

In 4–7, draw a figure of the indicated type conveniently placed on a coordinate system.

4. triangle

5. kite

6. right triangle

7. parallelogram

8. In right triangle *CAB* with m∠*A* = 90, *D* is the midpoint of $\overline{BC}$. $B = (7, 0)$ and $C = (0, 5)$. What is the length of $\overline{AD}$?

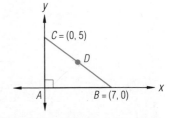

9. Fill in the blanks.
$\sqrt{4a^2 + 4b^2} = \sqrt{4(\underline{\ ?\ })} = \sqrt{\underline{\ ?\ }} \cdot \sqrt{\underline{\ ?\ }} = 2\sqrt{a^2 + b^2}$

10. An isosceles triangle has base 10 and altitude 11. Place this triangle conveniently on a coordinate system.

11. A rectangular metal sheet has length 4 meters and width 2.3 meters. If you wished to analyze this sheet with a computer, you might need to put it on a coordinate system. Show two convenient sets of locations for the vertices of the rectangle.

12. For the figure of Question 1, give justifications in this proof that *ABCN* is a parallelogram.

Conclusions	Justifications
1. $\overline{BC} \parallel \overline{LN}$; $\overline{AB} \parallel \overline{MN}$	**a.** _?_
2. *ABCN* is a parallelogram.	**b.** _?_

13. *L, M,* and *N* are the midpoints of the sides of △*DEF* below. If *DE* = 20, *EF* = 16, and *DF* = 24, what is the perimeter of △*LMN*?

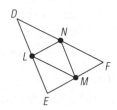

In 14 and 15, *RECT* below is a rectangle. *Y* and *D* are the midpoints of sides $\overline{RE}$ and $\overline{EC}$.

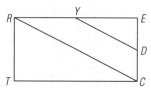

14. Explain why *YDCR* is a trapezoid.

15. If *RC* = 58 and *ED* = 20, find the lengths of all of the other segments drawn in the figure.

16. By placing a general rectangle in a convenient location, prove that the diagonals of a rectangle have the same midpoint.

17. Find the center of gravity of the vertices of the figure shown below. *(Lesson 11-4)*

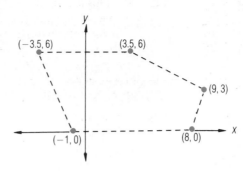

18. Find the center of gravity of the region bounded by the kite with vertices $(a, 0)$, $(0, b)$, $(-a, 0)$ and $(0, -c)$ graphed on page 546. *(Lesson 11-4)*

19. Let $V = (11, 21)$ and $L = (6, 33)$. Calculate each value.
 a. VL
 b. the slope of $\overline{VL}$
 c. the coordinates of the midpoint of $\overline{VL}$
  (Lessons 11-4, 11-2, 3-4)

20. Answer Question 19 if $V = (a, b)$ and $L = (c, d)$. *(Lessons 11-4, 11-2, 3-4)*

21. The circle at the right has center $(-2, 0)$. What is an equation for it? *(Lesson 11-3)*

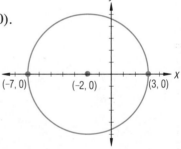

22. Twice one number plus three times a second number is 462. The sum of the numbers is 254. What are the numbers? *(Lesson 11-1, Previous course)*

23. Draw at least five quadrilaterals with different shapes. In each quadrilateral, connect the midpoints of the sides in order so as to form a smaller quadrilateral. What is true about all these smaller quadrilaterals?

11·6

Three-Dimensional Coordinates

Points in space can be located by using a **three-dimensional coordinate system.** For instance, to locate points in a room, let the origin be at a corner of the room where two walls and the floor intersect. With two coordinates, x and y, you can describe the location of an object on the floor. To describe an object in the room which is not on the floor (such as a light hanging from the ceiling), use a third number to indicate the height from the floor. This is the **z-coordinate.** Thus, if the light is 4 ft from the origin in the x-direction, 7 ft in the y-direction, and 8 ft in the z-direction (up), you could uniquely specify the position of the light by the **ordered triple** (4, 7, 8). The x-coordinate is 4, the y-coordinate is 7, and the z-coordinate is 8. The lines where the walls and floor meet are the **axes** of this 3-dimensional coordinate system.

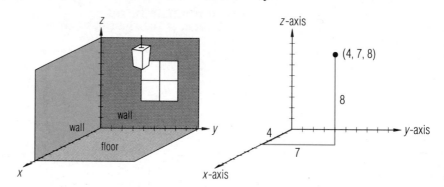

Now imagine extending each axis in its negative direction, as shown in the figure below. The positive direction is shown on each axis by a single arrowhead. The three axes are called the **x-axis,** the **y-axis,** and the **z-axis.** The ordered triple (x, y, z) represents a point in 3-space. The position of a point is given by its three distances from the origin (0, 0, 0). The following example shows how to locate points in three dimensions.

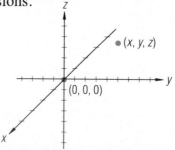

Example 1   Plot the point $R = (-5, 2, 1)$ on a three-dimensional coordinate system.

> **Solution**   To plot point R:
>
> **1.** Move 5 units backward (in a negative direction) on the x-axis.
> **2.** Move 2 units to the right parallel to the y-axis.
> **3.** Move 1 unit up parallel to the z-axis.
>
> It helps to think of the point as the back, upper, right vertex of a box with base dimensions 5 and 2, and height 1.

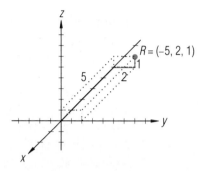

Many of the formulas for 2-dimensional coordinates have counterparts in three dimensions. For instance, the Distance Formula states that the distance between (x_1, y_1) and (x_2, y_2) in the coordinate plane is $\sqrt{(x_2 - x_1)^2 + (y_2 - y_1)^2}$. Its counterpart is the 3-dimensional Distance Formula below.

Distance Formula in Three Dimensions:

The distance between two points (x_1, y_1, z_1) and (x_2, y_2, z_2) is

$$\sqrt{(x_2 - x_1)^2 + (y_2 - y_1)^2 + (z_2 - z_1)^2}.$$

The proof of the formula is based on two applications of the Pythagorean Theorem.

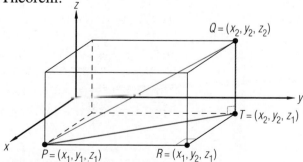

In right $\triangle PRT$, $PT^2 = RT^2 + PR^2$

In right $\triangle PTQ$, $PQ^2 = PT^2 + QT^2 = RT^2 + PR^2 + QT^2$.

So $\qquad PQ^2 = (x_2 - x_1)^2 + (y_2 - y_1)^2 + (z_2 - z_1)^2$.

The formula is found by taking the square root of each side.

Example 2 Find the distance between points P and Q, where $P = (-5, 2, 1)$ and $Q = (4, 0, -3)$.

Solution Let $P = (-5, 2, 1) = (x_1, y_1, z_1)$
and let $Q = (4, 0, -3) = (x_2, y_2, z_2)$.
Then
$$PQ = \sqrt{(x_2 - x_1)^2 + (y_2 - y_1)^2 + (z_2 - z_1)^2}$$
$$= \sqrt{(4 - -5)^2 + (0 - 2)^2 + (-3 - 1)^2}$$
$$= \sqrt{81 + 4 + 16}$$
$$= \sqrt{101}$$
$$\approx 10.05 \text{ units.}$$

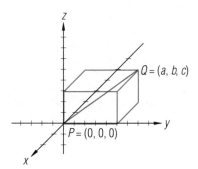

The Distance Formula for Three Dimensions helps to answer the question: What is the length of the diagonal of a box? A box with dimensions a, b, and c is conveniently located below with its edges on the axes, one endpoint of the diagonal at the origin, the other at (a, b, c).

Simply find PQ.

$$PQ = \sqrt{(a - 0)^2 + (b - 0)^2 + (c - 0)^2}$$
$$= \sqrt{a^2 + b^2 + c^2}$$

This proves the following formula.

Diagonal of a Box Formula:

In a box with dimensions a, b, and c, the length of the diagonal is

$$\sqrt{a^2 + b^2 + c^2}.$$

In Lesson 11-3, the equation for the circle with center (h, k) and radius r was given as $(x - h)^2 + (y - k)^2 = r^2$. The three-dimensional counterpart to the circle is the sphere. An equation for the sphere is analogous to the equation for a circle.

Theorem (Equation for a Sphere):

The sphere with center (h, k, j) and radius r is the set of points (x, y, z) satisfying

$$(x - h)^2 + (y - k)^2 + (z - j)^2 = r^2.$$

Proof

Since r is the radius, by the definition of sphere, the distance from (h, k, j) to (x, y, z) is r. That distance is given by the Distance Formula for Three Dimensions:

$$\sqrt{(x - h)^2 + (y - k)^2 + (z - j)^2} = r.$$

Squaring both sides results in the theorem.

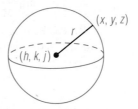

Example 3   Find an equation for the sphere with center $(3, 0, -1)$ and radius 8.

Solution   Here $(h, k, j) = (3, 0, -1)$. So $h = 3$, $k = 0$, and $j = -1$.
Also, $r = 8$. Substitute into the equation for a sphere.
$$(x - 3)^2 + (y - 0)^2 + (z - -1)^2 = 8^2$$
Simplify: $(x - 3)^2 + y^2 + (z + 1)^2 = 64$ is the desired equation.

Finally, the Midpoint Formula adapts easily to three dimensions.

Midpoint Formula in Three Dimensions:

If a segment has endpoints (a, b, c) and (d, e, f), then its midpoint is
$$\left(\frac{a + d}{2}, \frac{b + e}{2}, \frac{c + f}{2}\right).$$

You can verify the Midpoint Formula in Three Dimensions by calculating the distances between the endpoints and the midpoint, just as in two dimensions.

Covering the Reading

1. Any point in three dimensions can be located with an ordered __?__ .

2. *True* or *false*?   The intersection of two walls and the floor of a room can represent the origin of a coordinate system in three dimensions.

3. Draw a coordinate system and plot the points $B = (7, -1, -3)$ and $C = (0, -6, 1)$.

4. Find PQ where $P = (3, 7, -2)$ and $Q = (5, -11, 0)$.

5. In the box pictured below, calculate CF.

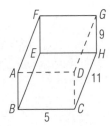

6. Find an equation for the sphere with center $(-5, 3, -10)$ and radius 13.

7. Refer to Question 4. Find the midpoint of $\overline{PQ}$.

8. Given the equation
$$(x - 18)^2 + (y - 5)^2 + (z + 11)^2 = 36.$$
   a. Where is the center of the sphere?
   b. What is the radius of the sphere?
   c. Give the coordinates of two points on the sphere.

Applying the Mathematics

9. A box has the following vertices: the origin, $(0, 1, 0)$, $(3, 0, 0)$, $(3, 1, 0)$, $(3, 1, 9)$, $(3, 0, 9)$, $(0, 0, 9)$, and $(0, 1, 9)$.
   a. Draw the box on a 3-dimensional coordinate system.
   b. Determine its volume.

10. In the rectangular box below, $D = (10, 1, 2)$ and F is the origin.
   a. Find the coordinates of points $A, B, C, E, G,$ and H.
   b. Determine the volume of the box.
   c. Determine its surface area.

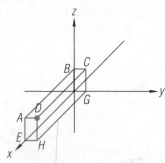

In 11 and 12, triangle ABC has vertices $A = (2, -1, 7)$, $B = (4, 0, -5)$, and $C = (-11, 8, 2)$.

11. Find the perimeter of $\triangle ABC$.

12. Find the midpoints of all the sides.

13. What is the length of the longest thin cylindrical tube that can be carried in a $20'' \times 40'' \times 5''$ carrying case?

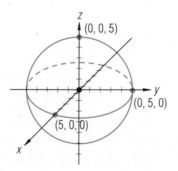

14. Find an equation for the sphere below with center $(0, 0, 0)$.

Review

15. A right triangle has sides of lengths 12, 16, and 20. To study this triangle on a coordinate plane, where would be a convenient place to locate its vertices? *(Lesson 11-5)*

16. a. The figure below is a(n) ___?___ .
  b. Use this figure to complete the sentence and prove: The segment joining the midpoints of the non-base sides of a(n) ___?___ is parallel to the bases. *(Lessons 11-5, 5-2)*

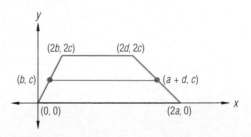

In 17 and 18, use the figure below. *P* and *L* are the midpoints of $\overline{QM}$ and $\overline{QN}$. *(Lesson 11-5)*

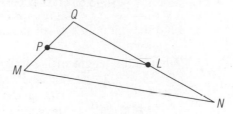

17. Prove: $\angle QLP \cong \angle QNM$.

18. If $QL = 3x$, $PL = 2x + 1$, and $QM = 4x$, find the perimeter of $\triangle QMN$.

19. Below, $\overline{AD}$ is a median of $\triangle ABC$.
a. Find the coordinates of *D*.
b. Calculate the length of $\overline{AD}$.
c. *True* or *false?* The center of gravity of triangular region *ABC* is on $\overline{AD}$. *(Lesson 11-4)*

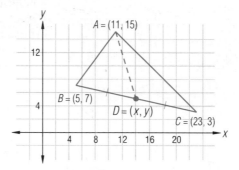

20. A triangle has vertices (4, -7), (-12, 5), and (9, -7). Find its perimeter. *(Lesson 11-2)*

21. Find the intersection of the lines with equations $5x - 2y = 15$ and $y = 6$. *(Lesson 11-1, Previous course)*

Exploration

22. Set up a coordinate system in your bedroom or classroom and determine the coordinates of the lights and windows.

23. What is a hypersphere? What is a hypercube?

Summary

In coordinate geometry, figures are described by equations or by giving coordinates of key points. To deduce a general property of a polygon using coordinates, it is efficient to place the polygon in a convenient location on the coordinate plane. Either the figure is placed with one vertex at the origin and one or more sides on axes, or the figure is placed so that it is symmetric to the x-axis or y-axis.

Three formulas are involved in the coordinate proofs of this chapter. Let (a, b) and (c, d) be two points. The slope of the line through them, $\frac{d - b}{c - a}$, gives a way of telling whether this line is perpendicular or parallel to another. The distance between these points, deduced using the Pythagorean Theorem, is $\sqrt{(c - a)^2 + (d - b)^2}$. This gives a way to tell whether segments are congruent. The midpoint of the segment joining the points is $\left(\frac{a + c}{2}, \frac{b + d}{2}\right)$. Many theorems about triangles and quadrilaterals which involve midpoints can be deduced using the Midpoint Formula.

Just as there are equations for lines, there are equations for circles. An equation for the circle with center (h, k) and radius r is
$$(x - h)^2 + (y - k)^2 = r^2.$$
A coordinate geometry of three dimensions can be built by extending the two-dimensional coordinate system. An ordered pair becomes an ordered triple. The equation for a circle has an analogous equation for a sphere. The Distance Formula and the Midpoint Formula have their three-dimensional counterparts. Many properties of three-dimensional figures can be deduced using three-dimensional coordinates. One example given in this chapter was the formula for the length of a diagonal of a box.

Vocabulary

Below are the most important terms and phrases for this chapter.
For these terms you should be able to give a general description and a specific example of each.

Lesson 11-1
coordinate geometry
analytic geometry

Lesson 11-2
Distance Formula

Lesson 11-3
equation for a circle

Lesson 11-4
mean
center of gravity
Midpoint Formula

Lesson 11-5
Midpoint Connector Theorem

Lesson 11-6
three-dimensional coordinate
    system
ordered triple, z-coordinate
x-axis, y-axis, z-axis
Distance Formula in Three
    Dimensions
Diagonal of a Box Formula
equation for a sphere
Midpoint Formula in Three
    Dimensions

Progress Self-Test

Directions: Take this test as you would take a test in class. Use a ruler and calculator. Then check your work with the solutions in the Selected Answers section in the back of the book.

In 1 and 2, *D, E,* and *F* are midpoints of the sides of △*ABC* below.

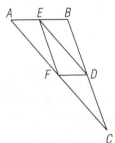

1. Explain why *BDFE* is a parallelogram.

2. If *AB* = 11 and *BC* = 22.3, find as many other lengths as you can.

3. Let *R* = (3, 4), *S* = (8, 4), and *T* = (11, 8). Find the perimeter of △*RST*.

4. What are the coordinates of the center of gravity of the vertices of the figure graphed below?

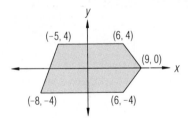

5. For the circle with equation $(x + 1)^2 + (y - 9)^2 = 25$, determine
   a. the center, **b.** the radius, and
   c. one point on the circle.

6. *Multiple choice.* Quadrilateral *ABCD* has coordinates *A* = (3, 6), *B* = (7, 9), *C* = (13, 1), and *D* = (9, -2). Most specifically, *ABCD* is a
   (a) rectangle   (b) rhombus
   (c) kite   (d) square.

7. Selkirk, Kansas, does not have a local airport. The nearest airports are in Goodland, about 60 miles north and 12 miles west of Selkirk, and in Garden City, about 36 miles south and 39 miles east of Selkirk. What is the flying distance from Goodland to Garden City?

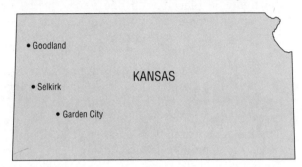

In 8 and 9, a rhombus *RHMB* is located on the coordinate system below. *E, I, O,* and *U* are midpoints of the sides.

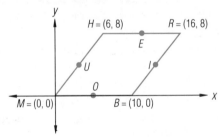

8. Give the coordinates of *E, I, O,* and *U*.

9. Prove: *EIOU* is a rectangle.

10. Give convenient coordinates for the vertices of a trapezoid.

11. Find *PQ* where *P* = (3, -1, 8) and *Q* = (-4, 9, 0).

12. What is an equation for a sphere with center (0, -19, 4) and radius 6?

13. Find the point of intersection of the lines $2x - 3y = 8$ and $4x - 5y = 20$.

14. Prove that the diagonals of the quadrilateral below have the same midpoint.

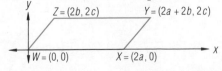

Chapter Review

Questions on **SPUR** Objectives

SPUR stands for **S**kills, **P**roperties, **U**ses, and **R**epresentations.
The Chapter Review questions are grouped according to the
SPUR Objectives for this chapter.

SKILLS deal with the procedures used to get answers.

There are no objectives for skills in this chapter.

PROPERTIES deal with the principles behind the mathematics.

▓ **Objective A:** *Using coordinates in individual figures, prove that segments in them are congruent, perpendicular, or parallel.*
(Lessons 11-1, 11-2)

1. Prove that the triangle with vertices
   $A = (11, 2)$, $B = (23, 1)$, and $C = (2, 10)$
   is isosceles.

2. Prove that the triangle with vertices
   $X = (q, 0)$, $Y = (0, q)$, and $Z = (2q, 3q)$
   is a right triangle.

3. Determine whether the quadrilateral with
   vertices $A = (0, 5)$, $B = (0, 1)$, $C = (7, 4)$,
   and $D = (7, 9)$ is a trapezoid or kite.

4. Prove that $X = (-1, 10)$, $Y = (6, 8)$,
   $Z = (3, -2)$, and $W = (-4, 0)$ are vertices
   of a parallelogram.

▓ **Objective B:** *Using coordinates, prove theorems involving parallel or perpendicular sides, congruent segments, midpoints, or combinations of these in triangles and quadrilaterals.*
(Lessons 11-1, 11-2, 11-4, 11-5)

5. Prove that the four segments joining
   consecutive midpoints of the rectangle
   below all have the same length.

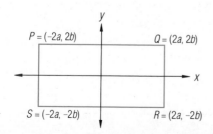

6. Prove that both pairs of opposite sides of
   the parallelogram below have the same
   length.

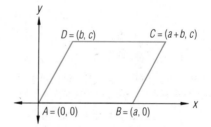

7. Prove that the diagonals of the square below
   are perpendicular to each other.

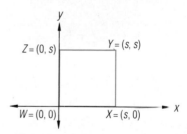

8. Use the figure below to prove that any
   isosceles triangle has two medians of the
   same length.

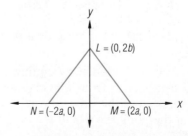

■ Objective C: Apply the Midpoint Connector Theorem. *(Lesson 11-5)*

In 9 and 10, W and Y are midpoints of $\overline{XV}$ and $\overline{XZ}$ in the figure below.

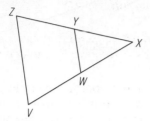

9. If $YW = 40$ and $WV = 41$, what other lengths can be determined?

10. Prove: $m\angle XWY = m\angle XVZ$.

In 11 and 12, *ABCD* below is a rhombus. *F* and *E* are midpoints of sides $\overline{BC}$ and $\overline{CD}$.

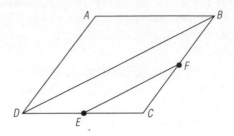

11. Explain why *BDEF* is a trapezoid.

12. If $BD = 10$ and $BC = 6$, find the lengths of as many other segments as possible.

USES deal with applications of mathematics in real situations.

■ Objective D: *Determine the center of gravity of a segment or a set of points.* (Lesson 11-4)

13. Think of the region below as a very thin sheet of metal with no weight except at its vertices. Find the center of gravity of its vertices.

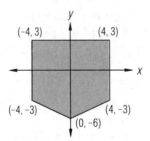

14. Locate the center of gravity of the vertices of this 3–4–5 right triangular region.

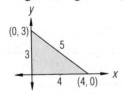

15. Where is the center of gravity of a segment located?

16. A meter stick is shortened by cutting it at a point 8 centimeters from one end and 3 centimeters from the other. What is the reading at the point on which the new stick balances?

■ Objective E: *Apply the distance and diagonal of a box formulas in real situations.* (Lessons 11-2, 11-6)

17. A car drives 5 miles north, 2 miles east, then another 6 miles north, and another 3 miles east. By plane, how far is the car from its starting point?

18. A ship is located 2.3 km south and 1.4 km west of a lighthouse. Another ship is 1.6 km south and 0.8 km east of the lighthouse.
 a. Draw a picture of this situation.
 b. Calculate the distance between the ships.

19. A storage niche is 8 inches by 12 inches by 24 inches. What is the longest dowel rod that can fit in it?

20. A wooden crate is 45 mm by 30 mm by 80 mm. What is the length of the longest straw that will fit in it?

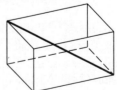

REPRESENTATIONS deal with pictures, graphs, or objects that illustrate concepts.

■ **Objective F:** *Determine the distance between two points in the coordinate plane. (Lesson 11-2)*

21. Calculate the distance between $(3, 5)$ and $(-7, -1)$.

22. What is the distance between (a, b) and the origin?

23. A triangle has vertices $(3, 2)$, $(3, 7)$, and $(6, 11)$. What is its perimeter?

24. What is the length of the longest side of trapezoid $ABCD$ if $A = (0, 0)$, $B = (3, 0)$, $C = (10, 1)$, and $D = (6, 1)$?

■ **Objective G:** *Write an equation for a circle given its center and radius, and vice versa. (Lesson 11-3)*

25. What is an equation for the circle with center $(8, -1)$ and radius 15?

26. The circle has center at $(0, 6)$. What is an equation for it?

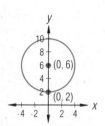

In 27 and 28, determine **a.** the center, **b.** the radius, and **c.** one point on the circle with the given equation.

27. $(x - 6)^2 + (y + 3)^2 = 169$

28. $x^2 + y^2 = 50$

In 29 and 30 graph.

29. $(x + 1)^2 + (y - 4)^2 = 9$

30. $x^2 + (y + 2)^2 = 1$

■ **Objective H:** *Determine the coordinates of the midpoint of a segment in the coordinate plane. (Lesson 11-4)*

31. Give the coordinates of the midpoint of the segment joining $(3, 2)$ and $(6, -2)$.

32. Give the coordinates of the midpoint of the segment joining $(2a, 2b)$ and $(0, 2c)$.

33. Give the slope of the segment connecting the origin to the midpoint of the segment with endpoints $(50, -10)$ and $(60, 70)$.

34. Let $A = (3, 0)$, $B = (4, 5)$, and $C = (9, 8)$. Find the length of the segment connecting B to the midpoint of $\overline{AC}$.

■ **Objective I:** *Give convenient locations for triangles and quadrilaterals in the coordinate plane. (Lesson 11-5)*

35. Give convenient coordinates of a rectangle placed on the coordinate plane so that it is symmetric to both the x-axis and the y-axis.

36. Give convenient coordinates for the vertices of an isosceles triangle.

37. Three consecutive vertices of a parallelogram are $(17, 5)$, $(0, 0)$, and $(8, 0)$. What is the fourth vertex?

38. Give convenient coordinates for the vertices of a kite with diagonals of lengths 30 and 48 if the other diagonal divides the symmetry diagonal in pieces of length 20 and 28.

■ **Objective J:** *Apply coordinate geometry in three dimensions. (Lesson 11-6)*

In 39 and 40, **a.** draw a coordinate system and plot the points. **b.** Find the midpoint of the segment joining them. **c.** Find the distance between them.

39. $P = (-2, 3, 6)$ and $Q = (0, -5, 1)$

40. $R = (13, -5, 8)$ and $S = (0, 16, -3)$

41. Find an equation for the sphere with center $(4, -3, 0)$ and radius 10.

42. Find the center and radius of the sphere $(x - 1)^2 + (y + 2)^2 + (z - 5)^2 = 4$.

■ **Objective K:** *Find the point of intersection of two lines in the coordinate plane. (Lesson 11-1, Previous course)*

In 43–45, find the point of intersecton of the lines by solving a system.

43. $\begin{cases} 2x + y = 5 \\ -x - 5y = 11 \end{cases}$

44. $\begin{cases} x + y = 180 \\ x - y = 25 \end{cases}$

45. $\begin{cases} y - 3x = 8 \\ \quad\quad x = 7 \end{cases}$

CHAPTER 12

Similarity

In 1970, the population of Saline, Michigan, was 4811. By 1980, the population had grown to 6483.

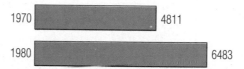

This *bar graph* depicts the change, but it has no "oomph." One way to make it more appealing is to use repetitions of congruent figures. Here each picture of a person represents 1000 people. Part of a picture is part of a thousand. The result is called a *picture graph*.

Still another way to compare data in a display is to show two figures of the same shape but of different size. The shorter figure represents the 1970 population, and the taller one represents the 1980 population. Since $\frac{6483}{4811}$ is about 1.35, the height of the 1980 figure is about 1.35 times the height of the 1970 figure.

However, the area of the 1980 figure is about $(1.35)^2 \approx 1.8$ or almost twice the area of the 1970 figure. And if these figures were three-dimensional, the volume of the 1980 figure would be about $(1.35)^3 \approx 2.5$ times the volume of the figure for 1970. Do you think the graph is misleading?

Figures with the same shape (but not necessarily the same size) are *similar figures*. The concept of *similarity* is as important in analyzing figures as the concept of congruence. In this chapter, you will learn how to draw similar figures, study their basic properties and the transformations relating them, and see a few of their many applications.

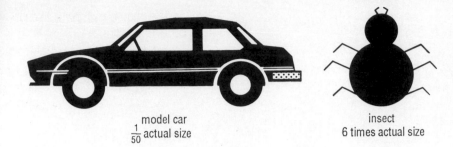

model car
$\frac{1}{50}$ actual size

insect
6 times actual size

Size Changes on a Coordinate Plane

Figures with different sizes but the same shape are found both in fun and serious pursuits. Model planes, model cars, model trains, dolls, and doll houses can all be considered as scale models of real figures played with for enjoyment. Clothes designers, inventors, architects, and city planners use scale models to see how an object will look without having to make it actual size. Scientists magnify small things like insects or the atom, or make models of large objects like the earth or our solar system, in order to study them.

Changing the size is remarkably easy if the figure is given on a coordinate plane. You need only multiply the coordinates of every point on the figure by a fixed number.

Example 1   In pentagon *ABCDE*, *A* = (-9, 15), *B* = (-15, -6), *C* = (0, 3), *D* = (12, 0), and *E* = (3, 12). Describe the result when all coordinates of points on this figure are multiplied by $\frac{2}{3}$.

Solution   First draw *ABCDE*. Then multiply the coordinates of the vertices of *ABCDE* by $\frac{2}{3}$. The resulting five image points are called *A'*, *B'*, *C'*, *D'*, and *E'* and are connected below.

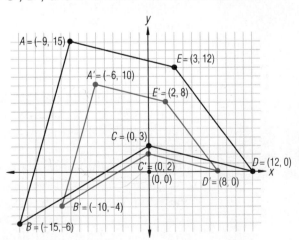

To describe the result, examine the preimage and the image sides closely. You could write:

  (1) Image and preimage sides seem to be parallel.
  (2) Image sides appear to be $\frac{2}{3}$ as long as preimage sides.

Closer examination gives something else:

  (3) The image of a point is between the preimage and the origin.

Do you see anything else?

Example 1 describes a transformation in which the image of (x, y) is $(\frac{2}{3}x, \frac{2}{3}y)$. This transformation is denoted $S_{\frac{2}{3}}$. To verify the first property of $S_{\frac{2}{3}}$ found in Example 1, you could focus on a segment and its image, say $\overline{AE}$ and $\overline{A'E'}$. Using slopes, it is easy to show that $\overline{AE} \parallel \overline{A'E'}$.

$$\text{slope of } \overline{AE} = \frac{12 - 15}{3 - -9} = \frac{-3}{12} = -\frac{1}{4}$$
$$\text{slope of } \overline{A'E'} = \frac{8 - 10}{2 - -6} = \frac{-2}{8} = -\frac{1}{4}$$

Since the slopes are equal, $\overline{AE}$ and $\overline{A'E'}$ are parallel.

Now we generalize this example. The transformation which maps (x, y) onto (kx, ky) is denoted by the symbol S_k. The number k is called the **magnitude** of S_k. Any number but zero can be the magnitude, but in this book $k > 0$ unless otherwise stated. This transformation has many important properties, all of which can be proved using coordinate geometry. Here are two important ones.

Theorem

Let S_k be the transformation mapping (x, y) onto (kx, ky).
Let $P' = S_k(P)$ and $Q' = S_k(Q)$. Then
(1) $\overleftrightarrow{P'Q'} \parallel \overleftrightarrow{PQ}$,
(2) $P'Q' = k \cdot PQ$.

Proof

Let $P = (a, b)$ and $Q = (c, d)$ be the preimages.
Then $P' = (ka, kb)$ and $Q' = (kc, kd)$.

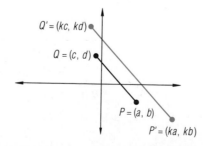

(1) $\overleftrightarrow{P'Q'}$ is parallel to $\overleftrightarrow{PQ}$ if the slopes are the same.

$$\text{slope of } \overleftrightarrow{P'Q'} = \frac{kd - kb}{kc - ka} = \frac{k(d - b)}{k(c - a)} = \frac{d - b}{c - a}$$

$$\text{slope of } \overleftrightarrow{PQ} = \frac{d - b}{c - a}$$

Thus $\overleftrightarrow{PQ} \parallel \overleftrightarrow{P'Q'}$.

(2) The goal is to show that $P'Q' = k \cdot PQ$.
From the Distance Formula,
$$PQ = \sqrt{(c - a)^2 + (d - b)^2}.$$
Also from the Distance Formula,

$$
\begin{aligned}
P'Q' &= \sqrt{(kc - ka)^2 + (kd - kb)^2} && \\
&= \sqrt{(k(c - a))^2 + (k(d - b))^2} && \text{Distributive Property} \\
&= \sqrt{k^2(c - a)^2 + k^2(d - b)^2} && \text{Power of a Product} \\
&= \sqrt{k^2((c - a)^2 + (d - b)^2)} && \text{Distributive Property} \\
&= \sqrt{k^2}\sqrt{(c - a)^2 + (d - b)^2} && \text{Square Root of a Product} \\
&= k\sqrt{(c - a)^2 + (d - b)^2} && \text{Since } k > 0, \sqrt{k^2} = k \\
&= k \cdot PQ. && \text{Substitution}
\end{aligned}
$$

Property (2) in the theorem is verified in Example 2.

Example 2   **a.** Find the images of $M = (2, 2)$ and $N = (-1, 3)$ under S_4.
b. Verify that $M'N' = 4MN$.

Solution   It helps to draw a figure.

a. $M' = (4 \cdot 2, 4 \cdot 2) = (8, 8)$
$N' = (4 \cdot -1, 4 \cdot 3) = (-4, 12)$

Graph the preimages and images.
The graph shows that the segment
and its image are parallel. That is
a good check that the points are
correctly graphed.

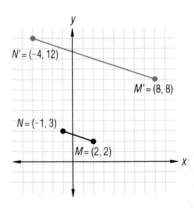

b. $M'N' = \sqrt{(8 - -4)^2 + (8 - 12)^2} = \sqrt{12^2 + (-4)^2}$
$= \sqrt{160} = \sqrt{16}\sqrt{10} = 4\sqrt{10}$
$MN = \sqrt{(2 - -1)^2 + (2 - 3)^2} = \sqrt{3^2 + (-1)^2} = \sqrt{10}$
So $M'N' = 4MN$.

Other properties of these transformations are proved in Lesson 12-3.

1. Name four occupations which use scale models.

In 2 and 3, refer to Example 1.

2. Verify that $\overline{B'C'} \parallel \overline{BC}$ by calculating slopes.

3. Verify that $B'C' = \frac{2}{3}BC$ by using the Distance Formula.

4. a. S_k is the transformation which maps (x, y) onto __?__.
   b. k is the __?__ of S_k.

5. Let $J = (5, -8)$, $K = (-6, 0)$, and $L = (-10, -4)$.
   a. Graph $\triangle JKL$ and its image under S_3.
   b. Describe the result.

6. Let $P = (-2, 11)$ and $Q = (3, -5)$. Let $P' = S_7(P)$ and $Q' = S_7(Q)$.
   a. What are the coordinates of P' and Q'?
   b. Show that the slopes of $\overline{QP}$ and $\overline{Q'P'}$ are equal.
   c. Show that $Q'P' = 7 \cdot QP$ using the Distance Formula.

7. Refer to the solution of Example 1. Verify property (3) for the points O, A', and A. (Hint: calculate distances.)

8. An artist wished to double the dimensions of the insect shown in this lesson. So the artist traced the insect onto graph paper. (This is shown at the right.) Then the coordinates of key points on the insect were multiplied by 2 and the image drawn. Repeat what the artist did using your own paper.

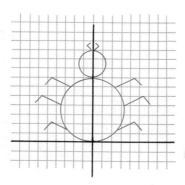

9. a. What is the image of (x, y) under S_1?
   b. Describe S_1.

10. Below is a scale drawing of the side of a cabin. If each unit on the paper is $\frac{1}{4}$ inch, and the figure is $\frac{1}{48}$ actual size, what is the height of the real cabin?

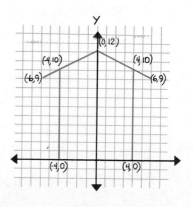

11. In three dimensions, S_k is the transformation mapping (x, y, z) onto (kx, ky, kz).
   a. Find the image of $P = (-3, 12, 4)$ under S_5. Call this point P'.
   b. Find the image of $Q = (2, -8, 0)$ under S_5. Call this point Q'.
   c. Using the Distance Formula in Three Dimensions, verify that $Q'P' = 5 \cdot QP$.

Review

12. In the figure below, $\overleftrightarrow{KL} \parallel \overleftrightarrow{FG}$ and M is the midpoint of $\overline{LF}$.
   a. Prove $\triangle KLM \cong \triangle GFM$.
   b. Prove $MG = MK$. *(Lessons 7-3, 6-7)*

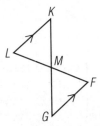

13. State the Figure Reflection Theorem. *(Lesson 4-2)*

14. Copy segment $\overline{AB}$ below. Construct its perpendicular bisector. *(Lesson 3-6)*

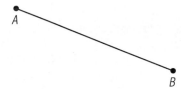

In 15–17, solve. *(Previous course)*

15. $\dfrac{2}{9} = \dfrac{3}{x}$

16. $\dfrac{2y - 5}{5} = \dfrac{3y + 14}{8}$

17. $AB - 9 = \frac{3}{4} \cdot AB$. (Here, A and B are points.)

Exploration

18. Use $\triangle JKL$ of Question 5.
   a. Multiply all the coordinates of the vertices by -3.
   b. Describe the figure that results.
   c. Generalize parts **a** and **b**.

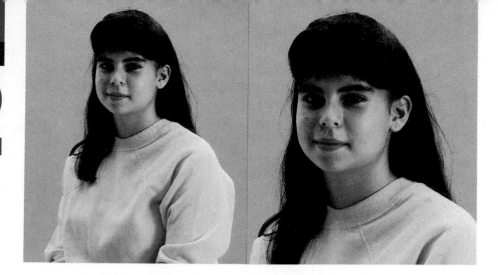

LESSON 12-2

Size Changes Without Coordinates

Not all figures, of course, are given on the coordinate plane. It sometimes is necessary to be able to change sizes of figures without coordinates. Below is a face made up of segments and circular arcs. Suppose you wanted to draw a face like this one, but 2.5 times as large. The number 2.5 is the **magnitude** or **scale factor** or **size change factor**.

To begin, choose a point in the plane. The point can be anywhere in the plane, but, for clarity, we select a point O outside the face. O is the **center** of a *size transformation*. Then choose and label key points on the face. Some key points are endpoints of the segments and the centers of the arcs. We have chosen A, B, C, D, E, F, G, and H. Draw rays from O through the named points.

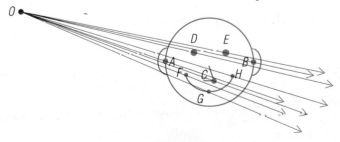

Now find the image of each point. Here is how to do it for point A.

Step 1. Measure OA.

Step 2. On $\overrightarrow{OA}$, locate A' so that $OA' = 2.5 \cdot OA$. That is, A' is 2.5 times as far from the center as A is. Point A' is the *size change image* of A.

Repeat steps 1 and 2 for all the labeled points of the figure. Connect the image points in the manner of the preimages. The result is shown below. Because the scale factor is greater than one, the image is larger than the preimage.

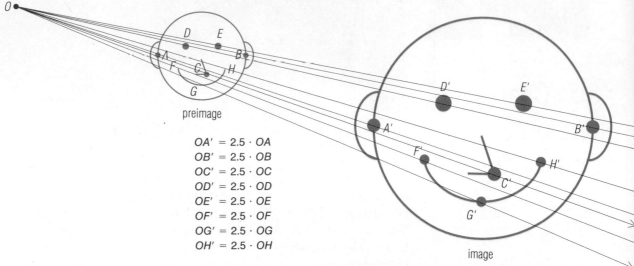

preimage

$OA' = 2.5 \cdot OA$
$OB' = 2.5 \cdot OB$
$OC' = 2.5 \cdot OC$
$OD' = 2.5 \cdot OD$
$OE' = 2.5 \cdot OE$
$OF' = 2.5 \cdot OF$
$OG' = 2.5 \cdot OG$
$OH' = 2.5 \cdot OH$

image

The same procedure can be used if the scale factor is less than or equal to one. Below is shown the face and its image when the scale factor is $\frac{1}{3}$ and the center is O. Notice OC'' is $\frac{1}{3}$ of OC. The image is now smaller than the preimage.

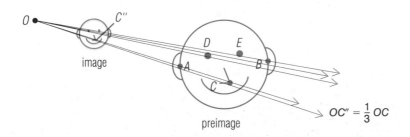

image

preimage

$OC'' = \frac{1}{3} OC$

The transformation described in this section has various names. It is called a **size change** or a **size transformation.** Some others call it a **dilation** or **dilatation.**

Definition:

Let O be a point and k be a positive real number. For any point P, let $S(P) = P'$ be the point on $\overrightarrow{OP}$ with $OP' = k \cdot OP$. Then S is the **size change with center O and magnitude k.**

When $k > 1$, S is called an **expansion.** When $0 < k < 1$, S is a **contraction.** When $k = 1$, S is called the **identity transformation** because each point coincides with its image, so the image is identical to the preimage. In this lesson you have seen an expansion with magnitude 2.5 and a contraction with magnitude $\frac{1}{3}$.

The next theorem relates a size change to the transformation S_k of the last lesson.

Theorem

The transformation S_k, where $S_k(x, y) = (kx, ky)$, is the size change with center $(0, 0)$ and magnitude k.

Proof

It must be shown that a point and its image under S_k satisfy the sufficient conditions of the definition of size change. So let $P = (a, b)$. Then $P' = (ka, kb)$ by the definition (meaning) of S_k.

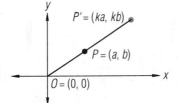

Two things need to be shown:
(1) P' lies on $\overrightarrow{OP}$, and
(2) $OP' = k \cdot OP$.

(1) P' lies on $\overrightarrow{OP}$ if the points O, P, and P' are collinear and in the same quadrant. O, P, and P' are collinear if the slope of $\overline{OP}$ equals the slope of $\overline{OP'}$.

$$\text{slope of } \overline{OP} = \frac{b - 0}{a - 0} = \frac{b}{a}$$

$$\text{slope of } \overline{OP'} = \frac{kb - 0}{ka - 0} = \frac{kb}{ka} = \frac{b}{a}$$

Thus O, P, and P' are collinear.

If a and b are not zero, the quadrant of (a, b) depends on the signs (positive or negative) of a and b. Since k is positive, the numbers a and ka have the same sign. Similarly, b and kb have the same sign. So (a, b) and (ka, kb) are in the same quadrant. If $a = 0$ or $b = 0$, then the points are on the axes and a similar argument can be given.

(2) Use the Distance Formula and algebraic simplification. This is similar to the proof in the last lesson.

$$OP = \sqrt{(a - 0)^2 + (b - 0)^2} \quad = \sqrt{a^2 + b^2}$$
$$OP' = \sqrt{(ka - 0)^2 + (kb - 0)^2} = \sqrt{(ka)^2 + (kb)^2}$$
$$= \sqrt{k^2a^2 + k^2b^2}$$
$$= \sqrt{k^2(a^2 + b^2)}$$
$$= \sqrt{k^2} \cdot \sqrt{a^2 + b^2}$$
$$= k\sqrt{a^2 + b^2} \text{ (because } k > 0)$$
$$= k \cdot OP$$

Although the proof of the above theorem is long, the theorem is worth it, because it enables you to work either with or without coordinates when doing size changes.

Questions

1. In the expansion of the face in this lesson, what are the center and magnitude?

2. In the contraction of the face in this lesson, what are the center and magnitude?

In 3 and 4, trace the drawing below. Find the image of the flag under:

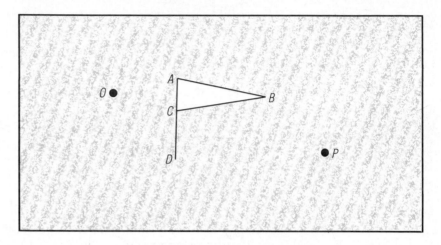

3. the size change with center O and magnitude 3;

4. the size change with center P, magnitude $\frac{3}{4}$.

5. Let S be a size transformation with scale factor 6 and center O. Let A be any point. Then S(A) is __?__ times as far from O as A is.

6. In the figure below, $A'B'C'D'$ is a size change image of $ABCD$ with center O.
   a. Is this size change an expansion or a contraction?
   b. If $OA = 10$ and $AA' = 4$, what is the magnitude of the size change?

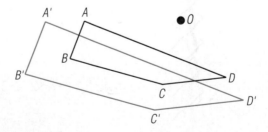

7. If k is the scale factor of an expansion, then __?__ .

8. If k is the scale factor of a contraction, then __?__ .

9. In order to show that the transformation S_k is a size change of magnitude k with center O, what two statements needed to be proved?

In 10–13, use the figure below. S is a size change with center O and $S(\triangle ABC) = \triangle A'B'C'$. The figure is a guide and not necessarily accurate.

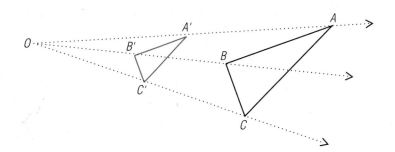

10. If $k = \frac{2}{3}$ and $OA = 9$, then $OA' = \underline{\ ?\ }$ and $AA' = \underline{\ ?\ }$.

11. If $OB = 5$ and $OB' = 3$, then $k = \underline{\ ?\ }$.

12. If $OC' = 2 \cdot OC$, then $k = \underline{\ ?\ }$.

13. If $\dfrac{OB}{OB'} = \dfrac{4}{3}$, then $k = \underline{\ ?\ }$.

In 14–16, trace each figure. Use a ruler to determine the center and the scale factor k for the size transformation represented. (The image is blue.)

14.

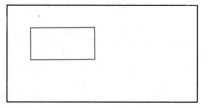

15.

16.

17. Draw a figure 1.5 times as large as the figure below.

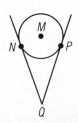

18. Trace $\triangle ABC$ below and draw its image under a size change with center A and magnitude $\frac{1}{3}$.

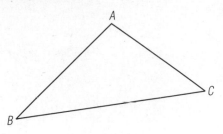

Review

19. Let $A = (0, -4)$, $B = (-13, \frac{1}{3})$, and $C = (7, 11)$. Find the image of $\triangle ABC$ under S_3. *(Lesson 12-1)*

20. Given $P = (9, 2)$, $Q = (-4, 8)$, and $R = (35, -10)$.
   a. Show that P, Q, and R are collinear.
   b. Show that P is between Q and R.
   c. Find the images P', Q', and R' of P, Q, and R under S_4.
   d. Show that P', Q', and R' are collinear.
   e. Show that P' is between Q' and R'. *(Lessons 12-1, 1-8)*

21. The rectangular field $ABCD$ pictured below is $300'$ by $400'$. What is the perimeter of $\triangle ABC$? *(Lessons 8-7, 8-1)*

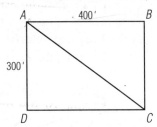

22. Is the figure of Question 21 traversable? *(Lesson 1-4)*

23. a. How many inches are there in a mile?
   b. How many millimeters are there in a kilometer?
   (Previous course)

24. Solve each equation. *(Previous course)*
   a. $\dfrac{z + 1}{2} = \dfrac{30}{40}$
   b. $\dfrac{M}{5} = \dfrac{6}{M}$

Exploration

25. Draw a pentagon (but not a regular pentagon). Draw the images of this pentagon under two size changes with the same magnitude but different centers, one inside the pentagon, one outside. (You pick the magnitude and the two centers.) How do the images compare?

You have now seen ways to find size changes with and without coordinates. Working without coordinates is more flexible because figures are not always given on a coordinate plane. However, coordinates enable some properties of size changes to be deduced rather easily. And, since any point can be the origin for a coordinate system, if a property of S_k can be deduced, then it holds for size changes with other centers.

In the questions of the last two lessons, you have been asked to verify some of the properties of size changes. The first of these is the most important property of size changes and was proved in Lesson 12-1.

Size Change Distance Theorem:

Under a size change with magnitude $k > 0$, the distance between any two image points is k times the distance between their preimages.

Remember the A-B-C-D properties of reflections and other isometries. Size changes may not preserve distances, but they preserve the other three. First, look at betweenness and collinearity.

Size transformations preserve betweenness and collinearity.

Proof

Let the images of P, Q, and R under size change S_k be P', Q', and R'. For betweenness, we need to show: If Q is between P and R, then Q' is between P' and R'.

Given: Q is between P and R.

Conclusions	Justifications
1. $PQ + QR = PR$	Def. of betweenness (meaning)
2. $k(PQ + QR) = k \cdot PR$	Multiplication Property of Equality
3. $k \cdot PQ + k \cdot QR = k \cdot PR$	Distributive Property
4. $k \cdot PQ = P'Q'$	Size Change Distance Theorem
$\quad k \cdot QR = Q'R'$	
$\quad k \cdot PR = P'R'$	
5. $P'Q' + Q'R' = P'R'$	Substitution (step 4 into step 3)
6. Q' is between P' and R'.	Def. of betweenness (suff. cond.)

Collinearity is preserved means that when three points are collinear, so are their images. But if three different points are collinear, one must be between the other two. So the image of that one is between the images of the other two, which means the images are collinear.

Because size changes preserve collinearity, the image of a line is a line. Because size changes preserve betweenness, the image of a segment is a segment, the image of a ray is a ray, and the image of an angle is an angle.

In Lesson 12-1, the following property was proved.

Theorem:

A line and its image under a size transformation are parallel.

You can use this theorem to quickly draw images of polygons.

Example   S is a size transformation with magnitude 0.6 and center O. Draw S(ABCD).

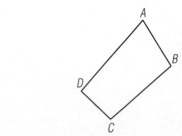

Solution S(ABCD) is determined by the images of A, B, C, and D. Draw guide rays $\overrightarrow{OA}$, $\overrightarrow{OB}$, $\overrightarrow{OC}$, and $\overrightarrow{OD}$. Measure OA: OA ≈ 56 mm. So OA' = 0.6 · OA = 0.6 · 56 mm ≈ 34 mm. This locates A'. Since $\overleftrightarrow{A'B'}$ ∥ $\overleftrightarrow{AB}$, find B' by drawing a line through A' parallel to $\overleftrightarrow{AB}$ which intersects $\overrightarrow{OB}$ in B'. Likewise, since $\overleftrightarrow{A'D'}$ ∥ $\overleftrightarrow{AD}$, find D by drawing a line through A' parallel to $\overleftrightarrow{OB}$ which intersects $\overrightarrow{OD}$ in D'. Continue this process until all the vertices of the image polygon are located.

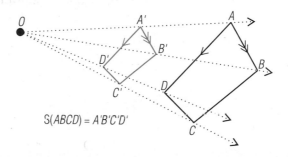

S(ABCD) = A'B'C'D'

In the Example, it certainly looks as if corresponding angles in ABCD and A'B'C'D' have the same measure. This can be proved easily. For instance, here is a proof that m∠ABC = m∠A'B'C'.

Conclusions	**Justifications**
1. $\overleftrightarrow{BC}$ ∥ $\overleftrightarrow{B'C'}$ $\overleftrightarrow{AB}$ ∥ $\overleftrightarrow{A'B'}$	A line and its image under a size transformation are parallel.
2. m∠ABO = m∠A'B'O m∠OBC = m∠OB'C'	∥ lines ⇒ corr ∠s =
3. m∠ABO + m∠OBC = m∠A'B'O + m∠OB'C'	Addition Property of Equality
4. m∠ABO + m∠OBC = m∠ABC m∠A'B'O + m∠OB'C' = m∠A'B'C'	Angle Addition Property
5. m∠ABC = m∠A'B'C'	Substitution (step 4 into step 3)

This proves that size transformations preserve angle measure. Combining this all into one theorem:

Size Change Theorem:

Under a size transformation:

(a) angle measure preserved;
(b) betweenness is preserved;
(c) collinearity is preserved; and
(d) lines and their images are parallel.

The preservation properties imply that images of figures are determined by images of key points.

> **Figure Size Change Theorem:**
>
> If a figure is determined by certain points, then its size change image is the corresponding figure determined by the size change images of those points.

The Figure Size Change Theorem was applied as early as Lesson 12-1 to find the image of a pentagon.

Questions

Covering the Reading

1. Suppose you know the lengths of a segment and its image under a size change. How can the magnitude of the size change be calculated?

2. *True* or *false*? The length of the image of a segment under a size transformation depends upon the location of the center of the size transformation.

3. *True* or *false*? Size transformations preserve distance.

4. A picture of an insect is k times actual size. If a leg on the picture is 3 cm long, how long is the leg on the actual insect?

5. Size transformations preserve __?__ , __?__ , and __?__ .

6. S is a size transformation of magnitude 2. If $S(\angle TJK) = \angle T'J'K'$ and $m\angle T'J'K' = 43$, find $m\angle TJK$.

7. Suppose $S(\overleftrightarrow{AB}) = \overleftrightarrow{CD}$. How are $\overleftrightarrow{AB}$ and $\overleftrightarrow{CD}$ related?

In 8 and 9, $S(A) = X$, $S(B) = T$, $S(C) = E$, and $S(D) = J$.

8. $S(\angle BCD) = $ __?__   **9.** If $m\angle BAD = 73$, then $m\angle$ __?__ .

10. If $S(TINY) = HUGE$, then $S(N) = $ __?__ .

Applying the Mathematics

11. Below, $\triangle DEF$ is a size transformation image of $\triangle ABC$ with center O. $AB = 6$, $BC = 8$, $EF = 20$, and $DF = 30$. Find each value.
  a. k, the magnitude of the size change
  b. DE
  c. AC

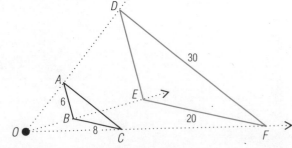

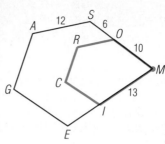

12. T is a size change with T(*MEGAS*) = *MICRO* and lengths as indicated at the left.
   a. What is the magnitude of T?
   b. What is the center of T?
   c. Give the value of *OR*.
   d. Give the value of *ME*.

In 13–15, trace each figure. Draw the image of the figure under the size change with center *P* and the given magnitude *k*.

13. $k = \frac{5}{6}$ **14.** $k = \frac{5}{6}$ **15.** $k = 4$

 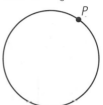 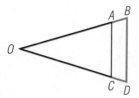

16. A photograph that measures 5 cm by 12 cm is enlarged to a width of 7 cm.
   a. Find the scale factor of the enlargement.
   b. Find the length of the enlargement.
   c. Find the areas of the photograph and its enlargement.
   d. How many times larger in area is the enlargement than the original?
   e. How many times larger in perimeter is the enlargement than the original?

17. Use the figure at the right.
   Given: S(△*OAC*) = △*OBD*,
   OA = 6, *AB* = 1,
   BD = 4, *OC* = 6.1.
   Find the lengths of as many other segments as you can.

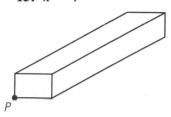

Review

18. Figure A below is a size change image of Figure B. Find the center and scale factor *k*. *(Lesson 12-2)*

Figure A   Figure B

19. Many road maps can be thought of as contractions of a part of the earth. Suppose 1 cm on a map equals 1 km on the earth. What is the scale factor of the contraction for this map? (That magnitude is the *scale* of the map.) *(Lesson 12-2)*

20. Suppose $P'Q'R'T'$ is the image of $PQRT$ under S_k with $P = (4, -6)$, $Q = (-9, 12)$, $R' = (5, 13)$, $T = (0, -8)$, and $P' = (2, -3)$. Find k and the coordinates of Q', R, and T'. *(Lesson 12-1)*

21. Nina and Kathryn are about to replace the anchor line for their boat. When they go fishing at their favorite spot on Lake Congora, which is about 15 feet deep, they like to be able to drift 9 feet from the location where they drop the anchor. How long should the anchor line be? *(Lesson 8-7)*

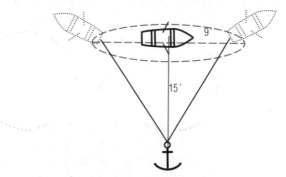

22. Complete this hierarchy for isometries. *(Lesson 6-6)*

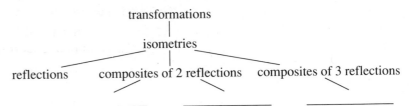

In 23 and 24, suppose $\dfrac{2x}{k} = \dfrac{b}{y}$. *(Previous course)*

23. Find k if $x = 9$, $b = 7$, and $y = 50$.

24. If $x = 1$ and $y = 1$, what can you say about the value of k?

25. Solve for t: $\dfrac{t+3}{100} = \dfrac{t-5}{200}$. *(Previous course)*

Exploration

26. a. Does the definition of size change given in Lesson 12-2 hold in three dimensions or must it be modified? If so, how would you modify it?
   b. What properties mentioned in this lesson are preserved with size changes of three dimensions?

27. Consider this conjecture:
   If $MNOP$ is a square, then $S_k(MNOP)$ is a square.
   a. Draw an instance of this conjecture.
   b. Is this conjecture true? If so, prove it. If not, draw a counterexample.

Proportions

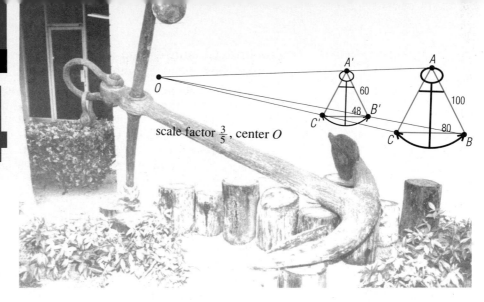

scale factor $\frac{3}{5}$, center O

A **ratio** is a quotient of two numbers, $\frac{m}{n}$ or m/n. Sometimes the ratio m/n is written $m:n$. In a ratio $\frac{m}{n}$, m and n must be quantities of the same kind, such as lengths, populations, or areas. (If the quantities are of different kinds, $\frac{m}{n}$ is called a *rate*.)

Ratios appear whenever there is a size change. For example, above is pictured the size change with center O and magnitude $\frac{3}{5}$. Then, by the Size Change Distance Theorem,

$$A'B' = \tfrac{3}{5} \cdot AB \quad \text{and} \quad B'C' = \tfrac{3}{5} \cdot BC.$$

Consequently, $\dfrac{A'B'}{AB} = \dfrac{3}{5}$ and $\dfrac{B'C'}{BC} = \dfrac{3}{5}.$

Thus in a size transformation, the ratios of image lengths to pre-image lengths are equal; that is, $\frac{A'B'}{AB} = \frac{B'C'}{BC}$. That ratio is equal to the magnitude of the size change.

A statement that two ratios are equal is called a **proportion.** Each equation below is a proportion.

$$\frac{CB}{C'B'} = \frac{5}{3} \qquad \frac{2}{7} = \frac{x}{9} \qquad \frac{y+3}{5} = \frac{7}{y} \qquad \frac{A'B'}{AB} = \frac{B'C'}{BC}$$

You learned how to solve proportions in previous years and have reviewed them in questions in previous lessons. In this lesson, there are two more goals for proportions:

1. to learn some terms used to talk about proportions;
2. to derive other true proportions when given a true one.

Four numbers that form a true proportion are called **proportional.** The numbers 5, 3, 10, and 6, in that order, are proportional because $\frac{5}{3} = \frac{10}{6}$. The numbers 1, 2, 3, and 4 are not proportional, for $\frac{1}{2} \neq \frac{3}{4}$.

Proportional numbers are always around when there is a size change. For instance, when $\triangle ABC$ is a size transformation image of $\triangle XYZ$, you can say "The sides of the triangles are proportional." This means the three ratios of corresponding sides are equal.

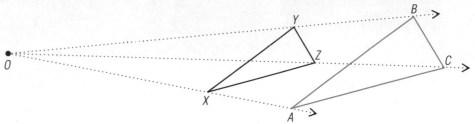

That is, $\frac{XY}{AB} = \frac{XZ}{AC} = \frac{YZ}{BC}$. You can equate any two of these ratios to form a true proportion.

$$\frac{XY}{AB} = \frac{XZ}{AC} \qquad \frac{XY}{AB} = \frac{YZ}{BC} \qquad \frac{XZ}{AC} = \frac{YZ}{BC}$$

Notice that in each proportion, *the numerators come from one figure and the denominators from the other*.

The four parts of a proportion have names and are numbered in order. The 1st and 4th terms are the **extremes** and the 2nd and 3rd terms are the **means.**

1st term $\longrightarrow$ $\dfrac{a}{b}$ $= \dfrac{c}{d}$ $\longleftarrow$ 3rd term
2nd term $\longrightarrow$ $\phantom{\dfrac{a}{b}}$ $\phantom{\dfrac{c}{d}}$ $\longleftarrow$ 4th term

$\dfrac{a}{b} = \dfrac{c}{d}$

extremes

means

In algebra, you learned the Means-Extremes Property: In any proportion, the product of the means equals the product of the extremes.

Theorem (Means-Extremes Property):

If $\dfrac{a}{b} = \dfrac{c}{d}$, then $ad = bc$.

Proof

Multiply both sides of $\dfrac{a}{b} = \dfrac{c}{d}$ by bd.

$$bd \cdot \frac{a}{b} = bd \cdot \frac{c}{d}$$

$$b \cdot d \cdot a \cdot \frac{1}{b} = b \cdot d \cdot c \cdot \frac{1}{d}$$

Since the product of a number and its reciprocal is 1, these products can be simplified.

$$ad = bc$$

Example $\triangle QRS$ is the image of $\triangle TUV$ under a size change with center O. If $QR = 10$, $RS = 15$, and $TU = 25$, find UV.

Solution The sides of the triangles are proportional.

Thus $\frac{TU}{QR} = \frac{UV}{RS}$. Substituting, $\frac{25}{10} = \frac{UV}{15}$.

Solve for UV, using the Means-Extremes Property.
$$25 \cdot 15 = 10 \cdot UV$$
$$UV = \frac{375}{10}$$
$$= 37.5$$

Check The magnitude of the size change is $\frac{10}{25} = .4$, which is the same as $\frac{15}{37.5}$.

When four numbers are proportional, many true proportions can be stated. For instance, if the proportional numbers are 30, 7.5, 20, and 5, the following is a true proportion.
$$\frac{30}{7.5} = \frac{20}{5}$$
You can *exchange the means* (or the *extremes*) to form two other true proportions.
$$\frac{30}{20} = \frac{7.5}{5} \qquad \frac{5}{7.5} = \frac{20}{30}$$
You can take *reciprocals* to form still other true proportions.
$$\frac{20}{30} = \frac{5}{7.5} \qquad \frac{7.5}{5} = \frac{30}{20}$$
These examples are generalized in the following theorem.

Theorem:

If $\frac{a}{b} = \frac{c}{d}$, then $\frac{a}{c} = \frac{b}{d}$ **(Means Exchange Property)**

and $\frac{b}{a} = \frac{d}{c}$ **(Reciprocals Property)**.

Proof

If $\frac{a}{b} = \frac{c}{d}$, then by the Means-Extremes Property, $ad = bc$.
Dividing both sides of $ad = bc$ by cd yields the Means Exchange Property.
Since $ad = bc$, by the Symmetric Property of Equality, $bc = ad$.
Dividing both sides of $bc = ad$ by ac yields the Reciprocals Property.

Questions

Covering the Reading

1. *Multiple choice.* Which is *not* a way of writing the ratio of 7 to 9?
   (a) 7 : 9   (b) 7/9
   (c) $\frac{7}{9}$ (d) 7.9

2. A ratio is a(n) __?__ of two numbers.

3. A proportion is a statement that two __?__ are __?__ .

4. Given $\frac{7}{x} = \frac{11}{y}$, name the
   a. extremes   b. means
   c. first term   d. 4th term
   e. 3rd term   f. 2nd term.

5. Suppose $\frac{r}{s} = \frac{t}{u}$. Make a conclusion using each justification.
   a. Means-Extremes Property
   b. Means Exchange Property
   c. Reciprocals Property

6. Form three true proportions using the numbers 2, 93, 62, and 3.

7. Why are the numbers 2, 4, 6, and 8 *not* proportional?

In 8 and 9, *ABCD* at the left is the image of *FGHE* under a size change with center *V*.

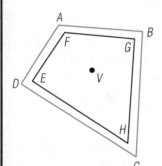

8. Fill in the space: $\frac{AB}{FG} = \frac{AD}{\Box}$.

9. If $FG = 10$, $AB = 12$, and $BC = 15$, what is *GH*?

10. a. What equation results if both sides of the equation $ad = bc$ are divided by bd?
    b. What equation results if both sides of the equation $ad = bc$ are divided by ac?

11. Suppose $\frac{u}{v} = \frac{w}{x} = \frac{y}{z}$. From this information, form three true proportions.

Applying the Mathematics

12. Solve for x: $\frac{a}{x} = \frac{b}{c}$.

In 13 and 14, $\triangle GJK$ at the left is a size change image of $\triangle GHI$.

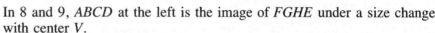

13. *True* or *false*?
    a. $\frac{GJ}{GH} = \frac{GK}{GI}$ b. $\frac{GH}{GJ} = \frac{GI}{GK}$ c. $\frac{JK}{HI} = \frac{GI}{GK}$

14. If $GH = 100$, $GJ = 130$, and $HI = 120$, then $JK =$ __?__ .

15. Weights and prices of fruit are often proportional. If 2.3 pounds of apples cost \$1.05, what should 4 pounds of apples cost?

16. a. If you bike 13 miles in $1\frac{1}{2}$ hours, at that rate how many miles would you bike in $2\frac{1}{2}$ hours?

b. If you drive m miles in h hours, at that rate how many miles can you drive in r hours?

17. If $wx = yz$, write three true proportions using w, x, y, and z.

Review

18. Suppose S is a size change of magnitude 1.5, and suppose $S(ABCDE) = UVWXY$. If m$\angle BDE = 47$ and $AE = 30$, find two other measures. *(Lessons 12-3, 12-2)*

19. Let S be a size transformation of magnitude $\frac{1}{2}$ centered at the origin. If $A = (16, -6)$ and $B = (10, 8)$, verify that the distance between $S(A)$ and $S(B)$ is half the distance between A and B. *(Lessons 12-3, 12-1)*

20. Trace the figure below. Draw the image of the figure under the size change with center H and magnitude $\frac{3}{5}$. *(Lesson 12-2)*

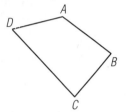

21. The distance between the lens and the negative is 2 inches. How far away from the lens must Ann place the photo paper if the developed picture is to be 5 times as large as the negative? *(Lesson 12-2)*

22. Finish this definition. Two figures α and β are congruent, written $\alpha \cong \beta$, if and only if __?__. *(Lesson 6-5)*

23. Given: $GHJKL$, FGL, and HIJ are regular polygons.
a. Prove: $\triangle FGL \cong \triangle HIJ$.
b. What is m$\angle GHI$? *(Lesson 7-6, 7-3)*

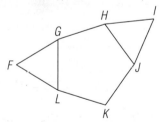

Exploration

24. Here are sets of numbers that could be lengths of sides of triangles.

$\{3, 4, 5\}$ $\{8, 6, 12\}$ $\{5, 4, 3\}$ $\{9, 12, 18\}$

$\{2, 4.5, 4\}$ $\{1.8, 2.4, 3\}$ $\{8, 16, 18\}$

a. Which sets could be paired so that one triangle is a size transformation image of the other?
b. What possible scale factors are there for each pair?
c. Could there be more than one scale factor for a pair? Why or why not?

Similar Figures

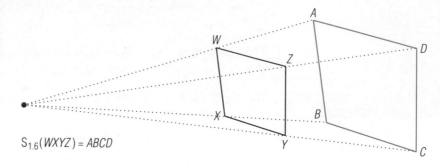

$S_{1.6}(WXYZ) = ABCD$

In geometry, the word "similar" has a very precise meaning. Quadrilaterals *ABCD* and *WXYZ* above are similar to each other. Triangles *ABC*, *PQR*, *SQT*, and *XYZ* below are also similar.

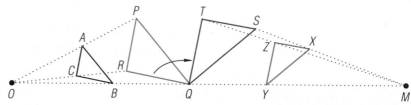

$\triangle PQR$ is a size change image of $\triangle ABC$.   (center *O*, magnitude 1.8)
$\triangle SQT$ is a rotation image of $\triangle PQR$.   (center *Q*, magnitude 90°)
$\triangle XYZ$ is a size change image of $\triangle SQT$.   (center *M*, magnitude 0.8)

The definition of *similarity transformation* encompasses all these possibilities.

Definition:

A transformation is a **similarity transformation** if and only if it is the composite of size changes and reflections.

A figure and its image under these transformations are called *similar*.

Definition:

Two figures F and G are **similar,** written **F ~ G,** if and only if there is a similarity transformation mapping one onto the other.

When the size changes have magnitude 1, then the similarity transformation is a composite solely of reflections. Figures and their images are then congruent. Thus two congruent figures are also similar.

Here is a hierarchy of transformations you have studied, with similarity transformations and size changes included.

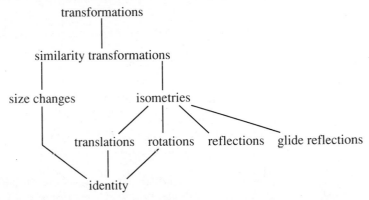

The basic properties of similar figures come from preservation properties of similarity transformations. Compare these lists.

Preserved under reflections
Angle measure
Betweenness
Collinearity
Distance

Preserved under size transformations
Angle measure
Betweenness
Collinearity

Those properties common to both columns are preserved by similarity transformations. Thus similarity transformations have the A-B-C preservation properties. However, distance is not preserved. Because size transformations are involved, similarity transformations multiply distance by a constant amount. Thus the ratios of image lengths to preimage lengths are equal.

Similar Figures Theorem:

If two figures are similar, then:
(a) corresponding angles are congruent;
(b) corresponding lengths are proportional.

The ratio of the length of an image to the length of a preimage is called the **ratio of similitude.** It is the product of the scale factors of all size transformations used in the composite similarity transformation. Unless otherwise specified, F ~ G with *ratio of similitude k* means that lengths in G divided by corresponding lengths in F equal *k*. As with congruence, corresponding vertices are put in order.

Example 1 In the figure, $r_\ell \circ S_{2.5}(ABCD) = WXYZ$, where the center of $S_{2.5}$ is point O.

a. If $m\angle B = 85$, what other angle has measure 85?
b. If $CD = 12$, what other length can be determined and what is this length?

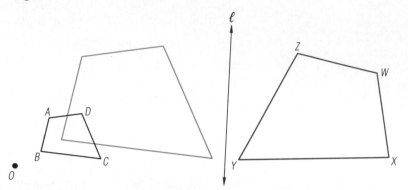

Solution The figures are similar, since $r_\ell \circ S_{2.5}$ is a composite of a reflection and a size change.

a. By the Similar Figures Theorem, corresponding angles are congruent:

$$\angle A \cong \angle W, \angle B \cong \angle X, \angle C \cong \angle Y, \text{ and } \angle D \cong \angle Z.$$

Since $m\angle B = 85$, so also $m\angle X = 85$.

b. By the Similar Figures Theorem, corresponding sides are proportional. These ratios equal 2.5, the ratio of similitude.

$$\frac{WX}{AB} = \frac{XY}{BC} = \frac{YZ}{CD} = \frac{ZW}{DA} = 2.5$$

Since $CD = 12$, the length of the corresponding side YZ can be determined.

$$\frac{YZ}{12} = 2.5$$
$$YZ = 12 \cdot 2.5 = 30$$

When examining similar figures, always look first for corresponding vertices. These give the pairs of congruent angles. Look next at corresponding sides.

Example 2 $\triangle ABC \sim \triangle TOP$ with lengths and angle measures as indicated.

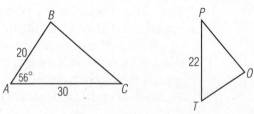

Find as many lengths and angle measures in $\triangle TOP$ as you can.

Solution Angle measures: $\angle T$ corresponds to $\angle A$. In similar figures, corresponding angles are congruent. So $m\angle T = m\angle A = 56$.

Lengths: Since corresponding sides are proportional, $\frac{PT}{CA} = \frac{TO}{AB} = \frac{OP}{BC}$.

Now substitute the three known lengths.

$$\frac{22}{30} = \frac{TO}{20} = \frac{OP}{BC}$$

Use the equality of the left and middle ratios.

$$\frac{22}{30} = \frac{TO}{20}$$

By the Means-Extremes Property, $30 \cdot TO = 440$, so

$$TO = \frac{440}{30} = 14\frac{2}{3} \approx 14.67.$$

Neither BC nor OP can be found using the Similar Figures Theorem.

In Example 2, enough information is given to determine all sides and angle measures in each triangle, but a theorem from trigonometry (the Law of Cosines) is needed. That theorem is not covered in this book.

Here is a problem you have learned to solve in previous years. Now you can analyze it using the language of similarity.

Example 3 A dollhouse is $\frac{1}{12}$ actual size. If a table in the house is an oval $6\frac{1}{2}''$ long and $4\frac{3}{8}''$ wide, how long and wide is the actual table it models?

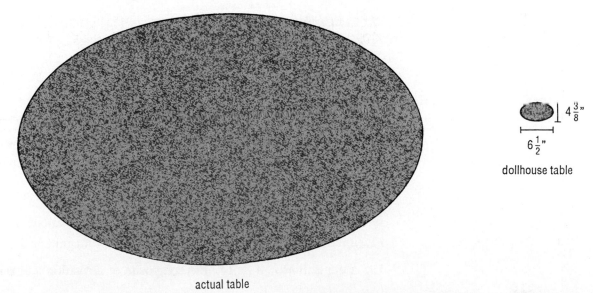

$4\frac{3}{8}''$

$6\frac{1}{2}''$

dollhouse table

actual table

Solution The two tables D (for doll) and A (for actual) are similar. So
A ~ D and the ratio of similitude is $\frac{1}{12}$.

Corresponding lengths are proportional. So

$$\frac{\text{dollhouse width}}{\text{actual width}} = \frac{\text{dollhouse length}}{\text{actual length}} = \frac{1}{12}.$$

Substitute for the doll house table dimensions and let L and W be the actual length and width.

$$\frac{4\frac{3}{8}}{W} = \frac{6\frac{1}{2}}{L} = \frac{1}{12}$$

Now solve. Since $\dfrac{4\frac{3}{8}}{W} = \dfrac{1}{12}$, $W = 12 \cdot 4\frac{3}{8}'' = 52\frac{1}{2}''$.

Since $\dfrac{6\frac{1}{2}}{L} = \dfrac{1}{12}$, $L = 12 \cdot 6\frac{1}{2}'' = 78''$.

Check $\frac{78}{6.5} = 12$ and $\frac{52.5}{4.375} = 12$, so the actual measurements are 12 times the measurements of the model.

Questions

Covering the Reading

In 1–3, use the sketch at the right.
Figure III is the image of
Figure I under $S \circ r_\ell$, where S
is the size transformation with
center C, magnitude 2.3.

I   II   III

1. $S \cdot r_\ell$ is what kind of transformation?

2. Figures I and III are __?__ .

3. Figures I and II are both __?__ and __?__ .

4. The symbol "~" is read __?__ .

5. Define: similar figures.

In 6–10, does every similarity transformation preserve the given property?

6. betweenness   7. angle measure   8. orientation

9. distance   10. "tilt"

In 11–14, is the transformation a similarity transformation?

11. a reflection   12. a size change with magnitude $\frac{1}{3}$

13. a translation   14. the composite of a rotation and a size change

590

In 15–17, *ABCDE* ~ *FGHIJ*. The ratio of similitude is $\frac{4}{7}$.

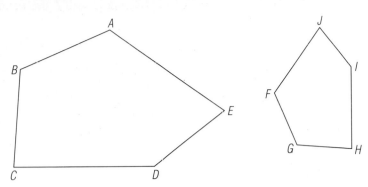

15. *True* or *false*? $m\angle I = \frac{4}{7} \cdot m\angle D$

16. Suppose *FJ* = 10.
   a. What other segment length can be determined?
   b. What is that length?

17. If *DE* = *x*, then *IJ* = __?__ .

Applying the Mathematics

18. A photograph measures 40 mm by 30 mm. The longer side of an enlargement measures 150 mm. What is the length of the shorter side of the enlargement?

19. a. Draw the image of the logo at the left under a size change with magnitude 2. Then draw an enlargement of the image with a scale factor of 1.5.
   b. How does the final image compare to the original logo?

20. If you were to enlarge the logo in Question 19 by a factor of 4, and then transform the image with a scale factor of $\frac{1}{5}$, using a different center than the first transformation, what would be the result?

21. Presto Printing makes cards which, when opened, have an outside boundary similar to that when they are folded. Find the width *w* of the card for the dimensions given.

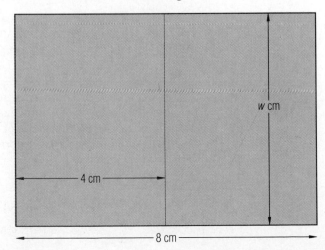

In the figure below, the two right cones are similar. $QS = 10$, $MZ = 5$. T and L are centers of the bases.

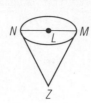
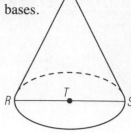

22. **a.** What is the ratio of similitude?
    b. If $ST = 6$, find LM.

23. $\triangle ABC \sim \triangle DEF$. If $BC = 12$, $DE = 8$, and $EF = 16$, find AB.

24. Let S be a similarity transformation and ℓ and m be lines. Tell whether the statement is true or false and justify your answer.
    a. $S(\ell) \parallel \ell$
    b. If $\ell \parallel m$, then $S(\ell) \parallel S(m)$.

Review

25. If 3 cans of tuna cost $2.00, at this rate how much would 5 cans cost? *(Lesson 12-4)*

26. Given $\dfrac{a}{b} = \dfrac{c}{d}$. *True* or *false*?

    a. $\dfrac{a}{c} = \dfrac{b}{d}$ **b.** $\dfrac{a + b}{b} = \dfrac{c + d}{d}$

    c. $\dfrac{a}{d} = \dfrac{c}{b}$ *(Lesson 12-4)*

27. In the figure at the left, $\triangle ABC$ is the image of $\triangle DBE$ under a size change.
    a. *True* or *false*? $\overleftrightarrow{DE} \parallel \overleftrightarrow{AC}$ **b.** *True* or *false*? $\dfrac{BD}{AB} = \dfrac{ED}{AC}$
    c. Solve for x. *(Lessons 12-4, 12-3, 12-2)*

28. A spherical rubber ball has an outside diameter of 10 cm. The ball is hollow and the rubber is 1 cm thick. How much rubber is used in making the ball? *(Lesson 10-7)*

29. In triangles XYZ and APD, $\angle X \cong \angle A$, $\angle Y \cong \angle P$, and $\angle Z \cong \angle D$.
    a. Is $\triangle XYZ$ necessarily congruent to $\triangle APD$?
    b. Justify your answer to **a**. *(Lesson 7-2)*

Exploration

30. Scale models are objects that are similar to larger objects. Find a scale model. For the scale model you find:
    a. What is the ratio of similitude?
    b. A length of $1''$ on the model corresponds to what length on the larger object it models?

31. In Example 2, BC can be found using a theorem called the Law of Cosines. Look in some other book to find out what this "law" is.

The Fundamental Theorem of Similarity

In the last lesson, a similarity transformation was defined as a composite of size changes, reflections, rotations, or translations. Similar figures may be 2-dimensional or 3-dimensional because a similarity transformation can be done in three dimensions just as easily as in two. Any point can be the center of the size change and any real number the scale factor. The characteristics of corresponding parts that hold for similar plane figures hold for similar space figures—corresponding distances are multiplied by the scale factor and corresponding angles are congruent.

In similar figures, perimeters, areas, and volumes satisfy a very important relationship, which is the subject of this lesson.

Example 1 Two models of the same schooner (a boat with front and rear masts) are made. Each is similar to the original, so they are similar to each other. The bigger model is 120 cm long, the smaller 30 cm long.

a. How do their heights compare?
b. How do the areas of their sails compare?
c. How do the volumes of their hulls (the bodies of the boats) compare?

30 cm

120 cm

Solution

a. Corresponding lengths in similar figures are proportional. Thus

$$\frac{\text{height of large schooner}}{\text{height of small schooner}} = \frac{\text{length of large schooner}}{\text{length of small schooner}} = \frac{120 \text{ cm}}{30 \text{ cm}} = 4.$$

So the height of the large schooner is 4 times that of the small schooner.

b. Let the dimensions of a sail in the small schooner be b and h. The sail's area is thus $\frac{1}{2}bh$. The dimensions of the corresponding sail in the larger schooner must be $4b$ and $4h$, because the ratio of lengths is 4. So the corresponding sail's area is $\frac{1}{2} \cdot 4b \cdot 4h = 8bh$. Thus the areas of sails in the large schooner are 16 times those of the small schooner.

c. Think of the smaller hull as being made up of small cubes with sides s. The larger hull is made up of the same number of cubes, each of side $4s$.

$$\frac{\text{volume of part of larger hull}}{\text{volume of part of smaller hull}} = \frac{(4s)^3}{s^3} = \frac{64s^3}{s^3} = 64$$

The volume of the larger hull is 64 times the volume of the smaller.

The ratio of similitude in Example 1 is 4. Lengths in the smaller model are multiplied by 4 to yield corresponding lengths in the larger model. Areas are multiplied by 16, which is 4^2, and volumes are multiplied by 64, which is 4^3. All this verifies the *Fundamental Theorem of Similarity,* which applies to all plane or solid figures.

Fundamental Theorem of Similarity:

If $G \sim G'$ and k is the ratio of similitude, then

(a) $\text{Perimeter}(G') = k \cdot \text{Perimeter}(G)$ or $\dfrac{\text{Perimeter}(G')}{\text{Perimeter}(G)} = k$;

(b) $\text{Area}(G') = k^2 \cdot \text{Area}(G)$ or $\dfrac{\text{Area}(G')}{\text{Area}(G)} = k^2$; and

(c) $\text{Volume}(G') = k^3 \cdot \text{Volume}(G)$ or $\dfrac{\text{Volume}(G')}{\text{Volume}(G)} = k^3$.

Proof

(a) Perimeter is just the sum of the lengths. Suppose lengths $a, b, c, d, e, \ldots$ make up the perimeter of G. Then lengths $ka, kb, kc, kd, ke, \ldots$ make up the perimeter of G'.

$$\begin{aligned}
\text{Perimeter}(G') &= ka + kb + kc + kd + ke + \ldots \\
&= k(a + b + c + d + e + \ldots) \\
&= k \cdot \text{Perimeter}(G)
\end{aligned}$$

(b) Let A = the area of G. Then you could think of the area of G as the sum of areas of A unit squares. Then the area of G' is the sum of areas of A squares k units on a side. Since each square in G' has area k^2,

$$\text{Area of G'} = A \cdot k^2 = k^2 \cdot \text{Area of G.}$$

(c) The argument is identical to that in part (c) of Example 1, except that you should use k for the ratio of similitude and make it apply to more than schooners.

Example 2 $\triangle ABC \sim \triangle DEF$. Give the ratios of the perimeters and areas of those triangles.

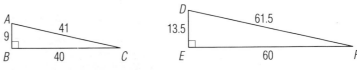

Solution Use the Fundamental Theorem of Similarity. The ratio of similitude is $\frac{60}{40} = 1.5$. So the ratio of perimeters is 1.5 and the ratio of areas is 1.5^2, which is 2.25.

Check The perimeters and areas can be calculated directly.

$\triangle ABC$ $\triangle DEF$

Perimeter = 9 + 40 + 41   Perimeter = 13.5 + 60 + 61.5
          = 90 units   = 135 units
Area   = $\frac{1}{2} \cdot 40 \cdot 9$ Area   = $\frac{1}{2} \cdot 13.5 \cdot 60$
          = 180 square units   = 405 square units

Thus ratio of perimeters = $\frac{135}{90}$ = 1.5

ratio of areas = $\frac{405}{180}$ = 2.25.

The Fundamental Theorem of Similarity can be verified by looking at area formulas. Here are some area formulas: $A = \pi r^2$ (circles), $A = \ell w$ (rectangles), $A = \frac{1}{2} h(b_1 + b_2)$ (trapezoids), L.A. = ph (cylinders or prisms). Notice that each area formula involves the product of two lengths. (That's why the result is measured in *square* units.) So if every length is multiplied by k, the area will be multiplied by k^2.

Volume formulas also verify the Fundamental Theorem of Similarity. Consider some volume formulas: $V = \ell wh$ (boxes), $V = \frac{4}{3}\pi r^3$ (spheres), $V = \frac{1}{3}Bh$ (pyramids or cones). Each formula involves the product of three lengths. (For pyramids or cones, it looks as if there are only two lengths multiplied, but B is an area, so B itself is the product of two lengths.) When each length is multiplied by k, the volume will be multiplied by k^3.

To summarize the basic properties of measures in similar figures: If two figures are similar with ratio of similitude k, then

corresponding angle measures are equal;
corresponding lengths and perimeters are in the ratio k;
corresponding areas and surface areas are in the ratio k^2;
corresponding volumes are in the ratio k^3.

Some people remember the Fundamental Theorem of Similarity by remembering the units in which objects are measured. Since volume is measured in cubic units, the ratio of volumes of similar figures is k^3. Since area and surface area are measured in square units, the ratio of areas or surface areas of similar figures is k^2. Since lengths and perimeter are measured in linear units, the ratio of linear measures in similar figures is k^1, which is k.

Questions

Covering the Reading

1. Here are two similar boxes.

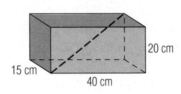 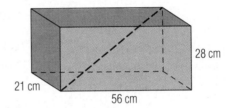

   a. What is the ratio of the lengths of their longest diagonals?
   b. What is the ratio of the areas of their largest faces?
   c. What is the ratio of their volumes?

2. Area is a product of __?__ lengths.

3. Volume is a product of __?__ lengths.

4. The ratio of similitude of two figures is $\frac{5}{3}$. Find the ratio of their
   a. perimeters   b. areas
   c. volumes   d. corresponding sides.

5. $R \sim R'$, $k = 4$, and Volume(R) = 34 cubic units. Find Volume(R').

6. $G \sim G'$, $k = \frac{2}{3}$, and Area(G) = 72 square meters. Find Area(G').

7. Two squares have sides 5 in. and 13 in. Find the ratio of their perimeters.

8. a. Find the area of $\triangle ABC$ at the left.
   b. If $\triangle ABC \sim \triangle EFG$ with ratio of similitude 5, what is the area of $\triangle EFG$?

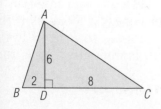

9. **a.** Find the perimeter of △*ABC* in Question 8.
   b. Find the perimeter of △*EFG* in Question 8.

10. **a.** Find the volume and surface area of right cylinder Q below.
    b. Let cylinder R be the image of cylinder Q under a size change with magnitude 3. Cylinder R will have __?__ times the volume of cylinder Q and __?__ times the surface area.
    c. Find the volume and surface area of cylinder R.

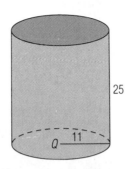

11. Corresponding sides of two similar pyramids are 8 and 12 inches.
    a. Find the volume of the larger solid, if the smaller has volume 100 cubic inches.
    b. Find the volume of the smaller solid, if the larger has volume 100 cubic inches.

12. Two similar nonregular 15-gons have perimeters of 20 ft and 28 ft, respectively. What is the ratio of the length of a side of the smaller to the length of the corresponding side of the larger?

13. On two similar solid brass statues of Martin Luther King, Jr., the length of the left ear on one is 3 cm and on the other is 5 cm.
    a. If the base area of the larger statue is 50 cm², find the base area of the smaller statue.
    b. The volume of brass used to make the smaller was 216 cm³. What volume of brass was used to make the larger?

14. The volumes of two spheres are 288π and 7776π cubic mm.
    a. What is a ratio of similitude for these spheres?
    b. What is a ratio of their surface areas?

15. *Multiple choice.* The bases of two quadrangular prisms are similar with ratio of similitude 1.5, but the prisms have the same height. What is the ratio of the volumes?

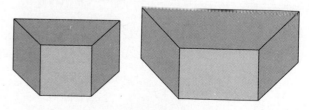

(a) 1.5   (b) 2.25
(c) 3   (d) 4.5
(e) cannot be determined from the given information

Martin Luther King, Jr.

16. Below, Figure Q ~ Figure R. Name the ratio of similitude. *(Lesson 12-5)*

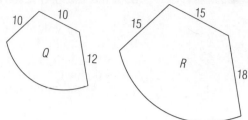

17. $\triangle ABC \sim \triangle DEF$ with ratio of similitude 2.5. If $AB = 3$, $BC = 5$, and m$\angle B = 135$, find as many lengths and angle measures in $\triangle DEF$ as you can. *(Lesson 12-5)*

18. A comic strip measures 6″ by 2″. The smaller sides of a reduction measure $\frac{1}{2}$″. What are the lengths of the larger sides of the reduction? *(Lesson 12-5)*

19. Given $\frac{x}{10} = \frac{11}{y}$. Find three other true proportions involving these numbers. *(Lesson 12-4)*

20. A goal post and its shadow are shown. The sides of the goal post cast shadows 20 meters long. The crossbar is 3 m high; the post part beneath the crossbar casts a shadow 8 m long. What is the height of the goalpost? *(Lesson 12-4)*

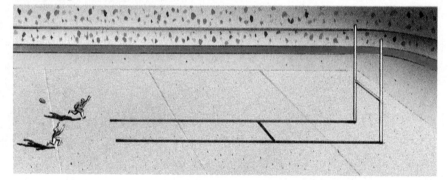

21. A can of tennis balls usually holds three, as pictured at the left. What percent of the volume of the can is outside the balls? (Hint: Let r be the radius of the can and proceed from there.) *(Lesson 10-7)*

22. In the Exploration to Lesson 12-5, you were asked to find a scale model of an actual object. Weigh the scale model you found. If the actual object were made from the same materials, what would be its weight?

12-7

Can There Be Giants?

Giants are common characters in children's stories; an example is the giant from *Jack and the Beanstalk*. Saturday morning cartoons often have giant creatures with human shape. But according to the *Guinness Book of World Records,* the tallest man on record was Robert Wadlow from Alton, Illinois. On June 27, 1940, at age 22, he was measured at 8 feet, 11.1 inches. Wadlow was about 1.5 times the height of a typical male. Can humans be much taller? The Fundamental Theorem of Similarity provides the answer.

Let's look at what the theorem reveals, using an example from a famous novel. In *Gulliver's Travels,* Jonathan Swift writes about Gulliver visiting the land of Brobdingnag, where the Brobding-nagians are similar to us but 12 times as tall. Their volume, and thus their weight, would be 12^3 times ours. Since $12^3 = 1728$, they would weigh about 1728 times what we weigh. If you weigh 140 pounds, a similar Brobdingnagian would weigh 241,920 pounds! They would support this weight on feet covering a region whose area is only 12^2 or 144 times what we stand on. So each bone of a Brobdingnagian would have to carry 12 times as much weight as ours.

Even champion weightlifters seldom lift more than twice their body weight—and when they do, it is only for a few seconds. You can imagine what lifting 12 times your weight would do. It would quickly break your bones!

You might think that a giant's body would find some way of dealing with the extra weight. But it can't. Wadlow had to wear a brace to support his weight. He had an accident involving the brace and cellulitis set in. Eighteen days after his height was measured in June, 1940, he died in Manistee, Michigan.

Animals in nature have developed within the constraints imposed by the Fundamental Theorem of Similarity. Elephants have legs with large horizontal cross-sectional surface areas to support their great weight. Thoroughbred race horses have skinny legs which enable them to run fast, but the legs are small for their bodies and break easily. When a thoroughbred falls, its legs often break. Draught horses do not have this problem, but they are slow. A mosquito can walk on the surface of water without sinking. It is so light that it will not break the surface tension of the water. It also has thin legs which are fine to support its light body. But that body has a relatively large surface area. Should a raindrop force the body into the water, the surface tension acts like glue on the body's surface and the thin legs cannot pull the mosquito from the water.

The amount of food needed by an animal is proportional to its volume. The Brobdingnagians would consume 1728 times the food needed by Gulliver. A person like Gulliver needs about 19 calories per day per pound of body weight (perhaps 3000 calories) to maintain body weight. The Brobdingnagians would require 1728 times 3000 calories daily to maintain their body weights. That's a lot of food.

Gulliver also visited the land of Lilliput, where people were $\frac{1}{12}$ his height. For Gulliver as for us, a new coat would require about two square yards of material. Clothing is proportional to surface area and is multiplied by k^2, the square of the ratio of similitude. So the Brobdingnagians would require 12^2 or 144 times as much material. The Lilliputians, being $\frac{1}{12}$ Gulliver's height, would require only $(\frac{1}{12})^2$ or $\frac{1}{144}$ times the two square yards needed by Gulliver. Thus similarity answers questions about clothing and food needs as well as the properties of giants.

■ ■ ■ ■ ■ ■ ■ ■ ■ ■

Example 1 In 1987, Domino's® Pizza sold 12″-diameter pizzas with cheese and one topping for $6.05 (plus tax). Suppose they base their prices on the amount of ingredients and the pizzas have the same thickness. Then what should they charge for a 14″-diameter pizza?

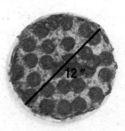 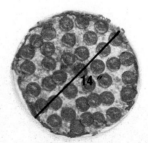

Solution The pizza tops are similar with $k = \frac{14}{12} = \frac{7}{6}$. An immediate response is to charge $\frac{7}{6} \cdot \$6.05$. This is not correct because the crust and toppings are proportional to the *area*, not the linear dimensions. Thus the price, based only on amount of ingredients, would be $\$6.05 \cdot (\frac{7}{6})^2 = \$6.05 \cdot \frac{49}{36} \approx \$8.23$.

Example 2 A solid clay figurine weighs 5 kilograms. A similar one which is twice as tall stands next to it. Could a 4-year old child pick up the taller figurine?

Solution Weight is dependent upon volume. Thus the multiplying factor for weight is the cube of the ratio of similitude, in this case 2^3. The taller figurine weighs $2^3 \cdot 5 = 40$ kg (about 90 pounds). Most children of 4 would not be able to pick up the figurine, and many adults would be surprised at the weight of the figurine.

The Fundamental Theorem of Similarity was known to Euclid, but the structural applications to giants were not recognized until over 1800 years later by the Italian scientist Galileo. He considered this discovery as important as his most famous discovery that when heavier-than-air objects of different weights are dropped from the same height, they fall to the ground at the same time.

Questions

Covering the Reading

In 1–3, according to *Gulliver's Travels*,

1. Brobdingnagians are __?__ times the height of Gulliver, and weigh __?__ times as much.

2. Lilliputians are __?__ times the height of Gulliver and weigh __?__ times as much.

3. Brobdingnagians are __?__ times the height of Lilliputians and weigh __?__ times as much.

4. Who was Robert Wadlow?

In 5–8, consider an imaginary giantess 27 feet tall, which is about 5 times the height of an average woman. If the giantess and woman had similar shapes, how would the quantities compare?

5. weight

6. nose lengths

7. area of bottom of foot

8. wrist circumference

9. *True* or *false?* Champion weightlifters often lift weights five times their own weight.

10. *True* or *false?* Prices of pizza are proportional to their diameters.

11. Why does an elephant need thicker legs for its height than a mosquito?

12. A scale model is $\frac{1}{15}$ actual size. If it is made from the same materials as the original object, then its weight will be __?__ the weight of the object. The amount of paint to cover the exterior will be __?__ times the paint used to cover the original.

13. Two similar solid clay figurines are 40 cm and 50 cm tall. If the shorter one weighs 8 kg, how much will the taller one weigh?

14. A pizza store manager calculates that the ingredients in a 16″ pizza cost the store $1.50. At this rate, what do the ingredients cost in a 12″ pizza with the same thickness?

15. Suppose two boxes have congruent bases, but one box is twice the height of the other.
 a. Are the boxes similar?
 b. How do their volumes compare?
 c. How do their surface areas compare?

16. If a 6-foot-tall basketball player weighs 200 lb, what would you expect a similarly shaped, 7-foot-tall player to weigh?

17. The surface area of the earth is about 13 times that of the moon.
 a. What is the ratio of their radii, considering them both to be spheres?
 b. What is the ratio of their volumes?

18. A hexagon has area 70 units². What is the area of its image under a size change of magnitude $\frac{2}{5}$? *(Lesson 12-6)*

19. Below, $\triangle PQR \sim \triangle MST$. Find as many missing lengths and angle measures as possible. *(Lessons 12-5, 12-4)*

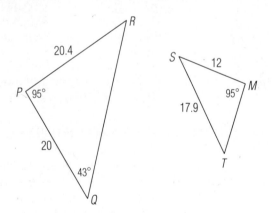

20. Define: similar figures. *(Lesson 12-5)*

21. Draw the image of $\triangle ABC$ below under a size change with center P, magnitude 4. *(Lesson 12-3)*

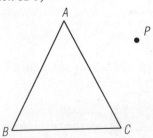

22. Use the figure below.

Given: K is the midpoint of $\overline{FJ}$.

The segments $\overline{KI}$ and $\overline{KG}$ are parallel to $\overline{FH}$ and $\overline{HJ}$, respectively.

Prove: $\triangle FGK \cong \triangle KIJ$. *(Lesson 7-3)*

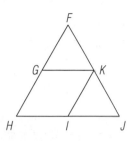

Exploration

23. Below are the men's world weightlifting records as of October 1, 1988, in the clean and jerk.

a. Calculate the ratios of weight lifted to weightlifter's maximum weight.

b. What trends do you see?

c. Give an explanation for any trends you find.

Naim Suleymanoglu

Weight Class	Men	Country	C & J
52.0 kg	He Zhuoqiang	China	153.0 kg
56.0 kg	Neno Terziiski	Bulgaria	171.0 kg
60.0 kg	Naim Suleymanoglu	Turkey	190.0 kg
67.0 kg	Mikhail Petrov	Bulgaria	200.5 kg
75.0 kg	Alexander Varbanov	Bulgaria	215.5 kg
82.5 kg	Asen Zlatev	Bulgaria	225.0 kg
90.0 kg	Anatoli Khrapaty	USSR	235.0 kg
100.0 kg	Pavel Kuznietsov	USSR	241.5 kg
110.0 kg	Yuri Zacharevich	USSR	250.5 kg
Over 110.0 kg	Leonid Taranenko	USSR	265.5 kg

24. Find the costs of two different size pizzas (with the same ingredients) at a local pizza parlor.

a. What is the ratio of the diameters of the pizzas?

b. What is the ratio of the costs of the pizzas?

c. Are costs based on area?

d. What are the costs in making a pizza?

12-8

The SSS Similarity Theorem

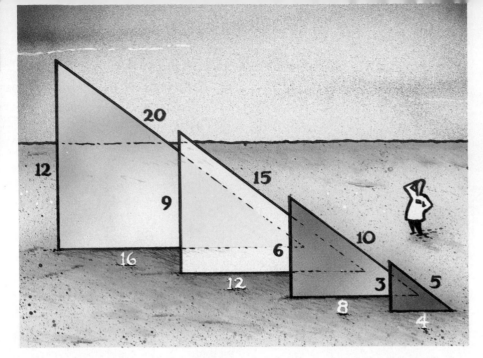

Recall the SSS Congruence Theorem: If three sides of one triangle are congruent to three sides of a second triangle, then the triangles are congruent.

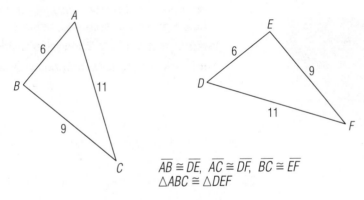

$\overline{AB} \cong \overline{DE},\ \overline{AC} \cong \overline{DF},\ \overline{BC} \cong \overline{EF}$
$\triangle ABC \cong \triangle DEF$

There is also an SSS Similarity Theorem. For it, the sides of the triangles need to be proportional. That is, their ratios must be equal. Below, each ratio of corresponding sides equals 2: $\frac{12}{6} = \frac{22}{11} = \frac{18}{9}$. The SSS Similarity Theorem asserts that $\triangle ABC \sim \triangle GHI$.

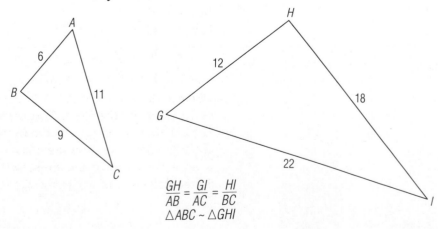

$\dfrac{GH}{AB} = \dfrac{GI}{AC} = \dfrac{HI}{BC}$
$\triangle ABC \sim \triangle GHI$

SSS Similarity Theorem:

If the three sides of one triangle are proportional to the three sides of a second triangle, then the triangles are similar.

Proof

Draw As usual, the first task is to draw a figure and state the given and what is to be proved in terms of that figure.

Given: $\dfrac{XY}{AB} = \dfrac{YZ}{BC} = \dfrac{XZ}{AC}$.

Prove: $\triangle ABC \sim \triangle XYZ$.

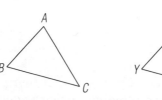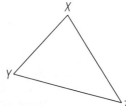

Analyze The idea is to prove that there is a size transformation image of $\triangle ABC$ which is *congruent* to $\triangle XYZ$. Then the definition of similar figures (sufficient condition) shows the triangles are similar.

Write Let $k = \dfrac{XY}{AB}$. Then by transitivity, $k = \dfrac{YZ}{BC}$ and $k = \dfrac{XZ}{AC}$. Apply *any* size transformation with magnitude k to $\triangle ABC$.

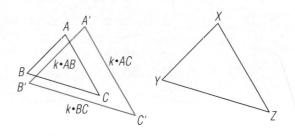

In the image $\triangle A'B'C'$, $A'B' = k \cdot AB$, $B'C' = k \cdot BC$, and $A'C' = k \cdot AC$.

But $k \cdot AB = \dfrac{XY}{AB} \cdot AB = XY$

$\quad k \cdot BC = \dfrac{YZ}{BC} \cdot BC = YZ$

$\quad k \cdot AC = \dfrac{XZ}{AC} \cdot AC = XZ$.

Thus the three sides of $\triangle A'B'C'$ have the same lengths as the sides of $\triangle XYZ$. So by the SSS Congruence Theorem, $\triangle A'B'C' \cong \triangle XYZ$. The definition of congruence tells us there is an isometry mapping $\triangle A'B'C'$ onto $\triangle XYZ$. So there is a composite of a size change (the one we started with) and an isometry mapping $\triangle ABC$ onto $\triangle XYZ$. By the definition of similarity, $\triangle ABC \sim \triangle XYZ$.

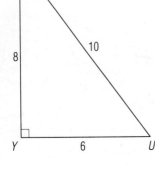

Example 1 *True* or *false*?   A triangle with sides 3, 4, and 5 is similar to a triangle with sides 8, 6, and 10.

Solution Put the sides in order and take the ratios:

$$\frac{6}{3} \qquad \frac{8}{4} \qquad \frac{10}{5}$$

Since all the ratios are equal, the triangles are similar.
The answer is *true*.

Check $3^2 + 4^2 = 5^2$ and $6^2 + 8^2 = 10^2$, so both triangles are right triangles. Since $\angle I$ and $\angle Y$ are both right angles, $\angle I \cong \angle Y$.

In Example 1, the ratio of similitude is either 2 or $\frac{1}{2}$, dependent on which triangle is first. The corresponding sides tell you which vertices correspond. Write the similarity with vertices in corresponding order. Here you could write $\triangle AEI \sim \triangle UOY$. This tells which corresponding angles are congruent. For instance, $\angle E \cong \angle O$. Similar right triangles form the basis for the trigonometry concepts introduced in Chapter 14.

Example 2 Given the two triangles below with sides and approximate angle measures as indicated.

a. Ratios of which sides are equal?
b. Are the triangles similar?
c. Find the measure of each angle of $\triangle XYZ$.
d. $\triangle BAC \sim$ __?__

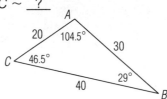

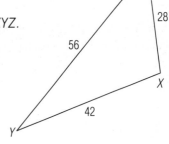

Solution

a. The shortest side in $\triangle ABC$ would have to correspond to the shortest in $\triangle XYZ$. In general, the sides correspond in order of their lengths. Write the extended proportion.

$$\frac{28}{20} = \frac{42}{30} = \frac{56}{40}. \text{ That is, } \frac{XZ}{AC} = \frac{XY}{AB} = \frac{YZ}{BC}.$$

b. Since all three ratios of sides are equal, the triangles are similar due to the SSS Similarity Theorem.

c. The congruent angles are opposite the corresponding sides.
$\overline{BC}$ corresponds to $\overline{YZ}$, so $\angle A \cong \angle X$, so $m\angle X \approx 104.5$.
$\overline{AC}$ corresponds to $\overline{XZ}$, so $\angle B \cong \angle Y$, so $m\angle Y \approx 29$.
$\overline{AB}$ corresponds to $\overline{XY}$, so $\angle C \cong \angle Z$, so $m\angle Z \approx 46.5$.

d. Using the correspondence of angles, $\triangle BAC \sim \triangle YXZ$.

Covering the Reading

In 1 and 2, the triangles are similar.

    a. Determine the corresponding vertices.

    b. Find a ratio of similitude.

    c. Determine as many missing angle measures or side lengths as possible.

1.

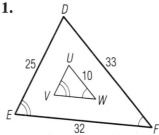

2.

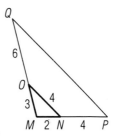

3. If $\triangle RST \sim \triangle UVW$, name two ratios equal to $\frac{RS}{UV}$.

4. One way to prove $\triangle ABC \sim \triangle DEF$ is to find a size change image of $\triangle ABC$ that is __?__ to $\triangle DEF$.

5. State the SSS Similarity Theorem.

6. *True* or *false*?   The right triangle with sides 5, 12, and 13 is similar to the right triangle with sides 60, 65, and 25.

7. *True* or *false*?   The right triangle with sides 20, 21, and 29 is similar to the right triangle with sides 41, 9, and 40.

Applying the Mathematics

8. a. Are these two triangles similar?

    b. Why or why not?

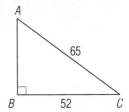

9. The two triangles below are similar by the SSS Similarity Theorem.

    a. Write the similarity with the vertices in proper order.

    b. Describe a similarity transformation which maps the smaller triangle onto the larger.

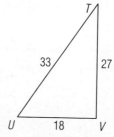

10. Given: X is the midpoint of $\overline{WY}$.
   V is the midpoint of $\overline{WZ}$.
   Prove: $\triangle WXV \sim \triangle WYZ$.

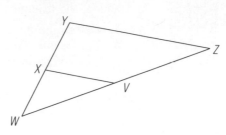

11. An altitude of $\triangle ABC$ is k times the altitude of $\triangle PQR$ and the base of $\triangle ABC$ is k times the base of $\triangle PQR$. Explain why the two triangles might not be similar.

Review

12. If there were a person $\frac{1}{6}$ as tall as you are and with your physique, the person would weigh __?__ times as much as you. This weight would be supported by __?__ times the area that supports you. *(Lesson 12-7)*

13. A certain box 10″ high holds 20 lb of paper when filled. How many pounds of paper would be in a similar box 13″ high filled with the same kind of paper? *(Lessons 12-7, 12-6)*

14. A right triangle has area 120 cm^2. A similar right triangle has area 30 cm^2. The length of the hypotenuse of the larger triangle is __?__ times the length of the hypotenuse of the smaller triangle. *(Lesson 12-6)*

15. The radius of a sphere is tripled to create a new sphere. If the original sphere had volume 36π units^3, what is the volume of the new sphere? *(Lesson 12-6)*

16. $\triangle DEF$ is the image of $\triangle ABC$ under a size change of magnitude 5. Then $\triangle ABC$ is the image of $\triangle DEF$ under a size change of magnitude __?__ . *(Lesson 12-2)*

17. The given formula finds what quantity in what figure?
   (Lessons 10-6, 10-5)
   a. $V = \frac{1}{3}Bh$ **b.** S.A. $= 2\ell w + 2wh + 2\ell h$
   c. $p = a + b + c$ **d.** $V = \pi r^2 h$
   e. L.A. $= \pi r \ell$

18. *Multiple choice.* $\frac{2x + 10}{2} =$
   (a) $\frac{x + 5}{2}$ (b) $x + 5$
   (c) $x + 10$ (d) $2x + 5$ *(Previous course)*

Exploration

19. Is there an SSSS Similarity Theorem for quadrilaterals? If so, how do you know? If not, draw a counterexample.

12-9

The AA and SAS Similarity Theorems

For each triangle congruence theorem there is a counterpart triangle similarity theorem. In the triangle similarity theorems, "A" still denotes a pair of congruent angles but "S" denotes a *ratio* of corresponding sides.

Three triangle similarity theorems are used more often than the others.

Triangle Congruence Theorem	Triangle Similarity Theorem
SSS ———————————————→	SSS
SAS ———————————————→	SAS
ASA ——————\	
AAS ——————→	AA

The strategy used in proving all these triangle similarity theorems is the same. A size change is applied to one triangle so that its image is congruent to the other triangle. The key decision is the choice of the magnitude k of the size change. Once that is done, the only other thing to do is to identify the triangle congruence theorem to use. That turns out always to be the corresponding triangle congruence theorem.

AA Similarity Theorem:

If two triangles have two angles of one congruent to two angles of the other, then the triangles are similar.

Proof

Given: Triangles ABC and XYZ with $\angle A \cong \angle X$ and $\angle B \cong \angle Y$.
Prove: $\triangle ABC \sim \triangle XYZ$.

The congruent angles signal the corresponding vertices. This indicates the corresponding sides and enables a picture to be drawn.

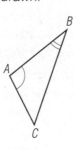
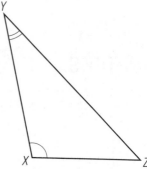

Since $\overline{XY}$ and $\overline{AB}$ are corresponding sides, let $k = \frac{XY}{AB}$ be the magnitude of a size transformation applied to $\triangle ABC$.

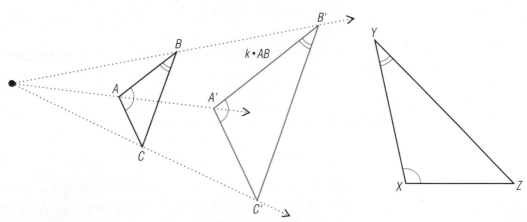

Then
$$A'B' = k \cdot AB$$
$$= \frac{XY}{AB} \cdot AB$$
$$= XY.$$

Also, since size transformations preserve angle measure, $\angle A \cong \angle A'$ and $\angle B \cong \angle B'$. With transitivity, $\angle A' \cong \angle X$ and $\angle B' \cong \angle Y$. So $\triangle A'B'C' \cong \triangle XYZ$ by the ASA Congruence Theorem. Thus $\triangle ABC$ can be mapped onto $\triangle XYZ$ by a composite of size changes and reflections.
So $\triangle ABC \sim \triangle XYZ$.

Example 1   Given the triangles at the right
with lengths and congruent
angles as indicated.
a. Prove that the
triangles are similar.
b. Find the ratio
of similitude.
c. Find AC.

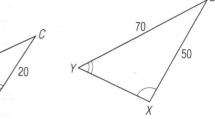

Solution

a. $\angle A \cong \angle X$ and $\angle B \cong \angle Y$, so $\triangle ABC \sim \triangle XYZ$ by the
AA Similarity Theorem.

b. The ratio of similitude is any of the equal ratios $\frac{XY}{AB} = \frac{YZ}{BC} = \frac{XZ}{AC}$. Use
sides $\overline{BC}$ and $\overline{YZ}$ whose lengths are known: $\frac{YZ}{BC} = \frac{70}{20} = \frac{7}{2}$.
(The ratio would be $\frac{2}{7}$ if you considered the triangles in reverse order.)

c. Substituting into the proportion $\frac{YZ}{BC} = \frac{XZ}{AC}$, $\frac{70}{20} = \frac{50}{AC}$, from which
$AC = \frac{100}{7} = 14\frac{2}{7}$.

Another triangle similarity theorem is the *SAS Similarity Theorem*.
You are asked to prove it in the Questions.

SAS Similarity Theorem:

If, in two triangles, the ratios of two pairs of corresponding
sides are equal and the included angles are congruent, then
the triangles are similar.

Example 2   **Given:** T is the midpoint of $\overline{PS}$;
Q is the midpoint of $\overline{PR}$.
Prove: $\triangle PTQ \sim \triangle PSR$.

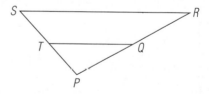

Analyze   Since T and Q are midpoints, the ratio of two pairs of
corresponding sides is 2:1. The angle included by these sides is in
both triangles.

Write

Conclusions	Justifications
1. $PT = \frac{1}{2} PS$, $PQ = \frac{1}{2} PR$	definition of midpoint (meaning)
2. $\frac{PT}{PS} = \frac{1}{2}$, $\frac{PQ}{PR} = \frac{1}{2}$	Mult. Prop. of Equality
3. $\angle P \cong \angle P$	Reflexive Prop. of Congruence
4. $\triangle PTQ \sim \triangle PSR$	SAS Similarity Theorem (steps 2, 3)

Questions

Covering the Reading

In 1 and 2, the triangles are similar.
- **a.** Determine the correspondence for the vertices.
- **b.** Find a ratio of similitude.
- **c.** Determine as many missing angle measures or side lengths as possible.

1.

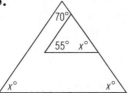

2.

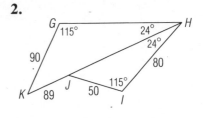

3. State the AA Similarity Theorem.

4. For each triangle similarity theorem, give the corresponding triangle congruence theorem.
- **a.** SSS Similarity Theorem
- **b.** AA Similarity Theorem
- **c.** SAS Similarity Theorem

In 5–9, each figure contains two triangles. **a.** Are the triangles similar? **b.** If so, what triangle similarity theorem guarantees their similarity?

5.

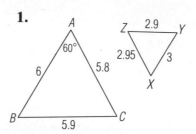

6.

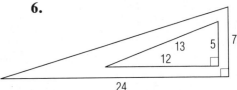

7.

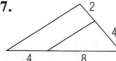

8.

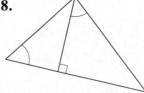

9.

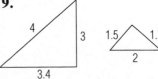

10. The triangles below are similar.
   a. What is the magnitude of a size change applied to △*PQR* which would cause its image to be congruent to △*XYZ*?
   b. How do you know the image of the smaller triangle would be congruent to the larger?

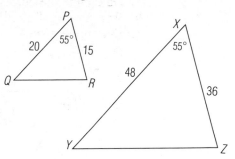

11. Prove the SAS Similarity Theorem using the figure below.
   Given: ∠*A* ≅ ∠*X*.
   $$\frac{AB}{XY} = \frac{AC}{XZ}.$$
   Prove: △*ABC* ~ △*XYZ*.
   (Hint: Use the general idea of the proofs of the other two triangle similarity theorems.)

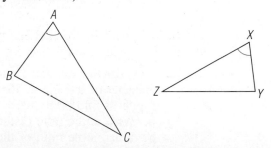

12. In the beach chair pictured below, $\overline{AE}$ and $\overline{BD}$ intersect at *C*, and $\overleftrightarrow{AB} \parallel \overleftrightarrow{DE}$. Prove that the triangles are similar.

13. Use the figure at the right.
   Given: *WY* = 3 · *VY*
              XY = 3 · *YZ*.
   Prove: △*WXY* ~ △*VZY*.

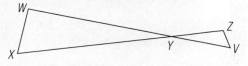

14. A garage casts a shadow 5 meters long. At the same time, a meter stick casts a shadow 1.2 meters long. Determine the height of the garage.

Review

15. a. Are triangles *LMN* and *PQR,* pictured here, similar?
  b. If so, why? If not, why not? *(Lesson 12-8)*

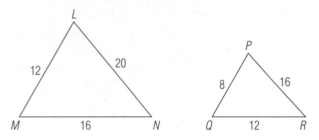

16. Consider the sun and Jupiter to be of similar shape. The equatorial diameter of the sun is 865,400 miles. The equatorial diameter of Jupiter is 88,000 miles.
  a. What is the ratio of the surface area of the sun to that of Jupiter?
  b. What is the ratio of the volume of the sun to that of Jupiter?
    (Lessons 12-7, 12-6)

17. Find the image of path *HIJHG* under a size change with center *G,* magnitude $\frac{3}{4}$. *(Lesson 12-3)*

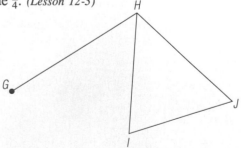

18. Solve for *x*: $\dfrac{x^2}{90} = \dfrac{3}{10}$. *(Lesson 12-4)*

Exploration

19. Is there an HL Similarity Theorem and an SsA Similarity Theorem for triangles? If so, how do you know? If not, draw a counterexample.

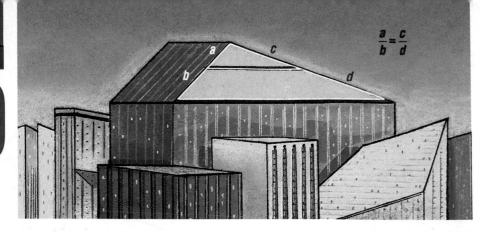

$$\frac{a}{b} = \frac{c}{d}$$

The Side-Splitting Theorem

Above is pictured an asymmetric roof. Amazingly, the parallel beams split the sides of the roof into proportional lengths. This result is called the Side-Splitting Theorem, and its proof depends on similar triangles.

Side-Splitting Theorem:

If a line is parallel to a side of a triangle and intersects the other two sides in distinct points, it "splits" these sides into proportional segments.

Proof

A figure is drawn at the right.

Given: $\overleftrightarrow{PQ} \parallel \overleftrightarrow{BC}$.

Prove: $\dfrac{AP}{PB} = \dfrac{AQ}{QC}$.

$\angle 1 \cong \angle 2$ and $\angle 3 \cong \angle 4$ since $\parallel$ lines $\Rightarrow$ corr. $\angle$s $=$. Thus, by the AA Similarity Theorem, $\triangle APQ \sim \triangle ABC$. Thus in these triangles, corresponding sides are proportional.

$$\frac{AB}{AP} = \frac{AC}{AQ}$$

Now we split AB and AC into two parts.

$$\frac{AP + PB}{AP} = \frac{AQ + QC}{AQ}$$

Separate the fractions, as you might do in algebra.

$$\frac{AP}{AP} + \frac{PB}{AP} = \frac{AQ}{AQ} + \frac{QC}{AQ}$$

$$1 + \frac{PB}{AP} = 1 + \frac{QC}{AQ}$$

Subtract 1 from both sides.

$$\frac{PB}{AP} = \frac{QC}{AQ}$$

Use the Reciprocals Property.

$$\frac{AP}{PB} = \frac{AQ}{QC}$$

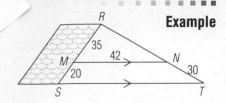

Example Suppose beams $\overline{MN}$ and $\overline{ST}$ are parallel and split the sides of the roof into the lengths as shown at the left. (All lengths are in decimeters. One decimeter = $\frac{1}{10}$ meter.)

a. Find the length of $\overline{RN}$.   **b.** Find ST.

Solution

a. From the Side-Splitting Theorem, $\dfrac{RM}{MS} = \dfrac{RN}{NT}$.

Substitute. $\dfrac{35}{20} = \dfrac{RN}{30}$

Solve for RN. $20 \cdot RN = 30 \cdot 35$

$RN = 52.5$ decimeters

b. $\triangle RMN \sim \triangle RST$ so $\frac{RM}{RS} = \frac{MN}{ST}$. Substituting, $\frac{35}{55} = \frac{42}{ST}$. Thus $35 \cdot ST = 42 \cdot 55$ and $ST = 66$ decimeters.

The converse of the Side-Splitting Theorem is also true: A line intersecting two sides of a triangle and forming proportional segments is parallel to the third side. You may use it to conclude that lines are parallel.

Side-Splitting Converse:

If a line intersects $\overrightarrow{OP}$ and $\overrightarrow{OQ}$ in distinct points X and Y so that $\dfrac{OX}{XP} = \dfrac{OY}{YQ}$, then $\overleftrightarrow{XY} \parallel \overleftrightarrow{PQ}$.

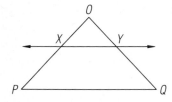

Proof

Analyze   It looks like the triangles are similar. Prove this first. Then corresponding angles can be used to get the parallel lines.

Write   **Given is** $\dfrac{OX}{XP} = \dfrac{OY}{YQ}$.

Using the Reciprocals Property, $\dfrac{XP}{OX} = \dfrac{YQ}{OY}$.

Adding 1 to both sides ($\frac{OX}{OX}$ to the left side, and $\frac{OY}{OY}$ to the right), and adding the fractions,

$$\frac{OX + XP}{OX} = \frac{OY + YQ}{OY}.$$

Since $OX + XP = OP$ and $OY + YQ = OQ$, substituting,

$$\frac{OP}{OX} = \frac{OQ}{OY}.$$

Thus, in the triangles, two pairs of sides are proportional. Also, by the Reflexive Property, $\angle XOY \cong \angle POQ$. So $\triangle OPQ \sim \triangle OXY$ by the SAS Similarity Theorem. The corresponding angles in the similar triangles are congruent, so $\angle OPQ \cong \angle OXY$. These are corresponding angles for the lines $\overleftrightarrow{XY}$ and $\overleftrightarrow{PQ}$ with transversal $\overleftrightarrow{OP}$. Since corr. $\angle s = \Rightarrow \parallel$ lines, $\overleftrightarrow{XY} \parallel \overleftrightarrow{PQ}$.

Questions

1. Given $m \parallel \overleftrightarrow{XY}$, finish the proportions.

   a. $\dfrac{AC}{AX} = \underline{} = \underline{}$

   b. $\dfrac{AB}{BY} = \underline{}$

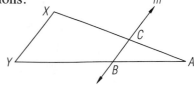

2. In the triangle below at the left, if $\overleftrightarrow{BC} \parallel \overleftrightarrow{DE}$, then $CE = \underline{}$.

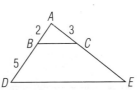
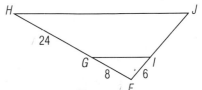

3. In the triangle above at the right, if $\overleftrightarrow{GI} \parallel \overleftrightarrow{HJ}$ then $FJ = \underline{}$.

4. Given $\overleftrightarrow{MN} \parallel \overleftrightarrow{PQ}$, $MP = 6$, $NQ = 5$, $ON = 30$, $MN = 14$. Find each number.

   a. $\dfrac{NQ}{ON}$ b. $\dfrac{MP}{MO}$ c. MO d. OP

   e. $\dfrac{ON}{OQ}$ f. $\dfrac{OM}{OP}$ g. $\dfrac{MN}{PQ}$ h. PQ

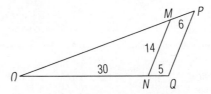

5. In Question 4, what is the magnitude of the size change S with center O and $S(\triangle MNO) = \triangle PQO$?

6. *Multiple choice.* $\dfrac{x + y}{x} =$

   (a) $1 + y$ (b) $1 + \dfrac{y}{x}$ (c) $\dfrac{y}{x}$ (d) none of these

7. *Multiple choice.* $\dfrac{z}{z} + \dfrac{y}{z} =$

   (a) $\dfrac{z + y}{2z}$ (b) $\dfrac{z + y}{z^2}$ (c) $\dfrac{z + y}{z}$ (d) none of these

8. State the Side-Splitting Converse.

9. Below, the horizontal beam splits the sides of this asymmetric roof. If $AB = 20$, $BD = 30$, and $AE = 60$, find AC and CE.

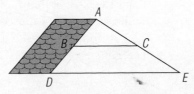

10. Given $\overleftrightarrow{DE} \parallel \overleftrightarrow{AC}$, $\overleftrightarrow{EF} \parallel \overleftrightarrow{AB}$; lengths as indicated below.
   a. Find *DB*.
   b. Find *FA*.
   c. ∠*A* and ∠*AFE* are __?__ angles.
   d. Write a true proportion using *BD*, *DA*, *CF*, and *FA*.

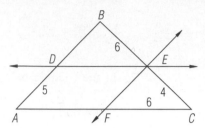

11. Given *m* ∥ *n*, then the Side-Splitting Theorem guarantees $\dfrac{x}{y} = \dfrac{z}{w}$.
Write five other true proportions involving *x*, *y*, *z*, and *w*.

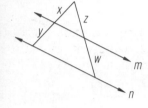

12. Fill in the justifications for the proof of the following generalization of the Side-Splitting Theorem:

If *m* ∥ *n* ∥ *p*, then $\dfrac{a}{b} = \dfrac{c}{d}$.

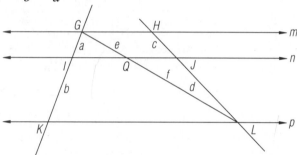

Conclusions	Justifications
1. $\dfrac{a}{b} = \dfrac{e}{f}$	**a.** __?__
2. $\dfrac{e}{f} = \dfrac{c}{d}$	**b.** __?__
3. $\dfrac{a}{b} = \dfrac{c}{d}$	**c.** __?__

13. 8th, 9th, and 10th Streets are parallel. Given the distances on Rasci Road, find *x* and *y*, the distances on Elm Street between these streets.

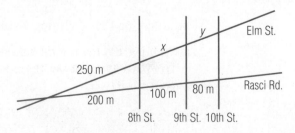

14. Refer to the figure below.
Given: $\overleftrightarrow{BE}$ bisects $\angle ABC$;
$\overline{AE} \perp \overline{AB}$; $\overline{DC} \perp \overline{CB}$.
Prove: $\triangle ABE \sim \triangle CBD$. *(Lesson 12-9)*

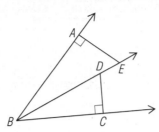

In 15–17, determine from the markings and other information if the pair of triangles is similar. If so, indicate the corresponding vertices and state the theorem or definition that justifies your conclusion. *(Lessons 12-9, 12-8)*

15.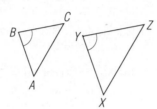

16.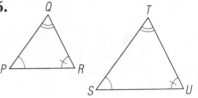

17.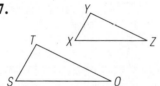
$$\frac{ST}{XY} = \frac{TO}{YZ} = \frac{OS}{ZX}$$

18. $ABCDE \sim JFGHI$ with sides and angle measures as indicated below. Find as many missing lengths and angle measures as possible. *(Lesson 12-5)*

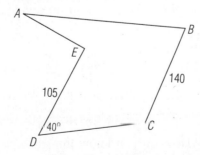

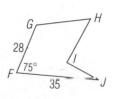

19. On a certain map, a distance of 150 miles is 4 inches. If two cities are $2\frac{1}{2}$ inches apart on the map, what is the actual distance between them? *(Lesson 12-4)*

20. Let S be a size change of magnitude 5 centered at the origin. Graph $S(\triangle PQR)$ if $P = (2, -.6)$, $Q = (-1.4, 0)$, and $R = (.8, 1.2)$. *(Lesson 12-1)*

21. In the figure below, $AB = AC$, and D and E split $\overline{BC}$ into three equal segments. Carefully trace the figure (or use an automatic drawer) and draw $\overline{AD}$ and $\overline{AE}$. Do they trisect $\angle BAC$? That is, do they split $\angle BAC$ into three angles of equal measure? Justify your answer.

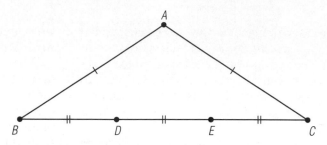

22. Here is how to divide a line segment $\overline{AB}$ into n congruent parts. (The figure shows the case $n = 5$.)

Step 1.   Draw any ray $\overrightarrow{AC_1}$ that is not collinear with $\overrightarrow{AB}$. (Make C_1 close to A for convenience.)

Step 2.   Mark off n segments AC_1, C_1C_2, C_2C_3, … of equal lengths on $\overrightarrow{AC_1}$.

Step 3.   Draw $\overline{BC_n}$. (Below, $n = 5$ so $\overline{BC_5}$ is drawn.)

Step 4.   Draw parallels to $\overline{BC_n}$ through C_1, C_2, C_3, etc.

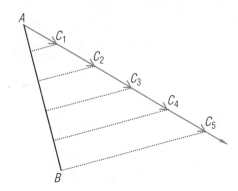

a. Follow the algorithm to divide $\overline{AB}$ below into 5 equal parts.

b. How do you know that each part of $\overline{AB}$ in the figure above is $\frac{1}{5}$ of $\overline{AB}$?

Summary

In the coordinate plane, a size change centered at the origin can be achieved by multiplying coordinates of points by a given scale factor. Since a coordinate system can be created with any point as the origin, size transformations can be centered anywhere. Size transformations can occur in two or three dimensions.

Two figures are similar if and only if one can be mapped onto the other by a composite of reflections and size transformations. In similar figures, angles and their images are congruent. Lengths of image segments are k times the lengths of preimage segments, where k is a positive number called the ratio of similitude. Areas of images are k^2 times the areas of their preimages. Volumes of images are k^3 times the volumes of their preimages. These relationships between two similar figures help explain why large animals need relatively thicker legs than small animals, and why there cannot be giants.

When one quantity is k times another, then the ratio of the quantities equals k. An equality of two ratios is called a proportion. Whenever there are similar figures, lengths are proportional. Solving proportions can help you determine unknown measurements.

The ability to draw or construct similar figures is necessary in the making of scale drawings, toys or scale models, maps, blueprints, and other diagrams. It is just as important to know when figures are similar. For triangles, the conditions guaranteeing similarity correspond to those for congruence. The most commonly used are SSS, AA, and SAS; A indicates equal angle measures and S indicates equal ratios of sides.

Vocabulary

Below are the most important terms and phrases for this chapter.
For the starred (*) terms you should be able to give a definition of the term.
For the other terms you should be able to give a general description and a specific example of each.

Lesson 12-1
S_k, magnitude

Lesson 12-2
*size change
size transformation
dilation, dilatation
center of size transformation
magnitude
scale factor
size change factor
size change image
*expansion
*contraction
*identity transformation

Lesson 12-3
Size Change Distance Theorem
Size Change Theorem
Figure Size Change Theorem

Lesson 12-4
*ratio, rate,
*proportion, proportional
means, extremes
Means-Extremes Property
Means Exchange Property
Reciprocals Property

Lesson 12-5
*similarity transformation
*similar figures
ratio of similitude
Similar Figures Theorem

Lesson 12-6
Fundamental Theorem of
    Similarity

Lesson 12-8
SSS Similarity Theorem

Lesson 12-9
AA Similarity Theorem
SAS Similarity Theorem

Lesson 12-10
Side-Splitting Theorem
Side-Splitting Converse

Progress Self-Test

Directions: Take this test as you would take a test in class. Use a ruler. Then check your work with the solutions in the Selected Answers section in the back of the book.

1. Trace the figure. Draw the image of $\triangle ABC$ under a size transformation with center O, magnitude $\frac{3}{4}$.

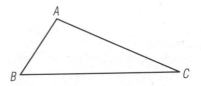

2. Draw the image of $\overline{DE}$ under a size change with center F, magnitude 2.8.

3. *Multiple choice.* Size changes preserve
(a) angle measure
(b) distance
(c) area
(d) volume.

4. In Question 1, how does the area of $\triangle ABC$ compare with the area of its image?

5. Define: similar figures.

In 6–8, use the figure below, in which $\overleftrightarrow{WX} \parallel \overleftrightarrow{YZ}$.

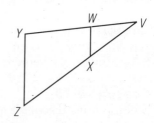

6. $\frac{VW}{WY} = \underline{\quad ? \quad}$

7. If $VW = 11$, $WY = 13$, and $VZ = 30$, what is VX?

8. If $WX = 8$, $YZ = 20$, and $WV = 10$, find VY.

9. If $\frac{a}{b} = \frac{c}{d}$, write three other true proportions using a, b, c, and d.

10. In the figure below, $\overleftrightarrow{AB} \parallel \overleftrightarrow{DE}$. If $AC = 32$, $CE = 24$, and $DC = 20$, find BC.

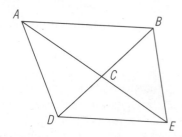

11. $QUAD \sim FOUR$ with sides and angle measures as indicated below. Find as many missing lengths and angle measures as possible.

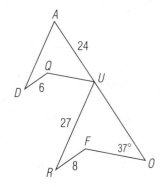

12. Two figures are similar and the ratio of corresponding sides is $5 : 1$. What is the ratio of their volumes?

13. A solid figurine is 4″ tall and weighs 5 pounds. What will a similar figurine of the same material weigh if it is 12″ tall?

In 14 and 15, are the triangles similar? If so, why?

14.

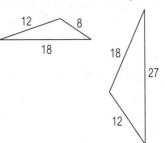

15.

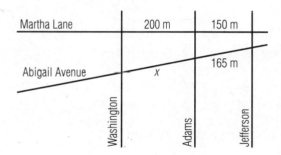

$\overrightarrow{AB} \parallel \overrightarrow{DE}$

16. Washington, Adams, and Jefferson streets are parallel. Given the distances on Martha Lane, find *x,* the length on Abigail Avenue between Washington and Adams.

Martha Lane	200 m	150 m
Abigail Avenue	*x*	165 m

Washington Adams Jefferson

17. A photo slide is 5 cm by 3 cm. If a similar print from the slide is 25 cm in its shorter dimension, what is its longer dimension?

18. A man 2 meters tall has a foot 30 cm long. If a man with a similar physique were 0.4 meters tall, how long would his foot be?

19. If there were a person 6 times as tall as you, the person would weigh about __?__ times as much. This weight would be supported by about __?__ times the area.

20. Let S be a size change of magnitude $\frac{1}{3}$ centered at the origin. Graph S($\triangle ABC$) if $A = (6, -2)$, $B = (9, 0)$, and $C = (-30, 10)$.

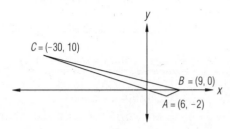

Chapter Review

Questions on **SPUR** Objectives

SPUR stands for **S**kills, **P**roperties, **U**ses, and **R**epresentations.
The Chapter Review questions are grouped according to the
SPUR Objectives for this chapter.

SKILLS deal with the procedures used to get answers.

■ **Objective A:** *Draw size transformation images of figures.* *(Lessons 12-2, 12-3)*

In 1–4, first trace the figure.

1. Draw the image of △*ABC* under a size change with center·*O*, magnitude 1.5.

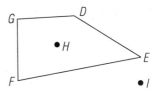

2. Draw the image of △*ABC* under a size transformation with center *A*, magnitude 0.8.

3. Draw the image of *DEFG* under a size transformation with center *I*, scale factor $\frac{2}{3}$.

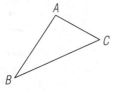

4. Draw the image of *DEFG* under a size change with scale factor $\frac{5}{3}$, center *H*.

5. Describe the image of *DEFG* in Question 4 under a size change with center *F*, magnitude 1.

■ **Objective B:** *Find the lengths in figures by applying the Side-Splitting Theorem and the Side-Splitting Converse.* *(Lesson 12-10)*

6. Given: S is a size transformation and S(△*JKL*) = △*JMN*. What is the value of *LN*?

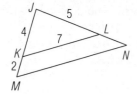

In 7 and 8, use the figure below. $\overleftrightarrow{NP} \parallel \overleftrightarrow{QS}$, *MP* = 30, and *PS* = 120.

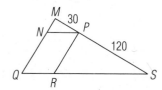

7. If *QR* = 25, what must *RS* be in order for $\overleftrightarrow{PR}$ to be parallel to $\overleftrightarrow{MQ}$?

8. If *MQ* = 90, then *MN* = ___?___ .

9. If $\overline{AB} \parallel \overline{CD}$, find *DE*.

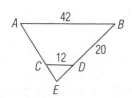

10. Below, if $\overleftrightarrow{WV} \parallel \overleftrightarrow{UT}$, what is *SW*?

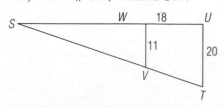

■ **Objective C:** *Find angle measures, lengths, perimeters, areas, and volumes in similar figures.* (*Lessons 12-5, 12-6*)

In 11 and 12, $\overline{TU} \parallel \overline{WX}$.

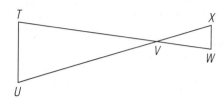

11. If $TV = 10$, $VW = 5$, and $VX = 6$, what is VU?

12. If $TU = 70$, $XW = 42$, and $TV = 112.5$, what other length can be found?

13. *PENTA ~ HOURS* with sides and angle measures as indicated below. Find as many missing lengths and angle measures as possible. (Be careful about which vertices correspond.)

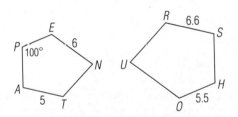

14. A hexagon has area 20 cm^2 and a smallest side with length 6 cm. A similar hexagon has a smallest side of length 8 cm. What is the area of this similar hexagon?

15. A right triangle has hypotenuse 10 and two angles with measures 57 and 33. What are the angle measures in a similar triangle whose hypotenuse has length 5?

16. A prism has volume 64 cubic meters. What is the volume of a similar prism $\frac{3}{4}$ as high?

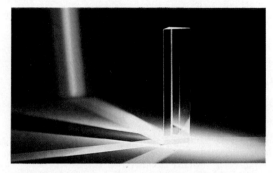

17. A polygon has area 100. What is the area of its image under a size change of magnitude 2.5?

18. In Question 1, if $\triangle A'B'C'$ is the image of $\triangle ABC$, how do the areas of $\triangle A'B'C'$ and $\triangle ABC$ compare?

PROPERTIES deal with the principles behind the mathematics.

■ **Objective D**: *Recognize and apply properties of size transformations and similar figures.* (*Lessons 12-2, 12-3, 12-5, 12-6, 12-7*)

19. Refer to the figure in Question 6.
   a. What is the center of S?
   b. What is the magnitude of S?
   c. *True or false?* $\overleftrightarrow{MN} \parallel \overleftrightarrow{KT}$.

20. *Multiple choice.*
   Size changes do *not* preserve
   (a) angle measure
   (b) betweenness
   (c) collinearity
   (d) distance.

21. How are the volumes of similar figures related to the ratio of similitude?

22. $\triangle RST$ is the image of $\triangle OQP$ under a size change.

   a. Trace the figure and locate the center of the size change.
   b. What is the magnitude of the size change?
   c. Find the lengths of $\overline{RT}$ and $\overline{ST}$.

23. If two figures are similar and the ratio of their areas is 4:1, what is the ratio of the lengths of corresponding sides?

24. One kite has sides of lengths 12, 12, 14, and 14. Another has sides of lengths 6, 6, 7, and 7.
 a. Must they be similar?
 b. If so, why? If not, why not?

■ **Objective E:** *Given a true proportion, find other true proportions with the same terms.* (*Lesson 12-4*)

25. If $\frac{m}{a} = \frac{t}{e}$, write three other true proportions using m, a, t, and e.

26. *Multiple choice.* If $\frac{u}{v} = \frac{w}{x}$, which is true?

(a) $\frac{u + v}{v} = \frac{w + v}{x}$ (b) $\frac{u}{v} = \frac{x}{w}$

(c) $\frac{u + v}{v} = \frac{w + x}{x}$ (d) $\frac{u}{x} = \frac{w}{v}$

27. Write three true proportions involving the numbers 8, 12, 24, and 16.

28. If the Means Exchange Property is applied to $\frac{3}{x} = \frac{4}{5}$, what proportion results?

■ **Objective F:** *Determine whether or not triangles are similar using the AA, SAS, or SSS Similarity Theorems.* (*Lessons 12-8, 12-9*)

29. One triangle has sides 40, 45, and 50.
 a. Is this triangle similar to a second triangle with sides 10, 9, and 8?
 b. If so, why? If not, why not?

In 30 and 31, are the triangles similar? If so, why? If not, why not?

30.

31.

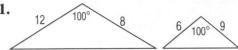

32. *ABDC* is a trapezoid with $\overleftrightarrow{AB} \parallel \overleftrightarrow{CD}$ and diagonals intersecting at *E*.
 Prove: $\triangle ABE \sim \triangle DCE$.

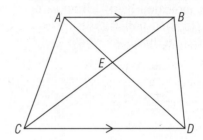

33. Refer to the figure below.
 Given: $\overline{AC} \perp \overline{BD}$, $BC = x$,
 $AC = 2x$, and $DC = 4x$.
 Prove: $\triangle ABC \sim \triangle DAC$.

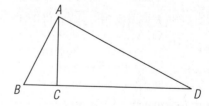

USES deal with applications of mathematics in real situations.

■ **Objective G:** *Identify and determine proportional lengths and distances in real situations.*
(*Lessons 12-4, 12-5, 12-10*)

34. First Street runs north-south. Elm, Maple, and Pine run east-west. Distances between them are as indicated. There is 2000 ft of frontage on Slant Street between Elm and Maple. How much frontage is there on Slant Street between Maple and Pine?

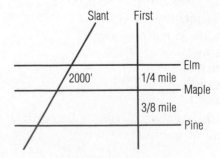

35. A photograph is 5″ by 8″. If a similar photograph is 10″ in its longer dimension, what is its shorter dimension?

36. 1.5 meters from its bottom, a slide is 1.3 m tall. If the slide runs for 4 m along the ground, what is its height at its highest point? (Round your answer to the nearest 0.1 m.)

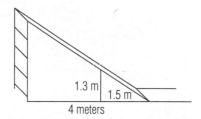

1.3 m
1.5 m
4 meters

37. At 4 PM, a tree casts a shadow 9 meters long. At the same time, a vertical meter stick casts a shadow 60 cm long. How tall is the tree?

38. If 4 pounds of navel oranges cost $1.89, what should 5 pounds of navel oranges cost?

39. TV screens are nearly all similar. If a 9″ screen (measured along a diagonal) is 7″ wide, how wide is a 26″ screen?

■ **Objective H:** *Apply the Fundamental Theorem of Similarity in real situations. (Lessons 12-6, 12-7)*

40. A solid figurine is 20 cm tall and weighs 3 kg. How much will a similar figurine of the same material weigh if it is 32 cm tall?

41. If a 10-inch-diameter pizza costs $5.89, and cost is proportional to ingredients, what should a 16-inch-diameter pizza with the same kinds of ingredients cost?

42. Dolls are often $\frac{1}{12}$ actual size. The same material used for a real coat can be used to make how many doll coats?

43. An elephant 16 feet high can weigh 7 tons. (A ton is 2000 pounds.) If a similarly shaped elephant were 1 foot high, how many pounds would it weigh?

44. If there were a person 8 times as tall as you are with your physique, the person would weight about __?__ times as much. This weight would be supported by about __?__ times the area.

45. *True* or *false*? Larger animals need thicker legs than smaller animals to hold their weight.

REPRESENTATIONS deal with pictures, graphs, or objects that illustrate concepts.

■ **Objective I:** *Use the definition of size transformations for figures on the coordinate plane. (Lesson 12-1)*

In 46–48, A = (6, -5), B = (-10, 0), C = (-3, 8), D = (12, 20).

46. Graph *ABCD* and its image under $S_{\frac{1}{2}}$.

47. Graph *ABCD* and its image under $S_{2.5}$.

48. List the coordinates of the image of *ABCD* under S_k.

49. Let O = (0, 0, 0) and P = (-5, -8, 11).
  a. Find P′, the image of P under S_4.
  b. Verify that $OP' = 4 \cdot OP$.

50. Let S be a size transformation of magnitude 5.
  a. Using the graph, find S(P), S(Q), and S(R).
  b. Fill in the blank and answer the question. Prove that the distance between S(P) and S(Q) is __?__ times the distance between P and Q.
  c. Verify that the slope of $\overline{PQ}$ equals the slope of the line through S(P) and S(Q).
  d. Verify that S(P), S(Q), and S(R) are collinear.
  e. Verify that S(Q) is between S(P) and S(R).

P = (1, 4)
Q = (2, -1)
R = (3, -6)

Logic and Indirect Reasoning

The 15 clues below are from a famous puzzle called "Who Owns the Zebra?" (This puzzle dates from the 1950s, before the dangers of smoking were widely recognized.)

1. There are five houses, each of a different color and inhabited by men of different nationalities, with different pets, drinks, and cigarettes.
2. The Englishman lives in the red house.
3. The Spaniard owns the dog.
4. Coffee is drunk in the green house.
5. The Ukranian drinks tea.
6. The green house is immediately to the right (*your* right) of the ivory house.
7. The Old Gold smoker owns snails.
8. Kools are smoked in the yellow house.
9. Milk is drunk in the middle house.
10. The Norwegian lives in the first house on the left.
11. The man who smokes Chesterfields lives in the house next to the man with the fox.
12. Kools are smoked in the house next to the house where the horse is kept.
13. The Lucky Strike smoker drinks orange juice.
14. The Japanese man smokes Parliaments.
15. The Norwegian lives next to the blue house.

Now, who drinks water? And who owns the zebra?

"Who Owns the Zebra?" is famous partially because nothing in the clues seems to have anything to do with water or zebras. Consequently, it doesn't seem like there is enough information to figure out the answer to the question. However, by carefully using logic and ruling out possibilities, the owner of the zebra can be determined.

The logic in these puzzles is the same as the logic used in mathematics. Instead of reasoning from clues, mathematicians reason from postulates. Instead of finding out who owns the zebra or who drinks water, mathematicians try to find out what is true about figures or numbers or other mathematical ideas.

In the first ten chapters of this book, you were introduced to all of the postulates that are needed in Euclidean geometry. You may not have realized that there were no new postulates, no new assumptions in Chapters 11 and 12. Nor are there any new assumptions in the remainder of this book. The postulates you have seen are sufficient to deduce any theorem of Euclidean geometry.

However, there are two types of proofs in mathematics—direct and indirect—and thus far you have been asked only to write direct proofs. In this chapter, you will learn about the logic of indirect reasoning and see and write some indirect proofs. Indirect reasoning is used to solve logic puzzles like "Who Owns the Zebra?" and also to prove many theorems. You may find some indirect proofs easier to write than direct proofs.

13-1

The Logic of Making Conclusions

The battle of Waterloo is one of the subjects in logic puzzles by Charles Dodgson. See Example 3 on page 632.

To begin the study of logic, we examine a proof similar to some you have written before. In this case, however, we have identified each statement with a letter so that the logic becomes clearer.

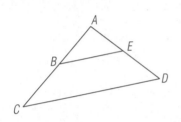

Given: $\overline{BE} \parallel \overline{CD}$. p
Prove: $\triangle ABE \sim \triangle ACD$. r

Conclusions	Justifications	
1. $\angle ABE \cong \angle ACD$, $\angle AEB \cong \angle ADC$ q	$\parallel$ lines $\Rightarrow$ corr. $\angle$s $=$	$p \Rightarrow q$
2. $\triangle ABE \sim \triangle ACD$ r	AA Similarity Theorem	$q \Rightarrow r$

Recall that a justification for a conclusion is a true if-then statement with the conclusion as the consequent. Notice how this idea is used in step 1 of the above proof. $p \Rightarrow q$ is the justification for concluding q from the given p. The general logical principle is called the *Law of Detachment* because q is "detached" from $p \Rightarrow q$. It is a generalization of the common sense idea that when $p \Rightarrow q$ is a true statement and p is true, q follows.

Law of Detachment:

If you have a statement or given information p and a justification of the form $p \Rightarrow q$, you may conclude q.

Conclusions can be antecedents for making other conclusions. In step 2, from the conclusion q and the justification $q \Rightarrow r$, the conclusion r follows. Having steps 1 and 2, you can conclude that $p \Rightarrow r$. The proof can be diagrammed as follows:

$$p \Rightarrow q$$
$$q \Rightarrow r$$

from which you can conclude $p \Rightarrow r$.

The logical idea is the *Law of Transitivity*. (It is sometimes called the *Transitive Property of Implication*.)

> **Law of Transitivity:**
>
> If $p \Rightarrow q$ and $q \Rightarrow r$, then $p \Rightarrow r$.

Logical principles can be applied to everyday thinking.

Example 1 A commercial states:
> If you want to be popular, you should dress well.
> If you dress well, you should wear brand X jeans.
> What conclusion is desired?

Solution Assign variables for the statements.
   p: You want to be popular.
   d: You dress well.
   j: You wear brand X jeans.
The commercial states:
> If p, then d. If d, then j. Using the symbol for $\Rightarrow$,
> you can write $p \Rightarrow d$ and $d \Rightarrow j$.
By the Law of Transitivity, you can conclude $p \Rightarrow j$. In words:
> If you want to be popular, you should wear brand X jeans.

Of course, the commercial wants you to believe that $p \Rightarrow d$ and $d \Rightarrow j$ are true statements. Many people would *not* accept these statements as true. Recall from Chapter 2 that if an antecedent is not true, you cannot trust any conclusion made from it. If either $p \Rightarrow d$ or $d \Rightarrow j$ is false, you have no reason to automatically conclude $p \Rightarrow j$.

The Law of Transitivity is used often in algebra. Each step in many algebra problems is a conclusion based on the previous step. The end result (r) is often not obvious from the given information (p).

p	$3n + 18 > 16$	Given
$\Rightarrow q$	$3n > -2$	Addition Property of Inequality ($p \Rightarrow q$)
$\Rightarrow r$	$n > -\frac{2}{3}$	Multiplication Property of Inequality ($q \Rightarrow r$)

Because of the Law of Transitivity, you can conclude $p \Rightarrow r$:
   If $3n + 18 > 16$, then $n > -\frac{2}{3}$.

In Example 1, the justifications were properties of inequality and operations and the logic was "behind the scenes." But sometimes the justifications you might use are part of the given information. Then the logical laws themselves become the justifications. This is shown in Example 2, in which the given statements (1) and (2) are used as justifications.

Example 2 What conclusions can be made from the following?
(1) Every rhombus is a kite.
(2) The diagonals of a kite are perpendicular.
(3) *BUSM* is a rhombus.

Solution First put the conditionals in if-then form. Call (3) *r,* for the special instance of figure *BUSM*.

(1) $r \Rightarrow k$: If a figure is a rhombus, then it is a kite.
(2) $k \Rightarrow p$: If a figure is a kite, then its diagonals are perpendicular.

From (1) and (2), using the Law of Transitivity, you can conclude
$r \Rightarrow p$:   If a figure is a rhombus, then its diagonals are perpendicular.
From r and $r \Rightarrow p$, using the Law of Detachment, you can conclude p:
    The diagonals of *BUSM* are perpendicular.
Since the given statements (1)–(3) are true, the conclusion should be true.

Check   Statements (1) and (2) are theorems we have proved, so they are true. Now draw a situation in which (3) is true also. That is, draw a picture of a rhombus *BUSM*. Don't make it special. Do its diagonals seem perpendicular? Yes, the conclusion checks.

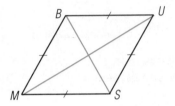

Lewis Carroll, the Englishman [1832-1898] best known for writing *Alice in Wonderland,* was a logician. That is, he studied the process of reasoning. Under his given name, Charles L. Dodgson, he wrote books on logic. Here is a puzzle from one of his books.

Example 3 Given these statements, what can you conclude using all the statements?
(1) My gardener is well worth listening to on military subjects.
(2) No one can remember the battle of Waterloo, unless he is very old.
(3) Nobody is really worth listening to on military subjects, unless he can remember the battle of Waterloo.

Solution   Assign a letter to each statement or clause in the statement.
    p: A person is worth listening to on military subjects.
    q: A person can remember Waterloo.
    r: A person is very old.
Now analyze the givens.
    (1) is merely *p,* for the special instance of the gardener.
    (2) is $q \Rightarrow r$.
    (3) is $p \Rightarrow q$.
From (2) and (3), using the Law of Transitivity, you get $p \Rightarrow r$.
Together with (1), using the Law of Detachment, you get r as applied to the gardener. Lewis Carroll's desired conclusion: My gardener is very old.

Charles Dodgson (1832-1898)

1. Why is "Who Owns the Zebra?" famous?

2. What two kinds of proofs are there in mathematics?

3. Which two logical principles are used in the proof which begins this lesson?

4. If p is given and $p \Rightarrow q$ is true, then __?__ can be concluded.

In 5–8, what can be concluded from the given statements?

5. (1) Every square is a rectangle.
   (2) Every rectangle is a parallelogram.

6. (1) Every triangle with two congruent sides has at least two congruent angles.
   (2) If a triangle is isosceles, then it has two congruent sides.

7. (1) Your teeth will be whiter if you use Toothdazzle.
   (2) The whiter your teeth are, the more popular you will be with the opposite sex.

8. (1) If a figure is a prism, then the figure is a polyhedron.
   (2) A figure is a polyhedron if it is a pyramid.

9. Explain how the Law of Transitivity is used when solving the sentence $7(x - 12) < 70$.

In 10–13, assume this statement is true: If a tennis player has won Wimbledon, then the player is world class. Using the Law of Detachment only, what (if anything) can you conclude if you also know the given statement is true?

10. Martina Navratilova has won Wimbledon.

11. Boris Becker has won Wimbledon.

12. Gabriela Sabatini has not won Wimbledon (as of 1989).

13. Arthur Ashe won the U.S. Open Tennis Tournament in 1968.

14. What can you conclude from these two statements?
    (1) A triangle has two congruent angles if it is equilateral.
    (2) $\triangle ABC$ has two congruent angles.

In 15–18, in some states if a person has a driver's license, then the person's age is greater than or equal to 16. Tell what you can conclude in these states from this statement if you also know the following:

15. Joe has a driver's license.   16. Jamie drives a car legally.

17. Florence is 18 years old.   18. Isabel does not drive a car.

Martina Navratilova won the singles title at Wimbledon, England, July 6, 1985.

19. Use the drawing at the right.
    a. Make a conclusion using the Law of
       Detachment. Justify your conclusion.
    b. Make a second conclusion using the
       Law of Transitivity.

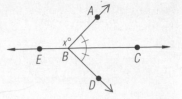

20. Lewis Carroll asked if this reasoning is correct. Is it?
    (1) Dictionaries are useful.
    (2) Useful books are valuable.
    Conclusion: Dictionaries are valuable.

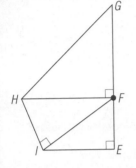

21. Use the drawing at the left. $HI = 4$, $EF = 6$, $EI = 8$, and $FG = 10$.
    a. Find *FI*.   b. Find *FH*.   c. Find *GH*.
    d. *Multiple choice.* Which of the following has *not* been used in
       finding *GH*?
       (i) Law of Detachment   (ii) Law of Transitivity
       (iii) Pythagorean Theorem   (iv) All of these are used.

22. Use the drawing for Question 21.
    Explain why $GH^2 = FG^2 + HI^2 + IE^2 + EF^2$.

Review

23. The height of a pyramid is doubled and the dimensions of its
    rectangular base are tripled. What happens to its volume?
    (Lesson 10-6)

24. The height of a cylinder is doubled and the diameter of its circular
    base is tripled. What happens to its volume? *(Lesson 10-5)*

25. What is the sum of the measures of the angles of a convex pentagon?
    (Lesson 5-7)

26. Give the definition of trapezoid. *(Lesson 5-2)*

27. Draw a counterexample to this statement: If a quadrilateral has two
    consecutive sides congruent, then it is a kite. *(Lessons 5-2, 2-2)*

28. a. Graph the lines with equations $y = 2x + 1$ and $y = 2x + 2$.
    b. Are these lines parallel or intersecting?
    c. Are these lines horizontal, vertical, or oblique?
       (Lessons 3-4, 1-3)

29. Expand: **a.** $(x - y)^2$; **b.** $(a - (-q))^2$. *(Previous course)*

Exploration

30. Let *p* be the statement "*ABCD* is a rectangle." Find as many theorems
    as you can of the form $p \Rightarrow q$, and for each tell what *q* means for
    rectangle *ABCD*.

31. Examine the clues in "Who Owns the Zebra?" Make a conclusion that
    is not given in the clues.

13-2

Negations

Jane is studying for the next test.

Indirect reasoning is based on the idea of *negation*. The **negation** of a statement *p*, called ***not-p,*** is a statement that is true whenever statement *p* is false and is false whenever statement *p* is true.

Statement: You study for the next test.
Negation: You do not study for the next test.

The above example shows that you can often write the negation by changing the verb. If the verb is negative, then the negation has a positive verb.

p: The quadrilateral *ABCD* is not a parallelogram.
not-p: The quadrilateral *ABCD* is a parallelogram.

Changing something other than the verb will not necessarily give the negation. But the word "not" can be avoided by considering all alternatives.

p: $\triangle ABC$ is isosceles.
not-p: $\triangle ABC$ is scalene.

t: $\angle A$ is a right angle.
correct *not-t:* $\angle A$ is acute or $\angle A$ is obtuse.
incorrect *not-t:* $m\angle A = 45$.

The negation of a negation is the original statement. The statements *p* and *not-(not-p)* are identical.

Recall that from any conditional $p \Rightarrow q$, you can form its converse $q \Rightarrow p$. Let *p* = "a triangle is equilateral" and *q* = "a triangle has three acute angles."

Original $p \Rightarrow q$:   If a triangle is equilateral,
                              then it has three acute angles.
Converse $q \Rightarrow p$:   If a triangle has three acute angles,
                              then it is equilateral.

Here the original is true, the converse false.

Negating *both* parts of the original conditional gives a new conditional of the form *not-p* $\Rightarrow$ *not-q*, called the **inverse** of the original.

Inverse   *not-p* $\Rightarrow$ *not-q*:   If a triangle is not equilateral,
                                                it does not have three acute angles.

This inverse is false. There are triangles which are not equilateral but do have three acute angles.

However, if both parts of the original are negated and the antecedent and consequent are switched, a second *true* statement appears. This statement, of the form *not-q* $\Rightarrow$ *not-p,* is called the **contrapositive** of the original.

Contrapositive   *not-q* $\Rightarrow$ *not-p:* If a triangle does not have three
                                                acute angles, it is not equilateral.

Example 1   Given the conditional "If you live in California, then you need a mountain bicycle," write the converse, contrapositive, and inverse.

> **Solution**   Converse $q \Rightarrow p$:   If you need a mountain bicycle,
>   then you live in California.
> Contrapositive   *not-q* $\Rightarrow$ *not-p*:   If you do not need a mountain
>   bicycle, then you do not live in
>   California.
> Inverse   *not-p* $\Rightarrow$ *not-q*:   If you do not live in California, then
>   you do not need a mountain bicycle.

The given and all three statements in the solution of Example 1 are false. Both Example 1 and the equilateral triangle example preceding it verify the following law of logic.

Law of the Contrapositive:

A statement ($p \Rightarrow q$) and its contrapositive (*not-q* $\Rightarrow$ *not-p*) are either both true or both false.

To summarize: If a given statement is true, you may conclude that its contrapositive is true, but its converse and inverse may be either true or false. The Law of the Contrapositive used along with the Law of Detachment and the Law of Transitivity allows you to make many more conclusions.

Example 2   Given are two statements.
(1) Every square is a kite.
(2) Quadrilateral *POTS* is not a kite.
What conclusion can be made using both statements?

Solution In if-then form, (1) is: If a figure is a square, then it is a kite. This is a true statement; thus, the contrapositive is also true and may be stated as follows: If a figure is not a kite, then it is not a square. Now, since (2) *POTS* is not a kite, you can use the Law of Detachment to conclude that *POTS* is not a square.

You have now studied enough laws of logic to figure out many logic puzzles. Here is a version of another one of Lewis Carroll's puzzles. Notice how the Law of the Contrapositive and the Law of Transitivity are both used.

Example 3 Given these statements, what can you conclude?
(1) Babies are illogical.
(2) Any person who can manage a crocodile is not despised.
(3) Illogical persons are despised.

Solution First translate as many statements as possible into if-then form. To avoid lots of writing, use variables to name the parts of the statements.
Let *B:* A person is a baby.
      D: A person is despised.
      C: A person can manage a crocodile.
      I: A person is illogical.
Now (1) becomes $B \Rightarrow I$.
      (2) becomes $C \Rightarrow not\text{-}D$.
      (3) is $I \Rightarrow D$.
From (1) and (3) you can conclude (using transitivity) $B \Rightarrow D$. The contrapositive of (2) is $D \Rightarrow not\text{-}C$. So, using transitivity again, the conclusion is $B \Rightarrow not\text{-}C$. A baby cannot manage a crocodile.

Questions

Covering the Reading

In 1–4, give the negation of the statement.

1. The perimeter of an *n*-gon with side *s* is *ns*.

2. ∠*A* is acute.

3. You were not late for school today.

4. △*GHI* is scalene.

5. The negation of a statement p is written __?__.

In 6–9, give **a.** the converse; **b.** the contrapositive; and **c.** the inverse of the given statement.

6. If m$\angle T = 45$, then $\angle T$ is acute.

7. $p \Rightarrow q$

8. If $ax + by = c$, then $ax = c - by$.

9. You can get $10 for that old tape recorder when you bring it in Saturday.

In 10–12, *multiple choice*. The four choices are:
   (a) negation
   (b) converse
   (c) inverse
   (d) contrapositive.

10. If a statement is true, its __?__ must be true.

11. If a statement is true, its __?__ is false.

12. If a statement is false, its __?__ is false.

13. Give the contrapositive: If $\triangle ABC$ is not a right triangle, then the Pythagorean Theorem does not hold for $\triangle ABC$.

14. Make a conclusion using both of the following true statements.
   (1) If a network has only even vertices, it is traversable.
   (2) The network below is not traversable.

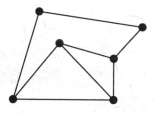

Applying the Mathematics

15. a. Make a conclusion using both these statements.
   (1) If $x = 3$, then $y = 4$.
   (2) $y = 5$
   b. Which two of the three laws—Detachment, Transitivity, or Contrapositive—are needed to make your conclusion?

16. If these three statements are true, what can be concluded using all of them?
   (1) $p \Rightarrow q$
   (2) $q \Rightarrow r$
   (3) *not-r*

17. Joanne had a date, but her mother truthfully told her, "If you don't apologize to your brother for the way you treated him, then you're not going out tonight." Joanne went on her date. Is it true that she apologized to her brother?

18. José heard the ad "If you try our product, you won't be sorry." Later on, José was not sorry. Does that mean he tried the product?

19. Make a conclusion from all these statements, adapted from Lewis Carroll.
(1) All unripe fruit is unwholesome.
(2) All these apples are wholesome.
(3) No fruit grown in the shade is ripe.

20. Make a conclusion using both these statements.
(1) All equilateral triangles have three 60° angles.
(2) m∠*ABC* = 59

Review

21. State the Law of Detachment. *(Lesson 13-1)*

22. Fill in the blank. Then make a conclusion from all the statements. *(Lessons 13-1, 5-2)*
(1) *ABCD* is a rhombus.
(2) If a figure is a rhombus, then it is a(n) __?__ .
(3) Opposite sides of a parallelogram are parallel.

23. Given: $\overline{AD} \parallel \overline{BC}$;
$\overline{AB} \parallel \overline{CD}$.
Prove: $\overline{AB} \cong \overline{CD}$. *(Lesson 7-6)*

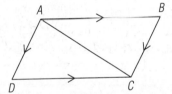

24. *Multiple choice.* In Question 23, what have you proved?
(a) In a parallelogram, opposite sides are parallel.
(b) In a parallelogram, opposite sides are congruent.
(c) If opposite sides of a quadrilateral are congruent, the figure is a parallelogram.
(d) If opposite sides of a quadrilateral are parallel, the figure is a parallelogram.
(Lesson 7-6)

In 25–28, solve. *(Previous course)*

25. $5x - 13 = 19x + 15$

26. $8(y - 3) = 7(3y + 1)$

27. $6r^2 = 150$

28. $(w + 5)^2 = 289$

Exploration

29. Make up your own logic puzzle like Example 3.

13-3

Ruling Out Possibilities

Indirect reasoning is based on the idea of ruling out possibilities. It is used even by animals or babies. If a baby knows that a toy is in either a parent's right hand or the parent's left hand, and the right hand is opened and found empty, the baby will know to look in the left hand for the toy. This innate principle of reasoning is called the *Law of Ruling Out Possibilities*.

Law of Ruling Out Possibilities:

When *p or q* is true and *q* is not true, then *p* is true.

You know every angle in a triangle is either acute, right, or obtuse. So if an angle in a triangle is not acute or right, then it is obtuse. There is no other possibility.

In real life, if words are not carefully defined, you may not be able to rule out possibilities so easily. For example, if a person is not young, that does not necessarily mean the person is old.

In the questions for this lesson, you are asked to solve some logic puzzles. These puzzles use the idea of ruling out possibilities again and again. Notice how little information is given. Yet you can deduce a great deal. The same happens in geometry.

Here are some hints for doing these puzzles: (1) Logic puzzles take a lot of time and analysis, so do not hurry. (2) Construct a grid and place an X in a square whenever something cannot occur. Place an O in the square when the situation *must* occur.

Example 1

Carol, Sue, Jill, Dave, and Jim each play a different instrument in the school band. The instruments they play are clarinet, cornet, flute, trombone, and tuba. From the clues below determine which instrument each student plays.

(1) Carol plays either the clarinet, cornet, or tuba.
(2) Sue does not play the flute.
(3) Dave does not play any of these instruments: trombone, cornet, flute, or clarinet.
(4) Jim plays either the tuba or the cornet.

Solution To solve this puzzle the grid below can be used. The first clue tells you that Carol does not play the flute and that Carol does not play the trombone. Two X_1s in the first row of the grid show this. (We call it X_1 so you can tell it comes directly from clue (1).) The third clue tells you four instruments Dave does not play. The four X_3s in the fourth row show this. Of course, this means that Dave must play the tuba. We show this with an O. Now we know that no one else plays the tuba, so we place four Xs in the column labeled "tuba."

	Clarinet	Cornet	Flute	Trombone	Tuba
Carol			X_1	X_1	X
Sue					X
Jill					X
Dave	X_3	X_3	X_3	X_3	O
Jim					X

You are asked to complete this puzzle in Question 7 at the end of this section.

Sometimes a single piece of given information may yield many conclusions, as in the following example.

Example 2

In Question 12 at the end of this lesson, clue (4) is "Neither Edgar nor the person named Voila is the guard or the teller." What can be concluded from that?

Solution At least five things can be concluded.
Edgar's last name is not Voila.
Edgar is not the guard.
Edgar is not the teller.
Voila is not the guard.
Voila is not the teller.

For Question 12 and other logic problems like it, a complicated grid is often very helpful. The grid should have a space for each *last name-first name* pair, for each *first name-bank job* pair, and for each *bank job-last name* pair. The grid below will do.

On this grid we have noted the possibilities which can be ruled out by clue (4).

Covering the Reading

1. Marilyn tosses a coin. The face that shows up is not "heads." You conclude that the face that shows up is "tails." What principle of reasoning have you used?

2. If statement m or statement n is true and m is not true, then ___?___ must be true.

3. Two different lines s and t in the same plane are not parallel. What can be concluded about s and t?

In 4–6, refer to Question 12 on the next page.

4. From clue (3) alone, who is known *not* to be the secretary?

5. Write at least two conclusions that follow from clue (1).

6. Write at least two conclusions that follow from clue (5).

7. Finish Example 1 of this lesson.

In 8 and 9, make a conclusion from the given information.

8. Line m is not parallel to plane X and m is not in plane X.

9. $ABCD$ is a trapezoid with $\overline{AB} \parallel \overline{CD}$, but $ABCD$ is not a parallelogram.

10. The **Trichotomy Law** for real numbers is: Of two real numbers a and b, either $a < b$, $a = b$, or $a > b$, and no two of these can be true at the same time. Suppose you know that $\sqrt{2} \neq \frac{41}{29}$. What can you conclude by using the Trichotomy Law?

11. Seven seniors, Joyce, Mike, Darlene, Gary, Wanda, Ken, and Brad, were asked about their career plans. These occupations were mentioned: lawyer, farmer, teacher, doctor, dentist, car dealer, and chemist. No occupation was selected by more than one student. Using the following clues, find out who mentioned which occupation.
(1) Joyce doesn't want to be a doctor, car dealer, or chemist.
(2) Mike doesn't want to be a doctor or car dealer either.
(3) Gary wants to be either a teacher, dentist, or farmer.
(4) Ken wants to be either a dentist or farmer.
(5) Brad doesn't want to be a car dealer.
(6) Darlene wants to be a dentist.

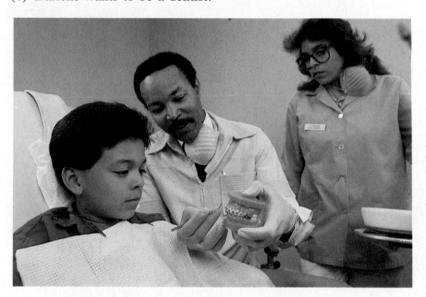

12. The Smalltown Bank has a teller, secretary, bookkeeper, guard, and manager named Mr. Farmer, Mr. Guinness, Ms. Landis, Ms. Voila, and Ms. Edwards, though not necessarily in that order. The two men are Edgar and Wilbur, while the three women are Catherine, Marjorie, and Shirley. From the clues below, determine the first and last names of each person and his or her position at the bank. (Hint: Use the grid on the previous page.)
(1) Neither Catherine nor Marjorie is the teller and neither is Ms. Edwards.
(2) Shirley is not the guard.
(3) The secretary is either Catherine or Ms. Landis.
(4) Neither Edgar nor the person named Voila is the guard or teller.
(5) Mr. Farmer, Edgar, and the bookkeeper have all worked at the bank for more than five years.

13. Consider this statement: "If Jackie is a good cook, I'll eat my hat!" Give the **a.** converse; **b.** inverse; and **c.** contrapositive. *(Lesson 13-2)*

In 14 and 15, make a conclusion from these three statements. *(Lessons 13-2, 13-1)*

14. (1) Every integer is a real number.
(2) Every natural number is an integer.
(3) The complex number *i* is not a real number.

15. (1) Every square is a rhombus.
(2) Diagonals in a kite are perpendicular.
(3) A figure is a kite if it is a rhombus.

16. Write the negation of this statement in two different ways:
$\triangle ABC$ is isosceles. *(Lessons 13-2, 2-7)*

17. Refer to the figure below.
Given: Diagonals of quadrilateral *ABED* intersect at *C*.
$\triangle ABC$ and $\triangle DCE$ are isosceles, both with vertex angle *C*.
Prove: $\triangle ACD \cong \triangle BCE$. *(Lesson 7-3)*

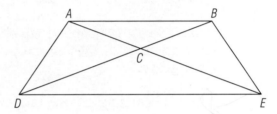

18. Given $A = (5, 3)$, $B = (-6, 3)$, $C = (-6, -2)$, $D = (5, -2)$.
a. What kind of figure is *ABCD*?
b. Show that $AC = BD$. *(Lessons 11-2, 5-2)*

19. Question 12 and Example 1 are adapted from puzzles found in *Pencil Puzzle Treasury,* by Wayne Williams, Grosset and Dunlap publishers, New York, 1978. Logic puzzles of this type can be found in *Games* magazine or magazines by Dell Publishing Co. and other places. Find an example of a logic puzzle different from the ones given in this lesson, or write one yourself!

Indirect
Proof

A lawyer, summing up a case for a jury, says, "The prosecutors assume the defendant–my client–committed the crime. Then my client would have been at the scene of the crime. But remember that we brought in witnesses and telephone records. These extra people and records demonstrate my client was on a farm 15 miles away. A person can't be in two places at one time! My client could not have been both on the farm and at the scene of the crime at the same time. So the assumption my client did the crime cannot be true. So it must be false. Ladies and gentlemen of the jury, the defendant is not guilty."

In this summing up, the lawyer has used indirect reasoning.

In **direct reasoning,** a person begins with given information known to be true. The Laws of Detachment and Transitivity are used to reason from that information to a conclusion. The proofs you have written so far in this book have been **direct proofs.**

In **indirect reasoning,** a person tries to rule out all the possibilities except the one thought to be true. This is exactly what you did in solving the logic puzzles of the last lesson. You marked Xs in boxes to show that certain possibilities could not be true. When you had enough Xs, you knew that only the possibility left could be correct.

You can rule out a possibility if you know it is false. But how can you tell that a statement is false? One way to tell is if you know its negation is true. For instance, suppose you know $y = 5$ is true. Then $y \neq 5$ is false. Suppose you know $\triangle ABC$ is isosceles. Then it is false to say it is scalene.

You also know a statement is false if it contradicts another statement known to be true. For instance, if your friend Lillian is a senior, then she cannot be a junior. If you know 5 is a solution to an equation, and there is only one solution to that equation, then 3 cannot be a solution. If one statement contradicts another, they are called *contradictory*.

Example 1 Let p be the statement: $\angle V$ is acute. Let q be: $\angle V$ is right. Are p and q contradictory?

Solution Yes. An acute angle has measure less than 90. A right angle has measure 90. A number cannot be both less than 90 and 90 at the same time, so an angle cannot be both acute and right at the same time.

Example 2 Let p: *ABCD* is a rhombus. Let q: *ABCD* is a rectangle. Are p and q contradictory?

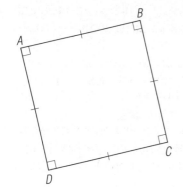

Solution No. p and q can be true at the same time. Square *ABCD* at the left is both a rhombus and a rectangle.

A **contradiction** is a situation in which two contradictory statements p and q are both asserted as true. Contradictions are false statements. In Example 1, the statement p *and* q ($\angle A$ is acute *and* $\angle A$ is right) is false, because p and q are contradictory. However, in Example 2, the statement p *and* q (*ABCD* is a rhombus *and ABCD* is a rectangle) is not necessarily false.

Sometimes it isn't so easy to tell whether a statement is true or false. Then you can employ the logic used by the lawyer in the situation described at the beginning of this lesson.

Step 1. If you think a statement is false, start by assuming it *for the moment* and reason from it. (The prosecutors thought the defendant was at the spot the crime was committed. The lawyer started with this assumption.)
Step 2. Using valid logic, try to make the reasoning lead to a contradiction or other false statement. (The lawyer argued that the defendant would then have had to be in two places at the same time.)
Step 3. Since the reasoning leads to a contradiction or other false statement, the assumed statement must be false. (The lawyer concluded that the defendant could not be at the scene of the crime.)

This logic exemplifies the *Law of Indirect Reasoning*. It is the fifth and last law of logic discussed in this book.

Law of Indirect Reasoning:

If valid reasoning from a statement p leads to a false conclusion, then p is false.

Example 3   Show that the statement $3(4 + 2x) = 6(x + 1)$ is never true.

Solution
Step 1.   Begin with the equation and reason from it as you would any normal equation to see what happens. First use the Distributive Property.
   $12 + 6x = 6x + 6$
Step 2.   Add -6x to each side. This leads to the conclusion $12 = 6$.
Step 3.   Since "12 = 6" is a false conclusion, by the Law of Indirect Reasoning, the original statement $3(4 + 2x) = 6(x + 1)$ is not true.

A proof using the Law of the Contrapositive, the Law of Ruling Out Possibilities, or the Law of Indirect Reasoning is called an **indirect proof.** The next two Examples suggest how to write indirect proofs.

Example 4   Use an indirect proof to show that $\sqrt{22200} \neq 149$.

Solution   No drawing is needed, so begin by analyzing the problem. There are only two possibilities here. Either $\sqrt{22200} = 149$ or $\sqrt{22200} \neq 149$. To show that the first possibility is false, reason from it to produce a contradiction. Write:

Either $\sqrt{22200} = 149$ or $\sqrt{22200} \neq 149$.
1. Assume $\sqrt{22200} = 149$.
2. Then, squaring both sides: $22200 = 149^2$.
However, by the definition of power,
$149^2 = 149 \cdot 149 = 22201$.
3. The two statements in step 2 are contradictory.
The assumption of step 1 has led to a false conclusion.
By the Law of Indirect Reasoning, the assumption of
step 1 is false. Thus $\sqrt{22200} \neq 149$.

Notice the steps in the proof. Start by stating all possibilities. Then pick an option you think is not true and make conclusions from it. Reason until you get a false conclusion. Then apply the Law of Indirect Reasoning to rule out that possibility. Rule out all possibilities until the statement you desire is the only one left.

Example 5 Use an indirect proof to show that no triangle has two obtuse angles.

Solution First rewrite in if-then form: If a figure is a triangle, then it does not have two obtuse angles. Now draw a representative triangle.

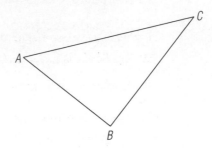

Either △ABC has two obtuse angles, say ∠A and ∠B, or it does not.
1. Assume both ∠A and ∠B are obtuse.
2. Then, by definition of obtuse, m∠A >90 and m∠B >90. By the Addition Property of Inequality, m∠A + m∠B >180. Then, because m∠C >0 for any angle in a triangle, m∠A + m∠B + m∠C > 180. But the Triangle-Sum Theorem says that m∠A + m∠B + m∠C = 180.
3. The last two statements in step 2 are contradictory. A false conclusion has been reached. By the Law of Indirect Reasoning, the assumption of step 1 is false. ∠A and ∠B cannot both be obtuse.

In Example 5, the following statement has been proved: (1) If a figure is a triangle, then it does not have two obtuse angles. Its contrapositive is: (2) If a figure has two obtuse angles, then it is not a triangle. By the Law of the Contrapositive, statement (2) is also true.

Questions

Covering the Reading

1. What kind of reasoning has the lawyer in this lesson used?

2. Beginning with $2 + 5x = 5x - 8$, a student added $-5x$ to each side and ended up with $2 = -8$. What should the student conclude?

3. Beginning with $\sqrt{2400} = 49$, a student squared both sides and wound up with $2400 = 2401$. What should the student conclude?

4. State the Law of Indirect Reasoning.

5. *Multiple choice.* Consider the equation $3(x - 2) = 3x - 2$. Which is true?
   (a) The equation has no solution (is never true).
   (b) The equation has one solution, 0.
   (c) The equation is true for all real numbers.

6. When are two statements contradictory?

7. By indirect reasoning, show that $\sqrt{9800} \neq 99$.

8. **a.** Draw a quadrilateral with three obtuse angles.
   b. By indirect reasoning, show that a quadrilateral cannot have all four angles obtuse.

Applying the Mathematics

In 9 and 10, give a statement contradictory to the given one.

9. $\triangle ABC$ is isosceles.

10. Coplanar lines m and n are parallel.

In 11–13, determine whether the statements are contradictory.

11. $m\angle A = 85$ and $\angle A$ is obtuse.

12. *GHIJ* is a trapezoid and *GHIJ* is a square.

13. Phil is older than 25 and Phil attends high school.

14. Either a triangle can have two right angles or it cannot.
    a. Show that one of these possibilities leads to a contradiction.
    b. Using the Law of Ruling Out Possibilities, what can you conclude?

15. **a.** Solve $-12x > 252$.
    b To do part **a**, did you use direct or indirect reasoning?

16. Refer to $\triangle ABC$ below.
    Given: $m\angle A > m\angle B > m\angle C$.
    Prove: $\triangle ABC$ is scalene.

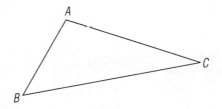

Review

17. (This puzzle is taken from *Quizzles,* by Wayne Williams, published by Grosset and Dunlap, 1976.) Mary, Isobel, Marcia, Grace, and Ruth are on the Grand Avenue School basketball team. Each girl has a different hair color. The hair colors are blond, red, auburn, black, and brunette. As it happens, no two girls on the team are the same height: they are 5'11", 5'10", 5'8", 5'7", and 5'6". From the clues given, try to determine the hair color and height of each of the girls on the team. (Hint: Use a grid like that shown in Lesson 13-3.)
    (1) Mary is taller than Ruth who is two inches taller than the redhead.
    (2) The brunette is not 5'8" tall.
    (3) Marcia and Mary are neither the tallest nor the shortest.
    (4) The girl with black hair is two inches taller than Ruth.
    (5) Isobel is taller than the blond, who is one inch taller than Grace.
    (Lesson 13-3)

18. Give the negation of this statement: $\triangle ABC \sim \triangle DEF$. *(Lesson 13-2)*

19. For the statement "If $\triangle ABC \sim \triangle DEF$, then $\angle A \cong \angle D$," write the
a. contrapositive, **b.** converse, and **c.** inverse.
d. which of these three statements is (are) true? *(Lesson 13-2)*

In 20 and 21, use the figure
at the right. $\overline{WV} \parallel \overline{ZY}$.

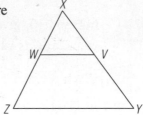

20. If $XW = 7$, $XV = 9$, and $VY = 11$, find WZ. *(Lesson 12-10)*

21. If $XW = 6$, $WZ = 3$, and $WV = 8$, find YZ. *(Lesson 12-3)*

22. Below, a rectangle is placed conveniently on a coordinate plane. Use the placement to prove: In any rectangle, the diagonals have the same length. *(Lesson 11-5)*

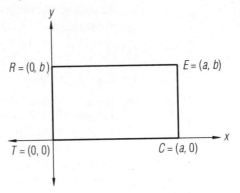

23. In everyday life, indirect reasoning is often used as follows. If you do A, then B will happen. B is horrible (or dangerous or some other bad thing). Therefore you should not do A. Give two examples of possible As and Bs.

13-5

Tangents to Circles and Spheres

This solar eclipse was photographed in space from an Apollo spacecraft. A solar eclipse observed from Earth is discussed on page 654.

Indirect reasoning has been used at least since the time of Euclid to deduce theorems. Early in this century, some mathematicians tried to see what could be deduced without indirect reasoning. These mathematicians allowed themselves to use only direct proofs. They were unable to find direct proofs for many important theorems for which there were indirect proofs. These attempts point out that indirect reasoning is necessary.

In this lesson, indirect reasoning is used to deduce two theorems about *tangents*. The word "tangent" comes from the Latin word meaning "touching." Think of a wheel (a circle) as tangent to a ramp (a line) as it rolls up or down the ramp. If the wheel and ramp are very hard, they are thought to have only one point in common.

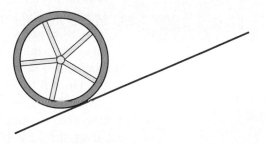

Definition

A **tangent to a circle** is a line which intersects the circle in exactly one point.

The point of intersection of a circle and the line is called the **point of tangency.**

Tangents to circles can be constructed easily, due to the following theorem. Notice how short its (indirect) proof is.

Theorem:

If a line is perpendicular to a radius of a circle at the radius's endpoint on the circle, then it is tangent to the circle.

Proof

Draw   Here is a figure and the theorem restated.
Given: ⊙O, $\overline{OP} \perp \ell$.
Prove: ℓ is tangent to the circle.

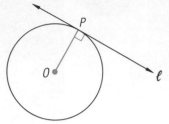

Analyze   It needs to be shown that no other point of ℓ is on the circle. Assume another point of ℓ is on the circle. This will lead to a contradiction.

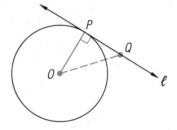

Write   Assume Q is another point on ℓ and on the circle. Since Q is on ℓ, $\triangle OPQ$ is a right triangle with hypotenuse $\overline{OQ}$. So $OQ > OP$. But since Q is on the circle, $OQ = OP$. The statement $OQ > OP$ and $OQ = OP$ is a contradiction. By the Law of Indirect Reasoning, the assumption must be false. So ℓ intersects the circle at exactly one point. By the definition of tangent (sufficient condition), ℓ is tangent to ⊙O.

The converse of this theorem is true, but its proof is longer. The proof uses the Law of the Contrapositive.

Theorem:

If a line is tangent to a circle, then it is perpendicular to the radius drawn to the point of tangency.

Proof

Draw   Below is a figure.
Restate the given and prove in terms of the figure.
Given: *m* is tangent to ⊙*O* at point *P*.
Prove: $\overline{OP} \perp m$.

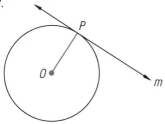

Analyze   The contrapositive is as follows:
Given: $\overline{OP}$ is not ⊥ to *m*.
Prove: *m* is not tangent to ⊙*O* at point *P*.

If the contrapositive is proven true, then the original statement is true.

Write   Since $\overline{OP}$ is not ⊥ to *m*, a different segment, $\overline{OQ}$, can be drawn from *O* perpendicular to *m*. Locate *R* on *m* so that *Q* is between *R* and *P* and *QR* = *QP*. Then △*OQR* ≅ △*OQP* because of the SAS Congruence Theorem. So *OR* = *OP*. This means *R* is on ⊙*O* (it is the same distance from *O* as *P*). So *m* contains two points on the circle. Thus *m* is not a tangent.

The contrapositive has been proved. By the Law of the Contrapositive, the original statement is true.

The two theorems of this lesson can be written as one if-and-only-if statement:

Radius-Tangent Theorem:

A line is tangent to a circle if and only if it is perpendicular to a radius at the radius's endpoint on the circle.

As you have learned, many properties of two-dimensional figures extend to three-dimensional figures. The idea of tangency extends very easily to spheres. A **tangent to a sphere** is a line or plane which intersects the sphere in exactly one point. That point is called the **point of tangency.** A common example of a plane tangent to a sphere is a ball resting on a ramp.

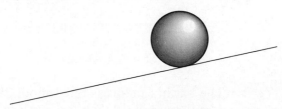

You can approximate the shape of the earth, moon, and sun with spheres. When the moon comes directly between the sun and a part of the earth, that part witnesses a *solar eclipse*. The figure here shows this but is misleading. The sun is relatively *much* bigger and these objects are *much* farther from each other.

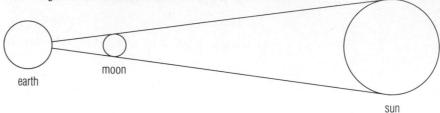

The lines in the above drawing are *common tangents* to the spheres of the moon and the sun. The tangent lines come very close to intersecting on the earth; at most only a small part of the earth sees a solar eclipse when it happens. If you ignore the earth in the drawing, then the drawing looks somewhat like a sphere and its size-change image. This means that there are proportions. These proportions can be used to calculate the radius of the sun.

- - - - - - - ■ ■ ■

Example   It is known that the moon is about 240,000 miles from the earth, the sun about 93,000,000 miles from the earth, and the moon's radius is 1080 miles. Estimate the radius of the sun.

Solution   First draw a picture. Here M and S are the centers of the sun and moon. N and T are points of tangency of a common tangent. The distances $EM = 240{,}000$, $ES = 93{,}000{,}000$, and $MN = 1080$ are known. ST is the radius of the sun.

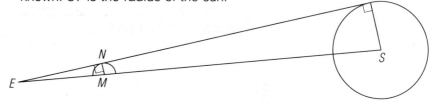

Because $\overline{MN}$ and $\overline{ST}$ are radii, they are perpendicular to $\overleftrightarrow{ET}$. Since $\angle E$ is common to $\triangle EMN$ and $\triangle EST$, by AA Similarity, $\triangle EMN \sim \triangle EST$. And so,

$$\frac{EM}{ES} = \frac{MN}{ST}.$$

Substituting for these lengths,

$$\frac{240000}{93000000} = \frac{1080}{ST}.$$

Simplify the fraction at the left to $\frac{24}{9300}$ before using your calculator! Solving this proportion, $ST = 418{,}500$ miles, quite close to the actual value of about 432,000 miles.

The earth's radius is only about 3960 miles, so the sun is well over 100 times bigger than the earth in its linear dimensions.

Covering the Reading

1. **a.** By definition, when is a line tangent to a circle?
    b. Give another condition sufficient for a line to be tangent to a circle.

2. ℓ is tangent to $\odot O$ below at P. Must ℓ be perpendicular to $\overline{OP}$?

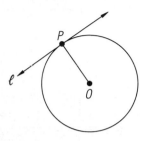

3. In the proof of the first theorem of this lesson, what contradiction is reached?

4. *Multiple choice.* The first two theorems of this lesson are
    (a) converses
    (b) inverses
    (c) contrapositives
    (d) negations.

5. To prove the second theorem in this lesson, what logical principle was applied?

6. **a.** About how many times larger than the moon is the sun?
    b. About how many times farther away from the earth is the sun than the moon?

7. $\overleftrightarrow{CA}$ below is a common tangent to circles P and Q at points A and B. If $CB = 5$, $AB = 10$, and the radius of circle Q is 3, what is the radius of circle P?

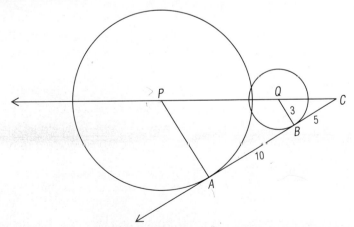

Applying the Mathematics

In 8–10, give a real-world example of the given mathematical idea.

8. a line tangent to a circle

9. a plane tangent to a sphere

10. a line tangent to a sphere

11. Use the given and the figure of Question 7. What is the length of $\overline{PQ}$?

12. a. Extend the if-and-only-if theorem of this lesson to apply to spheres.
   b. Is the extension true?

13. In the figure below at the left, $\overline{IZ}$ is tangent to sphere P at point I.
   a. Is $\overline{ZI} \perp \overline{IP}$?
   b. How many other tangents are there from point Z to sphere P?

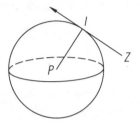
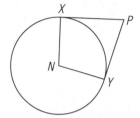

14. Refer to the figure above at the right.
   Given: Point P is outside $\odot N$;
   $\overline{PX}$ and $\overline{PY}$ are tangents to $\odot N$ at points X and Y.
   Prove: $PXNY$ is a kite. (You will have proved that the two tangents to circle N from point P have the same length. This is a theorem you should remember.)

15. Copy the figure below and draw the *four* common tangents to circles O and P.

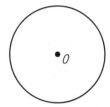

16. $\overline{PT}$ is tangent to $\odot O$ below at T. $PT = 12$ and $PO = 15$.
   a. What is the area of the circle?
   b. What is the distance from P to N, the point on the circle nearest to P?

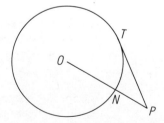

17. *Multiple choice.* Use the information in this lesson and assume that the earth and the sun have similar shape. Then the volume of the sun is about how many times the volume of the earth?
   (a) one thousand   (b) one million
   (c) one billion   (d) one trillion *(Lessons 12-6, 10-8)*

18. Give an indirect proof to show that $\sqrt{39,600} \neq 199$. *(Lesson 13-4)*

In 19 and 20, given the statements, **a.** what (if anything) can you conclude? **b.** What reasoning laws have you used?

19. (1) Either Julie walks to school or she rides her bicycle to school.
(2) Julie's bicycle is being repaired. *(Lesson 13-3)*

20. (1) All people who grew up in Mississippi have a southern accent.
(2) If you did not grow up in Mississippi, then you do not know the Ole Miss fight song.
(3) Murray does not have a southern accent. *(Lesson 13-2)*

21. a. Write the contrapositive of the statement: If a figure is a rectangle, then its diagonals are congruent.
b. Is the contrapositive true? *(Lesson 13-2)*

22. Draw the reflection line of the glide reflection mapping $\triangle ABC$ onto $\triangle XYZ$. *(Lesson 6-6)*

satellite view of the Mississippi Delta region of the United States

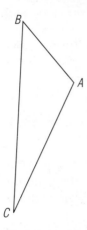

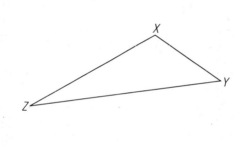

23. The drawing of the earth, sun, and moon in this lesson is nowhere near scale.
a. Draw a figure of the earth and the moon to scale using a tracing of the circle drawn at the left as the earth.
b. How far away would the sun be on the scale of your drawing and what would be its diameter?

24. Draw the relative positions of the moon, earth, and sun during an eclipse of the moon.

25. What is an annular eclipse?

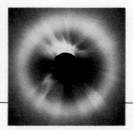

Total solar eclipse   2/26/79

When some people think of mathematics, they think of exactness. They think every question has exactly one answer. You know that isn't always the case. Some equations, like $x^2 = 49$, have more than one solution. Any proof can be done in many different ways. Estimation is one important part of mathematics. Probability and statistics are not exact.

Still, at times it is quite helpful to know there is exactly one of something, because then there is no possible confusion. It is said that the thing is **uniquely determined.**

In proofs, when a line or a circle or something else is uniquely determined, then it can be added to a given figure. It is called an **auxiliary** line or auxiliary circle, etc. Auxiliary lines were used in both proofs in the previous lesson.

For instance, if you are given a parallelogram, either diagonal is uniquely determined and can be an auxiliary line segment. The justification for this is part of the Point-Line-Plane Postulate studied in Chapter 1: Through two points, there is exactly one line. The phrase "exactly one" tells you that the line is uniquely determined.

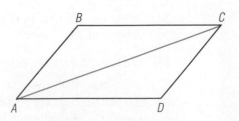

Parallelogram $ABCD$ with auxiliary segment $\overline{AC}$

If a figure is not uniquely determined, there are two possibilities. The first possibility is that there may be no such figure satisfying all the conditions. For instance, suppose you are given a parallelogram *ABCD* and want to draw a diagonal that bisects an angle. Although its angle bisectors are uniquely determined and diagonals are uniquely determined, you cannot be certain that a diagonal also is an angle bisector. They could be different lines. So you cannot add to this figure "a diagonal which is an angle bisector."

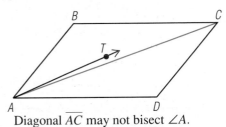

Diagonal $\overline{AC}$ may not bisect $\angle A$.
Angle bisector $\overrightarrow{AT}$ may not go through point *C*.

The second possibility is that many figures satisfy the condition(s). For instance, a segment has many bisectors. You could use a bisector of a segment in a proof but which bisector do you want?

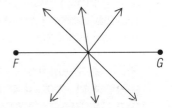

There are many bisectors of $\overline{FG}$.

A segment has exactly one midpoint. No one could speak of *the* midpoint unless there were only one. But uniqueness is not always so obvious. What about the number of lines parallel to a given line through a point not on it?

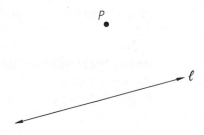

With algebra, it is easy to see that there is at least one parallel. It is the line through *P* with the same slope as ℓ. But is there more than one parallel? An indirect proof helps to deduce the answer, which is found in the next theorem.

Uniqueness of Parallels Theorem (Playfair's Parallel Postulate):

Through a point not on a line, there is exactly one parallel to the given line.

Proof

Since there is at least one parallel, the only other possibility is that there is more than one parallel. This is the situation to draw and the statement to reason from. A figure is drawn below.

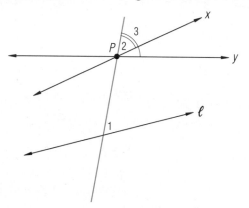

1. Assume there are two different lines x and y through P parallel to line ℓ.
2. Then angles 1 and 2 are corresponding angles, and so are angles 1 and 3. So, since // lines $\Rightarrow$ corr. $\angle$s =, $m\angle 1 = m\angle 2$ and also $m\angle 1 = m\angle 3$.
3. This means $m\angle 2 = m\angle 3$. But then the angle between lines x and y must have measure 0, which means the lines x and y are identical.
4. The last conclusion in step 3 contradicts the assumption of step 1. So we have reached a false conclusion. By the Law of Indirect Reasoning, the assumption of step 1 is false, so there is not more than one line through P parallel to ℓ. Since there is at least one such line, we can conclude that there is exactly one line through P parallel to ℓ.

Recall that a glide reflection is the composite of a reflection r_ℓ and a translation T in a direction parallel to ℓ. Here is a drawing of a point A and its image C under a glide reflection with reflecting line ℓ.

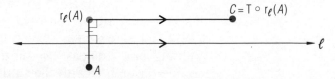

Notice how the Uniqueness of Parallels Theorem is used in the proof of the following theorem which was first stated in Lesson 6-6. This theorem, you may recall, helps to draw the reflecting line for a glide reflection if you know the location of a figure and its image.

Theorem:

In a glide reflection, the midpoint of the segment connecting a point to its image lies on the glide-reflection line.

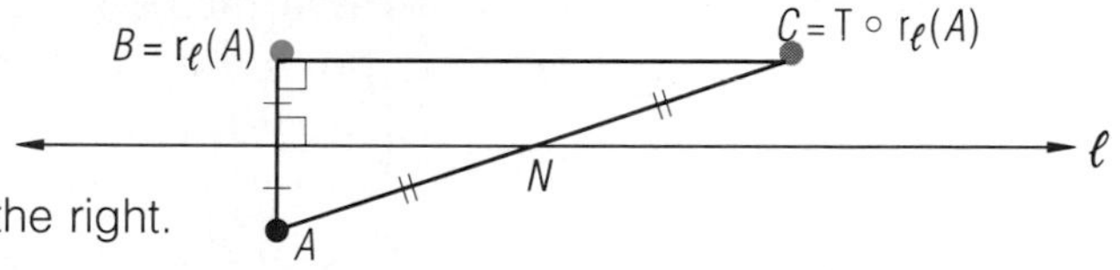

Proof

Use the figure at the right.

Given: $C = T \circ r_\ell (A)$,
where T is a translation parallel to ℓ.
N is the midpoint of $\overline{AC}$.

Prove: ℓ contains N.

Let $B = r_\ell (A)$ and let M be the midpoint of $\overline{AB}$. Now mark the figure.

From the Midpoint Connector Theorem, $\overleftrightarrow{MN}$ is parallel to $\overline{BC}$. But, from the definition of reflection, ℓ contains M, and because the translation T is parallel to ℓ, ℓ is parallel to $\overline{BC}$. Thus both ℓ and $\overleftrightarrow{MN}$ are parallel to $\overline{BC}$ through M. By the Uniqueness of Parallels Theorem, ℓ and $\overleftrightarrow{MN}$ must be the same line. Thus ℓ contains N.

The uniqueness of parallels statement is important in the history of mathematics. In fact, it ultimately changed the entire nature of mathematics.

Euclid began his geometry with ten assumptions, which today are called postulates, and with a number of definitions. Five of the postulates were algebraic in nature and caused no argument among mathematicians. The other five postulates were geometric and are given here in free translation.

Postulates of Euclid:

1. Two points determine a line segment.
2. A line segment can be extended indefinitely along a line.
3. A circle can be drawn with any center and any radius.
4. All right angles are congruent.
5. If two lines are cut by a transversal, and the interior angles on the same side of the transversal have a total measure of less than 180, then the lines will intersect on that side of the transversal.

You can see that the fifth postulate is much longer and more complex than the others. This bothered mathematicians, who felt that such a complicated statement should not be assumed true. For 2000 years they tried to prove the fifth postulate from Euclid's other assumptions.

Being unable to prove it, some mathematicians substituted simpler statements for it. The uniqueness of parallels property was first suggested by the Greek mathematician Proclus about A.D. 450, but it is known as *Playfair's Parallel Postulate* because it was used by the British mathematician John Playfair in the year 1795. The statement is proved as a theorem in this lesson based on assuming the Parallel Lines Postulate (// lines $\Rightarrow$ corr. $\angle$s =).

Other mathematicians substituted different statements for Playfair's Parallel Postulate. When they assumed there were no parallels to a line through a point not on it, they were able to develop a spherical geometry that could apply to the surface of the earth. When they assumed there was more than one parallel to a line through a point not on it, they developed types of geometry for other surfaces. These geometries are called *non-Euclidean*.

The works of these mathematicians greatly influenced *all* later mathematics. For the first time, postulates were viewed as statements *assumed* true instead of statements definitely true. After them, mathematicians experimented with a variety of algebras and geometries formed by modifying or changing postulates. Their experiments were at first thought to be merely a game, but are now considered quite important. Non-Euclidean geometries are important in physics in the theory of relativity. A useful algebra, different from what you have studied, is applied in the construction of computers.

Questions

Covering the Reading

In 1–3, tell whether the auxiliary figure is or is not uniquely determined.

1. a line through two points

2. a line parallel to a given line through a point not on it

3. a diagonal bisecting an angle of a quadrilateral

In 4 and 5, draw the reflecting line of the glide reflection mapping one figure onto the other.

4. 5.

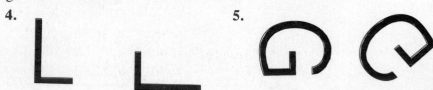

6. State Playfair's Parallel Postulate.

7. How many postulates were in Euclid's geometry?

8. How many of Euclid's postulates were geometric in nature?

9. Which of Euclid's postulates listed in the lesson most troubled mathematicians?

10. Can Playfair's Parallel Postulate be proved from the first four postulates of Euclid?

11. Geometries in which Playfair's Parallel Postulate is not true are called __?__ .

12. Since the discovery of non-Euclidean geometries, postulates have been viewed as __?__ rather than as statements which are definitely true.

Applying the Mathematics

In 13–18, use a ruler, compass, and protractor or an automatic drawer. Copy the drawing of $\triangle ABC$ for each question, then draw the given auxiliary figure. Tell whether the auxiliary figure is uniquely determined.

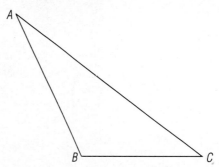

13. segment connecting A to the midpoint of $\overline{BC}$ (a median of the triangle)

14. perpendicular to $\overleftrightarrow{AB}$ through C (an altitude of the triangle)

15. reflection image of B over the line $\overleftrightarrow{AC}$

16. bisector of $\overline{AB}$

17. point E between A and B

18. point D on $\overrightarrow{AC}$ so that $AD = BC$

19. Draw a figure describing Euclid's fifth postulate. State the antecedent and consequent of that postulate in terms of your figure.

20. Euclid's first postulate is like what postulate in this book?

21. Euclid's third postulate is like what property of constructions?

22. *Multiple choice.* Which of these lines is parallel to the line with equation $3x + 2y = 5$ and contains the point $(10, 13)$?
   (a) $3x + 2y = 23$ (b) $2x - 3y = 23$
   (c) $3x + 2y = 56$ (d) $2x - 3y = 56$

23. $\overline{PT}$ is tangent to $\odot O$ at point T. If $PO = 20$ and $PT = 16$, what is the radius of $\odot O$? *(Lesson 13-5)*

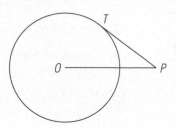

24. Show by indirect reasoning that a quadrilateral cannot have four acute angles. *(Lesson 13-4)*

In 25 and 26, given the statements, what (if anything) can you conclude using all the given statements and the rules of logic? *(Lessons 13-3, 13-2, 13-1)*

25. (1) You are elected President of the U.S. if you win the majority of electoral votes.
(2) In 1960, Richard Nixon was not elected President.

Richard Nixon delivered a campaign address at Dallas Memorial Auditorium.

26. (1) Miami won the football game 6–3.
(2) You can score six points in football by three safeties, two field goals, or one touchdown.
(3) Miami did not have any safeties or touchdowns.

In 27 and 28, consider kites, trapezoids, parallelograms, rhombuses, and rectangles. Name the types of quadrilaterals for which the property is always true. *(Lessons 5-5, 5-4, 5-2)*

27. The diagonals are congruent.

28. There is a pair of congruent sides.

29. What does the word *auxiliary* mean outside of mathematics?

30. a. Name five things outside of mathematics which are unique.
b. Name five things which are not unique.

31. Who owns the zebra?

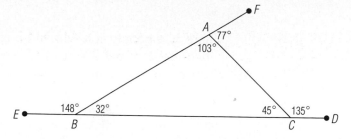

13-7

Exterior Angles

Above is pictured a triangle. At each vertex, one of its sides has been extended. The angles formed in this way are the *exterior angles* of the triangle. In this lesson and the next one, various techniques are applied to determine properties of exterior angles of triangles and other polygons.

Definition:

An angle is an **exterior angle** of a polygon if and only if it forms a linear pair with one of the angles of the polygon.

Above, the exterior angles are $\angle ABE$, $\angle ACD$, and $\angle FAC$. To distinguish exterior angles of a polygon from the polygon's own angles, the angles of the polygon are called **interior angles.** Measures of exterior angles in triangles are quite nicely related to the measures of the triangle's interior angles. Notice above that each exterior angle measure is the sum of the measures of two of the triangle's interior angles: $148 = 103 + 45$; $77 = 45 + 32$; and $135 = 103 + 32$. The general property is quite easy to prove using algebra.

Exterior Angle Theorem:

In a triangle, the measure of an exterior angle is equal to the sum of the measures of the two nonadjacent interior angles.

Proof

Draw   A triangle is shown here.

Given: $\triangle ABC$, exterior $\angle 4$.
Prove: $m\angle 4 = m\angle 2 + m\angle 3$.
Write   By the Triangle-Sum Theorem,
$$m\angle 1 + m\angle 2 + m\angle 3 = 180.$$
Since $\angle ACB$ and $\angle ACD$ form a linear pair,
$$m\angle 1 + m\angle 4 = 180.$$
So these sums of angle measures are equal to each other:
$$m\angle 1 + m\angle 4 = m\angle 1 + m\angle 2 + m\angle 3.$$
Subtracting $m\angle 1$ from each side,
$$m\angle 4 = m\angle 2 + m\angle 3.$$

There is a conclusion which directly follows from this theorem. Since m∠4 = m∠2 + m∠3, use the Equation to Inequality Property to conclude

　　　　m∠4 > m∠2
and　　m∠4 > m∠3.

The result is called the *Exterior Angle Inequality*.

Exterior Angle Inequality:

In a triangle, the measure of an exterior angle is greater than the measure of either nonadjacent interior angle.

Example 1　Refer to the figure below. If m∠APE = 35, what can be concluded about the other angle measures?

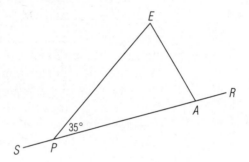

Solution　You can actually conclude something about each angle in the figure. m∠SPE = 145 by the Linear Pair Theorem.
Now, applying the Exterior Angle Inequality,
　　　　　　m∠E < 145
　　　and m∠EAP < 145.
The Exterior Angle Inequality also shows that m∠EAR > 35.

The Exterior Angle Inequality enables some properties of interior angles to be deduced. Below is a scalene triangle with sides and angles measured to the nearest millimeter and degree. Notice the smallest angle is opposite the smallest side; the largest angle is opposite the largest side. This important result is true in any triangle.

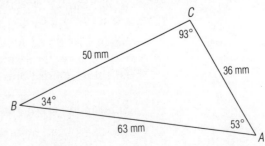

Unequal Sides Theorem:

> If two sides of a triangle are not congruent, then the angles opposite them are not congruent, and the larger angle is opposite the longer side.

Proof

First we draw a figure and state the given and to prove in terms of that figure.

Given: $\triangle ABC$ with $BA > BC$.
Prove: $m\angle C > m\angle A$.

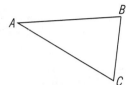

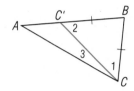

Angles opposite sides have already been explored in isosceles triangles. To use these results, draw an isosceles triangle as at the left by locating C' on $\overrightarrow{BA}$ so that $BC' = BC$. Then C' is between A and B because $BA > BC'$.

Conclusions	Justifications
1. Identify point C' on $\overrightarrow{BA}$ with $BC' = BC$.	On a ray, there is exactly one point at a given distance from an endpoint.
2. $m\angle 1 = m\angle 2$	Isosceles Triangle Theorem
3. $m\angle 2 > m\angle A$	Exterior Angle Inequality (with $\triangle CC'A$)
4. $m\angle 1 > m\angle A$	Substitution (step 2 into step 3)

[Comment: Now all that is left to show is that $m\angle BCA > m\angle 1$.]

5. $m\angle 1 + m\angle 3 = m\angle BCA$	Angle Addition Postulate
6. $m\angle BCA > m\angle 1$	Equation to Inequality Property
7. $m\angle BCA > m\angle A$	Transitive Property of Inequality (steps 4 and 6)

The contrapositive of any theorem is true, as you know. The contrapositive of the Isosceles Triangle Theorem is: If two angles in a triangle are not congruent, then the sides opposite them are not congruent. But which side is opposite the larger angle? Because of the Unequal Sides Theorem, the larger side cannot be opposite the smaller angle. All possibilities but one have been ruled out. The larger side must be opposite the larger angle.

Unequal Angles Theorem:

> If two angles of a triangle are not congruent, then the sides opposite them are not congruent, and the longer side is opposite the larger angle.

Example 2   In △QRS at the left, arrange the sides in order from shortest to longest.

Solution   From the Triangle-Sum Theorem,
$$m\angle Q + 88 + 49 = 180$$
so $m\angle Q = \ 43$
Since m∠Q is the smallest angle measure, $\overline{RS}$ is the shortest side.
Since m∠R is the largest, $\overline{QS}$ is the longest side. Thus the sides of △QRS from shortest to longest are: $\overline{RS}$, $\overline{RQ}$, $\overline{QS}$.

Questions

Covering the Reading

In 1 and 2, use the figure below.

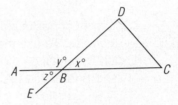

1. If m∠C = 50 and m∠D = 90, find
   a. *x*   **b.** *y*   **c.** *z.*

2. How is m∠ABD related to m∠C and m∠D?

In 3–5, sides of △FGI have been extended in the drawing below. For the named angle, give two angles with less measure.

3. ∠4

4. ∠5

5. ∠6

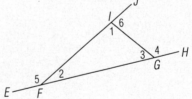

6. **a.** State the Exterior Angle Theorem..
   b. State the Exterior Angle Inequality.

In 7–10, use the triangles below.

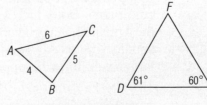

7. Name the largest angle of △ABC.

8. Name the smallest angle of △ABC.

9. Name the longest side of △DEF.

10. Name the shortest side of △DEF.

668

11. *True or false?* In an obtuse triangle, the longest side is opposite the obtuse angle.

12. In △*LUV, LU > UV > LV* and one angle has measure 60. Which angle is it?

13. Name the shortest segment in the figure below. (The figure is not necessarily drawn accurately.)

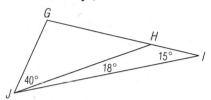

In 14 and 15, segments $\overline{PS}$ and $\overline{PR}$ trisect $\overline{QT}$ in right triangle *PQT* below.

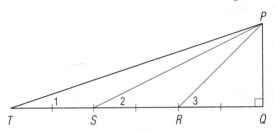

14. Prove: m∠3 > m∠1.   **15.** Prove: *PQ < PS.*

16. In △*UVW, X* is between *U* and *V*. If m∠*WXU* = 70, what can be concluded about
a. m∠*V*
b. m∠*U*
c. m∠*UWX?*

17. Below, $\overrightarrow{CB}$ bisects ∠*ACD.* In terms of *x* and *y,* find:
a. m∠*ACB*
b. m∠*CBD*
c. m∠*D.*

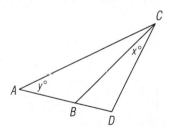

18. In △*PQR,* a student wanted to draw the line from *P* perpendicular to $\overline{QR}$ at its midpoint. **a.** Is this auxiliary line uniquely determined? **b.** If so, give the justification. If not, tell why not. *(Lesson 13-6)*

19. State Playfair's Parallel Postulate. *(Lesson 13-6)*

20. Are postulates definitely true? *(Lesson 13-6)*

21. How many postulates did Euclid use that are geometric? *(Lesson 13-6)*

22. Prove: The tangent lines to the endpoints of a diameter are parallel. *(Lesson 13-5)*

23. $\overrightarrow{AC}$ is a common tangent to $\odot O$ and $\odot P$ below. The radius of $\odot O$ is 3 cm and the radius of $\odot P$ is 8 cm. If $AB = 12$ cm, find AC. *(Lesson 13-5)*

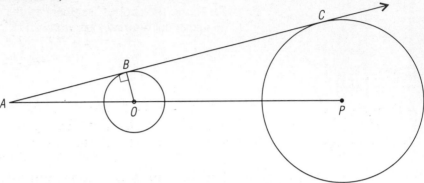

24. Solve $15(x - 7) = 3(19 + 5x)$. *(Lesson 13-4, Previous course)*

Exploration

25. a. Show that the Exterior Angle Inequality is not true for pentagons.
   b. Is the Exterior Angle Inequality true for quadrilaterals?

13-8

Exterior Angles of Polygons

Think of walking around a convex polygon. At each vertex, you must change direction. The amount of the change in direction is measured by an exterior angle at that vertex.

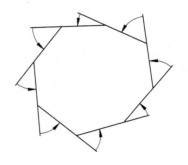

The total amount of change in direction, as you walk around, is the *sum of the measures of the exterior angles of the polygon,* where one exterior angle is picked at each vertex.

Since the sum of the *interior* angle measures gets larger as the number of sides of the polygon increases, you might think that the sum of exterior angle measures also increases. What is surprising is that the sum of the exterior angle measures does not increase. The sum is constant. It is the same as one revolution, 360°. It is the same amount as you turn in going around a circle.

Exterior Angles of a Polygon Sum Theorem:

In any convex polygon, the sum of the measures of the exterior angles, one at each vertex, is 360.

Proof

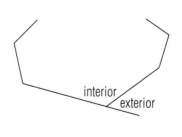

Consider any convex n-gon. It has n vertices. At each vertex, the measures of the interior angle and one exterior angle add to 180. So the sum of the interior and exterior angles at the n vertices is $(180n)$. But we know the sum of the interior angle measures is $180(n - 2)$ degrees. So form this equation (all measures are in degrees):

Sum of interior angles	+	sum of exterior angles	=	sum of all interior-exterior pairs.
$180(n - 2)$	+	x	=	$180n$

Solving this equation for x,

$$180n - 360 + x = 180n$$
$$-360 + x = 0$$
$$x = 360.$$

The previous theorem gives an alternate way of finding the number of degrees in each angle of a regular polygon.

Example The regular polygon at the left has 18 sides.

a. How many degrees are in each exterior angle?

b. How many degrees are in each interior angle?

Solution

a. The sum of the exterior angles is 360. Since the polygon is regular, all of the interior angles have the same measure. So all the exterior angles do also. There are 18 exterior angles, so each must have measure 20.

b. Each interior angle forms a linear pair with an exterior angle. Thus each interior angle has measure 160.

The idea of the Example is used in the computer language Logo to create regular polygons. In Logo, the command FORWARD traces a segment on a screen of a particular length. The command RIGHT turns the arrow clockwise the number of degrees you specify.

REPEAT simply does it as many times as indicated. Here is a Logo program for drawing a regular 18-gon in which each side has length 7. A side of length 7 is drawn, the tracer turns 20° clockwise for the exterior angle, and this is repeated 17 more times. Call the polygon REGGON. (If you stored REGGON in the machine, then you could call upon it later in some more complicated program.) Notice how short the program is.

```
TO REGGON
    REPEAT 18 [FORWARD 7 RIGHT 20]
END
```

To draw something that looks more like a circle, make the length of the segment smaller and the angle smaller. The following will look very much like a circle. Make the length 3, the turn 2°. This must be repeated 180 times to get all the way around.

```
TO 180GON
    REPEAT 180 [FORWARD 3 RIGHT 2]
END
```

The results of these programs are shown here.

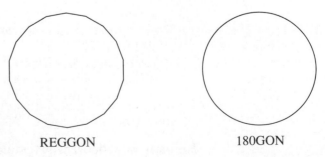

REGGON   180GON

1. A pentagon with some sides extended is drawn below.
a. Find a.
b. Find $a + b + c + d + e$.

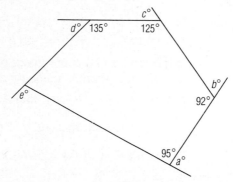

2. a. In a hexagon, the sum of the measures of the interior angles is _?_ .
b. The sum of the measures of the exterior angles is _?_ .

3. In an n-gon, give:
a. the sum of the measures of the interior angles;
b. the sum of the measures of the exterior angles.

4. Below is regular polygon *CONSIDERABLY*.
a. What is m∠*SIX*?   **b.** m∠*SID* = _?_

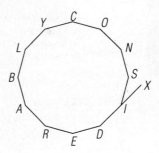

5. Write a Logo program that will draw a regular octagon with sides of length 12.

6. Write a Logo program that will draw a regular decagon with sides of length 5.

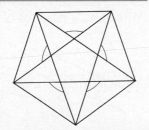

7. What will this Logo Program draw?
```
TO OBJECT
   REPEAT 30 [FORWARD 4 RIGHT 12]
END
```

8. A regular pentagon and its diagonals is drawn at the left. Five angles are marked in the figure. What is the sum of their measures?

9. Using an indirect proof, prove that no convex decagon has four right interior angles.

10. Refer to the figure at the right. If m∠CBD = 71, what can be concluded about
    a. m∠ABD
    b. m∠C
    c. m∠D? *(Lesson 13-7)*

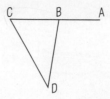

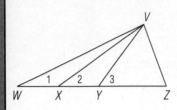

11. Refer to the figure at the left. Which angle is the smallest: 1, 2, or 3? Justify your conclusion. *(Lesson 13-7)*

In 12–14, *A* and *B* are given points. Draw the indicated figure. Tell whether the figure is uniquely determined. *(Lessons 13-6, 4-5, 2-5)*

12. point *C* on $\overleftrightarrow{AB}$ such that $AC = \frac{1}{2}AB$

13. point *C* such that $AC = CB$

14. point *C* such that $\triangle ABC$ is equilateral

15. A square and a circle each have area 400 square meters. Which has the larger perimeter? *(Lessons 8-3, 8-1)*

16. Where should you aim on wall *x* below to shoot a golf ball *G* off sides *x, y,* and *z* and into the hole at *H*? *(Lesson 6-4)*

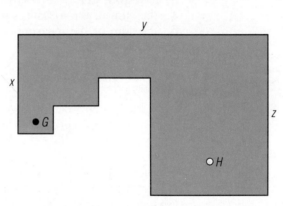

17. $\overline{AC}$ is a diagonal of rectangle *ABCD* below. $\overline{AC} \perp \overline{PB}$. Name all angles with the same measure as ∠*CAB*. *(Lesson 5-7)*

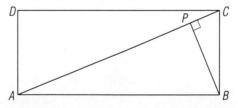

18. a. Run the Logo program for REGGON in this lesson. (You will need to find Logo software to do this.) Bring in a printout of what you get.
    b. Make up a Logo program of your own.

Summary

Every mathematical argument follows rules of logic. In this chapter, five rules are stated.

Law of Detachment: If you have a statement or given information p and a justification of the form $p \Rightarrow q$, you may conclude q.

Law of Transitivity: If $p \Rightarrow q$ and $q \Rightarrow r$, then $p \Rightarrow r$.

Law of the Contrapositive: A statement $p \Rightarrow q$ and its contrapositive $not\text{-}q \Rightarrow not\text{-}p$ are either both true or both false.

Law of Ruling Out Possibilities: When $p \text{ or } q$ is true and q is not true, then p is true.

Law of Indirect Reasoning: If valid reasoning from a statement p leads to a false conclusion, then p is false.

The last three of these laws are the logic used in indirect proofs. If you can prove that the contrapositive of a statement is true, then the statement is true. If you can rule out all possibilities but one, then the possibility left is true. If you reason from the negation of what you want to prove and arrive at a contradiction, then the negation is false. Thus what you want to prove must be true.

Indirect reasoning is used in everyday life, in puzzle problems, and throughout mathematics. In this chapter, indirect reasoning was applied in the proof of Playfair's Parallel Postulate, a very important postulate in the history of mathematics, and to prove theorems about tangents to circles and angles in triangles and polygons.

Vocabulary

Below are the most important terms and phrases for the chapter.
For the starred (*) terms you should be able to give a definition of the term.
For the other terms you should be able to give a general description and a specific example of each.

Lesson 13-1
Law of Detachment
Law of Transitivity (Transitive
    Property of Implication)

Lesson 13-2
negation, *not-p*
inverse
contrapositive
Law of the Contrapositive

Lesson 13-3
Law of Ruling Out Possibilities
Trichotomy Law

Lesson 13-4
direct reasoning, direct proof
indirect reasoning, indirect proof
*contradictory, *contradiction
Law of Indirect Reasoning

Lesson 13-5
*tangent to a circle
point of tangency
Radius-Tangent Theorem
tangent to a sphere, tangent
common tangents

Lesson 13-6
uniquely determined
auxiliary
Uniqueness of Parallels Theorem
    (Playfair's Parallel Postulate)
Postulates of Euclid
non-Euclidean

Lesson 13-7
*exterior angle
Exterior Angle Theorem
Exterior Angle Inequality
Unequal Sides Theorem
Unequal Angles Theorem

Lesson 13-8
Exterior Angles of a Polygon
    Sum Theorem
Logo

Progress Self-Test

Directions: Take this test as you would take a test in class. Then check your work with the solutions in the Selected Answers section in the back of the book.

1. Consider the statement: If a figure is a hexagon, then it is a polygon.
   a. Is the statement true?
   b. Write the inverse of this statement.
   c. Show that the inverse is false by drawing a counterexample.

2. Consider the statement: If two angles are adjacent, then they form a linear pair.
   a. Write the contrapositive of the statement.
   b. Is the contrapositive true?

3. $\angle A$ in $\triangle ABC$ is neither acute nor obtuse.
   a. What can you conclude?
   b. What law of logic have you used?

4. Write an argument to show why no triangle can have three angles all with measures under 50°.

5. Write an indirect proof to show that $\sqrt{80} \neq 40$.

6. What is the measure of an exterior angle of a regular duodecagon?

7. Write a Logo program that will draw a regular octagon with sides of length 6.

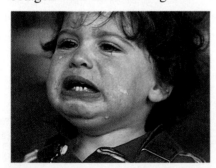

8. What (if anything) can you conclude using all the following statements?
   (1) All babies are happy.
   (2) If someone is teething, then that person is a baby.
   (3) Nate is sad.

9. *Multiple choice.* In the figure below, Y is between X and Z but the figure is not necessarily drawn accurately. Which is the shortest segment?
   (a) WX (b) WY (c) WZ
   (d) XY (e) XZ (f) YZ

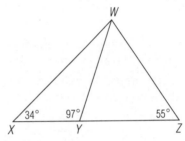

10. In the figure below, suppose m$\angle ABD = 120$. What can be concluded about
    a. m$\angle CBD$
    b. m$\angle C$
    c. m$\angle D$?

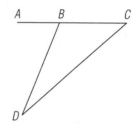

11. Until the discovery of non-Euclidean geometries, postulates were thought to be __?__ true. Now it is realized that they are only __?__ true.

In 12 and 13, give a justification for drawing the auxiliary line in this figure, or indicate that it cannot be justified.

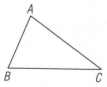

12. the line through C parallel to $\overleftrightarrow{AB}$

13. the bisector of $\angle B$ containing the midpoint of $\overline{AC}$

14. $\overline{PU}$ and $\overline{PT}$ are tangents to $\odot O$ below. If $\angle P$ is a right angle, what kind of quadrilateral is *OUPT*?

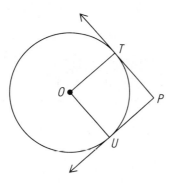

15. $\overrightarrow{CE}$ is a common tangent to $\odot A$ and $\odot B$. If $BD = 9$, $CD = 20$, and $CE = 50$, find the radius of $\odot A$.

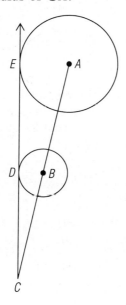

16. Four cards, the Jack, Queen, King, and Ace, are from four different centuries, the seventeenth, eighteenth, nineteenth, and twentieth. From the clues below, match each card to its century. (Note: the seventeenth century covers the years from 1601–1700; the eighteenth: 1701–1800; the nineteenth: 1801–1900; the twentieth: 1901–2000.)
1. The Queen is older than the King.
2. The Jack is exactly 100 years older than the Queen.
3. The Ace is older than the Jack.

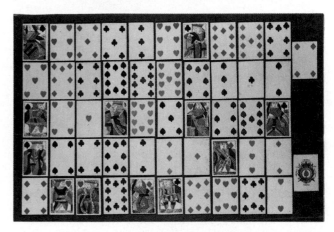

Chapter Review

Questions on **SPUR** Objectives

SPUR stands for **S**kills, **P**roperties, **U**ses, and **R**epresentations.
The Chapter Review questions are grouped according to the
SPUR Objectives for this chapter.

SKILLS deal with the procedures used to get answers.

■ **Objective A:** *Draw regular polygons using Logo programs.* *(Lesson 13-8)*

In 1 and 2, write a Logo program which will draw the following figures.

1. a regular hexagon with sides of length 10

2. a regular 360-gon with sides of length $\frac{1}{2}$

■ **Objective B:** *Determine measures of exterior angles in polygons.* *(Lesson 13-8)*

3. Refer to $\triangle XYZ$ below.
  a. Find $m\angle X$.
  b. Find $m\angle Y$.

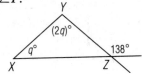

4. a. The sum of the measures of the exterior angles in a regular octagon is __?__ .
  b. The measure of each interior angle in a regular octagon is __?__ .

PROPERTIES deal with the principles behind the mathematics.

■ **Objective C:** *Write the converse, inverse, or contrapositive of a conditional.* *(Lesson 13-2)*

In 5–8, write **a.** the converse, **b.** the inverse, and **c.** the contrapositive of the statement. **d.** Tell which of these is (are) true.

5. If $x = 3$, then $x^2 = 9$.

6. If a figure is a rectangle, then it is a square.

7. All New Yorkers live in the U.S.

Times Square, New York City

8. Use the figure below. If $m\angle ABC = 40$, then $m\angle DBC = 140$.

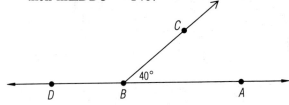

■ **Objective D:** *Follow the basic laws of reasoning to make conclusions.* *(Lessons 13-1, 13-2, 13-3, 13-4)*

In 9–15, using all the statements,
a. what (if anything) can you conclude?
b. What laws of reasoning have you used?

9. (1) If a figure is a rectangle, then it is a trapezoid.
  (2) *LOVE* is a rectangle.

10. (1) If corresponding angles formed by a transversal are congruent, then two lines are parallel.
    (2) If alternate interior angles formed by a transversal are congruent, then so are corresponding angles.

11. (1) If $x = 11$, then $y = 10$.
    (2) $y = 7$

12. (1) $x = 11$ or $y = 10$.
    (2) $y = 7$

13. (1) If $\ell \perp m$, then $m\angle A = 90$.
    (2) $m\angle A = 75$

14. (1) If you answer this correctly, you will make me feel good.
    (2) I will give you a hug if you make me feel good.
    (3) You answer this correctly.

15. The following is from Lewis Carroll.
    (1) No name in this list is unsuitable for the hero of a romance.
    (2) Names beginning with a vowel are always melodious.
    (3) No name is suitable for the hero of a romance, if it begins with a consonant.

16. Solving
    $(2x - 5)(3x + 4) = (x - 1)(6x - 1)$,
    Nella came up with the equation $-20 = 1$.
    a. What should Nella conclude?
    b. What law of logic is being used?

17. The area of a square is 48 mm². A certain teacher claims that the perimeter of that same square is 144 mm.
    a. What can you conclude?
    b. What rule of logic is being applied to answer part **a**?

18. a, b, c, d, and e are the numbers 1, 2, 3, 4, and 5 but not necessarily in that order. From the clues, match each of the variables and numbers.
    (1) d is not odd.
    (2) e is larger than c.
    (3) c and b are not primes.
    (4) d is larger than b.

■ **Objective E:** *Write indirect proofs. (Lesson 13-4)*

19. Explain why a quadrilateral cannot have four acute angles.

20. Give an indirect proof to show $\sqrt{2400} \neq 49$.

21. Give an indirect proof to show that $\sqrt{2} \neq \frac{239}{169}$.

■ **Objective F:** *Make deductions from properties of radii perpendicular to tangents. (Lesson 13-5)*

22. $\overline{AB}$ and $\overline{AC}$ are tangents to $\odot D$.
    a. What kind of figure is $ABDC$?
    b. What kind of figure is ABD?

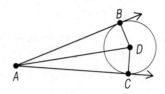

23. Use the figure above. If $AD = 41$ and $AC = 40$, find the circumference of $\odot D$.

In 24 and 25, $\overrightarrow{XZ}$ is a common tangent to $\odot O$ and $\odot P$ below.

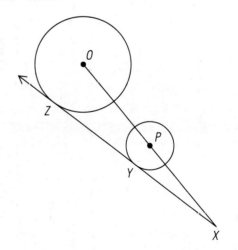

24. If $XY = 10$, $OZ = 8$, and $PY = 4$, find ZY.

25. If the radius of $\odot P$ is 15 mm, $XZ = 165$ mm, and $XY = 45$ mm, find the area of $\odot O$.

Objective G: *Justify auxiliary lines.* *(Lesson 13-6)*

In 26–29, give a justification for drawing the auxiliary line in this figure, or indicate that it cannot be justified.

26. diagonal $\overline{AC}$
27. line $\overleftrightarrow{CE}$ parallel to $\overline{AD}$
28. the bisector of $\angle B$
29. the $\perp$ bisector of $\overline{AB}$ and $\overline{CD}$

Objective H: *From given information, deduce which sides or angles of triangles are smallest or largest.* *(Lesson 13-7)*

In 30 and 31, refer to $\triangle ABC$ below.

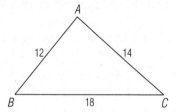

30. Name the largest angle.
31. Name the smallest angle.

In 32 and 33, the figures are not drawn accurately.

32. Name the sides of $\triangle DEF$ below in order from shortest to longest.

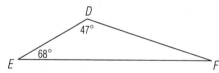

33. Refer to the figure *GHIJ* at the right. Name the shortest segment in the figure.

Objective I: *Use the Exterior Angle Inequality to determine angle measures.* *(Lesson 13-7)*

34. In $\triangle QRS$ below, if m$\angle QST = 132$, what can be concluded about
    a. m$\angle QSR$
    b. m$\angle Q$
    c. m$\angle R$?

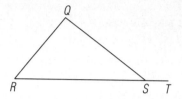

35. Refer to the figure below. Which angle is largest: 1, 2, 3, or 4? Explain your reasoning.

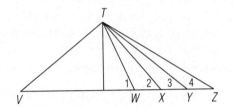

■ **Objective J:** *Apply laws of reasoning in real situations.* *(Lessons 13-1, 13-2, 13-3, 13-4)*

In 36–38, given the statements, what (if anything) can you conclude using the rules of logic?

36. (1) I am allowed to watch TV at 8 pm if I finish my homework.
(2) I am not allowed to watch TV at 8 pm.

37. (1) Either Mary is too old for camp or she can go to camp.
(2) Mary cannot go to camp.

38. (1) All bats are mammals.
(2) No mammal can live without air.
(3) Air is not found on the moon.

39. Ted is looking for his lost homework paper. It isn't in his notebook. It isn't in his school locker. So he concludes that it is at home.
a. What reasoning law has he used?
b. What is wrong with his reasoning?

There are no representations objectives in this chapter.

■ **Objective K:** *Know the history and impact of Playfair's Parallel Postulate on the development of geometry.* *(Lesson 13-6)*

40. How many geometric postulates were in Euclid's *Elements*?

41. State Playfair's Parallel Postulate.

42. How did the development of non-Euclidean geometry change the view of the truth of Euclid's postulates?

Trigonometry and Vectors

A ship, animal, or projectile that goes through the water or air is subject to two basic forces. There is the movement due to the ship's motor, the animal's muscles, or the projectile's initial impetus. There is also the force of the air or water currents. The mathematics that explains how these or other forces combine is the mathematics of *vectors*.

The height of the mast of a ship can be calculated without having to climb the mast. The finding of unknown distances like this is one of the basic applications of *trigonometry*. In the age before man-made satellites could map the earth (that is, before 1957), trigonometry enabled people to determine the locations of mountain peaks and other landmarks so that accurate maps could be made.

A knowledge of trigonometry and vectors is necessary to understand the physical world around us. Sometimes a full semester course is devoted to studying trigonometry. Similarly, there are full semester courses which cover vector ideas.

In this chapter, you are not expected to become expert in either of these areas of mathematics. Your goal should be to understand the meaning and applications of such things as sines, cosines, tangents, components of vectors, and addition of vectors, so that when you encounter these ideas in later courses they will not be totally new to you.

The study of both trigonometry and vectors utilizes properties of right triangles. Consequently, this chapter begins with a more in-depth look at these triangles.

14-1

Special Right Triangles

The diagonal from home plate to second base or from first base to third divides the baseball diamond into two isosceles right triangles. See Example 1.

Certain right triangles have such relationships among their sides and angles that they are considered special. These triangles occur in many situations that involve other polygons. By drawing the diagonals of a square, eight isosceles right triangles are formed. (Can you find all eight?) Suppose the congruent sides have length x and the hypotenuse has length c, as in the triangle at the right below.

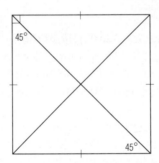
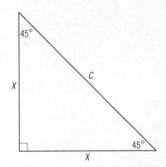

By the Pythagorean Theorem, $c^2 = x^2 + x^2$.
So $c^2 = 2x^2$.
Taking the positive square root, $c = x \cdot \sqrt{2}$.

The result is a relationship among the sides of any isosceles right triangle.

Isosceles Right Triangle Theorem:

In an isosceles right triangle, if a leg is x then the hypotenuse is $x\sqrt{2}$.

Notice that all isosceles right triangles are similar, because they all have the same angles: 45°, 45°, and 90°. Sometimes they are called **45-45-90 triangles**.

Example 1 A major league baseball diamond is a 90-ft square. In baseball, how far is it from home plate to second base?

Solution

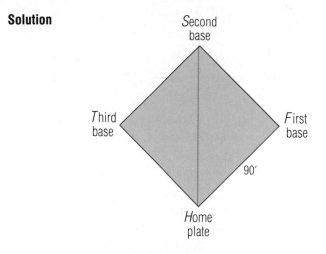

Triangle *HFS* is an isosceles right triangle with $\overline{HS}$ as its hypotenuse.

$HS = 90\sqrt{2}$ feet

≈ 127.3 feet

Another special right triangle is the **30-60-90 triangle.** It can be formed by any altitude of an equilateral triangle or by drawing diagonals in a regular hexagon. How many 30-60-90 triangles are in the drawing below at the right?

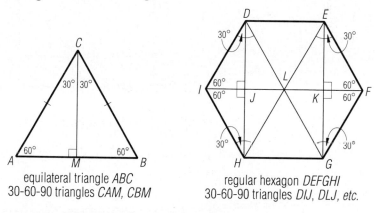

equilateral triangle *ABC*
30-60-90 triangles *CAM, CBM*

regular hexagon *DEFGHI*
30-60-90 triangles *DIJ, DLJ, etc.*

Again the lengths have a simple relationship.

30-60-90 Triangle Theorem:

In a 30-60-90 triangle, if the short leg is *x* then the longer leg is $x\sqrt{3}$ and the hypotenuse is 2*x*.

Proof

Here is a figure with the given and what is to be proved in terms of the figure.

Given: $\triangle ABC$ with $m\angle A = 30$, $m\angle B = 60$, $m\angle C = 90$. The shorter leg is opposite the smaller acute angle, so let $BC = x$.
Prove: (1) $AB = 2x$;
(2) $AC = x\sqrt{3}$.

The idea is to think of $\triangle ABC$ as half an equilateral triangle and use the Pythagorean Theorem.

(1) Reflect $\triangle ABC$ over $\overleftrightarrow{AC}$. Let $D = r_{\overleftrightarrow{AC}}(B)$. Reflections preserve distance, so $CD = x$. Since reflections preserve angle measure, the image $\triangle ADC$ is a 30-60-90 right triangle, with $m\angle ACD = 90$, $m\angle ADC = 60$, and $m\angle CAD = 30$. Thus, B, C, and D are collinear, and the big triangle ABD has three 60° angles making it equilateral with $AB = BD = 2x$.

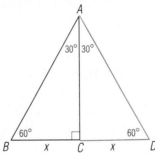

(2) Now, using $AB = 2x$, we can apply the Pythagorean Theorem to $\triangle ABC$ and get AC.

$$AC^2 + BC^2 = AB^2$$
$$AC^2 + x^2 = (2x)^2$$
$$AC^2 + x^2 = 4x^2$$
$$AC^2 = 3x^2$$

Taking the positive square root of each side,
$$AC = x\sqrt{3}.$$

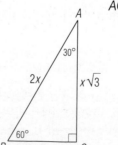

Example 2
A zoologist measured the length of a side of a cell in a natural beehive (a tessellation of regular hexagons) as 8.0 mm but forgot to measure the height h of each cell. Approximate the height to the nearest 0.1 mm.

Solution The figure below isolates one cell. DH is the desired height. $m\angle DIH = 120$ and $DI = IH$ from properties of a regular hexagon, so $\triangle DIJ$ is a 30-60-90 right triangle with hypotenuse 8.0. Let IJ, the shortest side, be x. Then, using the 30-60-90 Triangle Theorem, the hypotenuse $DI = 2x = 8.0$, so $x = 4.0$. Longer leg $DJ = x\sqrt{3} = 4\sqrt{3}$.

So
$$DH = 2 \cdot 4\sqrt{3}$$
$$= 8\sqrt{3}$$
$$\approx 13.9 \text{ mm.}$$

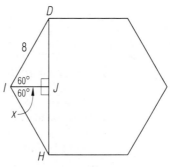

With these theorems, lengths can be found in some non-right triangles that contain 30, 45, or 60 degree angles.

Example 3 In $\triangle XYZ$, $m\angle Z = 45$, $m\angle Y = 30$, and $XY = 8$. Find XZ and YZ.

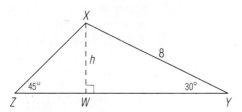

Solution Right triangles are needed, so an auxiliary line is drawn, the altitude from X to $\overline{YZ}$. This forms 45-45-90 right triangle XZW and 30-60-90 right triangle XYW. Now apply the theorems of this lesson. h, opposite the 30° angle in $\triangle XYW$, is half of 8, so $h = 4$, $YW = h\sqrt{3} = 4\sqrt{3}$. Since the left triangle is isosceles, $ZW = h = 4$. Adding, $YZ = 4 + 4\sqrt{3} \approx 10.93$. $XZ = h \cdot \sqrt{2} = 4\sqrt{2} \approx 5.66$

Check An accurate picture verifies these lengths.

Of course, you could always measure to get approximate lengths and angle measures in a triangle. One advantage of having the theorems of this lesson is that for these common triangles you do not have to measure. Another advantage is that they give exact values.

Questions

Covering the Reading

1. In an isosceles right triangle, each acute angle measures __?__ .

2. In a right triangle in which the hypotenuse is double one leg, the acute angles have measures of __?__ and __?__ .

3. In the drawing of regular hexagon *DEFGHI* near the start of this lesson, name some of its diagonals and all the 30-60-90 triangles.

4. *True* or *false*?
   a. All right triangles are similar.
   b. All right triangles with a 60° angle are similar.
   c. All isosceles right triangles are similar.

5. In Example 3, what is the measure of ∠*ZXY*?

6. In Example 3, what is the perimeter of △*XYZ*?

7. If one leg of an isosceles right triangle has length 10 cm, the hypotenuse has length __?__ .

8. A square has side *s*. What is the length of its diagonals?

9. If the shortest side of a 30-60-90 triangle is 6 cm, what are the lengths of the other two sides (to the nearest 0.1 cm)?

10. In Major League baseball, how far is it from first base to third base?

Applying the Mathematics

11. An equilateral triangle has a side of length *E* units. What is the length of one of its altitudes?

12. Suppose the cell of a natural beehive is a regular hexagon with a side of length 5 mm. What is the width of each cell? (The width is the distance between parallel sides.)

13. The hypotenuse of an isosceles right triangle is 100 feet. Find the dimensions of the other sides of the triangle.

14. Use the figure below. If *OL* = *h*, find the perimeter of △*BLT* in terms of *h*.

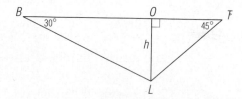

15. $\overline{BP} \perp \overline{AC}$ in rectangle $ABCD$ below. All triangles in the figure are similar to $\triangle ADC$. Name them with vertices in the correct order. *(Lesson 12-9)*

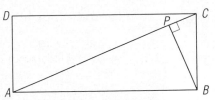

16. These triangles, all similar to each other, are not drawn very accurately. Find the values of a, b, and c. *(Lessons 12-5, 8-7)*

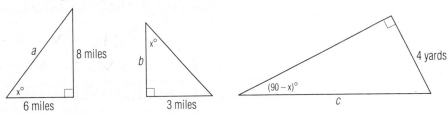

17. Solve for length DE. $\dfrac{30}{DE} = \dfrac{DE}{5}$ *(Lesson 12-4)*

18. The fraction $\frac{4}{\sqrt{3}}$ equals $\frac{4}{\sqrt{3}} \cdot \frac{\sqrt{3}}{\sqrt{3}}$, or $\frac{4\sqrt{3}}{3}$. This last form is easier to add to other multiples of $\sqrt{3}$, and is sometimes thought to be simpler. In this way, simplify:
   a. $\frac{5}{\sqrt{3}}$ **b.** $\frac{1}{\sqrt{2}}$ **c.** $\frac{3}{\sqrt{6}}$. *(Previous course)*

19. *Multiple choice.* $\sqrt{75} =$
   (a) $5\sqrt{3}$ (b) $25\sqrt{3}$ (c) $3\sqrt{5}$ (d) $3\sqrt{25}$ *(Previous course)*

20. *Multiple choice.* $\sqrt{16 + 16} =$
   (a) $2\sqrt{16}$ (b) $16\sqrt{2}$ (c) $4\sqrt{2}$ (d) 8 *(Previous course)*

21. A square and a circle each has area 400 square meters. Which has the larger perimeter? *(Lessons 8-9, 8-8, 8-3, 8-1)*

22. There are many triangles that could be considered special. One such triangle is formed by the side a, a shorter diagonal b, and a longer diagonal c of a regular heptagon.

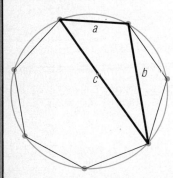

   a. Draw, as accurately as you can, a regular heptagon. A good way is to draw seven equally spaced points on a circle, as has been done at the left.

   b. Measure c, a, and b for your regular heptagon.
   Calculate $\left(\dfrac{c}{a}\right)^2 + \left(\dfrac{a}{b}\right)^2 + \left(\dfrac{b}{c}\right)^2$.

   Your answer should be very close to a whole number. Which whole number?

   c. Measure the three angles of this triangle. How do they seem to be related?

Lengths in Right Triangles

Constructing these house frames involves forming right triangles.

Occasionally the two means in a proportion are equal, as in
$$\frac{2}{10} = \frac{10}{50}.$$

When this happens, the number that appears twice is called a *geometric mean* of the other two numbers. Above, the truth of the proportion signifies that 10 is a geometric mean of 2 and 50.

Definition:

Let a, b, and g be positive numbers. g is a **geometric mean** of a and b if and only if
$$\frac{a}{g} = \frac{g}{b}.$$

The definition provides a way of calculating the geometric mean of any pair of positive real numbers.

Example 1   Find the geometric mean of 7 and 12.

Solution   Let g be the geometric mean. From the definition of geometric mean,
$$\frac{7}{g} = \frac{g}{12}.$$
Using the Means-Extremes Property,
$$g^2 = 84.$$
So
$$g = \pm\sqrt{84}.$$
From the definition of geometric mean, g is positive; so the geometric mean of 7 and 12 is $\sqrt{84}$.

Check $\sqrt{84}$ is about 9.17. Is $\frac{7}{9.17} \approx \frac{9.17}{12}$? Yes, $0.7634 \approx 0.7642$.

From the definition of geometric mean, if $\frac{a}{g} = \frac{g}{b}$ then $g^2 = ab$; thus $g = \sqrt{ab}$. This shows:

The geometric mean $\sqrt{ab}$ is always a number between a and b.
As you will explore in Question 21, it is always closer to the smaller
of a or b.

You may recall that the average of two numbers is called their
arithmetic mean. The arithmetic mean is exactly midway between
the numbers. Both kinds of means have applications in arithmetic,
algebra, and geometry. The name "geometric mean" comes from
relationships among lengths in any right triangle, relationships that
were discovered by the ancient Greeks and are in Euclid's *Elements*.

As usual, the small letters a and b are used for the lengths of the legs
of a right triangle, and c for the hypotenuse. The letter h is for the
altitude to the hypotenuse, which splits c into two lengths, x and y,
so $x + y = c$.

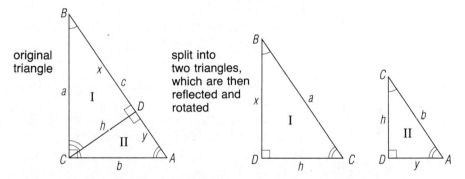

$m\angle A = m\angle BCD$ since both equal $90 - m\angle B$. So $\triangle I$, $\triangle II$,
and $\triangle ABC$ are all right triangles and each includes an angle
equal in measure to $\angle A$. Thus all three triangles are similar:
$\triangle ABC \sim \triangle CBD \sim \triangle ACD$. Since the triangles are similar,
corresponding sides are proportional. Now look for proportions
where the same quantity appears twice.

Consider triangles I and II. A length of a side in both is h.

$$\frac{x}{h} = \frac{h}{y}$$

For triangle I and the original (biggest) triangle, a is a side in both,
and for triangle II and the original triangle, b is a side in both.

$$\frac{x}{a} = \frac{a}{c} \quad \text{and} \quad \frac{y}{b} = \frac{b}{c}$$

Thus the altitude h and the legs a and b are geometric means of
other lengths. Almost everyone remembers these lengths by their
positions in the original triangle, as stated in the following theorem.

Right Triangle Altitude Theorem:

In a right triangle,
a. the altitude to the hypotenuse is the geometric mean of the segments into which it divides the hypotenuse; and
b. each leg is the geometric mean of the hypotenuse and the segment of the hypotenuse adjacent to the leg.

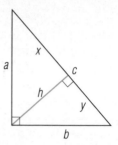

In the figure above, $h = \sqrt{xy}$, $a = \sqrt{cx}$, and $b = \sqrt{cy}$.

Example 2 $\overline{CD}$ is the altitude to the hypotenuse of right triangle ABC, as shown below. If $AD = 3$, $DB = 12$, find CD, CA, and CB.

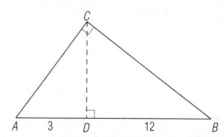

Solution CD is the geometric mean of AD and BD.

So $\qquad\qquad\qquad CD = \sqrt{3 \cdot 12} = \sqrt{36} = 6.$

CA is the geometric mean of BA and DA.

So $\qquad\qquad\qquad CA = \sqrt{15 \cdot 3} = \sqrt{45} = 3\sqrt{5}.$

CB is the geometric mean of AB and DB.

So $\qquad\qquad\qquad CB = \sqrt{15 \cdot 12} = \sqrt{180} = 6\sqrt{5}.$

Questions

Covering the Reading

In 1 and 2, find the geometric mean of the given numbers to the nearest hundredth.

1. 2 and 50   **2.** 9 and 12

3. *True* or *false*? If g is the geometric mean of a and b, and $a < b$, then g is closer to a than to b.

In 4–6, use the figure below.

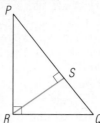

4. **a.** $m\angle P = m\angle \underline{\ ?\ }$
   b. $\triangle PRQ \sim \underline{\ ?\ } \sim \underline{\ ?\ }$

   c. $\dfrac{QS}{RQ} = \dfrac{RQ}{\underline{\ ?\ }}$

   d. $\dfrac{QS}{\underline{\ ?\ }} = \dfrac{RS}{PS}$

   e. RP is the geometric mean of $\underline{\ ?\ }$ and $\underline{\ ?\ }$.
   f. RS is the geometric mean of $\underline{\ ?\ }$ and $\underline{\ ?\ }$.
   g. RQ is the geometric mean of $\underline{\ ?\ }$ and $\underline{\ ?\ }$.

5. If $RS = 6$ and $PS = 9$, then $QS = \underline{\ ?\ }$.

6. If $RS = 6$ and $SQ = 4$, then $QR = \underline{\ ?\ }$.

7. Using the diagram below, find
   a. NS
   b. SE
   c. IE.

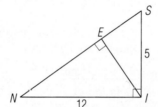

8. Below is the famous 3-4-5 right triangle. The altitude to the hypotenuse has been drawn. Find the lengths of x, y, and h.

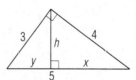

9. Refer to the figure below.
   a. Is $\triangle QRT \sim \triangle RST$?
   b. *True* or *false*? $m\angle QRS = 90$

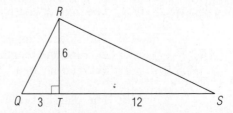

10. Nancy Weintraub taught the members of Girl Scout Troop 715 that they could use a notebook to estimate distances. To show them how, she used the lifeguard tower at Henson Beach. She held her notebook near her eye (5 feet off the ground) and moved back from the tower until she could sight both the top and bottom of the tower. Then she asked Amy Finch to estimate her (Nancy's) distance from the tower by pacing. Amy estimated 8 feet.

a. Which part of the right triangle altitude theorem could Nancy now use to find the height of the lifeguard tower?

b. How tall is the tower?

5 ft

11. Provide the missing justifications in this argument verifying the Pythagorean Theorem.

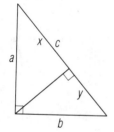

Conclusions	Justifications
1. a is the geometric mean of c and x. b is the geometric mean of c and y.	**a.** __?__
2. $a = \sqrt{cx}$, $b = \sqrt{cy}$	**b.** __?__
3. $a^2 = cx$, $b^2 = cy$	Multiplication Property of Equality
4. $a^2 + b^2 = cx + cy$	**c.** __?__
5. $a^2 + b^2 = c(x + y)$	**d.** __?__
6. $x + y = c$	Betweenness Theorem
7. $a^2 + b^2 = c^2$	**e.** __?__

Review

12. In Question 11, why is it inappropriate to use the Pythagorean Theorem as the justification for conclusion 7? *(Lesson 3-3)*

13. The sides of an equilateral triangle have length 5.
a. Find the length of an altitude of this triangle.
b. Find its area. *(Lesson 14-1)*

14. The diagonal of a square field has length 50 meters. What is the length of a side? *(Lesson 14-1)*

15. A prism has the same base as a pyramid but twice the height. How do their volumes compare? *(Lessons 10-7, 10-5)*

16. In the box below, if *all* pairs of vertices are connected, __
  a. how many of the segments have the same length as $\overline{AC}$?
  b. How many of the segments have the same length as $\overline{AG}$?
  (Lesson 9-2)

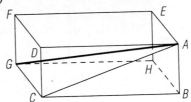

17. Refer to the figure at the right.
  Given: *BD = CE;*
             MB = CM;
             M is the midpoint of $\overline{DE}$.
  Prove: *ABMC* is a kite.
      (Lesson 7-3)

18. a. Find a fraction equal to $\frac{1}{\sqrt{3}}$ with no radical sign in its denominator.
  b. Find $\frac{1}{\sqrt{3}}$ to the nearest millionth. *(Previous course)*

19. Solve for *y:* $3y - 2 = y^2$. *(Previous course)*

Exploration

20. If a racer averages 120 mph for one lap and 200 mph for a second lap, the average speed for the two laps is not 160 mph, but 150 mph, the *harmonic mean* of 120 and 200.

  a. Look in a dictionary, or generalize this example, to find a formula for the harmonic mean of *x* and *y*.
  b. Using examples of the harmonic mean and the geometric mean of two positive numbers *a* and *b*, with *b < a*, is one always greater than the other? If so, which one is greater?

21. Which is larger, the geometric mean of two positive numbers or their arithmetic mean? Are the geometric and arithmetic means of two numbers ever equal?

14-3

The Tangent Ratio

In Example 3 of Lesson 14-1, measures of two angles and a non-included side in a triangle were given. That is the AAS condition. From this information, measures of all other angles and sides could be computed. In general, using trigonometry *all* sides and angles can be found whenever enough information is given for a triangle congruence condition. In this book you will learn how to do this with right triangles.

Consider two right triangles *ABC* and *XYZ* with a pair of congruent acute angles. The triangles might be formed by figures and shadows at the same time of day. Following custom, in the drawing at the right the side opposite angle *A* is called *a,* the side opposite angle *B* is called *b,* and so on. You should be careful to write small letters differently from capital letters.

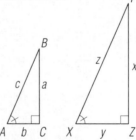

The triangles are similar because of AA Similarity.

Since corresponding sides are proportional, $\dfrac{a}{x} = \dfrac{b}{y}$.

By the Means-Exchange Property,

$$\frac{a}{b} = \frac{x}{y}.$$

The legs *a* and *x* are **opposite** the congruent angles *A* and *X*. The legs *b* and *y* are **adjacent to** angles *A* and *X*. This argument shows that in every right triangle, the ratio of lengths

$$\frac{\text{leg opposite angle } A}{\text{leg adjacent to angle } A}$$

is the same for the angle congruent to *A*. This ratio is called the *tangent of angle A.*

> **Definition:**
>
> In right triangle ABC with right angle C,
> the **tangent of** ∠**A,** written **tan A,** is $\dfrac{\text{leg opposite } \angle A}{\text{leg adjacent to } \angle A}$.

Tangents can be estimated by measuring.

Example 1   Estimate the tangent of an angle of 25°.

Solution   Draw a right triangle with a carefully measured 25° angle. Measure the leg opposite that angle. Using the triangle below, that leg is 24 mm. Then measure the leg adjacent to the angle; it is about 52 mm. The ratio of these lengths, $\frac{24}{52}$, is an estimate of the tangent of 25°.

The estimate can be converted to a decimal: $\frac{24}{52} \approx 0.46$.

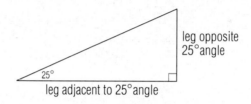

leg opposite 25° angle

25°

leg adjacent to 25° angle

You can write $\tan 25° \approx \frac{24}{52}$
or $\tan 25° \approx 0.46$.

Today, most people use calculators to approximate values of tangents. Every scientific calculator contains a [tan] key. To use this key, make sure your calculator is measuring angles in degrees (there are other ways, but they are not discussed in this text). To find the approximate value of tan 25°, use the following key sequence.

25 [tan]

Your calculator may display 0.4663077. That means tan 25° ≈ 0.4663077.

When the measure of an angle and one leg are known, the tangent enables you to find the length of the other leg.

Example 2 At a location 50 m from the base of a tree, the *angle of elevation* of the tree is 33°. Determine the height of the tree.

Solution The angle of elevation is $\angle A$ in the figure below.

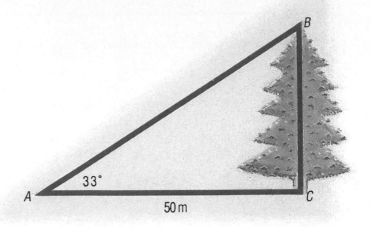

$$\tan 33° = \frac{\text{leg opposite } \angle A}{\text{leg adjacent to } \angle A}$$

$$\tan 33° = \frac{BC}{50}$$

Multiplying both sides by 50,

$$BC = 50 \cdot \tan 33°$$
$$= 50 \boxed{\text{x}} \ 33 \ \boxed{\text{tan}} \ \boxed{=}$$
$$\approx 32.47038$$
$$\approx 32 \text{ meters}.$$

The exact value of a tangent of an acute angle can be determined if you know the lengths of the two legs in a right triangle with that angle.

Example 3 In the right triangle below, find tan *D*.

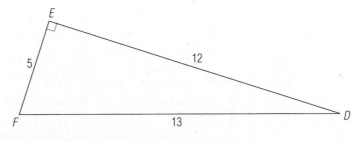

Solution $\tan D = \dfrac{\text{leg opposite } \angle D}{\text{leg adjacent to } \angle D} = \dfrac{EF}{ED} = \dfrac{5}{12}$

Tangents of angles in special triangles can be found exactly.

Example 4   Give an exact value for tan 60°.

Solution   Draw a 30-60-90 triangle.

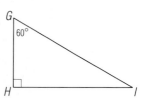

In △GHI, tan 60° = tan G = $\dfrac{\text{leg opposite }\angle G}{\text{leg adjacent to }\angle G}$ = $\dfrac{HI}{GH}$.

GH is the shorter leg. Call it x. Then $HI = x\sqrt{3}$.

Substituting, tan 60° = $\dfrac{x\sqrt{3}}{x}$ = $\sqrt{3}$.

Check   Press 60 [tan] on your calculator. You should get 1.732...,
which is approximately $\sqrt{3}$.

The tangent of an angle is an example of a **trigonometric ratio.**
Almost all scientific calculators have buttons for calculating three
trigonometric ratios. You will study the other two of these ratios in
the next lesson.

Questions

Covering the Reading

1. Draw a right triangle with a 40° angle, measure its sides, and use
those measurements to estimate tan 40°.

2. By measuring sides of △ABC below, estimate tan A.

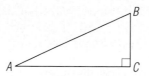

3. Using a calculator, approximate tan 73° to the nearest thousandth.

4. When the sun is 32° up from the horizon, the wall of a store casts a
shadow 25 meters long. How high is the wall?

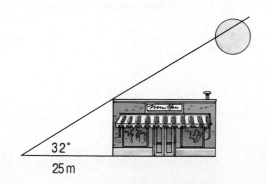

In 5 and 6, use $\triangle DEF$ below.

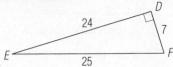

5. Calculate tan E.

6. Calculate tan F.

7. Give an exact value for tan 30°.

8. Give an exact value for tan 45°.

9. Draw a right triangle with legs of 4 units and 6 units. Use this triangle to estimate answers to the following questions.
   a. What is m∠A if tan $A = \frac{2}{3}$?
   b. What is m∠A if tan $A = \frac{3}{2}$?

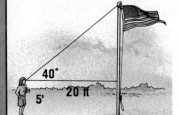

10. From eye level 5′ off the ground and 20′ away from a flagpole, a person has to look up at a 40° angle to see the top of the pole. How high is the pole?

11. Use the figure below. Of angles 1, 2, 3, and 4:
   a. Which has the largest tangent?
   b. Which has the smallest tangent?

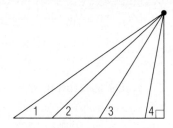

12. Without calculating, explain why tan 75° > tan 74°.

13. Use the figure below.
   a. Find tan BCD in triangle I.
   b. Find tan A in triangle II.
   c. Since m∠BCD = m∠A, tan BCD = tan A. Substitute in your answers from parts **a** and **b** into the equation tan BCD = tan A.
   d. What part of the Right Triangle Altitude Theorem have you proved?

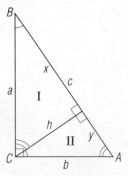

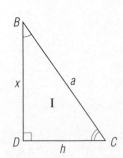

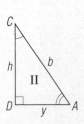

In 14 and 15, refer to the figure below.

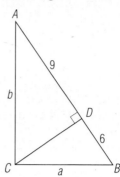

14. The altitude $\overline{CD}$ of a right triangle ABC splits the hypotenuse into segments of lengths 6 and 9. Find the lengths of the altitude and the two legs. *(Lesson 14-2)*

15. $\triangle ABC \sim$ ___?___ $\sim$ ___?___ *(Lesson 14-2)*

16. $ZONK$ is a trapezoid. $m\angle Z = m\angle O = 45$, $ZO = 24$, and $NK = 9$. Find the area of $ZONK$. *(Lesson 14-1)*

17. About how long a straw can fit into a box $3''$ by $4''$ by $8''$ in the way shown at the left? *(Lesson 11-6)*

18. Trace the figure below, in which $\ell \parallel m$.
   a. Draw $r_\ell \circ r_m(DAB)$.
   b. Describe this transformation. *(Lesson 6-2)*

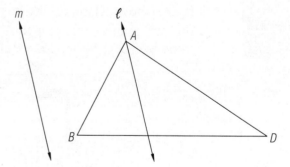

19. Choose three angle measures (other than 90) whose sum is 180. (For example, you could choose 25, 97, and 58.)
   a. Using a calculator, find the sum of the tangents of the numbers you have chosen.
   b. Calculate the product of the tangents of the numbers you have chosen.
   c. Repeat parts **a** and **b** with a different three numbers.
   d. Make a conjecture based on what you find.

14·4

The Sine and Cosine Ratios

The tangent is the ratio of the lengths of two legs in a right triangle. When a leg is compared to the hypotenuse, the *sine* or *cosine* ratio results.

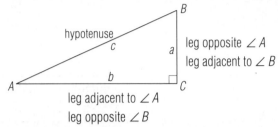

Definitions:

In right triangle *ABC* with right angle *C*,

the **sine of ∠A**, written **sin A**, is $\dfrac{\text{leg opposite }\angle A}{\text{hypotenuse}}$;

the **cosine of ∠A**, written **cos A**, is $\dfrac{\text{leg adjacent to }\angle A}{\text{hypotenuse}}$.

In the above triangle, $\sin A = \dfrac{a}{c}$ and $\cos A = \dfrac{b}{c}$.
For any angle congruent to *A*, these sine and cosine ratios are the same because the angles would be in similar right triangles.

Example 1 Right triangle *ABC* has side lengths as indicated. Find each value.

a. sin *A*   **b.** cos *A*
c. sin *B*   **d.** cos *B*

Solution

a. $\sin A = \dfrac{\text{leg opposite }\angle A}{\text{hypotenuse}} = \dfrac{5}{13} \approx 0.3846$

b. $\cos A = \dfrac{\text{leg adjacent to }\angle A}{\text{hypotenuse}} = \dfrac{12}{13} \approx 0.9231$

c. $\sin B = \dfrac{\text{leg opposite }\angle B}{\text{hypotenuse}} = \dfrac{12}{13} \approx 0.9231$

d. $\cos B = \dfrac{\text{leg adjacent to }\angle B}{\text{hypotenuse}} = \dfrac{5}{13} \approx 0.3846$

In Example 1, notice that $\sin A = \cos B$ and $\sin B = \cos A$. This is because the leg opposite either angle is the leg adjacent to the other. Angles *A* and *B* are also complementary. This is the origin of the term "cosine"; *cosine* is short for *complement's sine*.

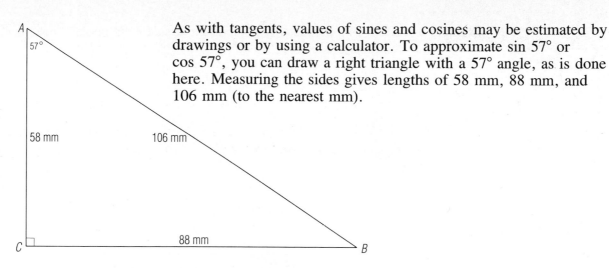

As with tangents, values of sines and cosines may be estimated by drawings or by using a calculator. To approximate sin 57° or cos 57°, you can draw a right triangle with a 57° angle, as is done here. Measuring the sides gives lengths of 58 mm, 88 mm, and 106 mm (to the nearest mm).

To two decimal places, sin 57° = $\frac{BC}{AB}$ ≈ $\frac{88}{106}$ ≈ .83 and cos 57° = $\frac{AC}{AB}$ ≈ $\frac{58}{106}$ ≈ .55. A calculator gives greater accuracy. For sin 57°, press 57 [sin].
An 8-digit display will show 0.8386706. So sin 57° ≈ .8387.
For cos 57°, press 57 [cos].
The display may show 0.544639. So cos 57° ≈ 0.5446.

Drawings and calculators usually give approximate values of sines and cosines. Exact values occur only when the lengths of sides are known exactly.

In special triangles, the exact values of sines, cosines, and tangents can be obtained because the sides are known exactly.

Example 2   Find exact values of sin 30° and cos 30°.

Solution   Sketch a triangle as shown at the left. This is a 30-60-90 triangle, so the legs are x and $x\sqrt{3}$ and the hypotenuse is $2x$.

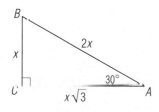

$$\sin 30° = \frac{x}{2x} = \frac{1}{2}$$
$$\cos 30° = \frac{x\sqrt{3}}{2x} = \frac{\sqrt{3}}{2}$$

Sines and cosines have a great number and variety of applications. The ancient Babylonians and Greeks measured triangles carefully, needing such measurements for navigation, surveying, and astronomy. The first table of trigonometric values was constructed by Claudius Ptolemy in the 2nd century A.D. Values like our present sine, cosine, and tangent values were first obtained by the German astronomer Regiomontanus (1436–1476). The abbreviations *sin*, *cos*, and *tan* are due to Euler.

Example 3 Suppose a particular type of ladder is safe if the angle it makes with the ground is from 65° to 80°.

a. How far up on a vertical wall can a 30-foot ladder of this type reach?

b. How far, at minimum, should it be placed from the base of the wall?

Solution First draw a picture.

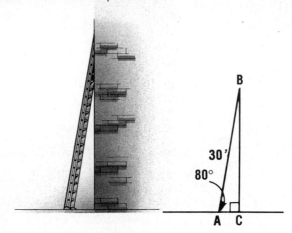

In the figure drawn, part **a** needs BC and part **b** needs AC.

a. The leg opposite 80° is desired. The hypotenuse is known. So the sine should be used.

$$\sin 80° = \frac{\text{leg opposite 80° angle}}{\text{hypotenuse}}$$

A calculator shows $\sin 80° \approx 0.985$.

Substituting: $0.985 \approx \dfrac{BC}{30}$.

Solve for BC. $BC \approx 30 \cdot 0.985 \approx 29.6$ feet

The ladder will reach about 29.6 feet high on the wall.

b. $\overline{AC}$ is the leg adjacent to the 80° angle. This suggests using the cosine.

$$\cos 80° = \frac{\text{leg adjacent to 80° angle}}{\text{hypotenuse}}$$

A calculator shows $\cos 80° \approx 0.174$. Substituting:

$$0.174 \approx \frac{AC}{30}$$

$$AC \approx 30 \cdot 0.174 \approx 5.2 \text{ feet.}$$

5.2 feet is 5 feet, 2.4 inches. You should place the ladder at least 5′ 3″ away from the wall. Otherwise the ladder is too close to perpendicular to be used safely.

Check The Pythagorean Theorem can check both answers at once.
Does $AC^2 + BC^2 = AB^2$?
Does $(5.2)^2 + (29.6)^2 = 30^2$?
The left side is 903.2, the right side is 900. This is close enough, given the approximations used for sin 80° and cos 80° and the rounding done to get 5.2 and 29.6.

1. Define: **a.** sin ∠A, **b.** cos ∠A.

2. In △MNO below, identify each segment.
   a. leg opposite ∠N
   b. hypotenuse
   c. leg adjacent to ∠M
   d. leg adjacent to ∠N

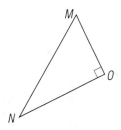

3. In △FGH below, find:
   a. sin F   **b.** cos F
   c. tan G   **d.** sin G.

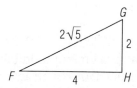

4. Give exact values of: **a.** sin 60° **b.** cos 60° **c.** tan 60°.

5. Give exact values of: **a.** sin 45° **b.** cos 45° **c.** tan 45°.

6. The figure below shows approximate lengths of the sides in a right triangle with angles of 42° and 48° and hypotenuse 15. Use these lengths to fill in the blanks.
   a. sin 48° ≈ __?__   **b.** cos 48° ≈ __?__
   c. tan 42° ≈ __?__   **d.** cos 42° ≈ __?__

7. Estimate to the nearest thousandth: **a.** sin 13.2° **b.** cos 13.2°.

8. **a.** How far up on a vertical wall can a 20′ ladder of the type in Example 3 safely reach?
   b. How far, at minimum, should the bottom be placed from the wall?

9. What is the farthest that the ladder of Example 3 should be placed from the wall?

10. a. Use a calculator to estimate sin 89° to the nearest ten-thousandth.
   b. Give a geometric reason why the value is so near 1.

11. In the triangles below, $\angle B \cong \angle B'$.
   a. By measuring, estimate sin B and sin B'.
   b. Are the results as expected?

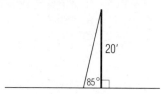

12. a. Of the angles 1, 2, 3, 4, and 5 pictured at the left, which angle has the largest sine?
   b. Which angle has the largest cosine?

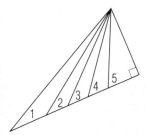

13. What length wire is needed as a brace for a 20-foot pole, if the brace is to make an angle of 85° with the ground?

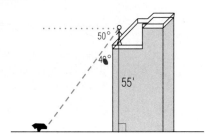

14. From the top of a building you look down at an object on the ground. If your eyes are 55 feet above the ground, and the angle of sight, called the *angle of depression*, is 50° below the horizontal, how far is the object from you?

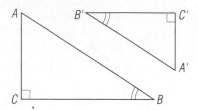

15. How tall is this building? *(Lesson 14-3)*

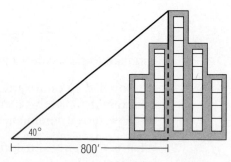

16. Refer to △*LMN* below. Estimate tan *N* by measuring *LM* and *LN* to the nearest mm. *(Lesson 14-3)*

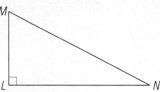

17. Find the geometric mean of 75 and 100 to the nearest hundredth. *(Lesson 14-2)*

18. Refer to the figure below. *(Lesson 14-2)*
    a. *RQ* is the geometric mean of __?__ and __?__ .
    b. *RT* is the geometric mean of __?__ and __?__ .
    c. *RS* is the geometric mean of __?__ and __?__ .

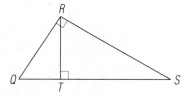

19. **a.** Write the converse, the inverse, and the contrapositive of the following statement:
       If *M* is between *P* and *Q*, then *PM* + *MQ* = *PQ*.
    b. Which of the statements you have written in part **a** are true?
    (Lessons 13-2, 1-9, 1-8)

20. Isosceles △*ABC* has vertex angle *A*. If its sides are 7, 7, and 12, find the length of the altitude from *A*. *(Lessons 8-7, 5-1)*

21. Rewrite without fractions or converting to decimals.

    a. $\dfrac{100}{\sqrt{2}}$;
                             b. $\dfrac{100}{\sqrt{2}} + 8\sqrt{2}$ *(Previous course)*

22. **a.** Fill in this table of values of the sine and cosine using your calculator.

x	$\sin x$	$\cos x$	x	$\sin x$	$\cos x$	x	$\sin x$	$\cos x$
0			30			60		
5			35			65		
10			40			70		
15			45			75		
20			50			80		
25			55			85		
						90		

    b. For which values of *x* does $(\sin x)^2 + (\cos x)^2 = 1$?

Aircraft departing from Los Angeles International Airport

Vectors

The air distance between Dallas/Fort Worth International Airport (DFW) and the Los Angeles International Airport (LAX) is the same in both directions. But if you look at the airline schedule, you will find that the scheduled time from LAX to DFW is less than the scheduled time from DFW to LAX. For instance, in 1989, American Airlines scheduled an average of 2 hours, 59 minutes for its flights from LAX to DFW, but 3 hours, 10 minutes from DFW to LAX. The difference is due to winds in the upper atmosphere which, in the United States, almost always go from west to east. These winds speed up planes going east (the approximate direction from LAX to DFW) and slow down planes going west. The mathematics of *vectors* helps to explain this idea.

A **vector** is a quantity that has both **magnitude** and **direction.** Here are some examples.

vector	its magnitude	its direction
northeast wind at 40 mph	40 mph	northeast
gravity on the surface of the earth	9.8 meters per second per second	downward
person pushing a refrigerator south with a force of 100 pounds	100 pounds	south

Vectors are represented by **directed line segments.** A directed line segment is drawn like a normal line segment, except that it has an arrow at one endpoint. For instance, drawn below is the directed line segment $\overrightarrow{OA}$ representing a northeast wind of 20 mph. Point O is the **initial point** of the vector and A is its **terminal point.** Its direction is 50° north of east (or 40° east of north) and its magnitude is 20, the distance OA. *Caution: Although a directed line segment is pictured like a ray, it is not a ray. It has a finite length; it does not continue forever.*

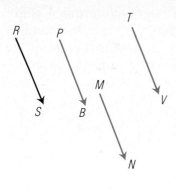

Two vectors are **equal vectors** if and only if they have the same direction and magnitude. You can draw a specific vector wherever you wish as long as it has the proper direction and magnitude. The vector $\overrightarrow{OA}$ started at the origin of a coordinate system, but a vector can start anywhere. The four vectors drawn at the left are equal: $\overrightarrow{RS} = \overrightarrow{PB} = \overrightarrow{MN} = \overrightarrow{TV}$.

Vectors are closely related to translations. Like a vector, a translation or slide is determined by its magnitude and direction. In a given translation, the segments connecting preimage to image points have the same direction and magnitude. This result can be stated in terms of vectors.

Theorem:

Two vectors are equal if and only if their initial and terminal points are preimages and images under the same translation.

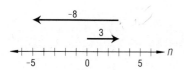

Remember when you learned to add positive and negative numbers? You were probably told you could picture the numbers by arrows. For instance, in adding 3 and -8, you drew arrows whose lengths were 3 and 8, but in opposite directions, as shown at the left. These arrows are, in fact, directed segments. You were adding vectors! Notice that you started the second arrow at the endpoint of the first. The sum was indicated by the endpoint of the second arrow. This is exactly the rule for adding vectors.

Definition:

The **sum** or **resultant** of two vectors $\overrightarrow{AB}$ and $\overrightarrow{BC}$, written $\overrightarrow{AB} + \overrightarrow{BC}$, is the vector $\overrightarrow{AC}$.

■ ■ ■ ■ ■ ■ ■ ■

Example 1   Given are two vectors $\overrightarrow{AB}$ and $\overrightarrow{BC}$. Draw their sum.

Solution   The sum is $\overrightarrow{AC}$.

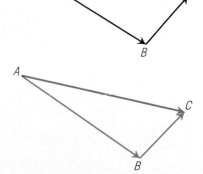

When the initial point of one given vector is not the terminal point of the other, you can still find the sum. Merely replace the second vector by an equal vector that *does* start at the terminal point of the first. In Example 2, the vectors are described by single boldface letters. The most common letters used are **u**, **v**, and **w**.

Example 2   With **u** and **v** as given, draw **u + v**.

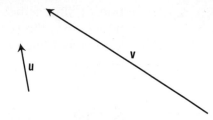

Solution   Use the directed segment for **v** that starts at the terminal point of **u**.

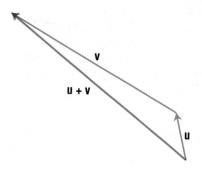

The significance of vector addition is that it models the way many physical forces in the world combine.

Example 3   A motorboat is traveling up a river at a speed that would be 25 miles an hour in still water. There is a current of 15 miles an hour coming down the river. How far will the motor boat travel in an hour?

Solution   Possible vectors are drawn here. The resultant is a vector that represents a speed of 10 mph up the river.

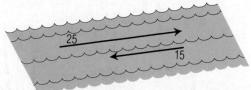

So, in a single hour, the boat will travel 10 miles up the river. (If the boat were traveling down the river, it would be with the current. So the resultant speed of the boat would be 25 + 15, or 40 mph down the river.)

Even when the current is in an oblique direction relative to the boat, the path and ground speed of the boat can be found by adding vectors.

Example 4
A motorboat is traveling due east at 20 miles an hour. There is a 5 mph current in the direction 40° west of south. In what direction will the motorboat move?

Solution   Draw a directed segment for each vector.

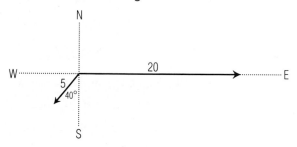

To find the sum, slide one of the vectors so its initial point is the terminal point of the other. Below, we moved the vector $\overrightarrow{OB}$ to have A as its initial point.

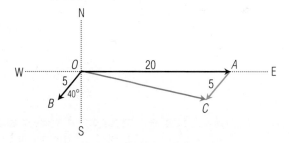

The resultant, which is the path of the boat, is in the direction of the vector $\overrightarrow{OC}$. The speed of the motorboat is indicated by the length of that vector. (Notice that the length of $\overrightarrow{OC}$ is less than the length of $\overrightarrow{OA}$. This is as you might expect, since the current is "fighting" the boat. In the last lesson of this chapter, you will learn how to determine the precise direction and magnitude of $\overrightarrow{OC}$.)

In Example 4, since $\overrightarrow{AC}$ and $\overrightarrow{OB}$ are of equal length and parallel, *OACB* is a parallelogram. For this reason, the addition of vectors is said to follow the **parallelogram rule.** That is, the sum of two noncollinear vectors $\overrightarrow{OA}$ and $\overrightarrow{OB}$ is the vector $\overrightarrow{OC}$ such that *OACB* is a parallelogram.

Questions

Covering the Reading

1. a. Why is the time scheduled for an airplane to travel from Los Angeles to Dallas/Fort Worth not the same as the time scheduled to travel from Dallas/Forth Worth to Los Angeles?
   b. Which trip usually takes longer?

2. Suppose a motorboat can travel at a maximum speed of 20 mph in still water. What is its maximum ground speed
   a. against a 4 mph current?
   b. with a 5 mph current?

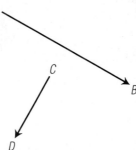

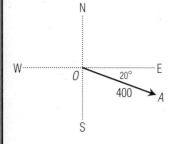

3. Name the initial point, terminal point, magnitude, and direction of the vector $\overrightarrow{OA}$, as shown at the left.

4. Draw a vector with magnitude 10 and direction 15° north of East.

5. By definition, when are two vectors equal?

6. Draw three vectors equal to the vector of Question 3.

7. What sum is pictured here?

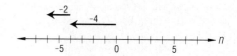

In 8–10, trace the vectors and then draw their sum.

8.

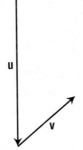

9.

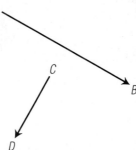

10.

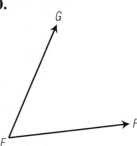

11. What is the parallelogram rule for adding vectors?

Applying the Mathematics

12. A motorboat is traveling north at a speed of 25 kilometers per hour in still water. There is a current going due east at 8 kilometers per hour. Draw a picture showing the direction in which the boat will move.

13. An airplane is traveling at a speed and direction that would be 540 mph in the direction 20° north of west in still air. The jet stream is pushing the plane at 180 mph in the direction 10° north of east. Draw a picture of these velocity vectors and show the direction in which the plane will move.

In 14–16, draw the possible vector.

14. the force of gravity (9.8 meters per second per second)

15. a person pushing a sofa in a direction 37° west of north with a force of 150 pounds

16. a person pushing a sofa in a direction 37° east of south with a force of 150 pounds

17. Draw **u + v + w**.

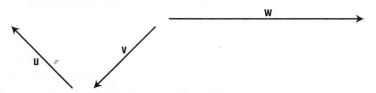

Review

18. In △XYZ, give the value of:
  a. sin X
  b. tan X
  c. cos Z. *(Lessons 14-4, 14-3)*

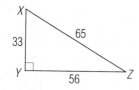

In 19 and 20, refer to △PQR at the left.

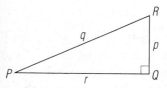

19. By measuring, determine tan R, sin R, and cos R (give answers to the nearest hundredth). *(Lessons 14-4, 14-3)*

20. *Multiple choice.* Which equals p? *(Lesson 14-4)*
  (a) q sin P   (b) q cos P   (c) r sin P   (d) r cos P

21. How long is a rope which supports this 8-meter-tall set from a play if the angle it makes with the stage is 43°? *(Lesson 14-4)*

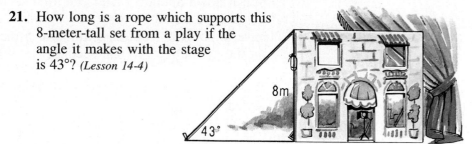

22. What is the exact value of cos 30°? *(Lessons 14-4, 14-1)*

23. Find the surface area of a sphere with radius 12. *(Lesson 10-9)*

24. Find the volume of a sphere with radius 12. *(Lesson 10-8)*

Exploration

25. a. Find out how long it takes by airplane to go from a nearby airport on a nonstop flight to some other location, and how long the return flight takes.
  b. Allowing some time for takeoff and landing (from 5 minutes at a smaller airport to 20 minutes at the largest airports), about how fast does the schedule assume the plane can travel? Is there any assumption about wind?

14-6

Properties of Vectors

A vector can describe the forces acting on a bullet.

Any vector can be placed so that its initial point is the origin. If its terminal point is (a, b), the vector is named (a, b). The **horizontal component** of (a, b) is a; the **vertical component** is b. This is the **ordered pair description of a vector.**

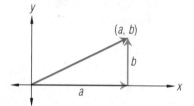

vector (a, b)
horizontal component a
vertical component b

The vector (a, b) can be interpreted as the resultant of a horizontal force a and a vertical force b. For instance, if a bullet is fired horizontally at an initial speed of 200 meters per second, gravity will pull it down about 5 meters the first second, and its location after one second could be described by the vector $(200, -5)$. (It would have to be fired from an altitude of 5 meters or more, so as not to hit the ground before one second.)

When vectors are described as ordered pairs, they can be easily added.

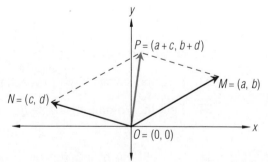

Vector Addition Theorem:

The sum of the vectors (a, b) and (c, d) is the vector $(a + c, b + d)$.

Proof

The idea is to use the parallelogram rule. We let $O = (0, 0)$, $M = (a, b)$, $N = (c, d)$, and $P = (a + c, b + d)$. To show that $\overrightarrow{OP}$ is the sum of $\overrightarrow{OM}$ and $\overrightarrow{ON}$, it needs to be shown that $OMPN$ is a parallelogram. For this, all that is needed is to show that $\overrightarrow{MP}$ and $\overrightarrow{ON}$ are equal vectors. They are equal if they have the same direction (slope) and magnitude (length). This is left to you in Question 14.

The Vector Addition Theorem can be exemplified using forces. To combine two forces, add their horizontal components and add their vertical components. If the bullet mentioned above is fired from a plane going 300 meters per second (about 675 mph), in the direction of the plane, its location after one second is $(200, -10) + (300, 0)$ which is $(500, -10)$.

Vector addition is so named because it has many of the properties of ordinary real number addition. These real number properties, in fact, help to prove the corresponding properties for vectors.

Properties of Vector Addition Theorem:

(1) Vector addition is commutative.
(2) Vector addition is associative.
(3) $(0, 0)$ is an identity for vector addition.
(4) Every vector (a, b) has an additive inverse $(-a, -b)$.

Proof

All the parts use the strategy of adding appropriate vectors and using the corresponding real number property.
(1) It must be shown that $(a, b) + (c, d) = (c, d) + (a, b)$. That is left to you.

(2) It must be shown that
$((a, b) + (c, d)) + (e, f) = (a, b) + ((c, d) + (e, f))$.

$$
\begin{aligned}
((a, b) + (c, d)) + (e, f) &= (a + c, b + d) + (e, f) && \text{Vector Addition Theorem} \\
&= ((a + c) + e, (b + d) + f) && \text{Vector Addition Theorem} \\
&= (a + (c + e), b + (d + f)) && \text{Associativity of real} \\
& && \text{number addition} \\
&= (a, b) + (c + e, d + f) && \text{Vector Addition Theorem} \\
&= (a, b) + ((c, d) + (e, f)) && \text{Vector Addition Theorem}
\end{aligned}
$$

(3) For any vector (a, b),
$$
\begin{aligned}
(a, b) + (0, 0) &= (a + 0, b + 0) && \text{Vector Addition Theorem} \\
&= (a, b). && \text{0 is identity for real} \\
& && \text{number addition.}
\end{aligned}
$$
Thus, $(0, 0)$ is an identity for vector addition.
(4) This is left to you.

Parts (1) and (2) of the Properties of Vector Addition Theorem are important because they imply that any number of vectors can be combined in any order. Part (2) of the Properties of Vector Addition Theorem is obvious when adding ordered pairs, but not so obvious with directed segments.

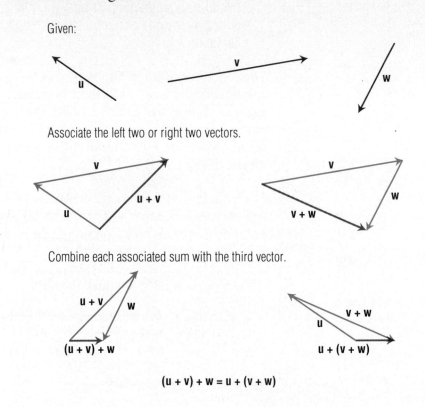

Given:

Associate the left two or right two vectors.

Combine each associated sum with the third vector.

$$(u + v) + w = u + (v + w)$$

The vector $(0, 0)$, called the **zero vector**, represents a force whose magnitude is zero. A helicopter is able to hover because the resultant of all the forces that act on it is the zero vector. The vectors (a, b) and $(-a, -b)$, whose sum is the zero vector, are called **opposite vectors.** If two teams engage in a tug-of-war, and neither is moving the other, the forces they have applied are opposite vectors.

There are operations with vectors other than vector addition. Perhaps the simplest is multiplication of a vector by a real number, called *scalar multiplication*.

The idea of scalar multiplication is simple. If 3 people each push with the same force **v**, then the total force is **v + v + v**. This is the force 3**v**.

It is easiest to give the general definition of scalar multiplication in terms of ordered pairs.

Definition:

Let k be a real number and (a, b) be a vector. Then $k(a, b)$, the **scalar multiple** of k and (a, b), is the vector (ka, kb).

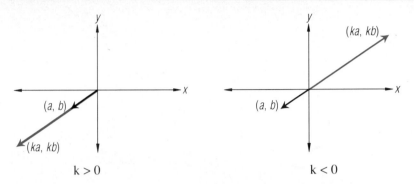

$k > 0$ $k < 0$

Recall that the point (ka, kb) is the image of (a, b) under a size change of magnitude k. Thus, when k is positive, the vector (ka, kb) has the same direction as (a, b) and k times the magnitude of (a, b). When k is negative, the vectors (a, b) and (ka, kb) have opposite directions.

Scalar multiplication has many properties, some of which are touched upon in the Questions.

Questions

Covering the Reading

1. Name the horizontal and vertical components of the vector $(2, 3)$.

In 2–5, add the vectors.

2. $(300, 15) + (100, 212)$

3. $(a, b) + (c, d)$

4. $(-9, 6) + (9, -6)$

5. $(0, 0) + (\frac{1}{2}, -\frac{\sqrt{3}}{2})$

6. Which of the vectors in Questions 2–5 are opposite vectors?

7. What vector is the additive identity?

8. A plane is traveling east at 250 meters per second. A bullet is fired backwards from the plane at 175 meters per second. Gravity pulls the bullet down 10 meters per second.
   a. What vector describes the effect of gravity in one second?
   b. What vector would describe the location of the bullet after one second if the plane were standing still?
   c. What vector describes the location of the bullet after one second taking into account the moving plane?

9. Below are 3 vectors **u**, **v**, and **w**.
  a. Draw (**u** + **v**) + **w**.
  b. Draw **u** + (**v** + **w**).
  c. What property is verified by the results of parts **a** and **b**?

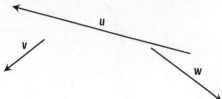

10. Write 2(-9, 5) as a single vector.

11. Draw the vectors (2, -1), 5(2, -1), and -5(2, -1).

12. The operation in Questions 10 and 11 is called __?__.

13. Given the vector $\overrightarrow{AB}$ as shown at the left, draw 4 $\overrightarrow{AB}$.

Applying the Mathematics

14. Finish the proof of the Vector Addition Theorem by showing that $\overrightarrow{MP}$ and $\overrightarrow{ON}$:
  a. are parallel;
  b. have the same length.

15. Prove that vector addition is commutative.

16. Prove that (a, b) and (-a, -b) are opposite vectors.

17. A plane is traveling at a ground speed (horizontally) of 350 mph and is descending at 1000 feet per minute. Convert these quantities to the same unit to find the slope of the vector describing the plane's path.

18. a. Determine whether this statement is true for all vectors (a, b) and (c, d) and scalar multiple k:
  $k[(a, b) + (c, d)] = k(a, b) + k(c, d).$
  b. What property have you proved or disproved in part **a**?

19. A vector has magnitude 2 and direction 30° north of east. What are its components?

Review

20. Here is a view of a refrigerator and wall from the top.

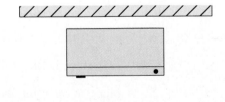

You pull on the refrigerator with a force of 80 lb perpendicular to and away from the wall. A friend pushes with a force of 60 lb parallel to the wall from left to right. Draw the two force vectors and their sum. *(Lesson 14-5)*

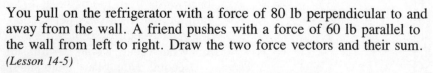

21. Draw the vector representing the velocity of a tornado traveling at 20 mph in the direction 35° north of east. *(Lesson 14-5)*

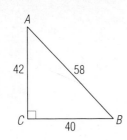

In 22 and 23, refer to △*ABC* at the left.

22. Give exact values for
   a. cos *A*
   b. tan *B*;
   c. sin *A*. *(Lessons 14-4, 14-3)*

23. *True* or *false*?   m∠*A* > m∠*B*. *(Lesson 13-7)*

24. Refer to △*DEF* below. By measuring, estimate:
   a. cos *D*
   b. tan *D*. *(Lessons 14-4, 14-3)*

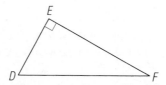

25. Without a calculator, give the value of tan 45°. *(Lessons 14-3, 14-1)*

26. Find the area of the shaded region between square *ABCD* and equilateral triangle *CDE*. *(Lessons 14-1, 8-5)*

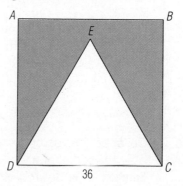

27. a. Draw a pair of vectors **u** and **v** and calculate their mean $\frac{1}{2}(\mathbf{u} + \mathbf{v})$. Then draw the mean.
   b. Do this with other pairs of vectors. Describe the mean geometrically.

28. The vectors in this lesson are two-dimensional. Suggest how three-dimensional vectors might be described and added.

14-7

Adding Vectors Using Trigonometry

You have seen vectors described in two ways in this chapter. First, they were described as directed segments. For instance, a wind of 25 mph in the direction 30° south of east could be described by the directed segment $\overrightarrow{OA}$ shown at the right. As directed segments, vectors can be added geometrically, by putting one segment at the end of the other.

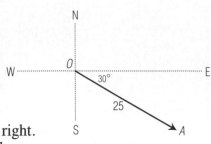

Second, vectors were described by ordered pairs. The ordered pair (8, 2) stands for the vector connecting (0, 0) to the point (8, 2). The sum of vectors (a, b) and (c, d) is the vector $(a + c, b + d)$. The properties of vectors are quite easily deduced from the description of vectors as ordered pairs.

Because it is so easy to add vectors as ordered pairs, it is natural to want to translate from directed segments to ordered pairs. This can be done using trigonometry.

Example 1   Describe the vector $\overrightarrow{OA}$ above with an ordered pair.

Solution   The desired ordered pair contains the coordinates of point A. Let $A = (x, y)$ as shown at the right. From the graph you can see that x is positive and y is negative. The absolute values of x and y are OB and BA. Now use trigonometry.

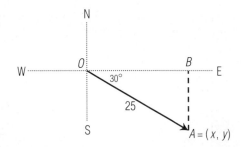

Since $\dfrac{OB}{OA} = \cos 30°,$

$$OB = OA \cos 30°$$
$$= 25 \cos 30°.$$

Similarly, because $\dfrac{BA}{OA} = \sin 30°,$

$$BA = OA \sin 30°$$
$$= 25 \sin 30°.$$

Now remember that the first coordinate of A is positive and the second coordinate is negative. Thus $A = (25 \cos 30°, -25 \sin 30°)$. With a calculator, you can find that $\cos 30° \approx 0.866$ and $\sin 30° = 0.5$, so $A \approx (21.65, -12.5)$.

In Example 1, because 30° is a special angle, you can find exact coordinates for point A. Because $\cos 30° = \frac{\sqrt{3}}{2}$ and $\sin 30° = \frac{1}{2}$, so $A = (12.5\sqrt{3}, -12.5)$. Usually you cannot find exact coordinates.

Example 2 Find the components of the vector whose magnitude is 150 and whose direction is 10° south of west.

Solution Draw a picture. The components of the vector are the coordinates of point C below. The picture includes a right triangle whose sides will give the coordinates of C.

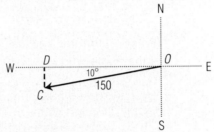

First notice that both coordinates of C are negative. Their absolute values are OD and DC.

Since $\cos 10° = \dfrac{OD}{OC}$,

$$OD = OC \cos 10°.$$

Since $\sin 10° = \dfrac{DC}{OC}$

$$DC = OC \sin 10°.$$

The x-component of C is $-OC \cos 10°$ and the *y*-component is $-OC \sin 10°$. With a calculator, you can get decimal approximations: $\overrightarrow{OC} \approx (-147.72, -26.05)$.

From Examples 1 and 2 you can see that one component of a vector is found using the sine of the given angle. The other component is found using the cosine. However, instead of memorizing formulas, it is usually easier to draw a picture each time and use the definitions of sine and cosine.

To go from the ordered pair description to one in terms of direction and magnitude, the tangent is required.

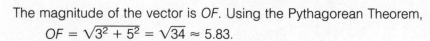

Example 3 Find the direction and magnitude of the vector (3, 5).

Solution Again, draw a picture. A sample is on the left.

The magnitude of the vector is *OF*. Using the Pythagorean Theorem,
$$OF = \sqrt{3^2 + 5^2} = \sqrt{34} \approx 5.83.$$

The direction can be found from m∠*FOE*. What we know is that
$$\tan\angle FOE = \tfrac{5}{3}.$$

To determine m∠*FOE,* press
$$5\; \boxed{\div}\; 3\; \boxed{=}\; \boxed{\text{INV}}\; \boxed{\text{tan}}.$$

(Pressing the $\boxed{\text{INV}}$ key just prior to the $\boxed{\text{tan}}$ key gives you the measure of the angle whose tangent is $\tfrac{5}{3}$.)

You should see 59.0362... displayed. This means that m∠*FOE* ≈ 59. So the direction of this vector is about 59° north of east, or you could say about 31° east of north.

The above examples provide algebraic tools to combine forces given their magnitudes and directions. Notice how many of the ideas of this chapter are applied in the next Example.

Example 4 To move a heavy box, one person pushes north with a force of 125 lb. A second person pushes northwest with a force of 100 lb. What is the magnitude and direction of the combined force?

Solution The force vectors are $\overrightarrow{OA}$ and $\overrightarrow{OB}$ as pictured at the left. The combined force is given by $\overrightarrow{OC}$, where $\overrightarrow{OC} = \overrightarrow{OA} + \overrightarrow{OB}$. *OACB* is a parallelogram.

It is easy to see that $\overrightarrow{OA} = (0, 125)$. Using the ideas of Examples 1 and 2, $\overrightarrow{OB} = (-100\cos 45°, 100\sin 45°) \approx (-70.7, 70.7)$. So $\overrightarrow{OC} = \overrightarrow{OA} + \overrightarrow{OB} \approx (0 + -70.7, 125 + 70.7) = (-70.7, 195.7)$.

The magnitude of $\overrightarrow{OC}$ is *OC*; $OC \approx \sqrt{(-70.7)^2 + 195.7^2} \approx 208.1$.

From the definition of tangent, $\tan\angle COD \approx \frac{195.7}{70.7} \approx 2.768$, so   m∠*COD* ≈ 2.768 $\boxed{\text{INV}}$ $\boxed{\text{tan}}$
$$\approx 70.1°.$$

The combined force is about 208 pounds in a direction 70° north of west (or 20° west of north).

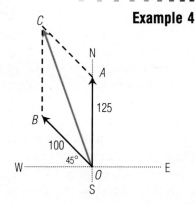

Questions

Covering the Reading

1. What are two ways of describing vectors?

In 2–5, find the components of the vector.

2.

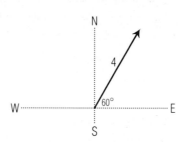

3.

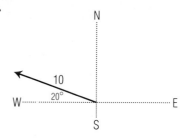

4.

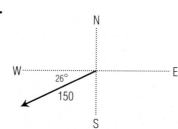

5.

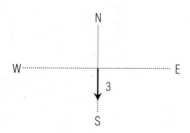

6. If tan $A = 0.532$ and A is an acute angle, estimate m$\angle A$ to the nearest degree.

In 7 and 8, give the direction and magnitude of the vector.

7.

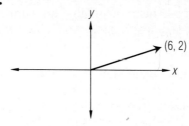

8.

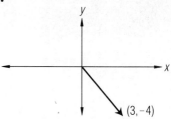

Applying the Mathematics

9. To move a crate, one person pushes east with a force of 130 pounds. A second person pushes 50° south of east with a force of 70 pounds. What is the magnitude and direction of the combined force?

10. A plane is flying at a speed and direction which, in still air, would be 550 mph, 25° north of west. There is a wind of 80 mph, 10° south of east. Give the resultant ground speed and direction of the plane.

11. From the top of a roof, a person throws a ball horizontally at 88 feet per second. The force of gravity pulls it down 32 feet in the first second. After one second, how far and in what direction from the person will the ball be?

12. Give the inverse of the vector (-7, 13). *(Lesson 14-6)*

13. Graph **u**, **v**, and **u + v** where **u** = (-5, 8) and **v** = (7, 0). *(Lesson 14-6)*

In 14 and 15, trace the given vectors. Then draw their sum. *(Lesson 14-5)*

14.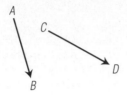

15.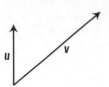

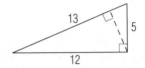

16. In a 5-12-13 right triangle, find the length of the altitude to the hypotenuse and the lengths of the segments into which the altitude splits the hypotenuse. *(Lesson 14-2)*

17. What is the area of △*STU* below? *(Lessons 14-1, 8-5)*

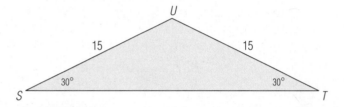

18. Make a conclusion using all of the following statements.
  a. No *x* is a *y*.
  b. If an animal is not a *y*, then the animal is not a *z*.
  c. Rudolph is a *z*. *(Lesson 13-4)*

19. Young children who play string instruments like the violin or cello often use instruments that are similar to, but smaller than, the adult-size instrument. An $\frac{1}{8}$-size cello is $\frac{1}{8}$ the volume of a full-size cello. How do the heights of these cellos compare? *(Lesson 12-6)*

20. a. Describe the figure formed by rotating circle *C* in space about line ℓ.
  b. Describe the figure formed by rotating circle *A* in space about line ℓ. *(Lesson 9-4)*

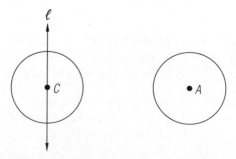

21. There is an operation on vectors called the *dot product*. Find out what the dot product of (*a*, *b*) and (*c*, *d*) is.

Summary

Right triangles are important because any triangle and thus any polygon can be split up into them, and because knowing only one acute angle and one side, all lengths are determined. Certain right triangles occur so often that they are special. The isosceles right triangle has angles of 45°, 45°, and 90° and sides of lengths x, x, and $x\sqrt{2}$. Any equilateral triangle can be split into two right triangles with angles of 30°, 60°, and 90° and sides with lengths x, $x\sqrt{3}$, and $2x$.

When the altitude to the hypotenuse of a right triangle is drawn, two triangles are formed, each similar to the original. Three of the resulting proportions involve a geometric mean, as one length appears as both means in the proportion. The altitude itself is the geometric mean of the segments into which it divides the hypotenuse. Either leg is the geometric mean of the hypotenuse and the segment of the hypotenuse closest to it.

When right triangles have congruent angles, they are similar and the ratios of corresponding sides in the triangles are equal. These ratios are called trigonometric ratios; three of them are the tangent, sine, and cosine of any angle. The trigonometric ratios can be estimated using an accurate drawing, or a scientific calculator, or calculated exactly if you are given lengths of sides in the triangle or are dealing with one of the two special triangles.

A vector is a quantity with a magnitude and a direction. Vectors may be described geometrically as directed line segments, or algebraically as ordered pairs. It is useful to be able to convert from either description to the other. Vectors can stand for forces, velocities, pressures, acceleration, and other physical quantities. Vector addition gives the result of combining forces or other quantities. The operation of vector addition has many of the properties of ordinary real number addition: commutativity, associativity, an identity, and inverses. Scalar multiplication yields vectors with the same or opposite directions but different magnitudes.

Vocabulary

Below are the most important terms and phrases for this chapter.
For the starred (*) items you should be able to give a definition of the term.
For the other items you should be able to give a general description and a specific example of each.

Lesson 14-1
45-45-90, 30-60-90 triangles
Isosceles Right Triangle Theorem
30-60-90 Triangle Theorem

Lesson 14-2
*geometric mean
arithmetic mean
Geometric Mean Theorem
Right Triangle Altitude Theorem

Lesson 14-3
leg adjacent to an angle
leg opposite an angle
*tangent of an angle
tan A, $\boxed{\text{tan}}$
trigonometric ratio

Lesson 14-4
*sine of an angle, sin A, $\boxed{\text{sin}}$
*cosine of an angle
cos A, $\boxed{\text{cos}}$

Lesson 14-5
vector, $\overrightarrow{AB}$, **v**
directed line segment
direction of vector
magnitude of vector
initial point, terminal point
equal vectors
*sum of two vectors
resultant of two vectors, **u** + **v**
parallelogram rule

Lesson 14-6
ordered pair description of a
    vector
horizontal component
vertical component
Vector Addition Theorem
Properties of Vector Addition
    Theorem
zero vector
opposite vectors
*scalar multiplication
*scalar multiple
*$k\,(a, b)$

Lesson 14-7
$\boxed{\text{INV}}$ $\boxed{\text{tan}}$

Progress Self-Test

Directions: Take this test as you would take a test in class. Use a ruler and calculator. Then check your work with the solutions in the Selected Answers section in the back of the book.

1. In right triangle *XYZ* below, estimate cos *Y* by measuring two sides. Give an answer to the nearest hundredth.

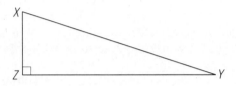

2. Refer to the figure below. Of the numbered angles, which has the smallest tangent?

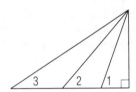

3. In right triangle *ABC* below, if $\sin B = \frac{9}{11}$, find cos *A*.

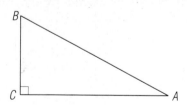

In 4 and 5, refer to the figure below. Suppose *XY* = 60, *XZ* = 45, and *ZY* = 75.

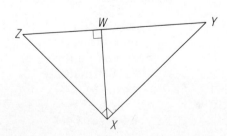

4. Find *WZ*.   **5.** Find *WY*.

In 6 and 7, use the figure below.

6. If *BC* = 6 and *BD* = 2, find *AB*.

7. *CD* is the geometric mean of __?__ and __?__.

In 8–10, use the figure below. If *AB* = 7, find:

8. *BC*   **9.** *AC*   **10.** *AD*.

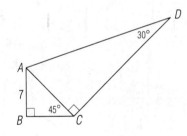

In 11 and 12, use triangle *DEF* below.

11. Find tan *D*.   **12.** Find cos *E*.

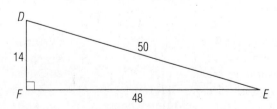

In 13 and 14, give the exact value.

13. sin 60°   **14.** tan 45°

15. Find the geometric mean of 18 and 30 to the nearest hundredth.

16. From eye level 5 ft above the ground, a person has to look up at an angle of 35° to see the top of a tree 40 ft away. How tall is the tree?

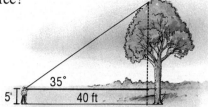

35°

5'   40 ft

17. How far up on a vertical wall can a 15-foot ladder reach if the angle it makes with the ground is 80°?

18. Trace the vectors below. Then draw their sum.

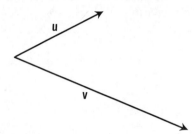

u

v

19. Use the vectors above.
a. Draw 2**v** + **u**.   **b.** Draw 2(**v** + **u**).

20. Draw an opposite of vector $\overrightarrow{AB}$ below.

A

B

21. Graph **u**, **v**, and **u** + **v**, where **u** = (-4, 2) and **v** = (0, -6).

22. Give the components of vector $\overrightarrow{OA}$ below.

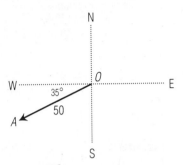

N

W   O   E
           35°
              50

A

S

23. Give the direction and magnitude of the vector (30, -16).

24. An airplane can travel at 700 kilometers per hour in still air. With a head wind of 150 kilometers per hour, how far could it travel in $3\frac{1}{2}$ hours?

25. A kayak is moved by a 4 mph current 25° west of north, and the kayaker is paddling at a speed of 8 mph in the direction 50° east of north. With a picture, show what direction the boat will move.

Chapter Review

Questions on **SPUR** Objectives

SPUR stands for **S**kills, **P**roperties, **U**ses, and **R**epresentations.
The Chapter Review questions are grouped according to the
SPUR Objectives for this chapter.

SKILLS deal with the procedures used to get answers.

■ **Objective A:** *Calculate lengths of sides in
isosceles right triangles and in 30-60-90 triangles.*
(Lesson 14-1)

1. In △ABC below, find AC and BC.

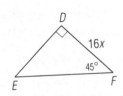

2. In △DEF above, find DE and EF.

3. A square has sides of length 12. What is the
length of a diagonal?

4. An equilateral triangle has sides of length q.
Find the length of an altitude.

In 5 and 6, use the figure below.

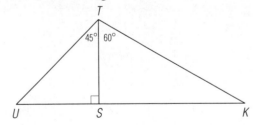

5. If ST = 7, find **a.** TU **b.** US **c.** SK
and **d.** TK.

6. If SK = 13, find **a.** ST **b.** SU and **c.** TK.

7. Refer to △XYZ at the right
with measures as marked.
Find YZ. (Hint: Draw an
altitude from X.)

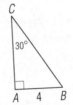

■ **Objective B:** *Determine sines, cosines, and
tangents from drawings. (Lessons 14-3, 14-4)*

8. Refer to △ABC below. By measuring,
determine m∠A (to the nearest degree), and
tan A, sin A, and cos A (to the nearest
hundredth).

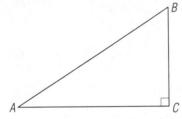

9. Refer to △DEF below. By measuring,
determine m∠E to the nearest degree, and
sin E, cos E, and tan E to the nearest
hundredth.

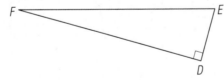

10. Draw a right triangle with legs of 3 units and
5 units. Use this triangle to estimate m∠A if
tan A = $\frac{3}{5}$.

In 11 and 12, use the figure below. Choose from
the numbered angles.

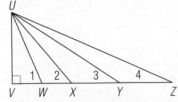

11. Which angle has the largest tangent?

12. Which angle has the largest sine?

Objective C: *Calculate sines, cosines and tangents of angles in right triangles.* *(Lessons 14-3, 14-4)*

In 13–16, use △ABC below. Give exact values for each.

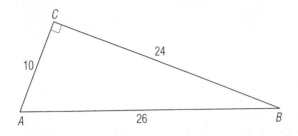

13. sin A

14. cos B

15. tan B

16. cos A

In 17–19, estimate to the nearest thousandth.

17. sin 57.5°

18. tan 22.1°

19. cos 1°

In 20–23, give exact values.

20. sin 30°

21. tan 60°

22. tan 45°

23. cos 45°

Objective D: *Calculate lengths using the Right Triangle Altitude Theorem.* *(Lesson 14-2)*

In 24–26, refer to the figure at the right below.

24. If AD = 9 and DB = 4, then CD = _?_.

25. If AC = 7 and AB = 12, then AD = _?_. ..

26. If DC = 12 and AD = 18, then BC = _?_.

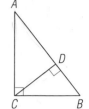

27. At the right is a 7-24-25 right triangle. Find the length of x, y, and z.

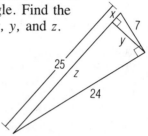

28. In △RQS below, $\overline{QR} \perp \overline{RS}$ and $\overline{RT} \perp \overline{QS}$. If RT = 4 and TS = 8, find

a. QT

b. QR

c. RS

d. QS.

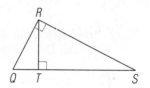

PROPERTIES deal with the principles behind the mathematics.

Objective E: *Draw the sum of two or more vectors.* *(Lessons 14-5, 14-6)*

In 29–31, trace the given vectors. Then draw their sum.

29.

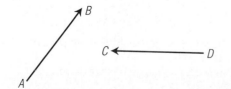

30.

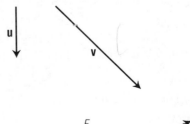

31.

32.

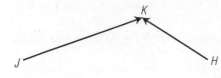

33.

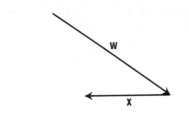

34.

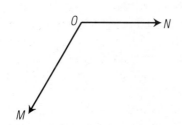

35. Trace the vectors and draw **u + v + w**.

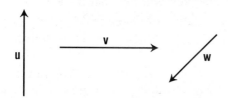

36. Use the vectors from Question 35.
  a. Draw 3 **v** + **w**. **b.** Draw 3 (**u** + **v**).

■ **Objective F:** *Know the definitions of sine, cosine, and tangent. (Lessons 14-3, 14-4)*

In 37–39, △*ABC* is a right triangle with right angle *C*. Define each expression.

37. cos *A*   **38.** sin *A*   **39.** tan *A*

In 40 and 41, use the figure below.

40. $\dfrac{MP}{MQ}$ is the tangent of which angle?

41. $\dfrac{MQ}{PQ}$ is the __?__ of angle *P*.

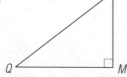

In 42 and 43, use right triangle △*ABC* below.

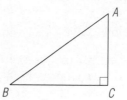

42. Write a ratio for tan *B*.

43. If cos *A* = *x,* find sin *B*.

■ **Objective G:** *Recognize and derive the geometric mean properties in right triangles. (Lesson 14-2)*

In 44–47, use the figure below.

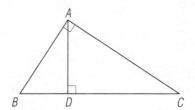

44. *AB* is the geometric mean of __?__ and __?__.

45. *AD* is the geometric mean of __?__ and __?__.

46. *AC* is the geometric mean of __?__ and __?__.

47. △*ABC* ~ △__?__ ~ △__?__

■ **Objective H:** *Identify the properties of vector addition. (Lesson 14-6)*

48. What vector is the additive identity?

49. Draw the inverse of the vector $\overrightarrow{AB}$.

50. Give the inverse of the vector (2, 9).

51. Using the vectors of Question 35, is it true that **u** + **v** = **v** + **u**?

■ **Objective I:** *Use sines, cosines, and tangents to determine unknown lengths in real situations.* *(Lessons 14-3, 14-4)*

52. From eye level 2 meters off the ground and 25 meters from a sculpture, a person has to look up at an angle of 20° to see the top of it. How high is the sculpture (including the base)?

53. When the sun is 57° up from the horizon, a tree casts a shadow 14 yards long. How tall is the tree?

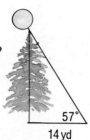

57°
14 yd

54. How far up a vertical wall does a 4-meter ladder reach if the angle it makes with the ground is 75°?

55. From the window of a building you look down at a clown in a parade. If your eyes are 60 feet above the clown, and the angle of sight, measured from the building, is 25°, how far is the clown from you?

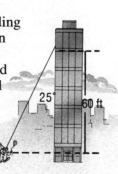

25°
60 ft

■ **Objective J:** *Use vectors for forces to determine combinations of forces.* *(Lesson 14-5, 14-7)*

56. A motorboat is traveling with a speed which, in still water, would be 30 mph, against a current of 10 mph. How far will the boat travel in 15 minutes?

57. An airplane can travel at 600 kilometers per hour in still air. With a tail wind of 100 kilometers per hour, how far could it travel in $2\frac{1}{2}$ hours?

In 58–59, Show the answer with a picture.

58. Two people are pushing a heavy crate. One exerts a force of 130 pounds in a westerly direction, the other 110 pounds in a northwesterly direction. In what direction will the crate move?

59. A rowboat is moved by a 6 mph current 30° south of east and by rowers, who row at 3 mph in the direction 40° west of south. In what direction will the boat travel?

60. In the situation of Question 58, give the magnitude and direction of the combined force.

61. In the situation of Question 59, give the magnitude and direction of the combined force.

■ **Objective K:** *Graph sums and scalar multiples of vectors represented as ordered pairs.* *(Lesson 14-6)*

In 62 and 63, graph **u**, **v**, and **u + v**.
62. **u** = (2, 1), **v** = (3, 2)
63. **u** = (-4, -3), **v** = (5, 0)
64. If **w** = (-9, 5), graph **w** and 2**w**.
65. Graph **v** and 3**v** when **v** = (6, 1).

■ **Objective L** *Convert directed segments to ordered pairs, and vice-versa.* *(Lesson 14-7)*

66. Give the components of the vector $\overrightarrow{OA}$ at the right.

67. Describe $\overrightarrow{OB}$ below as an ordered pair.

68. Give the direction and magnitude of the vector (1, 10).

69. Give the direction and magnitude of the vector (-31, -26).

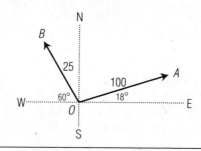

Further Work with Circles

Circles have been important figures since antiquity. The ancient Greeks believed that the sun, planets, and other celestial objects went around the earth in circles. The great scientist Galileo Galilei wrote in 1623:

> *. . . the universe . . . is written in the language of mathematics, and its characters are triangles, circles, and other geometrical figures, without which it is humanly impossible to understand a single word of it; without these, one is wandering about in a dark labyrinth.*

Already in this book you have seen circles arise from rather different sources:

as cross-sections of cylinders, cones, spheres, and other surfaces made by rotating a figure in three-dimensions;

as a limit of regular polygons;

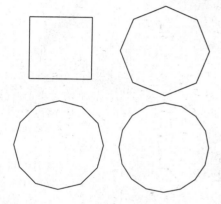

as containing shortest paths on the surface of a sphere;

as sets of points the same distance from a center.

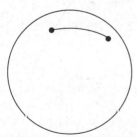

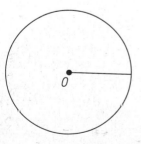

With these properties, the circle or arc is viewed as a whole. In this chapter, the measures of angles and segments associated with circles are examined in some detail. The results are very pretty and often quite surprising, and are related to further applications of this simple figure.

Chord Length and Arc Measure

Recall some information about angles and circles. An angle with its vertex at the center of a circle is a **central angle** of the circle. The arc of the circle on and in the interior of the angle is said to be **intercepted** by the angle. The **measure of the intercepted arc** is defined as the measure of its central angle.

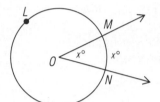

central angle MON and its intercepted arc $\overset{\frown}{MN}$.
$$m\angle MON = x°$$
$$m\overset{\frown}{MN} = x°$$

Above, $m\angle MON$ seems to be about 45, and arc $\overset{\frown}{MN}$ also measures $45°$. Since $45 = \frac{1}{8} \cdot 360$, the arc is about $\frac{1}{8}$ of the circle. $\overset{\frown}{MN}$ is a **minor arc** because its measure is less than $180°$. The **major arc** $\overset{\frown}{MLN}$ has measure $360° - 45°$, or $315°$. An arc with measure $180°$ is a **semicircle.**

If $\overset{\frown}{AB}$ is an arc of a circle, the segment $\overline{AB}$ is called the **chord of the arc** $\overset{\frown}{AB}$. When $\overset{\frown}{AB}$ is not a semicircle, the triangle determined by A, B, and center O is isosceles.

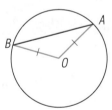

$\overline{AB}$ is the chord of $\overset{\frown}{AB}$.

You have learned that, in an isosceles triangle, the bisector of the vertex angle, the perpendicular bisector of the base, the altitude from the vertex, and the median from the vertex all lie on the same line. (See Lesson 5-1 if you have forgotten.) In the language of circles and chords, this leads to the following theorem.

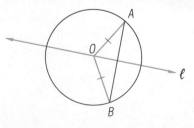

Chord-Center Theorem:

a. The line containing the center of a circle perpendicular to a chord bisects the chord.
b. The line containing the center of a circle and the midpoint of a chord bisects the central angle determined by the chord.
c. The bisector of the central angle of a chord is perpendicular to the chord and bisects the chord.
d. The perpendicular bisector of a chord of a circle contains the center of the circle.

Proof

Each part is only a restatement of a property of isosceles triangles.
a. This says the altitude to the base is a median.
b. This says the _?_ is also a(n) _?_ .
c. This says the _?_ is also a(n) _?_ .
d. This says the _?_ is also a(n) _?_ .

If two circles $\odot X$ and $\odot Y$ have equal radii, then one can be mapped onto the other by the translation mapping X to Y. So they are congruent. Of course, if they do not have equal radii, since isometries preserve distance, no isometry will map one onto the other.

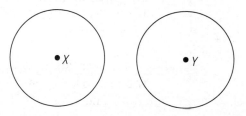

This proves that circles are congruent if and only if they have equal radii.

If two arcs in the same or congruent circles have the same measure, then they are congruent. In the circle below, you can rotate $\overset{\frown}{AB}$ about O by the measure of $\angle AOC$ to the position of $\overset{\frown}{CD}$. Then the chord $\overline{AB}$ rotates to $\overline{CD}$ also, and $\overline{AB} \cong \overline{CD}$. Thus, in a circle, arcs of the same measure are congruent and have congruent chords. This proves part **a** of the next theorem. The proof of part **b** is left for you as Question 14.

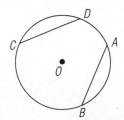

Arc-Chord Congruence Theorem:

In a circle or in congruent circles:
a. If two arcs have the same measure, they are congruent and their chords are congruent.
b. If two chords have the same length, their minor arcs have the same measure.

In circles with *different* radii, however, arcs of the same measure are not congruent. They are *similar*. And their chords are not congruent. This is pictured below.

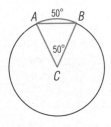

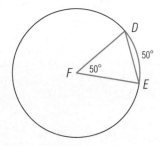

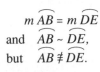

$m \overset{\frown}{AB} = m \overset{\frown}{DE}$
and $\overset{\frown}{AB} \sim \overset{\frown}{DE}$,
but $\overline{AB} \not\cong \overline{DE}$.

A natural question to ask is: Given the measure of an arc, can the length of its chord be found? This can always be done using trigonometry if the radius of the circle is known. If the arc measure is 60°, 90°, or 120°, it can be done without trigonometry.

Example 1   A circle has a radius of 10″. Find the length of a chord of
a. a 60° arc;   **b.** a 90° arc;   **c.** a 120° arc.

Solution   Always draw a picture.

a. △*AOB* is an isosceles triangle with a 60° vertex angle, so it is equilateral. So *AB* = 10″.

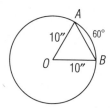

b. △*COD* is an isosceles right triangle. So $CD = 10\sqrt{2}'' \approx 14.14''$.

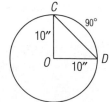

c. Draw the altitude $\overline{OG}$ to the base of △*OEF*. The two triangles formed are 30-60-90 triangles. $OE = 2 \cdot OG$, so *OG* = 5″. $GE = \sqrt{3} \cdot OG$, so $GE = 5\sqrt{3}''$, from which $FE = 10\sqrt{3}''$ or $FE \approx 17.32''$.

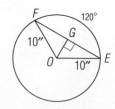

Example 1 provides a way of finding the length of a side of a regular hexagon, square, or equilateral triangle whose vertices are on a circle. Any polygon whose vertices lie on a given circle is called an **inscribed polygon.** The center of an inscribed regular polygon is the center of the circle.

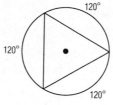
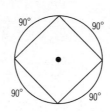
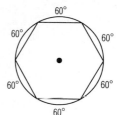

Using trigonometry, you can always find the length of a chord if you know its arc measure and the radius of the circle.

Example 2 Find the length of a chord of a 103° arc in a circle of radius 20 cm.

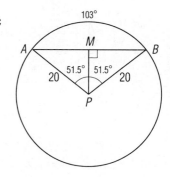

Solution A picture is drawn at the right. The length of $\overline{AB}$ is desired.

Because $\triangle PAB$ is isosceles with vertex angle P, if M is the midpoint of $\overline{AB}$, then $\overline{PM} \perp \overline{AB}$ and $\overline{PM}$ bisects $\angle APB$. Thus $\triangle APM$ is a right triangle and $m\angle APM = \frac{103}{2} = 51.5$. To find AM, use trigonometry.

$$\sin 51.5° = \frac{AM}{20}$$
$$AM = 20 \cdot \sin 51.5° \approx 15.65$$

Since M is a midpoint, $AB = 2 \cdot AM \approx 31.30$ cm.

Questions

Covering the Reading

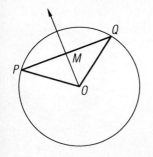

1. The measure of a minor arc of a circle is between __?__ and __?__ .

2. The measure of a major arc of a circle is between __?__ and __?__ .

In 3–6, use $\odot O$ pictured at the left.

3. If $m\angle POQ = 98$, then m $\overset{\frown}{PQ}$ = __?__ .

4. Explain why $\triangle OPQ$ is isosceles.

5. If $\overline{OM} \perp \overline{PQ}$, then $\overline{OM}$ __?__ $\overline{PQ}$.

6. If $\overrightarrow{OM}$ bisects $\angle POQ$, then $\overrightarrow{OM}$ __?__ $\overline{PQ}$.

7. Fill in the blanks in the proof of the Chord-Center Theorem.

8. *Multiple choice.*
Two circles are congruent if and only if their radii are

(a) parallel
(b) perpendicular
(c) equal in length
(d) none of these.

9. Refer to $\odot Z$ and $\odot A$ below.
True or false? If m$\angle Z$ = m$\angle A$, then $XY = BC$.

In 10–13, $\odot O$ at the right has radius 25 m.

10. Find the length of a chord of a 60° arc.

11. Find the length of a chord of a 90° arc.

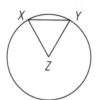

12. Find the length of a chord of a 120° arc.

13. Find the length of a chord of a 53° arc.

Applying the Mathematics

14. Complete this proof of part **b** of the Arc-Chord Congruence Theorem.

Given: $AB = CD$ in $\odot O$ as shown below.
Prove: m$\overarc{AB}$ = m$\overarc{CD}$.
(Hint: The measure of an arc equals
the measure of its central angle.)

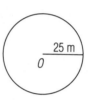

15. The circular hole with center Q shown at the right has a radius of 3 ft. A 5-foot board $\overline{XY}$ is to be wedged into the hole. What will be the distance from Q to $\overline{XY}$? (Hint: Draw some auxiliary radii and perpendiculars.)

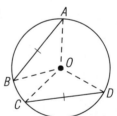

16. Regular hexagon *ABCDEF* is inscribed in $\odot H$.
Suppose $HA = 13$.
a. Find m$\angle AHB$.
b. Find the perimeter of *ABCDEF*.

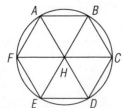

17. *LMNP* is a square inscribed in $\odot O$ at the right.
The radius of the circle is $6\sqrt{2}$. Find the
length of a side of the square.

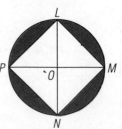

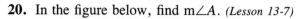

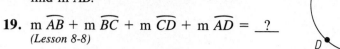

Review

In 18 and 19, use ⊙*Q* at the right.

18. If m $\widehat{ABC}$ = 178° and m $\widehat{BC}$ = 94°, find m $\widehat{AB}$.

19. m $\widehat{AB}$ + m $\widehat{BC}$ + m $\widehat{CD}$ + m $\widehat{AD}$ = __?__ *(Lesson 8-8)*

20. In the figure below, find m∠*A*. *(Lesson 13-7)*

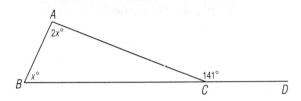

21. A square pyramid has a base with sides 2 m and height 1.4 m. What is its volume? *(Lesson 10-7)*

22. To rotate a figure -120°, you could reflect the figure over two lines where the acute angle between the lines has measure __?__ . *(Lesson 6-3)*

23. **a.** The measure of an angle of a regular *n*-gon is __?__ .
b. The measure of an angle of a regular octagon is __?__ . *(Lesson 5-7)*

Exploration

24. A polygon is **circumscribed** about a circle if each of its sides is tangent to the circle. At the right, a quadrilateral has been circumscribed about circle *O*.

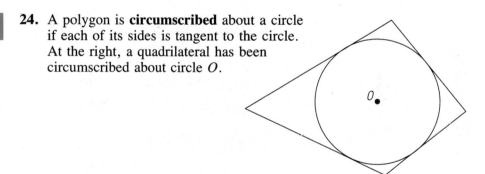

Experiment with various circles and polygons. Tell whether you think these conjectures are *true* or *false*.

   a. If a quadrilateral is circumscribed about a circle, then at least two of its sides are congruent.
   b. If a rectangle is circumscribed about a circle, then it is a square.
   c. If an isosceles trapezoid is circumscribed about a circle, then it is a rectangle.
   d. A polygon with an odd number of sides greater than 3 cannot be circumscribed about a circle.

15-2

Regular Polygons and Schedules

In many competitions, from baseball to chess to soccer to bowling, each competitor plays all the others. When each competitor (or team) plays each other competitor exactly once, it is called a **round-robin** tournament. Scheduling this, as you know if you have ever tried it, can be tricky. Suppose there are seven teams to be scheduled so that each plays the other six. The first thing you might do is number the teams 1 through 7. Now schedule a first week. One team doesn't play. That team gets a **bye.**

1 plays 2   3 plays 4   5 plays 6   7 bye

What about a second week? Try 1 playing 3. Perhaps 2 plays 4? Here's a possibility.

1 plays 3   2 plays 4   5 plays 7   6 bye

Now a third week. We just try to have teams play teams they haven't.

1 plays 4   2 plays 5   6 plays 7   3 bye

It seems easy. Here is a fourth-week schedule.

1 plays 5   2 plays 6   3 plays 7   4 bye

Another week. It's starting to get complicated. We keep looking back so as not to repeat.

1 plays 6   2 plays 3   4 plays 7   5 bye

How many weeks to go? Team 1 still has to play 7. So does 2. We make 2 the bye.

1 plays 7   3 plays 6   4 plays 5   2 bye

There's only one week left. Can you see what it should be?

___?___   ___?___   ___?___   ___?___

It doesn't seem hard. But perhaps we were lucky. What if there were more teams? It would be nice if there was some algorithm that automatically created the schedule. The algorithm described here is surprising in that it uses rotation and properties of regular polygons and circles.

Step 1   Let the 7 teams be vertices of an inscribed regular 7-gon (heptagon).

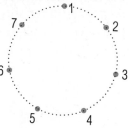

Step 2   (the first week) Draw a chord and all chords parallel to it. Because the polygon has an odd number of sides, no two chords have the same length. This is the first week's schedule

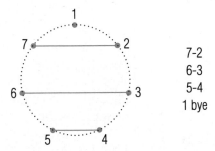

7-2
6-3
5-4
1 bye

Since the top chord joins 7 and 2, team 7 plays team 2 the first week. This is called a **pairing,** and is written 7-2. Also in the first week, team 6 plays team 3, team 5 plays team 4, and team 1 gets a bye. The full schedule will be completed when all sides and diagonals of the heptagons have been drawn.

Step 3   (the second week) Rotate the chords $\frac{1}{7}$ of a revolution. For example, the first week pairing 7-2 rotates into the pairing 1-3.

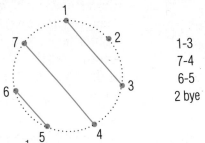

1-3
7-4
6-5
2 bye

Step 4   Continue rotating $\frac{1}{7}$ of a revolution for each week. Because in a week no two chords have the same length, no pairing repeats. In a total of seven weeks, the schedule is complete.

3rd week:	2-4	1-5	7-6	3 bye
4th week:	3-5	2-6	1-7	4 bye
5th week:	4-6	3-7	2-1	5 bye
6th week:	5-7	4-1	3-2	6 bye
7th week:	?	?	?	?

Again we leave the 7th week for you to figure out. It is easier this time.

The same procedure will not work with an even number of teams. If parallel chords are drawn using the vertices of a regular octagon, some will have the same length. So, as you rotate, you will repeat pairings.

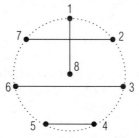

However, instead of putting the 8th team on the circle, it can be placed at the center of the circle. The radius joins team 8 and the bye in the above schedule. As you rotate the chords to make the schedule, rotate the radius too! This shows the surprising result: It takes as many weeks for a schedule of 7 teams as it does for a schedule of 8 teams. In general, it takes as many weeks for a schedule of $2n - 1$ teams as for a schedule of $2n$ teams.

With 7 teams there are 3 games for each of 7 weeks, or 21 pairings. Of these, 7 are sides of the regular heptagon, 7 are congruent shorter diagonals, and 7 are congruent longer diagonals. Scheduling a league of 7 or 8 teams thus has revealed some properties of the regular heptagon!

In the Questions, you should assume that all schedules are round-robin.

Questions

Covering the Reading

1. Complete the last week of pairings in the first schedule discussed in this lesson.

In 2–7, refer to the use of the regular heptagon to schedule teams.

2. How is a game between teams 4 and 6 pictured?

3. To find the pairings for the first week, all chords __?__ to a given chord are drawn.

4. How are the chords for one week related to the chords for the next week?

5. Complete the last week of pairings.

6. Where is an 8th team pictured to use this idea to schedule 8 teams?

7. Write a complete schedule for 8 teams.

8. A regular heptagon has diagonals of how many different lengths?

9. *True* or *false*? It takes as many weeks for a schedule of 9 teams as it does for a schedule of 10 teams.

Applying the Mathematics

10. a. To schedule 9 teams, what should be done first?
  b. Give the first two weeks of a schedule for 9 teams.
  c. Complete a schedule for 9 teams.
  d. How many diagonals does a nonagon have?
  e. Indicate what you can do to convert the schedule in **c** for 10 teams.

11. Explain why the algorithm of this lesson will not work for scheduling 6 teams. (Begin with the diagram at the left.)

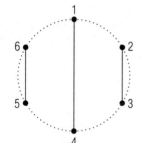

12. Make a complete schedule for a tournament with 6 teams.

13. Which two of the following descriptions of a point are used in the idea of scheduling?
  (a) dot
  (b) ordered pair
  (c) location
  (d) node of network

Review

14. $\overline{IB}$ is a chord in circle G. If $IB = 12$ and $IG = 10$, find the shortest distance from G to $\overline{IB}$. *(Lesson 15-1)*

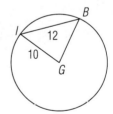

15. Find the length of a chord of a 120° arc in a circle of radius 45 mm. *(Lesson 15-1)*

16. Find the length of a chord of a 160° arc in a circle of radius 45 mm. *(Lesson 15-1)*.

17. Given: ℓ is tangent to $\odot E$ at C;
  $AD = DB$.
  Prove: $\overline{AB} \parallel \ell$. *(Lesson 15-1)*

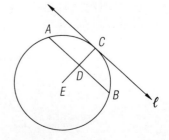

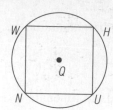

18. Square *WHUN* is inscribed in circle *Q* at the left. If the radius is $\sqrt{13}$ cm, find the perimeter of *WHUN*. *(Lesson 15-1)*

19. Willow, Lake, and Central are east-west streets. Greenwood and Landwehr are north-south streets. Milwaukee is oblique. What is the distance on Milwaukee from Lake to Willow? *(Lesson 12-8)*

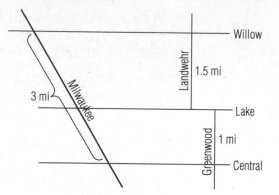

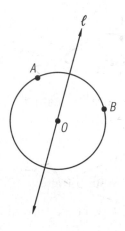

20. Trace the drawing at the left. Draw line *m* so that $r_m \circ r_\ell(A) = B$. *(Lesson 6-3)*

21. Trace △*ABC* below. Construct the perpendicular bisectors of its sides. *(Lesson 3-6)*

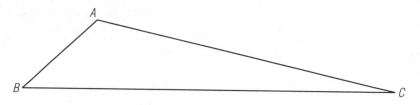

22. Solve for *x*: $100n - 200 + x = 100n$. *(Previous course)*

Exploration

23. a. Find a schedule for teams in a league involving your school or community.
    b. What factors affect schedules that this lesson does not mention?

15-3

The Inscribed Angle Theorem

The **picture angle** of a camera lens is a measure indicating how wide a field of vision can be captured in one photo. A normal camera lens in a Nikon 35 mm camera has a picture angle of 46°. A wide-angle lens may have a picture angle as large as 118°. A telephoto lens has a smaller picture angle, perhaps 18°.

Here is a situation in photography. You want to take a picture of a building, and you want to get the entire front of the building in your picture. (Assume the height of the building is not a problem.) Suppose you have only one normal lens with a 46° field. The diagram pictures the situation as seen from above.

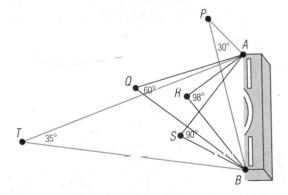

Let A and B be the endpoints of the building. If you stand at Q, m∠AQB is larger than 46, so the picture cannot include the entire front. The same is true for points R and S. But at points P and T, the whole front can be in the picture. There is a natural question: where are all the vertex points that make a 46° angle with points A and B? The answer is surprising. It is found by considering *inscribed angles* in a circle.

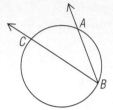

Inscribed angle ABC intercepts arc $\overset{\frown}{AC}$.

Consider some inscribed angles A, B, and C which intercept the same arc $\overset{\frown}{MN}$. You should measure these angles and then measure $\angle MON$ to determine m $\overset{\frown}{MN}$.

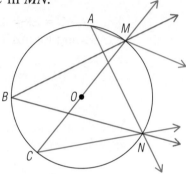

Above, you should find that m$\angle A$ = m$\angle B$ = m$\angle C$ $\approx$ 37, and m $\overset{\frown}{MN}$ $\approx$ 74°. These are instances of a surprising relationship which is true of all inscribed angles and their intercepted arcs.

Inscribed Angle Theorem:

In a circle, the measure of an inscribed angle is one-half the measure of its intercepted arc.

The steps of the proof depend on the position of the center O relative to the inscribed $\angle ABC$. There are three possibilities. They are referred to as Case I, Case II, and Case III.

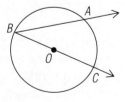

Case I: O lies on a side of $\angle ABC$.

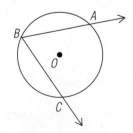

Case II: O is in the interior of $\angle ABC$.

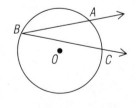

Case III: O is in the exterior of $\angle ABC$.

Proof

For all three figures the given and to prove are the same.

Given: ∠ABC inscribed in ⊙O.

Prove: $m\angle ABC = \frac{1}{2} \cdot m\overset{\frown}{AC}$.

Case I: The auxiliary segment $\overline{OA}$ is required. Since △AOB is isosceles, $m\angle B = m\angle A$. Call this measure x. By the Exterior Angle Theorem, $m\angle AOC = 2x$.

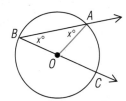

Because the measure of an arc equals the measure of its central angle,
   $m\overset{\frown}{AC} = 2x = 2 \cdot m\angle B$.
Solving for $m\angle B$, $m\angle B = \frac{1}{2} m\overset{\frown}{AC}$.

Case I proves that $m\angle B = \frac{1}{2} m\overset{\frown}{AC}$ when one ray of ∠B contains point O. This result is used in the proofs of Case II and Case III.

Case II: The auxiliary ray $\overrightarrow{BO}$ is needed.

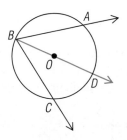

$$
\begin{aligned}
m\angle ABC &= m\angle ABD + m\angle DBC &&\text{(Angle Addition Postulate)}\\
&= \tfrac{1}{2}m\overset{\frown}{AD} + \tfrac{1}{2}m\overset{\frown}{DC} &&\text{(by the result of Case I)}\\
&= \tfrac{1}{2}(m\overset{\frown}{AD}+m\overset{\frown}{DC}) &&\text{(Distributive Property)}\\
&= \tfrac{1}{2}m\overset{\frown}{AC} &&\text{(Arc Addition, substitution)}
\end{aligned}
$$

Case III: The proof is like that for Case II.
For Case III, $m\angle ABC = m\angle ABD - m\angle CBD$.

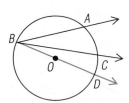

You are asked to finish the steps in Question 11.

The Inscribed Angle Theorem is easy to apply.

Example 1 Four points, A, B, C, and D, split a circle into arcs with measures as shown. Find the measures of the angles of $ABCD$.

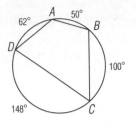

Solution

$$m\angle A = \tfrac{1}{2}\, m\overparen{BCD} = \tfrac{1}{2}(100° + 148°) = 124$$
$$m\angle B = \tfrac{1}{2}\, m\overparen{ADC} = \tfrac{1}{2}(62° + 148°) = 105$$
$$m\angle C = \tfrac{1}{2}\, m\overparen{DAB} = \tfrac{1}{2}(62° + 50°) = 56$$
$$m\angle D = \tfrac{1}{2}\, m\overparen{ABC} = \tfrac{1}{2}(50° + 100°) = 75$$

Check The four angle measures add up to 360° as they should for a quadrilateral. Furthermore, the measures look correct.

The next Example demonstrates a surprising consequence of the Inscribed Angle Theorem.

Example 2 Let $\overparen{PQR}$ be a semicircle. Find $m\angle PQR$.

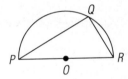

Solution Complete the circle.

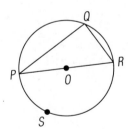

From the inscribed Angle Theorem, $m\angle \overparen{PQR} = \tfrac{1}{2}\overparen{PSR}$. Since $\overparen{PSR}$ is also a semicircle, $m\overparen{PSR} = 180°$. Thus $m\angle PQR = \tfrac{1}{2} \cdot 180 = 90$.

Example 2 proves the following.

Theorem:

An angle inscribed in a semicircle is a right angle.

What about the camera problem? The answer is given in Example 1 of the next lesson.

Covering the Reading

1. What is the picture angle of a camera lens?

2. Use the diagram at the right. A person stands at point *P* to take a picture of the house. Will the entire front of the house be in the picture:
   a. if the person uses a normal camera lens?
   b. if the person uses a telephoto lens?
   c. if the person uses a wide-angle lens?

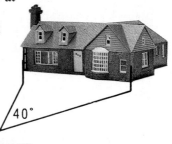

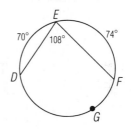

3. Use the circle below at the left. What is m∠*ABC*?

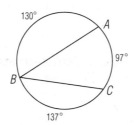

4. In the circle above at the right, what is m $\overparen{DGF}$?

5. An angle inscribed in a semicircle has what measure?

In 6 and 7, $\overline{MN}$ is a diameter of ⊙*O*, as pictured at the right below.

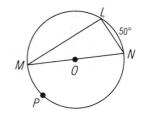

6. a. m $\overparen{ML}$ = __?__
   b. m $\overparen{MPN}$ = __?__

7. a. m∠*M* = __?__
   b. m∠*N* = __?__
   c. m∠*L* = __?__
   d. △*LMN* is a(n) __?__ triangle.

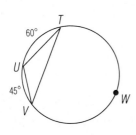

8. Use the figure at the left.
   a. △*TUV* is __?__ in the circle.
   b. m∠*U* = __?__

9. In the figure at the right, $\overline{YW}$ and $\overline{XZ}$ are diameters.
   a. m∠*WOZ* = __?__
   b. m∠*Y* = __?__

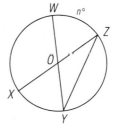

10. The proof of the Inscribed Angle Theorem has three cases. How do the cases differ?

11. Write a proof for Case III of the Inscribed Angle Theorem.

12. Use the figure below. Find the measures of the four angles of the quadrilateral.

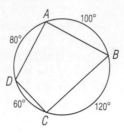

13. $\overline{AC}$ contains the center of the circle at the right. Calculate the measures of as many angles as you can.

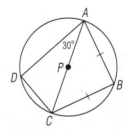

14. In $\odot O$ below, m$\angle M = 35$ and m$\angle P = 92$. If $MP = NQ$, find m $\overset{\frown}{MP}$.

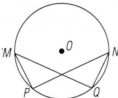

15. Fill in the justifications in this proof that in a circle, if two inscribed angles intercept the same arc, then they have the same measure.

Given: Inscribed angles AMB and ANB.
Prove: m$\angle AMB$ = m$\angle ANB$.

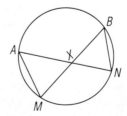

Conclusions	Justifications
1. m$\angle AMB = \frac{1}{2}$ m$\overset{\frown}{AB}$	**a.** ?
2. m$\angle ANB = \frac{1}{2}$ m$\overset{\frown}{AB}$	**b.** ?
3. m$\angle AMB$ = m$\angle ANB$	**c.** ?

16. Use the given of Question 15.
Prove: $\triangle AXM \sim \triangle BXN$.

17. Twelve teams are in a league. Each team is to play each other once. Make up a schedule for the first week that can be rotated into a schedule for every other week. *(Lesson 15-2)*

18. Find the perimeter of an equilateral triangle inscribed in a circle of radius 24. *(Lesson 15-1)*

19. Regular pentagon *VWXYZ* is inscribed in ⊙*P* at the right.
   a. What is m$\widehat{WX}$?
   b. If *PW* = 50, find the perimeter of the pentagon. *(Lesson 15-1)*

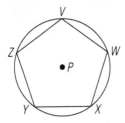

20. Square *ABCD* is inscribed in circle *O*. Square *EFGH* is circumscribed around circle *O*. In terms of *r*, the radius of circle *O*, express:
   a. the area between the circle and *EFGH*;
   b. the area between *ABCD* and the circle.
   c. Which is larger, the area in part **a** or the area in part **b**?
   (Lessons 15-1, 8-9)

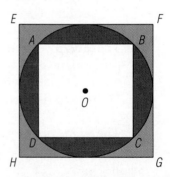

21. The length of a ballroom is twice its width and its area is 280 square yards. How long is it from one corner of the ballroom to the opposite corner? *(Lessons 8-7, 8-3, 8-1)*

22. In the figure below, *STICKEMUP* is a regular nonagon. *S* is the midpoint of $\overline{NT}$. What is m∠*PSN*? *(Lesson 5-7)*

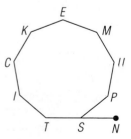

23. Examine a camera in your household or in a store. What is its normal picture angle? (You may need to refer to the instruction manual.)

Locating the Center of a Circle

Suppose you bought a circular coffee table and wished to place it on its base so that it balanced properly. To do this you need to find the center of the table. In Lesson 3-6 you learned how to do this by drawing perpendicular bisectors of chords. That method for locating the center of a circle is called the *perpendicular bisector method*.

There is a second method which relies on a theorem proved in the previous lesson: If an inscribed angle is a right angle, then its arc is a semicircle. So the segment connecting its endpoints is a diameter. Draw two diameters and you have the center.

The *right angle method* for locating the center of the circle:

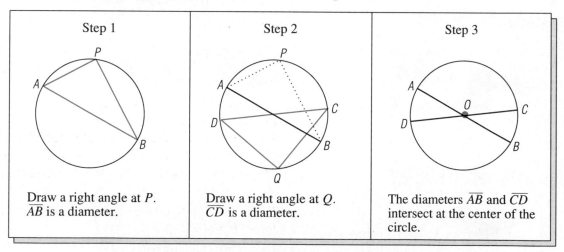

Step 1	Step 2	Step 3
Draw a right angle at P. $\overline{AB}$ is a diameter.	Draw a right angle at Q. $\overline{CD}$ is a diameter.	The diameters $\overline{AB}$ and $\overline{CD}$ intersect at the center of the circle.

This method is often used by people in drafting; the right angles are drawn with T-squares or metal ells. You can also use the corner of a piece of typing paper.

You can apply the construction of the center of a circle to the camera problem of Lesson 15-3.

.... ■■■

Example 1   A camera has a 46° field of vision. Where can a person stand to get the entire front of the building in one picture?

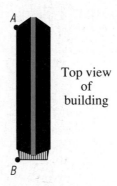

Top view
of
building

Solution   Consider a point P so that $m\angle APB = 46$. The front of the building will just be in the picture if you stand at point P. Think of $\overline{AB}$ as a chord of an arc in a circle also containing P.

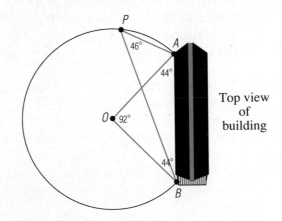

Top view
of
building

Step 1.   Determine $m\overset{\frown}{AB}$.

Since $m\angle P = \frac{1}{2} m\overset{\frown}{AB}$,

$$m\overset{\frown}{AB} = 2 \cdot m\angle P = 92°.$$

Step 2.   Find the center O of this circle.
The center is the point O so that $m\angle AOB = 92$. Since $\triangle AOB$ is isosceles, $m\angle OAB = m\angle OBA = 44$. Draw the 44° angles at A and B. Their sides intersect at O.

Step 3.   Draw $\odot O$ with radius OA.
Any point P on the major arc $\overset{\frown}{AB}$ of the circle will satisfy $m\angle APB = 46$.

If you stand anywhere on major arc $\overset{\frown}{AB}$, the front of the building will exactly fit into the picture. Inside the circle you will only get part of the building. Outside the circle you will get more than the building.

To determine the distance to the place to stand, you need to calculate the radius of the circle. This can be done using trigonometry.

Example 2   A photographer wishes to photograph a building 130′ long with a lens that has an 80° field of vision. If she stands in front of the middle of the building, at least how far from the building should she be?

Solution   Let $\overline{QS}$ be the front of the building, as shown below. R is the midpoint of $\overline{QS}$.

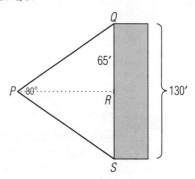

With the 80° lens, the photographer needs to stand at P. $\overline{PR} \perp \overline{QS}$ and PR is the minimum distance from the building. Since $\overleftrightarrow{PR}$ is the perpendicular bisector of $\overline{QS}$, $QR = 65′$ and $PQ = PS$. So $\triangle PQS$ is isosceles and $\overrightarrow{PR}$ bisects $\angle QPS$. So $m\angle RPQ = 40$. Now use trigonometry.

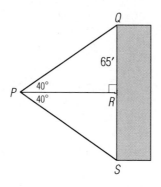

$$\frac{65}{PR} = \tan 40°$$

$$65 = PR \cdot \tan 40°$$

$$\frac{65}{\tan 40°} = PR$$

$$77.5′ \approx PR$$

If the photographer stands at least 77.5′ from the building, the picture will show the entire front.

Check $\angle Q$ is the larger acute angle in $\triangle PQR$, so PR should be greater than QR, which it is.

1. Trace the circle below at the left. Find its center using the right angle method.

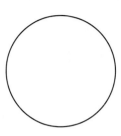

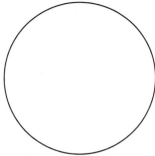

2. Trace the circle above at the right. Construct its center using the perpendicular bisector method.

3. Suppose your camera lens has a 56° field of vision. Trace the building at the left and diagram where you could stand so that $\overline{AB}$, the building's front, just fits into your picture.

4. In Question 3, assume $AB = 60$ yards. If you wanted to stand in front of the middle of the building, at least how far from the building would you need to stand?

5. Each year, the classes at Emmy Noether H.S. take class pictures on the steps to the main entrance. The steps are 50 meters long.

  a. A photographer has an 88° wide-angle lens and wants to stand in front of the middle of the steps as close to the students as possible. Where should the photographer stand?

  b. At the same time other people want to take pictures of the class. If they all have 88° wide-angle lenses and want to be as close as possible, where can they stand?

6. Trace points *A*, *B*, and *C* below. Use the perpendicular bisector method to construct the circle through points *A*, *B*, and *C*. (Hint: think of $\overline{AB}$ and $\overline{BC}$ as chords of the circle.)

7. Triangle *DEF* is inscribed in a circle. Draw that circle.

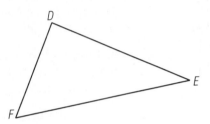

8. At the left is an arc of a circle. Trace the arc and locate the center of the circle.

9. Draw a circle using the bottom of a can or bottle. Find the center of the circle using a sheet of paper and the right angle method.

10. *IJKL* is a quadrilateral inscribed in circle *P*.
m∠*ILK* = *x* and m∠*IJK* = *y*.
   a. Which arc measures 2*x*°?
   b. Which arc measures 2*y*°?
   c. What is 2*x* + 2*y*?
   d. What is the sum of the measures of angles *ILK* and *IJK*?
   e. What is the sum of the measures of angles *LIJ* and *LKJ*?
   f. What does this prove about opposite angles in an inscribed quadrilateral? *(Lesson 15-3)*

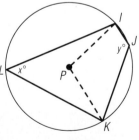

11. *BEHIVS* is a regular hexagon. The diagonals from *V* are drawn.
   a. Find the measures of the numbered angles.
   b. *True* or *false*?   △*BEV* is a right triangle. *(Lesson 15-3)*

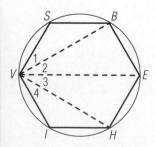

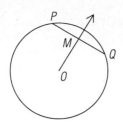

12. $\overline{PQ}$ at the left is a chord of $\odot O$.
  a. If M is the midpoint of $\overline{PQ}$, then __?__.
  b. If $\overrightarrow{OM} \perp \overline{PQ}$, then __?__.
  c. If $\overrightarrow{OM}$ bisects $\angle POQ$, then __?__. *(Lesson 15-1)*

13. The __?__ of a chord of a circle contains the center of the circle.
  (Lesson 15-1)

14. In $\odot O$ at the right, $PQ = 12$ and
  PQ is 8 units away from
  the center. What is OQ?
  (Lesson 15-1)

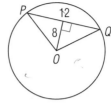

15. Use the figure below. $\overline{AB}$ is a diameter of $\odot C$. $\triangle BCD$ is equilateral.
  a. Find the measures of as many angles as you can.
  b. If $BD = x$, then what is the length of $\overline{AC}$?
  c. If $BD = 7$, what is the length of $\overline{AD}$? *(Lessons 15-3, 15-1)*

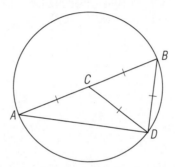

16. a. Give the contrapositive of this statement: If a figure is a rectangle, then its diagonals are congruent.
  b. Is the contrapositive true? *(Lesson 13-2)*

17. Sod is to be put on a circular golf course putting green 50′ in diameter. How much sod is needed? *(Lesson 8-9)*

Exploration

18. Each of the three circles below overlaps the other two. The three chords common to each pair of circles are drawn. They seem to have a point in common. Experiment to decide whether this is always true.

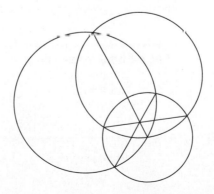

15-5

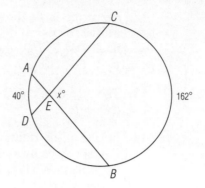

Angles Formed by Chords or Secants

Each side of a central angle or an inscribed angle intersects the circle. In this lesson and the next one, other angles for which both sides intersect a circle will be discussed. The Inscribed Angle Theorem enables angle measures to be determined even for these angles. First, consider an angle whose vertex is in the interior of a circle. For instance, consider the situation pictured below at the left, where two chords $\overline{AB}$ and $\overline{CD}$ intersect at E. Given m$\overset{\frown}{AD} = 40°$ and m$\overset{\frown}{BC} = 162°$, what is x?

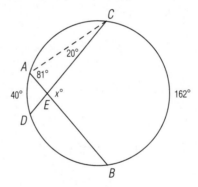

To find m$\angle CEB$, draw the auxiliary segment $\overline{AC}$, as done above. Now $\angle A$ and $\angle C$ are inscribed angles whose measures are half their arcs. So m$\angle A = 81$ and m$\angle C = 20$. $\angle CEB$ is an exterior angle of $\triangle ACE$. Its measure is the sum of these two angles. Thus, $x = 101$.

The argument can be generalized and proves the following startling theorem.

Angle-Chord Theorem:

> The measure of an angle formed by two intersecting chords is one-half the sum of the measures of the arcs intercepted by it and its vertical angle.

Example 1 In ⊙O at the left, m$\overarc{XY}$ = 200° and m$\overarc{VW}$ = 66°. Find m∠XQY.

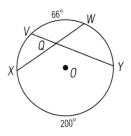

Solution   m∠XQY = $\frac{1}{2}$(m$\overarc{XY}$ + m$\overarc{VW}$)

$= \frac{1}{2}$(200 + 66)

$= \frac{1}{2}$(266)

= 133

The measure of the angle between chords can be found even when the lines containing the chords intersect in the exterior of the circle. Such lines are called **secants**.

Definition:

A **secant** is a line that intersects a circle in two points.

Below at the left, ∠E is formed by two secants and ∠E intercepts the two arcs $\overarc{AC}$ and $\overarc{BD}$ with measures 84° and 26°. To find m∠E, draw $\overline{AD}$, as pictured below at the right.

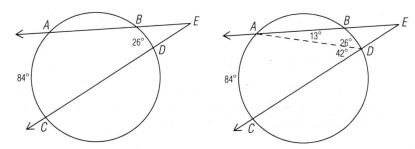

Again there are two inscribed angles, and one of them is ∠ADC, an exterior angle of △ADE. By the Exterior Angle Theorem,

$$m\angle A + m\angle E = m\angle ADC.$$

Solving for m∠E, $m\angle E = m\angle ADC - m\angle A$

$= \frac{1}{2} m\overarc{AC} - \frac{1}{2}m\overarc{BD}.$

Substituting, $= \frac{1}{2} \cdot 84 - \frac{1}{2} \cdot 26$

$= 42 - 13$

$= 29.$

Generalizing the argument proves the following theorem.

Angle-Secant Theorem:

The measure of an angle formed by two secants intersecting outside a circle is half the difference of the arcs intercepted by it.

Example 2 In ⊙R below, m$\overset{\frown}{KTM}$ = 195° and m$\overset{\frown}{JL}$ = 51°. Find m∠P.

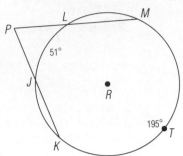

Solution From the Angle-Secant Theorem,

$$m\angle P = \tfrac{1}{2}(m\overset{\frown}{KTM} - m\overset{\frown}{JL})$$
$$= \tfrac{1}{2}(195 - 51)$$
$$= \tfrac{1}{2} \cdot 144$$
$$= 72.$$

In doing these problems, you have a choice between drawing the auxiliary segments and calculating, or memorizing a theorem. You should be able to do both.

Questions

Covering the Reading

1. Use the figure at the right. Find the measures of the numbered angles.
   a. m∠1 = ___?___
   b. m∠2 = ___?___
   c. m∠3 = ___?___
   d. m∠4 = ___?___

In 2 and 3, use the figure at the right.

2. What additional arc measure(s) do you need in order to find m∠1?

3. Suppose $\overline{XZ}$ is a diameter. Find m∠1.

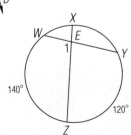

4. a. Using the diagram at the right, is enough information given to find m∠F?
   b. If so, find m∠F. If not, what more do you need to know?

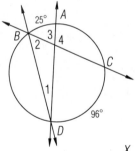

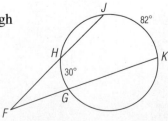

5. In the figure below, m$\widehat{LP}$ = 80° and m$\widehat{MO}$ = 50°.
Find:
   a. m∠MQO
   b. m∠N.

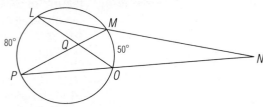

6. Define: secant.

Applying the Mathematics

7. A point *P* is outside ⊙*O*. How many secants of ⊙*O* contain *P*?

8. Use the circle below. Given: m$\widehat{RU}$ = 101° and $\overline{RS}$ ⊥ $\overline{TU}$. Find m$\widehat{ST}$.

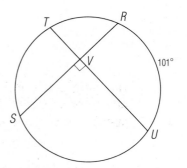

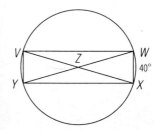

9. Rectangle *VWXY* is inscribed in the circle at the left. m$\widehat{WX}$ = 40°.
   a. What is the measure of the acute angle between the diagonals?
   b. What is m∠VYW?

10. Use the figure below. If m$\widehat{BD}$ = 53° and m∠C = 45, what is m$\widehat{AE}$?

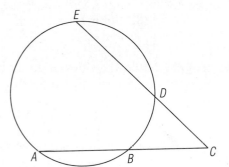

Review

11. Find the center of the circular arc at the right using the perpendicular bisector method. Then complete the whole circle. *(Lesson 15-4)*

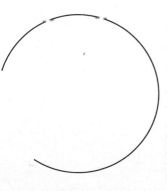

12. Suppose you have a camera with a picture angle of 118°. At least how far in front of the middle of the house shown would you need to stand to photograph the entire front? *(Lesson 15-4)*

13. Find the measure of each angle of *ABCDE* at the right. *(Lesson 15-3)*

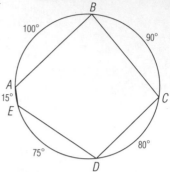

14. Create a round-robin schedule for ten teams. *(Lesson 15-2)*

15. A chord is 7 inches away from the center of a circle with radius $12\frac{1}{2}$ inches. Find the length of the chord. *(Lesson 15-1)*

16. a. State the Quadratic Formula.
   b. Use the Quadratic Formula to solve $2x^2 + 5x - 1 = 0$.
   (Previous course)

17. Solve for x: $x^2 - 30 = 34$. *(Previous course)*

18. Solve for y: $y + 12 > 21$. *(Previous course)*

Exploration

19. The sides of an inscribed pentagon *ABCDE* below are extended to form a **pentagram**, a five-pointed star.
   a. What is the sum of the measures of angles, *F, G, H, I,* and *J*, if the pentagon is regular?
   b. What is the largest and smallest this sum can be if the inscribed pentagon is not regular?

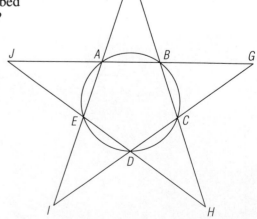

762

Angles Formed by Tangents

In the previous lesson, angles were formed by chords or secants. In this lesson, angles which have at least one side tangent to a circle are explored. Recall that a tangent line intersects a circle at exactly one point, and a radius drawn to the point of tangency is perpendicular to the tangent line.

Consider first the angle formed by a tangent and a chord through the point of tangency. $\overleftrightarrow{BC}$ is tangent to $\odot O$ below at B and $m\widehat{AB} = 75°$.

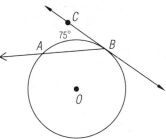

To find $m\angle ABC$, draw the diameter containing B and O. The semicircle $\widehat{BAD}$ has measure 180°, so $m\widehat{AD} = 105°$.

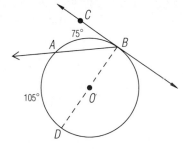

Thus $m\angle ABD = \frac{1}{2} \cdot 105 = 52.5$. Now, since $\overleftrightarrow{CB} \perp \overline{BD}$, $\angle CBA$ is complementary to $\angle ABD$. So $m\angle CBA = 37.5$. In general,

$$m\angle ABC = 90 - m\angle ABD$$
$$= \frac{1}{2} \cdot 180 - \frac{1}{2} \cdot m\widehat{AD}$$
$$= \frac{1}{2}(180 - m\widehat{AD})$$
$$= \frac{1}{2} m\widehat{AB}.$$

This proves the following theorem.

Tangent-Chord Theorem:

The measure of an angle formed by a tangent and a chord is half the measure of the intercepted arc.

Angles between tangents and secants are calculated just as angles between secants.

Tangent-Secant Theorem:

The measure of the angle between two tangents, or between a tangent and a secant, is half the difference of the intercepted arcs.

Proof

Consider secant $\overleftrightarrow{AB}$ and tangent $\overrightarrow{EC}$ at point C, forming $\angle E$, as below. Given $m\widehat{AC} = x°$ and $m\widehat{BC} = y°$, it needs to be shown that $m\angle E = \frac{1}{2}(x - y)$.

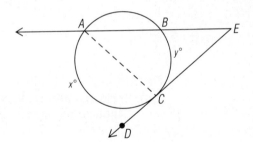

Draw $\overline{AC}$. Now $m\angle DCA = \frac{1}{2}x$ and $m\angle EAC = \frac{1}{2}y$. But $\angle DCA$ is an exterior angle of $\triangle ACE$. So

$$m\angle DCA = m\angle EAC + m\angle E.$$

Thus
$$m\angle E = m\angle DCA - m\angle EAC$$
$$= \frac{1}{2}x - \frac{1}{2}y$$
$$= \frac{1}{2}(x - y).$$

The proof for an angle between two tangents is similar. It is left to you as Question 6.

Example 1   Refer to the figure at the right.
$\overrightarrow{AB}$ is tangent to the circle at B.
Find $m\angle A$.

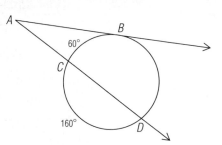

Solution   The circle measures 360°, so $m\widehat{BD} = 140°$.

$$m\angle A = \tfrac{1}{2}(m\widehat{BD} - m\widehat{BC})$$
$$= \tfrac{1}{2}(140 - 60)$$
$$= 40$$

Example 2   Refer to the figure at the left. $m\angle P = 30$. What is $m\widehat{QSR}$?

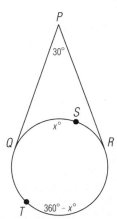

Solution   Let $m\widehat{QSR} = x°$. Then $m\widehat{QTR} = 360° - x°$.
By the Tangent-Secant Theorem,

$$m\angle P = \tfrac{1}{2}(m\widehat{QTR} - m\widehat{QSR})$$
$$= \tfrac{1}{2}((360 - x) - x).$$

Substituting and solving for x,

$$30 = \tfrac{1}{2}(360 - 2x)$$
$$= 180 - x.$$

So $x = 150$.

Check   When $x = 150$, $360 - x = 210$. Does $m\angle P$ equal half the difference of the two arcs? Yes, 30 is half of $210 - 150$.

Questions

Covering the Reading

1. $\overleftrightarrow{BC}$ is tangent to $\odot A$ below at B. If $m\widehat{BD} = 110°$, find:
   a. $m\angle ABC$
   b. $m\angle DBC$.

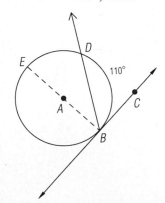

In 2–4, use the figure below. $\overline{PT}$ is tangent to circle O at point S.

2. m$\angle P$ = ___?___

3. m$\angle TSR$ = ___?___

4. *True* or *false*?
m$\angle RSP = \frac{1}{2}$ m$\widehat{RQS}$.

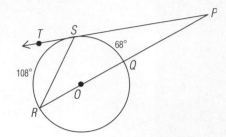

5. $\overline{AB}$ and $\overline{AC}$ are tangents to the circle
at B and C. Find the measures of
the indicated angles.
 a. $\angle ABD$
 b. $\angle CAB$
 c. $\angle ACD$

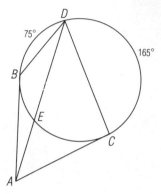

In 6 and 7, use the drawing below.

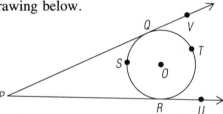

6. Prove that m$\angle P = \frac{1}{2}$ (m$\widehat{QTR}$ − m$\widehat{QSR}$). (Hint: Draw $\overline{QR}$ and use an
exterior angle of $\triangle PQR$.)

7. If m$\angle P = 25$, find the measures of arcs $\widehat{QSR}$ and $\widehat{QTR}$.

Applying the Mathematics

8. Match the angles at the left with the ways to compute measures at
the right.
 a. angle between two chords
 b. angle between two secants
 c. angle between two tangents
 d. angle between secant and
 tangent
 e. angle between chord and
 tangent
 f. inscribed angle
 g. central angle

    (i)   the intercepted arc
   (ii) $\frac{1}{2}$ the intercepted arc
  (iii) $\frac{1}{2}$ the sum of the
           intercepted arcs
  (iv) $\frac{1}{2}$ the difference of the
           intercepted arcs

9. Given: $\overrightarrow{CB}$ and $\overrightarrow{CD}$ are tangent to $\odot A$ at B and D.
Prove: m$\widehat{BD} = 180 - m\angle C$.

10. $\overrightarrow{PR}$ is tangent to $\odot O$ below at R. If m$\angle P = 41$, what is m$\overset{\frown}{QR}$?

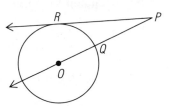

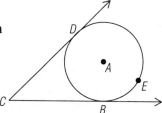

11. At the left, $\overleftrightarrow{ST}$ is tangent to $\odot X$ at T. If m$\angle RTS = 125$, find m$\overset{\frown}{TR}$.

12. Refer to the figure at the right. Graph on a number line the possible measures of angle C.

Review

13. Use the figure below. Find the measure of the indicated angle. *(Lessons 15-5, 15-3)*

    a. 2
    b. 3
    c. 4
    d. E

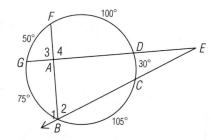

In 14 and 15, use the figure below.

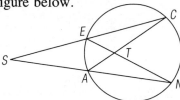

14. If m$\angle S = 23$ and m$\overset{\frown}{CN} = 85°$, find m$\overset{\frown}{AE}$.

15. **a.** Are triangles ANT and ECT similar? *(Lessons 15-3, 12-7)*
    b. Are triangles ANT and ECT congruent? *(Lesson 7-2)*

16. Suppose you have a camera with a picture angle of 38°. Trace the building below and diagram where you could stand so that the building's front just fits into your picture. *(Lesson 15-4)*

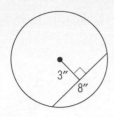

17. An 8″ chord is 3″ from the center of the circle at the left. What is the area of the circle? *(Lessons 15-1, 8-9)*

18. The measures of the exterior angles of a quadrilateral are $4x$, $8x - 23$, $9x + 7$, and $5x - 40$.
a. What is x?
b. What is the measure of each interior angle? *(Lesson 13-7)*

19. Below, $ABCD \sim JKHG$. Find as many missing lengths and angle measures as you can. *(Lesson 12-5)*

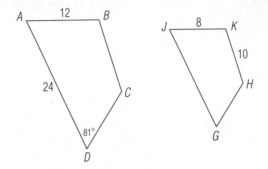

20. If $\dfrac{4}{x} = \dfrac{q}{10}$, write three other true proportions. *(Lesson 12-4)*

21. A sphere has diameter 24 mm.
a. Find its volume.
b. Find its surface area. *(Lessons 10-9, 10-8)*

Exploration

22. Recall that from two to five times a year the moon comes between the earth and sun, with a situation like that diagrammed here. When that happens, an eclipse of the sun occurs for part of the earth.

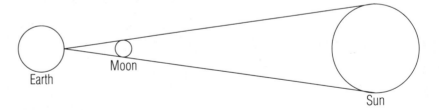

This picture is not to scale. The earth is roughly 7290 miles in diameter, the moon roughly 2160 miles. The moon is about 240,000 miles from the earth. The angle between the tangents is the angle of vision the moon and sun occupy in the sky. Find the measure of this angle. (You will need to use trigonometry.)

LESSON

15-7

Lengths of Chords, Secants, and Tangents

Usually if there are different-looking figures for a theorem, you would expect a different proof for each figure. In the theorem below, the surprise is that the same proof works, letter for letter, for two quite different figures. The theorem is simple, but amazing, and was known to Euclid.

Secant Length Theorem:

Suppose one secant intersects a circle at A and B, and a second secant intersects the circle at C and D. If the secants intersect at P, then
$$AP \cdot BP = CP \cdot DP.$$

Proof

Given: $\odot O$; secants $\overleftrightarrow{AB}$ and $\overleftrightarrow{CD}$ intersect at P.
Prove: $AP \cdot BP = CP \cdot DP$.
There are two figures, depending on whether P is inside or outside the circle.

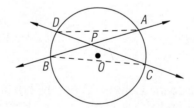
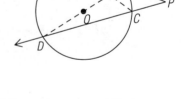

Analyze $AP \cdot BP$ will equal $CP \cdot DP$ if it can be proved that $\frac{AP}{CP} = \frac{DP}{BP}$. This suggests forming triangles and trying to prove them similar. Follow the conclusions and justifications, first for the left figure, then for the right figure.

Write	**Conclusions**	**Justifications**
	1. Draw $\overline{DA}$ and $\overline{BC}$.	Two points determine a line.
	2. $\angle BAD \cong \angle BCD$ $\angle ADC \cong \angle ABC$	In a $\odot$, inscribed angles intercepting the same arc are congruent.
	3. $\triangle DPA \sim \triangle BPC$	AA ~ Theorem (steps 2 and 3)
	4. $\frac{AP}{CP} = \frac{DP}{BP}$	Corresponding sides of similar figures are proportional.
	5. $AP \cdot BP = CP \cdot DP$	Means-Extremes Property

Example 1 Given chords $\overline{AB}$ and $\overline{CD}$ intersecting at P, with lengths as shown. Find PB.

Solution

$$PA \cdot PB = PC \cdot PD$$

Substituting, $\quad 3 \cdot PB = 5 \cdot 6$
$$= 30.$$
So $\quad\quad\quad\quad PB = 10.$

Example 2 Given secants $\overleftrightarrow{A_1B_1}$ and $\overleftrightarrow{A_2B_2}$ intersecting at P, with lengths as shown. Find A_2B_2.

Solution A_2B_2 is found by first getting PB_2 and then subtracting PA_2 from it.

$$PA_1 \cdot PB_1 = PA_2 \cdot PB_2$$
Substituting, $\quad 400 \cdot 1000 = 500 \cdot PB_2$
so $\quad\quad\quad\quad 800 = PB_2.$
Since $\quad\quad A_2B_2 = PB_2 - PA_2,$
$$A_2B_2 = 800 - 500 = 300.$$

The Secant Length Theorem has a surprising application. Suppose a circle and point P are given. For any secant through P intersecting the circle in two points A and B, there is a product $AP \cdot BP$. This product is a number, and it is the *same* number for any secant through P which intersects the circle! In Example 2, it is the number 400,000.

$$PA_1 \cdot PB_1 = PA_2 \cdot PB_2$$
$$= PA_3 \cdot PB_3$$
$$= PA_4 \cdot PB_4$$

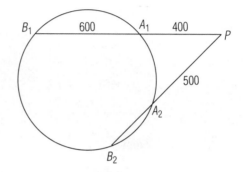

This is true for points P interior to the circle also. In Example 1, the product $PA \cdot PB$ is the number 30. The Swiss geometer

Jacob Steiner [1796–1863] called the product the **power of the point _P_ for the circle _O_.**

The power of a point external to a circle is easily calculated if you know the length of a tangent from _P_ to ⊙_O_.

Tangent Square Theorem:

The power of point _P_ for ⊙_O_ is the square of the length of a segment tangent to ⊙_O_ from _P_.

Proof

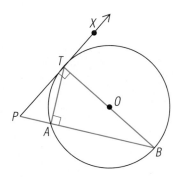

Draw   A figure is at the left.
Given: Point _P_ outside ⊙_O_ and $\overleftrightarrow{PX}$ tangent to ⊙_O_ at _T_.
Prove: The power of point _P_ for ⊙_O_ is PT^2.
Write   Draw $\overrightarrow{TO}$ which intersects ⊙_O_ at _B_. Let $\overline{PB}$ intersect ⊙_O_ at _A_ and _B_. Since $\overline{PT} \perp \overline{TB}$ and $\angle TAB$ is inscribed in a semicircle, $\triangle PTB$ is a right triangle with altitude $\overline{TA}$. Thus $PT^2 = PA \cdot PB$ by the Right Triangle Altitude Theorem. Thus the power of point _P_ for ⊙_O_ is PT^2.

Since $PT^2 = PA \cdot PB$, $PT = \sqrt{PA \cdot PB}$. Thus the length of a tangent $\overline{PT}$ to a circle from a point is the geometric mean of the lengths of segments of a secant drawn from that point.

■ ■ ■ ■ ■ ■ ■ ■

Example 3 $\overleftrightarrow{AR}$ is tangent to the circle. If $AP = 3$ and $AR = 6$, find AQ and PQ.

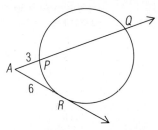

Solution   Use the Tangent Square Theorem: $AP \cdot AQ = AR^2$.
Substituting, $3 \cdot AQ = 6^2$
                              $3 \cdot AQ = 36$.
So $AQ = 12$.
Then $PQ = AQ - AP$
                                      $= 12 - 3$
                                      $= 9$.

Some problems involving the power of a point require solving a quadratic equation.

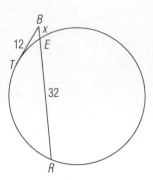

Example 4   Given that $\overleftrightarrow{BT}$ is tangent to the circle, $BT = 12$, and $ER = 32$, find BE.

Solution   From the Tangent Square Theorem,
$$BE \cdot BR = BT^2$$
$$BE \cdot (BE + ER) = BT^2.$$
Let $BE = x$. Substituting for BT, BE, and ER,
$$x(x + 32) = 144.$$
So $x^2 + 32x - 144 = 0.$
Use the Quadratic Formula:
$$x = \frac{-32 \pm \sqrt{1024 + 576}}{2} = \frac{-32 \pm \sqrt{1600}}{2} = \frac{-32 \pm 40}{2}.$$
So $x = 4$ or $x = -36$. Ignoring the impossible negative value for BE, $BE = 4$.

Questions

Covering the Reading

1. In the figure at the right, $DP \cdot DT = \underline{\ ?\ }$.

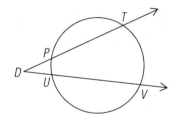

In 2 and 3, refer to the figure at the left.

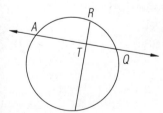

2. $AT \cdot TQ = \underline{\ ?\ }$

3. If $AT = 6$, $TQ = 4$, and $TR = 3$, then $TP = \underline{\ ?\ }$.

4. Refer to the figure at the right.
Let $TW = 3$, $WX = 3$, and $TU = 2$.
   a. Calculate TV.
   b. What is the power of point T for this circle?
   c. Calculate UV.

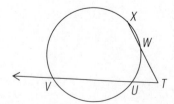

5. In Example 1, what is the power of point *P*?

In 6 and 7, refer to the figure at the left.

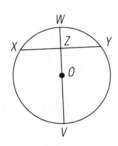

6. *JQ* is the geometric mean of __?__ and __?__.

7. If *JX* = 2 and *XY* = 6, then *JQ* = __?__.

8. Refer to the figure with two intersecting chords at the right.
   a. *x* = __?__
   b. The power of *P* in this circle is __?__.

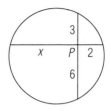

Applying the Mathematics

9. Use ⊙*K* below, with $\overleftrightarrow{JB}$ tangent to ⊙*K* at *B*. If *JI* = 10, *JA* = 8, and *AE* = 12, find *HI*.

10. In ⊙*O* at the left, diameter *WV* = 16. If $\overline{XY} \perp \overline{WV}$ and *XY* = 10, find *WZ*.

In 11 and 12, use the figure below. $\overline{BD}$ and $\overline{AC}$ intersect at *P* and $\overleftrightarrow{BA}$ and $\overleftrightarrow{CD}$ intersect at *X*. *True* or *false*? Carefully explain your response.

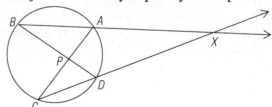

11. If *PA* = *PD*, then *PB* = *PC*.

12. It is impossible to have m$\overarc{BC}$ = m$\overarc{AD}$.

13. Is the Secant Length Theorem true if the word "circle" in it is replaced by "sphere"? That is, if *A*, *B*, *C*, and *D* are points on a sphere, does *PA* · *PB* = *PC* · *PD*? Explain your answer.

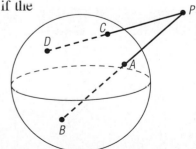

14. Find the measure of each angle in △*BDC* below. *(Lessons 15-6, 15-5)*

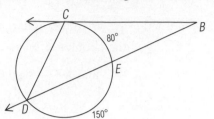

15. $\overrightarrow{XY}$ and $\overrightarrow{XZ}$ are tangent to ⊙*O* at the right at *Y* and *Z*. If m∠*X* = 45, find m$\overset{\frown}{YZ}$. *(Lesson 15-6)*

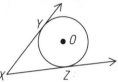

16. Find the measure of ∠*A* below. *(Lesson 15-5)*

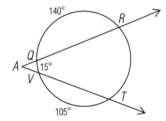

In 17 and 18, suppose you had a camera with a 64° picture angle. A top view of a building is shown at the left.

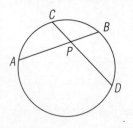

17. Draw where you can stand so that the entire front of the building will be seen in your picture. *(Lesson 15-4)*

18. If the building is 48 meters across, at least how far in front of the middle of the building would you need to stand? *(Lesson 15-4)*

19. In right triangle *ABC* at the right, find:
 a. *AC*
 b. tan *B*
 c. sin *A*
 d. cos *B*.
 (Lessons 14-4, 14-3, 8-7)

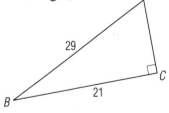

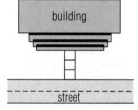

20. a. Is the Secant Length Theorem true if the secants intersect *on* the circle?
 b. If true, prove it. If not true, show a counterexample.

21. Is it possible for the lengths of the segments of two intersecting chords (*AP, BP, CP,* and *DP* in the figure at the left) to be four consecutive integers?

The Isoperimetric Inequality

Suppose you have 100 feet of fencing. How can you arrange it to provide the largest pen for the hogs? Here are some possibilities.

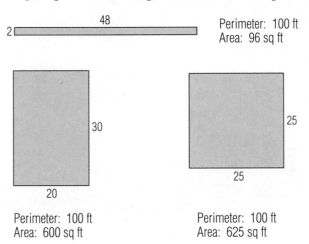

2 | 48

Perimeter: 100 ft
Area: 96 sq ft

30

20

Perimeter: 100 ft
Area: 600 sq ft

25

25

Perimeter: 100 ft
Area: 625 sq ft

Of the figures above, the square has the most area. It is the best quadrilateral shape for this purpose. But there is an even better shape than the square. Consider making the play area circular.

If $\qquad C = 100$ ft,

then $\qquad 2\pi r = 100$ ft.

Thus, $\qquad r = \frac{100}{2\pi} = \frac{50}{\pi} \approx 15.92$ ft.

With the radius known, the area can be calculated.

$$A = \pi r^2$$
$$\approx \pi(15.92)^2$$
$$\approx 796 \text{ sq ft}$$

Circumference: 100 ft
Area: 796 sq. ft.

The circle has about 171 sq ft more area than the square, even though it has the same perimeter!

The result, that the circle gives the most area, is the *Isoperimetric Theorem*. (The prefix "iso-" means "same.")

Isoperimetric Theorem:

Of all plane figures with the same perimeter, the circle has the most area.

The proof of this theorem requires advanced calculus, a subject usually not studied until college. The reason the proof is difficult is that it requires discussing all sorts of curves.

Pictured below are two such curves. At the left is an ellipse which is close to circular and thus encloses a good amount of area for its perimeter. At the right is a nonconvex curve with the same perimeter as the ellipse. As you can see, it encloses very little area for its perimeter.

Using the Isoperimetric Theorem, the maximal area for any perimeter p can be found. The steps in the proof are like those done above for the circle. The result is known as the *Isoperimetric Inequality*.

Isoperimetric Inequality:

If a plane figure has area A and perimeter p, then

$$A \leq \frac{p^2}{4\pi}.$$

Proof

Suppose the figure is a circle. Then its radius is $\frac{p}{2\pi}$ and its area is $\pi(\frac{p}{2\pi})^2$. This expression simplifies to $\frac{p^2}{4\pi}$. So for a circle, $A = \frac{p^2}{4\pi}$. The area of any other figure must be less than $\frac{p^2}{4\pi}$, so $A \leq \frac{p^2}{4\pi}$.

Example 1 Suppose a figure has perimeter 30 cm.

a. What is its largest possible area?

b. What is its smallest possible area?

Solution

a. The largest possible area is given by the Isoperimetric Inequality with $p = 30$.

$$A \le \frac{30^2}{4\pi}$$

$$= \frac{900}{4\pi}$$

$$\le 71.62 \text{ sq cm (approximately)}$$

The largest possible area, about 71.62 sq cm, occurs when the figure is a circle.

perimeter: 30
area: $\frac{900}{4\pi} \approx 71.62$

perimeter: 30
area: close to zero

b. The area can be as small as you want, but not zero. You can write, "The minimum is as close to zero as you like."

The inequality $A \le \dfrac{p^2}{4\pi}$ can be solved for p.

Multiply both sides by 4π. $\qquad\qquad\qquad\qquad 4\pi A \le p^2$

Rewrite the inequality to put p^2 on the left. $\qquad p^2 \ge 4\pi A$

Take the positive square root of each side. $\qquad p \ge \sqrt{4\pi A}$

Thus of all plane figures with a given area A, the perimeter p is at least $\sqrt{4\pi A}$. This result is a second way of stating the Isoperimetric Theorem.

Isoperimetric Theorem:

Of all plane figures with the same area, the circle has the least perimeter.

If the area of a circle is A, the perimeter (circumference) of a circle is $\sqrt{4\pi A}$. Any other figure with this area has a greater perimeter.

Example 2 Suppose a square and a circle both have area 25 sq ft. Show that the perimeter (circumference) of the circle is smaller than the perimeter of the square.

Solution The square's area is 25 sq ft, so a side is 5 ft, and its perimeter is 20 ft. For the circle, $A = 25$, so $p = \sqrt{4\pi(25)} = \sqrt{100\pi}$, or about 17.72 ft. Since $17.72 < 20$, the circle needs less perimeter to enclose the same area. It is more efficient.

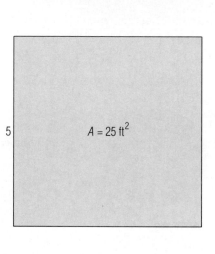

$A = 25\ \text{ft}^2$

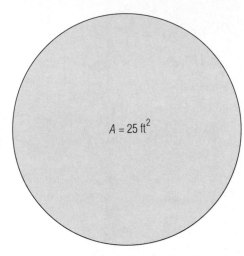

$A = 25\ \text{ft}^2$

Questions

Covering the Reading

1. Of all rectangles with perimeter 100 ft, what are the dimensions of the one with the most area?

2. **a.** Of all figures with perimeter 100 ft, which has the most area?
   b. What is that area?

3. If a figure has perimeter 100 ft, what is its least possible area?

4. Consider all figures with area 600 square meters. Which has the least perimeter?

5. Draw a non-polygonal figure that has a small area for its perimeter.

6. Draw a polygon with a small area for its perimeter.

7. A circle has area 9π sq cm. What is its circumference?

8. A square has area 9π sq cm. What is its perimeter?

9. Which answer should be larger, that for Question 7 or that for Question 8?

10. Complete the statements.
    a. Of all figures with the same area, the __?__ has the __?__ perimeter.
    b. Of all figures with the same perimeter, the __?__ has the __?__ area.

11. **a.** A fence encloses pentagonal region *ABCDE* at the right. Find the area of this region.
    b. Find the area of the largest region that could be enclosed by this fence.

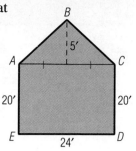

12. If a rectangle has perimeter 4*s*, then its sides can be called $s - t, s + t, s - t,$ and $s + t$.
    a. What is the area of this rectangle?
    b. For what value of *t* is the area the largest?

13. Refer to ⊙*O* at the right. Suppose *XY* = 8, *YZ* = 20, and *XW* = 10.
    a. Find *WV*.
    b. What is the power of point *X*?
    (Lesson 15-7)

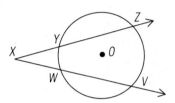

14. In the circle at the left, *AE* = 16, *BE* = 14, *CE* = 18. Find *DE*. *(Lesson 15-7)*

In 15 and 16, refer to ⊙*O* at the right. $\overrightarrow{AB}$ is tangent at point *B*.

15. If m∠*A* = 40, find
    a. m$\widehat{BD}$
    b. m$\widehat{BC}$. *(Lesson 15-6)*

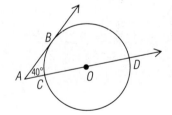

16. Find m∠*CBD*. *(Lesson 15-3)*

17. In the figure at the left, find *x*. *(Lesson 15-5)*

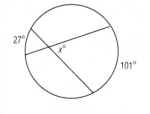

18. What is the measure of each interior angle of a regular decagon? *(Lesson 13-8)*

19. State **a.** the converse, **b.** the inverse, and **c.** the contrapositive of the following statement: If we finish the next lesson, our class will have done every lesson in the book. *(Lesson 13-2)*

20. Calculate $\sqrt[3]{\pi}$ to the nearest hundredth. *(Lesson 10-3)*

21. Give dimensions and draw a picture of a polygon whose perimeter is 100 feet and whose area is greater than 625 square feet.

15-9

The Isoperimetric Theorems in Space

The role the circle plays in 2-dimensional relationships between area and perimeter is played by the sphere in 3-dimensional relationships between volume and surface area.

To emphasize the similarities, mathematicians use the same term, "isoperimetric," to indicate "same boundary." Again, a proof of the theorem requires advanced mathematics.

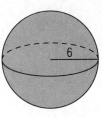

> **Isoperimetric Theorem (space version):**
>
> Of all solids with the same surface area, the sphere has the most volume.

The theorem can be verified in different ways. First is with an example. Below, the sphere and the cylinder have the same surface area, 144π square units.

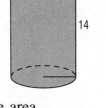

surface area
of sphere $= 4\pi r^2$
$= 144\pi$ sq units

surface area
of cylinder $= \text{L.A.} + 2B$
$= 2\pi rh + 2\pi r^2$
$= 144\pi$ sq units

Which has the greater volume? Their volumes can be easily found from formulas.

volume
of sphere $= \frac{4}{3}\pi r^3$
$= 288\pi$ units^3

volume
of cylinder $= Bh$
$= \pi r^2 h$
$= 224\pi$ units^3

The sphere has 64π cubic units more volume than the cylinder, almost 30% more volume. In fact, the sphere is the most efficient container. You would see spherical containers if they didn't roll!

A common experience provides a second verification. Suppose you blow air into a paper bag. The bag, being unable to stretch to change its surface area, will tend to assume a shape as close to a sphere as it can. If you blow in more air than the sphere can hold, the bag will burst.

Now, rather than a constant boundary, keep the interior constant. To do this, consider shapes with the same volume. The plastic container that holds a gallon of milk, but uses the least amount of plastic, would be shaped like a sphere. Soap bubbles consist of some soapy water and a fixed volume of air trapped inside. Because of surface tension, the bubble takes a shape to minimize the surface area surrounding the trapped air. That shape is a sphere.

Isoperimetric Theorem (space version):

Of all solids with the same volume, the sphere has the least surface area.

The following example verifies the theorem numerically.

Example A cube and a sphere have volume 1000 cubic meters. Calculate their surface areas.

Solution First draw figures and write down relevant formulas.

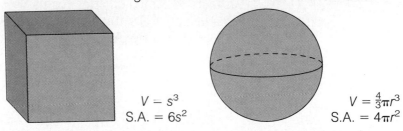

$$V = s^3$$
$$S.A. = 6s^2$$

$$V = \tfrac{4}{3}\pi r^3$$
$$S.A. = 4\pi r^2$$

For the cube, $1000 = s^3$, so $s = \sqrt[3]{1000} = 10$.
The surface area of the cube $= 6s^2 = 600$ square meters.
For the sphere, $1000 = \tfrac{4}{3}\pi r^3$,
$$\frac{750}{\pi} = r^3$$
$$238.7 \approx r^3.$$
Take the cube root to find $r \approx 6.2$.
The surface area of the sphere $= 4\pi r^2 \approx 4 \cdot \pi \cdot 6.2^2 \approx 483$ square meters. The sphere has considerably less surface area than the cube. The cube "wastes" surface because of its flat faces and corners.

Just as a two-dimensional figure can have a large perimeter and a small area, so a three-dimensional figure can have a large surface area inside a very small volume. Think of sponges like the natural and artificial ones pictured here. The artificial sponge has the shape of a retangular solid with volume 12 cubic inches, whereas the natural sponge is more irregular. Both sponges are nonconvex curved surface with many nooks, and both sponges can be enclosed in a space whose volume is small. The nooks give the sponges a large surface area compared to space they occcupy. This large irregular surface enables sponges to hold a lot of water. Some water is held because in almost any position some of the surface is under it. Other water clings to the large surface just the way the inside of a glass remains wet after you pour out its contents.

The Isoperimetric Theorems involve square and cube roots, π, polygons, circles, polyhedra, and spheres. They explain properties of fences, soap bubbles, and sponges. They demonstrate the broad applicability of geometry and the unity of mathematics. Many people enjoy mathematics due to the way it connects diverse topics. Others like mathematics for its uses. Still others like the logical way mathematics fits together and grows. We have tried to provide all these kinds of experiences in this book and hope that you have enjoyed it.

Questions

Covering the Reading

1. Of all the figures with the same surface area, the __?__ has the most __?__.

2. Of all the figures with the same volume, the __?__ has the least __?__.

3. Which statement, that of Question 1 or Question 2, explains the shape of a soap bubble?

4. The surface area of a solid is 600 square meters. To the nearest 100 cubic meters, what is the largest possible volume of the solid?

5. In Question 4, what is the least possible volume?

6. A cube has volume 8 cubic units. What is its surface area?

7. Explain why sponges are able to hold so much water.

Applying the Mathematics

8. The Water Pik company has claimed that its charcoal filter Instapure®, designed to be placed between a cigarette and a smoker's mouth, has over 6 acres of surface area.
   a. Can this claim possibly be true?
   b. If so, why would anyone want to have so much surface area? If not, why can't the claim be true?

9. a. A sphere has volume 36π cubic meters. What is its surface area?
   b. Give dimensions for a cylinder with volume 36π cubic meters. What is the surface area of the cylinder you identify?
   c. Give dimensions for a right cone with volume 36π cubic meters. What is its surface area?
   d. According to the Isoperimetric Inequality, the surface area in part **a** is __?__ than the surface area in parts **b** or **c**.

10. The plastic milk container that would have the least material for a given amount of milk would be shaped like a sphere. Why are milk containers *not* spheres?

11. A sphere has surface area $x \cdot \pi$. Find its volume in terms of x.

Review

12. Consider all plane figures whose area is 12 square meters.
    a. Which has the smallest perimeter?
    b. What is the perimeter? *(Lesson 15-8)*

13. A circle and a square both have perimeters of 96 inches.
    a. Calculate their areas.
    b. Which has the smaller area? *(Lesson 15-8)*

14. $\overrightarrow{QM}$ is tangent to $\odot X$ below at L. If $NQ = 6$ and $PN = 12$, find QL. *(Lesson 15-7)*

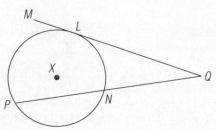

15. $\overline{DE}$ is a diameter of $\odot O$ below, and $\overline{AB} \perp \overline{DE}$. Prove that AC is the geometric mean of CD and CE. *(Lesson 15-7)*

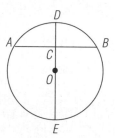

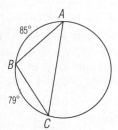

In 16 and 17, $\triangle ABC$ is inscribed in the circle at the left.

16. What are the measures of the angles of $\triangle ABC$? *(Lesson 15-3)*

17. What is the smallest side of $\triangle ABC$? *(Lesson 13-7)*

18. Draw a net for a juice can. *(Lesson 9-7)*

19. It is 457 miles from Boston to Buffalo. It is 436 miles from Buffalo to New York City. From only this information, what can you say about the distance from Boston to New York City? *(Lesson 1-9)*

Exploration

20. According to legend, the first person to use the Isoperimetric Inequality was Dido, the queen of Carthage.
  a. Where is, or was, Carthage?
  b. How did Dido use this inequality? (Hint: Look in an encyclopedia or dictionary under Dido.)

21. Develop an Isoperimetric Inequality for space. That is, find a relationship between the volume V and surface area S.A. of any space figure.

Summary

The theorems and applications of this chapter are related to many of the ideas you have studied in earlier chapters. Scheduling using properties of circles and regular polygons utilizes networks, where points are nodes. For the places to take a photo so that an entire object fits into the photo, points are locations.

Perpendicular lines are important in circles. A line perpendicular to a chord bisects the chord if and only if it contains the center of the circle. If the sides of an inscribed angle are perpendicular, then the angle intercepts a semicircle. These theorems give ways of finding the center of a circle.

The chapter includes congruence and similarity also. In a circle or in congruent circles, arcs of the same measure are congruent if and only if they have congruent chords. Inscribed angles which intercept the same arc are congruent. If two chords $\overline{AB}$ and $\overline{CD}$ intersect at point E, $\triangle EAC$ and $\triangle EBD$ are similar. As a result, $AE \cdot BE = CE \cdot DE$. Amazingly, this theorem holds if the word "secant" is substituted for "chord" and A, B, C, and D are the points at which two secants intersect the circle.

Relationships between measures of angles and arcs are all derived from the definition that the measure of an arc is equal to the measure of its central angle. Other angles are measured by:

central angle—intercepted arc
inscribed angle—half the intercepted arc
angle between chords—
        half the sum of the intercepted arcs
angle between secants or tangents—
        half the difference of the intercepted arcs

The Isoperimetric Theorems relate perimeters, areas, and volumes of figures. In two dimensions: Of all figures with the same perimeter, the circle has the most area. Of all figures with the same area, the circle has the least perimeter. In three dimensions: Of all figures with the same surface area, the sphere has the most volume. Of all figures with the same volume, the sphere has the least surface area. Many properties of real objects can be explained by these theorems.

Vocabulary

Below are the most important terms and phrases for this chapter.
For the starred (*) term you should be able to give a definition of the term.
For the other terms you should be able to give a general description and a specific example of each.

Lesson 15-1
intercepted arc
measure of the intercepted arc
Chord-Center Theorem
Arc-Chord Congruence Theorem
inscribed polygon
circumscribed polygon

Lesson 15-2
round-robin, bye, pairing

Lesson 15-3
picture angle of a lens
inscribed angle
Inscribed Angle Theorem

Lesson 15-4
right angle method
  for finding center of circle
perpendicular bisector method
  for finding center of circle

Lesson 15-5
Angle-Chord Theorem
*secant
Angle-Secant Theorem
pentagram

Lesson 15-6
Tangent-Chord Theorem
Tangent-Secant Theorem

Lesson 15-7
Secant Length Theorem
power of a point
Tangent Square Theorem

Lesson 15-8
Isoperimetric Theorem
Isoperimetric Inequality

Lesson 15-9
Isoperimetric Theorem
  (space version)

Progress Self-Test

Directions: Take this test as you would take a test in class. Then check your work with the solutions in the Selected Answers section in the back of the book. You will need a straightedge, compass, and protractor.

1. Find the center of the circle that contains points *C, D,* and *E* as shown below.

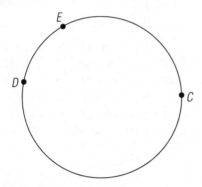

2. Schedule five teams for a round-robin tournament.

3. ℓ is tangent to $\odot O$ below at *Q*. If $\overline{OQ}$ intersects chord $\overline{XY}$ at the midpoint *M* of $\overline{XY}$, explain why $\ell \parallel \overline{XY}$.

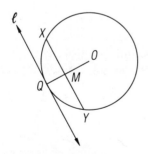

4. Square *JKLM* is inscribed in $\odot P$ below. If the radius of $\odot P$ is 30, find the perimeter of *JKLM*.

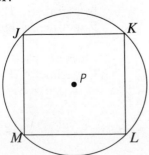

In 5 and 6, use the figure at the right, where $m\widehat{DC} = 80°$ and $m\angle DEC = 110$.

5. Find $m\angle B$.

6. Find $m\widehat{AB}$.

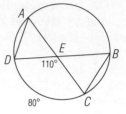

7. In $\odot Z$ below, $m\widehat{US} = 30°$, $m\widehat{UV} = 80°$, and $m\widehat{ST} = 140°$. Find $m\angle R$.

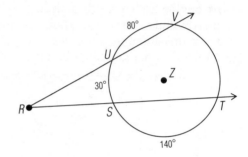

8. $\overrightarrow{PT}$ and $\overrightarrow{PU}$ are tangents to $\odot O$ below at *T* and *U*. If $m\widehat{UT} = 90°$, explain why *PUOT* is a square.

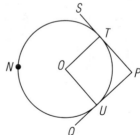

9. In circle *O* below, if $AQ = 19$, $BQ = 40$, and $CQ = 38$, find *QD*.

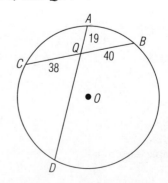

10. In ⊙G below, if $WX = 12$, $XY = 16$, and $WZ = 10$, find ZV.

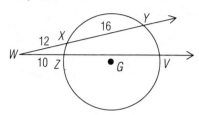

11. A clerk has 30 cm of a small wire screen to "fence in" some supplies on a desk.
  a. How should the screen be shaped to fence in the most area?
  b. What is this area?

12. A sphere and a cube both have volume 240 cubic feet. Which has the larger surface area?

In 13 and 14, refer to the stage below. You have a camera lens with a 64° picture angle.

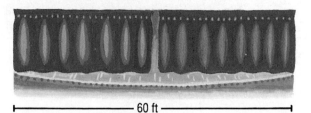

├─────────── 60 ft ───────────┤

13. Draw a picture indicating where you can stand so that the entire stage will be seen in your picture.

14. How near to the center of the stage in the middle of the audience can you stand and still photograph the entire stage?

Chapter Review

Questions on **SPUR** Objectives

SPUR stands for **S**kills, **P**roperties, **U**ses, and **R**epresentations.
The Chapter Review questions are grouped according according to the
SPUR Objectives for this chapter.

SKILLS deal with the procedures used to get answers.

■ **Objective A:** *Calculate lengths of chords of arcs.*
(Lesson 15-1)

1. A regular hexagon is inscribed in ⊙*O* below
   at the left. If the radius of ⊙*O* is 12, what is
   the length of each side of the hexagon?

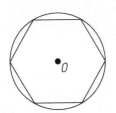
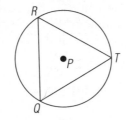

2. Equilateral triangle *QRT* is inscribed in circle
   P above at the right. If *QP* = 15, find the
   perimeter of △*QRT*.

In 3 and 4, *ABCD* is a square inscribed in ⊙*O* at
the right below. *AB* = 12√2.

3. Find *OB*.

4. Find the area of the
   shaded region.

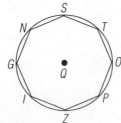

5. A circle has radius 55 mm. Find the length
   of a chord of a 144° arc.

6. Regular octagon *STOPZIGN* is inscribed in
   ⊙*Q* at the right.
   a. What is m$\widehat{IZ}$?
   b. If *QT* = 15, find
      the perimeter of
      the octagon.

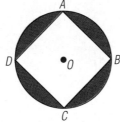

■ **Objective B:** *Calculate measures of inscribed
angles from measures of intercepted arcs, and
vice-versa. (Lesson 15-3)*

In 7–9, use the circle
at the right.

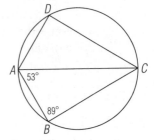

7. Find m$\widehat{CB}$.

8. Find m$\widehat{ADC}$.

9. Find m∠*D*.

In 10 and 11, △*PQR* is inscribed in the circle
below at the right.

10. Find m∠*Q*.

11. Find m∠*P*.

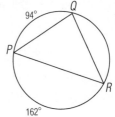

■ **Objective C:** *Calculate measures of angles
between chords, secants, or tangents, from
measures of intercepted arcs, and vice-versa.*
(Lessons 15-3, 15-5, 15-6)

In 12 and 13, use
circle Z at the right.

12. If m$\widehat{DG}$ = 100°
   and m$\widehat{EF}$ = 140°,
   what is m∠*EHF*?

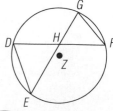

13. If m∠*EHD* = 51 and m$\widehat{GF}$ = 37°, what other
   arc measure can be found, and what is that
   measure?

14. Below, m$\widehat{BC}$ = 30° m$\widehat{DE}$ = 125°. Find the measures of as many angles in the figure as you can.

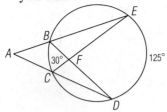

In 15–17, use ⊙L below with measures as marked.

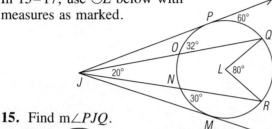

15. Find m∠PJQ.
16. Find m$\widehat{ON}$.
17. Find m∠PJM.

▧ **Objective D:** *Locate the center of the circle given sufficient information using the right angle or perpendicular bisector method.* *(Lesson 15-4)*

In 18 and 19, trace the circle. Then find its center using the right angle method.

18.

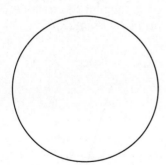

19.

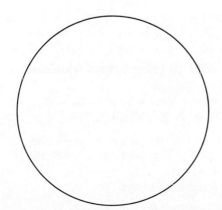

20. Trace the three points below. Draw the circle through them.

A •   B •

• C

21. Trace the figure below. Draw the circle containing all vertices of △DEF.

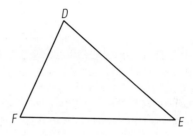

In 22 and 23, find the center of the circle containing the circular arc. Draw the entire circle.

22.   **23.**

▧ **Objective E:** *Apply the Secant Length Theorem.* *(Lesson 15-7)*

24. *A, B, C,* and *D* all lie on ⊙*Q* below. If *AX* = 12, *XB* = 40, and *DX* = 48, find *CX*.

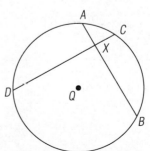

In 25 and 26, refer to ⊙O.

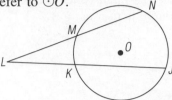

27. $\overleftrightarrow{QR}$ is tangent to ⊙Z below at R. If QR = 8 and QX = 4, find YX.

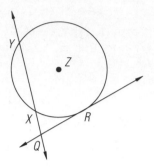

25. If LN = 20, MN = 15, and LJ = 25, find KJ.

26. If LM = 6, MN = 7, and KJ = 8, find LK.

PROPERTIES deal with the principles behind the mathematics.

■ **Objective F:** *Make deductions from properties of radii perpendicular to chords, and know sufficient conditions for radii to be perpendicular to them.* *(Lesson 15-1)*

In 28–30, given ⊙O, $\overline{AB} \perp \overline{CD}$, and $\overline{OA} \perp \ell$. Justify each statement. Be careful. One statement cannot be justified.

28. DE = EC

29. OE = EB

30. $\ell \parallel \overline{CD}$

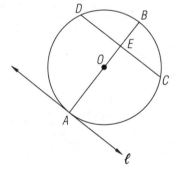

31. Use ⊙P below.
Given: W is the midpoint of $\overline{XY}$.
Prove: △ZYX is isosceles.

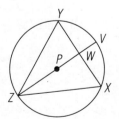

■ **Objective G:** *Make deductions from properties of inscribed angles formed by chords, tangents, or secants.* *(Lessons 15-3, 15-5, 15-6)*

In 32 and 33, ABDC at the right is a rectangle.

32. Explain why $\overline{BC}$ is a diameter.

33. Suppose m$\widehat{AB}$ = x. What is m∠ACB?

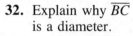

34. Below, $\overleftrightarrow{AB}$ is tangent to circle O at B. Prove: m∠ABD = m∠C.

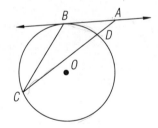

■ **Objective H:** *Apply the Isoperimetric Inequalities to determine which figures have the most or least area, perimeter, or volume.* *(Lessons 15-8, 15-9)*

35. Consider all plane figures with area of 800 square feet.
a. Which has the least perimeter?
b. What is the perimeter?

36. **a.** Of all rectangles with perimeter 2000 centimeters, which has the most area?
b. What is that area?

37. A circle and a square both have perimeters of 32 inches.
  a. Calculate their areas.
  b. Which has the larger area?

38. The surface area of a solid is 10,000 square meters. What figure has the largest volume for this surface area?

39. a. Of all boxes with surface area 48 square feet, which has the most volume?
  b. What is that volume?

40. A sphere and a cylinder both have volume 20,000 cubic meters.
  a. Can you tell which has the larger surface area?
  b. Why or why not?

USES deal with applications of mathematics in real situations

■ **Objective I:** *Given the angle width of a lens and the width of an object, determine the set of points from which the object will fit in the picture.* *(Lesson 15-4)*

In 41 and 42, a photographer wants to take a picture the entire length of a football field (from *A* to *B*). A scale drawing is made. The 50-yard line bisects the segment connecting the goal posts. Let $AB = 120$ yards.

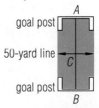

41. a. Locate all points where the photographer could stand to exactly fit $\overline{AB}$ if the camera lens has a picture angle of 62°.
  b. At least how far from *C* will the photographer be if he stands on the 50-yard line?

42. a. Locate all points where the photographer could stand to exactly fit $\overline{AB}$ if the camera lens has a picture angle of 84°.
  b. At least how far from *C* will the photographer be if he stands on the 50-yard line?

■ **Objective J:** *Apply the Isoperimetric Inequalities in real situations.* *(Lessons 15-8, 15-9)*

43. a. Of all containers that can hold a liter of orange juice, what shape container has the least surface area?
  b. Why is this shape seldom used?

44. A farmer is making a pigpen with 60 feet of fencing.
  a. What is the area of the most efficient rectangle?
  b. What is the area of the most efficient shape?

45. Draw a figure with a large perimeter for its area.

46. Identify a figure with a large surface area for its volume.

REPRESENTATIONS deal with pictures, graphs, or objects that illustrate concepts.

■ **Objective K:** *Make a schedule for a round-robin tournament.* *(Lesson 15-2)*

47. Four teams need to be scheduled for a round-robin tournament. Picture the schedule using chords of circles, and write a complete schedule.

48. Schedule a round-robin tournament for 11 teams, $A-K$.

49. Schedule a round-robin tournament for 12 teams, $A-L$.

This glossary contains definitions or descriptions of many of the terms used in this book. The numbers in parentheses following each term indicate a page on which that term is further discussed.

Named theorems are not listed here. To find the page number on which they are located, consult the index or the section in the back entitled THEOREMS.

acute angle   An angle whose measure is greater than 0 and less than 90. (113)

adjacent angles   Two nonstraight and nonzero angles are adjacent if and only if a common side is interior to the angle formed by the noncommon sides. (114)

algorithm   A sequence of steps leading to a desired end. (141)

alternate interior angles   Angles formed by two lines and a transversal whose interiors are partially between the lines and on different sides of the transversal. (234)

altitude   The distance between the bases of a trapezoid (384); the segment from a vertex perpendicular to the line containing the opposite side; also, the length of that segment (379). The distance between the planes of the solid (422); the length of a segment from the vertex perpendicular to the plane of the base of a pyramid or cone (429). Also called *height*.

angle   The union of two rays (its **sides**) that have the same endpoint (its **vertex**). (106)

antecedent   The "if" clause in an if-then statement. Also called *hypothesis*. (65)

arc   A path from one point (node) of a network to another point (its endpoints or vertices) (20). A part of a circle connecting two points (its endpoints) on the circle. (396)

area   The number of nonoverlapping unit squares or parts of unit squares that can be fit into a region. (355)

automatic drawer   Computer software that enables a geometric figure to be constructed from input by the user. (170)

auxiliary figure   A figure that is added to a given figure. (658)

axis of a cone   The line through the cone's vertex and the center of its base.   (428)

base angles of a trapezoid   Two angles whose vertices are the endpoints of a base of the trapezoid. (215)

base angles of an isosceles triangle   Two angles of an isosceles triangle whose vertices are the endpoints of a base of the triangle. (206)

base of a trapezoid   Either of two parallel sides of a trapezoid. (215)

base   See *cylindric solid*. See *conic solid*.

betweenness of numbers   A number is between two others if it is greater than one of them and less than the other. (40)

betweenness of points   A point is between two other points on the same line if its coordinate is between their coordinates. (40)

biconditional statement   An if and only if statement that includes a conditional and its converse. (83)

bisector of a segment   The midpoint or any plane, line, ray, or segment which intersects a segment at its midpoint. (141)

bisector of an angle   The ray in the interior of an angle that divides the angle into two angles whose measures are equal. (116)

box   A right parallelepiped whose base is a rectangle. (424)

Cartesian plane   See *coordinate plane*.

center of a regular polygon   The point in the plane of the polygon which is equidistant from all its vertices. (335)

center of rotation   A point which is its own image under the rotation. (267)

center   See *circle*. See *rotation*.

central angle of a circle   An angle whose vertex is the center of the circle.   (396)

chord   A segment whose endpoints are on a given circle. (397)

circle   The set of all points in a plane at a certain distance (its **radius**) from a certain point (its **center**). (84)

circumference of a circle   The perimeter of a circle, which is the limit of the perimeters of inscribed polygons. (397)

circumscribed polygon about a circle   A polygon with each of its sides tangent to the circle. (739)

clockwise orientation   The order in which the vertices of a polygon are given whereby the interior of the polygon is on the right. Also, the direction in which the hands move on a nondigital clock. (188)

clockwise rotation The direction designated as the negative direction from a preimage to its corresponding image in a rotation; expressed by a negative magnitude. (267)

coincide Contain exactly the same points. (192)

collinear points Points that lie on the same line. (6)

compass An instrument for drawing circles. (141)

complementary angles Two angles whose measures sum to 90. (114) Also called *complements*.

composite The result of applying the operation of composition to two transformations s followed by t, denoted by t ∘ s. (260)

composition The operation of combining two transformations s followed by t by mapping each point *P* onto t(s(*P*)). (260)

concentric circles Two or more circles with the same center. (331)

conclusion The result of a deduction. (65) See *consequent*.

conditional A statement of the form If-then... (65)

cone The surface of a conic solid whose base is a circle. (428)

congruence transformation A transformation that is a reflection or composite of reflections; also called *isometry* or *distance-preserving transformation*. (280)

congruent figures Two figures such that one is the image of the other under a translation, a reflection, a rotation, or any composite of these. (279, 439)

conic section The intersection of a plane with the union of two right conical surfaces that have the same vertex and whose edges are opposite rays. (436)

conic solid The set of points between a given point (its **vertex**) and all points of a given region (its **base**), together with the vertex and the base. (428)

conjecture An educated guess or opinion. (218)

consecutive angles In a polygon, two angles whose vertices are endpoints of the same side.

consecutive sides In a polygon, two sides with an endpoint in common. (93)

consecutive vertices In a polygon, endpoints of a side. (93)

consequent The "then" clause in an if-then statement. Also called *conclusion*. (65)

construction A drawing which is made using only an unmarked straightedge and a compass following certain prescribed rules. (141)

contraction A size change with magnitude less than one. (570)

contradiction A situation in which two contradictory statements are both asserted. (646)

contradictory statements Two statements that cannot both be true at the same time. (646)

contrapositive A conditional resulting from negating and switching the antecedent and consequent of the original conditional. (636)

converse The conditional statement formed by switching the antecedent and consequent of a given conditional. (76)

convex polygon A polygon whose interior is a convex set. (94)

convex set A set in which all segments connecting points of the set lie entirely in the set. (61)

coordinate axes A pair of perpendicular coordinatized lines in a plane (14); three mutually perpendicular coordinatized lines in space (521).

coordinate geometry Reasoning done with figures whose points are identified with coordinates in the plane or space. (521)

coordinate plane A plane on which points are described as ordered pairs of real numbers. Also called *Cartesian plane*. (14)

coordinatized line A line on which every point is identified with exactly one number and every number is identified with a point on the line. (8)

coplanar Figures that lie in the same plane. (10)

corollary An easily proved theorem that follows from another theorem. (230)

corresponding parts Angles and sides that are images of each other under a transformation or other correspondence. (292)

cosine of an acute angle The ratio $\dfrac{\text{leg adjacent to the angle}}{\text{hypotenuse}}$ in a right triangle. (702)

counterclockwise orientation The order taken of the vertices of a polygon when the interior is on the left. (188)

counterclockwise rotation   The direction designated by a positive magnitude to indicate the rotation from a preimage to its corresponding image. (267)

counterexample to a conditional   A situation for which the antecedent is true and the consequent is false. (66)

cube   A box whose dimensions are all the same. (10)

cube root   The number whose cube is a given number. (480)

cylinder   The surface of a cylindric solid whose base is a circle. (423)

cylindric solid   The set of points between a region (its **base**) and its translation image in space, including the region and its image. (422)

decagon   A polygon with ten sides. (93)

deduction   The process of making justified conclusions. (521)

degree   Unit of measure used for the measure of an angle, arc, or rotation. (107)

degree measure of a major arc $\overset{\frown}{ACB}$ of ⊕O $360° - mAB$. (396)

degree measure of a minor arc $\overset{\frown}{AB}$ of ⊙O   The measure of the central angle AOB. (396)

diagonal of a polygon   A segment connecting nonconsecutive vertices of the polygon. (93)

diameter of a circle or sphere   A segment connecting two points on the circle or sphere and containing the center of the circle or sphere; also, the length of that segment. (84, 433)

dilation   Also called *dilatation*. See *size change*.

dimensions of a box   The lengths of the three edges of a box which meet at a single vertex. (421)

dimensions of a rectangle   The lengths of the two sides of a rectangle which meet at a single vertex. (367)

direct reasoning (proofs)   Reasoning (proofs) using the Law of Detachment and/or the Law of Transitivity. (645)

direction of a translation   The direction given by any ray from a preimage point through its image point. (261)

discrete line   A line made up of points with space between them. (5)

distance between two points   The absolute value of the difference of their coordinates on a coordinatized line. (9)

dodecahedron   A polyhedron with twelve faces. (454)

edge   Any side of a polyhedron's faces. (449)

ellipse   The conic section formed by a plane which intersects only one of the right conical surfaces. (436)

empty set   See *null set*.

endpoint   See *arc*; *segment*.

ends of a kite   The common vertices of the equal sides of the kite. (223)

equiangular polygon   A polygon with all angles of equal measure. (360)

equidistant   At the same distance. (82)

equilateral polygon   A polygon with all sides of equal length. (358)

equilateral triangle   A triangle with all three sides equal. (94)

Euclidean geometry   The collection of propositions about figures which includes or from which can be deduced those given by the mathematician Euclid around 250 B.C. (36, 176)

expansion   A size change with magnitude greater than one. (570)

exterior angles   Angles formed by two lines and a transversal whose interiors contain no points between the two lines. (234) Angles which form linear pairs with angles of a polygon. (665)

extremes of a proportion   The first and fourth terms of the proportion. (582)

face of a polyhedron   Any of the polygonal regions that form the surface of the polyhedron. (449)

figure   A set of points. (30)

fundamental region   A region used to tessellate a plane. (362)

geometric mean of the positive numbers *a* and *b*   The positive number g such that $\dfrac{a}{g} = \dfrac{g}{b}$. (690)

glide reflection   The composite of a reflection and a translation parallel to the reflecting line; also called a *walk*. (287)

great circle of a sphere   The intersection of a sphere and a plane that contains the center of the sphere. (433)

height of a cylindric solid   The distance between the planes of the bases. Also called *altitude*. (422)

height of a conic solid   The length of a segment from the vertex perpendicular to the plane of the base. Also called *altitude*. (429)

heptagon   A polygon with seven sides. Also called *septagon*. (93)

hexagon   A polygon with six sides. (93)

hexahedron   A polyhedron with six faces. (449)

horizontal component of a vector   The first component in the ordered pair description of a vector. (714)

horizontal line   A line parallel to the horizon. (5)   A line with equation $y = k$. (16)

hyperbola   The conic section formed by a plane which intersects both of the right conical surfaces. (436)

hypotenuse   The side opposite the right angle in a right triangle. (327)

hypothesis   See *antecedent*.

icosahedron   A polyhedron with twenty faces. (454)

identity transformation   A transformation in which each point coincides with its image. (570)

if and only if statement   A statement consisting of a conditional and its converse. (83)

if-then statement   See *conditional*.

image   The result of applying a transformation to a preimage. (254)

image of a figure   The set of all images of points in the figure. (163)

included angle   The angle of a polygon whose vertex is the common point of two consecutive sides of the polygon. (311)

included side   The side of a polygon which is the intersection of two consecutive angles of the polygon. (312)

indirect reasoning (proofs)   Reasoning (proofs) using the Law of the Contrapositive, the Law of Ruling Out Possibilities, or the Law of Indirect Reasoning. (647)

inscribed angle in a circle   An angle whose vertex is on the circle and whose sides each intersect the circle at a point other than the vertex. (746)

inscribed polygon   A polygon whose vertices all lie on the same circle. (737)

instance of a sentence   A situation for which the sentence is true. (65)

interior angles   Angles formed by two lines and a transversal whose interiors are partially between the lines. (234)

interior of a figure   If a figure separates the plane into two parts, one bounded and one not, the bounded part (94)

interior of an angle   A nonzero angle separates the plane into two sets of points. If the angle is not straight, the convex set is the interior of the angle. (106)

intersection of two sets   The set of elements which are in both the sets. (87)

inverse   A conditional resulting from negating the antecedent and consequent of the original conditional. (636)

isometry   A transformation that is a reflection or composite of reflections. Also called *congruence* or *distance-preserving transformation*. (280)

isosceles trapezoid   A trapezoid with a pair of base angles equal in measure. (215)

isosceles triangle   A triangle with two or more equal sides. (94)

justification   The definition, postulate, or theorem which enables a conclusion to be drawn. (120)

kite   A quadrilateral with two distinct pairs of consecutive sides of the same length. (214)

lateral edge of a conic surface   Any segment connecting its vertex to a point on its base. (428)

lateral face of a polyhedron   Any face other than a base. (427)

lateral surface   The surface of a conic or cylindric solid other than the base. (422, 428)

lattice point   Points in the coordinate plane with integer coordinates. (18)

leg   A side of a right triangle that includes the right angle. (327)

length   The distance between two points measured along the segment or an arc joining them. (41)   A side of a rectangle. (357)

line   An undefined geometric term. (35). See *Point-Line-Plane Postulate* on p. 35 or p. 801.

line of reflection   The line over which a preimage is reflected. Also called *reflecting line*. (156)

linear pair   Two nonstraight and nonzero angles that are adjacent and whose noncommon sides are opposite rays. (114)

Logo   A computer language used to create drawings. (672)

magnitude   See *size change*.

magnitude of a rotation $\pm m\angle POP'$, where P' is the image of P under the rotation and O is its center. (267)

magnitude of a translation   The distance between any point and its image. (261)

major arc $\overset{\frown}{AB}$ of $\odot O$ The points of $\odot O$ that are on or exterior to $\angle AOB$. (396)

mapping   A transformation; a transformation *maps* a preimage onto an image. (255)

matrix   A rectangular array of rows and columns. (4)

mean   The sum of a set of numbers divided by the number of numbers in the set. Also called *average* or *arithmetic mean*. (537) See also *geometric mean*.

meaning half of a definition   The conditional in a definition whose antecedent includes the word being defined. (83)

means of a proportion   The second and third terms of the proportion. (582)

median of a triangle   The segment connecting a vertex of the triangle to the midpoint of the opposite side. (208)

midpoint of a segment   The point on the segment equidistant from the segment's endpoints. (81)

minor arc $\overset{\frown}{AB}$ of $\odot O$ The points of $\odot O$ that are on or interior to $\angle AOB$. (396)

n-gon   A polygon with n sides. (93)

negation of a statement   A statement (called *not-p*) that is true whenever statement p is false and is false whenever statement p is true. (635)

net   A two-dimensional figure that can be folded on its segments or curved on its boundaries into a three-dimensional surface. (449)

network   A union of points and segments (arcs) in which each segment or arc contains only its endpoints. (20)

node   The endpoint of an arc in a network. (20) See also *vertex*.

non-Euclidean geometries   A geometry in which the theorems are not the same as those in Euclidean geometry. (241)

nonagon   A polygon with nine sides. (93)

nonconvex set   A set that is not convex. (61)

nonoverlapping regions   Regions that do not share interior points. (368)

null set   The set with no elements. Also called *empty set*. (88)

oblique cylinder   A non-right cylinder. (423)

oblique line   A line that is neither horizontal nor vertical. (5)

oblique prism   A non-right prism. (423)

obtuse angle   An angle whose measure is greater than 90 and less than 180. (113)

obtuse triangle   A triangle with an obtuse angle. (118)

octagon   A polygon with eight sides. (93)

octahedron   A polyhedron with eight faces. (454)

opposite rays $\overrightarrow{AB}$ and $\overrightarrow{AC}$ are opposite rays if and only if A is between B and C. (42)

opposite vectors   Two vectors whose sum is the zero vector. (716)

ordered pair   The pair of numbers (a, b) identifying a point on a coordinate plane. (14)

ordered triple   Three numbers (a, b, c) identifying a point in a three-dimensional coordinate system. (550)

overlapping triangles   Triangles that have interior points in common. (323)

parabola   The conic section formed by a plane parallel to an edge of the conical surface. (436)

parallel lines   Two coplanar lines which have no points in common or are identical. (36)

parallelepiped   A prism whose base is a parallelogram. (424)

parallelogram   A quadrilateral with two pairs of parallel sides. (213)

parallelogram rule   The sum of two noncollinear vectors $\overrightarrow{OA}$ and $\overrightarrow{OB}$ is the vector $\overrightarrow{OC}$ such that $OACB$ is a parallelogram. (711)

pentagon   A polygon with five sides. (93)

perimeter of a polygon   The sum of the lengths of its sides. (356)

perpendicular   Two segments, rays, or lines such that the lines containing them form a 90° angle. (132)

perpendicular bisector of a segment   The line passing through the midpoint of the segment and perpendicular to the segment. (141) The plane that is perpendicular to the segment and contains the midpoint of the segment. (439)

perpendicular line to a plane   A line perpendicular to every line in the plane through their intersection. (418)

perspective drawing   A drawing of a figure made to look as it would in the real world. (25)

pi, π   The ratio of the circumference to the diameter of a circle. (397)

picture angle of a camera lens   An angle measure indicating how wide a field of vision can be captured in one photo. (745)

pixel   A dot on a TV or computer screen or other monitor. (4)

plane   An undefined geometric term. (35) See *Point-Line-Plane Postulate* on p. 35 or p. 801.

plane figure   A set of points that are all in one plane. (10)

plane geometry   The study of figures which lie in the same plane. (30)

plane section   The intersection of a three-dimensional figure with a plane. (434)

point   An undefined geometric term. (35) See *Point-Line-Plane Postulate* on p. 35 or p. 801.

point of tangency   The point at which a tangent to a circle (sphere) intersects the circle (sphere). (653)

polygon   The union of three or more coplanar segments (its **sides**) such that each segment intersects exactly two others, one at each of its endpoints (its **vertices**). (92)

polygonal region   The union of a polygon and its interior. (94)

polyhedron   A three-dimensional surface which is the union of polygonal regions and which has no holes. (Plural **polyhedra**) (449)

postulate   A statement assumed to be true. Also called *axiom*. (35)

power of the point P for the circle O   For any secant through P intersecting circle O at A and B, the product $PA \cdot PB$. (771)

preimage   The original figure in a transformation. (156)

prism   The surface of a cylindric solid whose base is a polygon. (423)

proof   A sequence of justified conclusions, leading from what is given or known to a final conclusion. (120)

proportion   A statement that two ratios are equal. (581)

proportional numbers   Four numbers that form a true proportion. (581)

proposition   A postulate or theorem.

protractor   A tool commonly used to measure angles. (107)

pyramid   The surface of a conic solid whose base is a polygon. (428)

Pythagorean triple   A set of three numbers that can be lengths of sides of a right triangle. (394)

quadrilateral   A polygon with four sides. (93)

radius of a circle or sphere   A segment connecting the center of a circle or a sphere with a point on that circle or sphere; also, the length of that segment. (plural **radii**) (84, 433)

ratio   A quotient of two numbers, $\frac{m}{n}$, $m{:}n$ or m/n. (581)

ratio of similitude   The ratio of the lengths of corresponding segments in similar figures. (587)

ray   The ray with endpoint A and containing B is the union of $\overline{AB}$ and the set of all points for which B is between each of them and A. (42)

rectangle   A quadrilateral with four right angles. (213)

rectangular solid   The union of a box and its interior. (421)

reflecting line   The line over which a preimage is reflected. Also called *line of reflection*. (156)

reflection   The transformation which associates each point with its reflection image. (164)

reflection image of a point P over a line m   If P is not on m, the point Q such that m is the perpendicular bisector of $\overline{PQ}$. If P is on m, P itself. (157)

reflection image of a point *A* over a plane *M*   If *A* is not on *M*, the point *B* such that *M* is the perpendicular bisector of $\overline{AB}$. If *A* is on *M,* the point *A* itself. (439)

reflection-symmetric figure   A figure F for which there is a reflection r_m such that r_m(F) = F. (192, 440)

region   The union of a polygon or circle and its interior. More generally, any connected two-dimensional figure that has an area. (94)

regular polygon   A convex polygon whose angles are all congruent and whose sides are all congruent. (334)

regular polyhedron   A convex polyhedron whose faces are all congruent regular polygons. (454)

regular pyramid   A pyramid whose base is a regular polygon and whose lateral faces are congruent isosceles triangles. (473)

rhombus   A quadrilateral with four equal sides. (213)

right angle   An angle whose measure is 90. (113)

right triangle   A triangle with one right angle. (118)

right cylinder   A cylinder formed when the direction of translation of the base is perpendicular to the plane of the base. (423)

right prism   A prism formed when the direction of translation of the base is perpendicular to the plane of the base. (423)

rotation   The composite of two reflections over intersecting lines; the transformation "turns" the preimage onto the final image about a fixed point (its **center**). Also called *turn*. (267)

round-robin tournament   A tournament in which each competitor plays each other competitor exactly once. (740)

scalar multiplication   The operation combining the real number *k* and the vector (*a, b*) resulting in the vector (*ka, kb*). (717)

scalene triangle   A triangle with no sides of the same length. (94)

secant to a circle   A line that intersects the circle in two points. (759)

segment   The set consisting of the distinct points *A* and *B* (its **endpoints**) and all points between *A* and *B*.   Also called *line segment*. (40)

semicircle   An arc of a circle whose endpoints are the endpoints of a diameter of the circle. (396)

side   One of the segments whose union is a polygon; also, the length of that segment. (93) See *angle*.

similar figures   Two figures for which there is a similarity transformation mapping one onto the other. (586)

similarity transformation   A composite of size changes and reflections. (586)

sine of an acute angle   The ratio $\dfrac{\text{leg opposite the angle}}{\text{hypotenuse}}$ in a right triangle. (702)

size change   The transformation S such that, for a given point *P* and a positive real number *k* (its **magnitude)** and any point O (its **center**), S(*P*) = *P′* is the point on $\overrightarrow{OP}$ with *OP′* = *k•OP*.   The transformation in which the image of (*x, y*) is (*kx, ky*). Also called *size transformation* or *dilation*. (570)

skew lines   Lines that do not lie in the same plane. (421)

slant height of a cone   The length of a lateral edge of the cone. (429)

slant height of a regular pyramid   The altitude from the vertex on any one of the lateral faces of the pyramid. (429)

slide   See *translation*.

slope   For a line in the coordinate plane containing (x_1, y_1) and (x_2, y_2), the number $\dfrac{y_2 - y_1}{x_2 - x_1}$. (128)

small circle of a sphere   The intersection of a sphere and a plane that does not contain the center of the sphere. (433)

solid   The union of the boundary and the region of space enclosed by a surface. (421)

solid geometry   The study of figures in three-dimensional space. (30)

space   The set of all possible points. (30)

sphere   The set of points in space at a fixed distance (its **radius**) from a point (its **center**). (433)

square   A quadrilateral with four equal sides and four right angles. (213)

square root   The number whose square is a given number. (390)

straight angle   An angle whose measure is 180. (113)

straightedge   An instrument for drawing the line through two points and which has no marks for determining length. (141)

subroutine   An algorithm used within another algorithm. (143)

sufficient condition *p* is a sufficient condition for *q* means "if *p*, then *q*." (340)

sufficient condition half of a definition The conditional in a definition whose consequent includes the word being defined. (83)

sum of two vectors See *vector addition.*

supplementary angles Two angles whose measures sum to 180. Also called *supplements.* (114)

surface The boundary of a three-dimensional figure.(421)

symmetry line A reflecting line for a reflection-symmetric figure. (192)

symmetry plane A plane *M* for a space figure *F* such that $r_M(F) = F$. (440)

tangent of an acute angle The ratio

$$\frac{\text{leg opposite the angle}}{\text{leg adjacent to the angle}}$$ in a right triangle. (697)

tangent to a circle or sphere A line or plane which intersects the circle or sphere in exactly one point. (651)

tessellation A covering of a plane with congruent nonoverlapping copies of the same region. (362)

tetrahedron A polyhedron with four faces. (449)

theorem A geometric statement deduced from postulates, definitions, or previously deduced theorems. (36)

three-dimensional figure A geometric figure or real object that does not lie in a single plane. (10)

torus A surface formed by rotating a circle about a line in space which contains no point on or interior to the circle. (456)

transformation A correspondence between two sets of points such that each point in the preimage set has a unique image, and each point in the image set has exactly one preimage. (255)

translation The composite of two reflections over parallel lines. Also called *slide.* (261)

trapezoid A quadrilateral with at least one pair of parallel sides. (214)

traversable network A network in which all the arcs may be traced exactly once without picking up the tracing instrument. (20)

triangle A polygon with three sides. (93)

triangulate To split a polygon into nonoverlapping triangles. (384)

two-dimensional figures Plane figures that do not lie in a single line. (10)

turn See *rotation.*

union of two sets The set of elements which are in either or both of the sets. (87)

unit cube A cube in which every edge has length one unit. (478)

unit square A square in which each side has length one unit. (367)

vanishing point (line) The point (line) at which several lines of a drawing appear to meet at a distance from the viewer's eye. (25)

vector A quantity that has both magnitude and direction. (708)

vector addition The operation combining two vectors (*a, b*) and (*c, d*), resulting in (*a + c, b + d*) (their **sum**). (714)

vertex (plural **vertices**) The endpoint of an arc of a network. (20) See also *angle; node; polygon.*

vertex angle The angle included by equal sides in an isosceles triangle. (206)

vertex of a polyhedron Any vertex of the polyhedron's faces. (449)

vertical angles Two nonstraight and nonzero angles whose sides form two lines. (114)

vertical component of a vector The second component in the ordered pair description of a vector. (714)

vertical line A line perpendicular to the horizon. (5) A line with equation $x = h$. (16)

volume The number of unit cubes or parts of unit cubes that can be fit into a solid. (478)

walk See *glide reflection.*

zero angle An angle whose measure is zero. (113)

zero vector The vector with zero magnitude; the vector (0, 0). (716)

SYMBOLS

Arithmetic and Algebra

$>$	is greater than
$<$	is less than
$\neq$	is not equal to
$\leq$	is less than or equal to
$\geq$	is greater than or equal to
$\approx$	is approximately equal to
π	pi
$|x|$	absolute value of x
$\sqrt{n}$	positive square root of n
$\sqrt[3]{n}$	cube root of n

Geometric Figures and Measures

$\overleftrightarrow{AB}$	line through A and B
$\overrightarrow{AB}$	ray starting at A and containing B
$\overline{AB}$	segment with endpoints A and B
AB	distance from A to B
$\angle ABC$	angle ABC
m $\angle ABC$	measure of angle ABC
$\llcorner$	right angle symbol
$n°$	n degrees
$\overarc{AB}$	minor arc with endpoints A and B
$\overarc{ADB}$	arc with endpoints A and B containing D
$\text{m}\overarc{AB}$	measure of arc AB in degrees
Area(F)	area of figure F
Volume(F)	volume of figure F
$\triangle ABC$	triangle with vertices A, B, and C
$ABCD...$	polygon with vertices A, B, C, D, ...
$\odot O$	circle with center O

Geometric Relations

$//$	is parallel to
$\perp$	is perpendicular to
$\cong$	is congruent to
$\sim$	is similar to

Logic and Sets

$\Rightarrow$	if-then (implication)
$\Leftrightarrow$	if and only if
$\{ ... \}$	set
$\{ \}, \varnothing$	empty or null set
N(E)	the number of elements in set E
P(E)	the probability of an event E
$\cap$	intersection (of sets)
$\cup$	union (of sets)

Trigonometry

tan A	tangent of $\angle A$
sin A	sine of $\angle A$
cos A	cosine of $\angle A$

Transformations

r_m	reflection over line m
$r_m(P)$	reflection image of point P over line m
$r(P)$	reflection image of point P
$T(P)$	tranformation image of point P
$T_1 \circ T_2$	composite of transformation T_2 followed by T_1
S_k	size change of magnitude k
A'	image of point A
A''	image of point A'

Coordinates and Vectors

(x, y)	ordered pair x, y
(x, y, z)	ordered triple x, y, z
$\overrightarrow{AB}$	vector with initial point A and terminal point B
$\mathbf{v}$	vector $\mathbf{v}$
(a, b)	vector with initial point $(0, 0)$ and endpoint (a, b)
$\mathbf{u} + \mathbf{v}$	resultant of two vectors
$k(a, b)$	scalar k times vector (a, b)

Calculator keys

$\boxed{\pm}$ or $\boxed{+/-}$	opposite
$\boxed{y^x}$ or $\boxed{x^y}$	powering function
$\boxed{\text{INV}}$, $\boxed{\text{2nd}}$, or $\boxed{\text{F}}$	second function
$\boxed{\text{EE}}$ or $\boxed{\text{EXP}}$	scientific notation
$\boxed{1/x}$ reciprocal	$\boxed{\text{INV}}$ inverse function
$\boxed{\sqrt{}}$ square root function	$\boxed{\text{sin}}$ sine function
$\boxed{x^2}$ squaring function	$\boxed{\text{cos}}$ cosine function
$\boxed{\text{tan}}$ tangent function	$\boxed{\pi}$ pi

Computer commands

2 * 3	$2 \cdot 3$
4 / 3	$4 \div 3$
3 ^ 5	3^5
> =	$\geq$
< =	$\leq$
< >	not equal to
SQR(N)	$\sqrt{n}$
IF...THEN	THEN statement to be executed only if IF part is true.

POSTULATES

Postulates are statements that are assumed true. The postulates listed below may be different from those found in other geometry books.

Postulates of Euclidean Geometry

Point-Line-Plane Postulate:
a. **Unique line assumption:** Through any two points, there is exactly one line.
b. **Dimension assumption:** Given a line in a plane, there exists a point in the plane not on the line. Given a plane in space, there exists a point in space not on the line.
c. **Number line assumption:** Every line is a set of points that can be put in a one-to-one correspondence with the real numbers, with any point on it corresponding to 0 and any other point corresponding to 1.
d. **Distance assumption:** On a number line, there is a unique distance between two points.
(Lesson 1-7, p. 35)

Some Postulates from Arithmetic and Algebra

Postulates of Equality
Reflexive Property of Equality: $a = a$
Symmetric Property of Equality: If $a = b$, then $b = a$.
Transitive Property of Equality: If $a = b$ and $b = c$, then $a = c$.

Postulates of Equality and Operations
Addition Property of Equality: If $a = b$, then $a + c = b + c$.
Multiplication Property of Equality: If $a = b$, then $ac = bc$.
Substitution Property of Equality: If $a = b$, then a may be substituted for b in any expression.

Postulates of Inequality and Operations
Addition Property of Inequality: If $a < b$, then $a + c < b + c$.
Multiplication Property of Inequality: If $a < b$ and $c > 0$, then $ac < bc$.
If $a < b$ and $c < 0$, then $ac > bc$.
Equation to Inequality Property: If a and b are positive numbers and $a + b = c$, then $c > a$ and $c > b$.
Transitive Property of Inequality: If $a < b$ and $b < c$, then $a < c$.

Postulates of Operations
Commutative Property of Addition: $a + b = b + a$
Commutative Property of Multiplication: $ab = ba$
Distributive Property: $a(b + c) = ab + ac$ *(Lesson 1-7, p. 37)*

Triangle Inequality Postulate: The sum of the lengths of two sides of any triangle is greater than the length of the third side. *(Lesson 1-9, p. 46)*

Angle Measure Postulate:
a. **Unique measure assumption:** Every angle has a unique measure from 0° to 180°.
b. **Two sides of line assumption:** Given any ray $\overrightarrow{VA}$ and any number x between 0 and 180, there are unique rays $\overrightarrow{VB}$ and $\overrightarrow{VC}$ such that $\overrightarrow{BC}$ intersects line $\overleftrightarrow{VA}$ and $m\angle BVA = m\angle CVA = x$.
c. **Zero angle assumption:** If $\overrightarrow{VA}$ and $\overrightarrow{VB}$ are the same ray, then $m\angle AVB = 0$.
d. **Straight Angle Assumption:** If $\overrightarrow{VA}$ and $\overrightarrow{VB}$ are opposite rays then $m\angle AVB = 180$.
e. **Angle Addition Property:** If $\overrightarrow{VC}$ (except for point V) is in the interior of $\angle AVB$, then $m\angle AVC + m\angle CVB = m\angle AVB$. *(Lesson 3-1, p. 108)*

Corresponding Angles Postulate: If two coplanar lines are cut by a transversal so that two corresponding angles have the same measure, then the lines are parallel. *(Lesson 3-4, p. 127)*

Parallel Lines Postulate: If two lines are parallel and are cut by a transversal, corresponding angles have the same measure. *(Lesson 3-4, p. 127)*

Reflection Postulate:
Under a reflection:
a. There is a 1–1 correspondence between points and their images.
   This means that each preimage has exactly one image and each image comes from exactly one preimage.
b. If three points are collinear, then their images are collinear.
   Reflections preserve collinearity. The image of a line is a line.
c. If *B* is between *A* and *C,* then the image of *B* is between the images of *A* and *C.*
   Reflections preserve betweeness. The image of a line segment is a line segment.
d. The distance between two preimages equals the distance between their images.
   Reflectons preserve distance.
e. The image of an angle is an angle of the same measure.
   Reflections preserve angle measure. (Lesson 4–2, p. 164)
f. A polygon and its image, with vertices taken in corresponding order, have opposite orientations.
   Reflections switch orientation. (Lesson 4–6, p. 189)

Area Postulate:
a. **Uniqueness Property:** Given a unit region, every polygonal region has a unique area.
b. **Rectangle Formula:** The area of a rectangle with dimensions ℓ and w is ℓw.
c. **Congruence Property:** Congruent figures have the same area.
d. **Additive Property:** The area of the union of two non-overlapping regions is the sum of the ares of the regions. *(Lesson 8–3, p. 368)*

Volume Postulate:
a. **Uniqueness Property:** Given a unit cube, every polyhedral solid has a unique volume.
b. **Box Volume Formula:** The volume of a box with dimensions ℓ, w, and h is ℓwh.
c. **Congruence Property:** Congruent figures have the same volume.
d. **Additive Property:** The volume of the union of two nonoverlapping solids is the sum of the volumes of the solids. *(Lesson 10–3, p. 479)*
e. **Cavalieri's Principle:** Let I and II be two solids included between parallel planes. If every place P parallel to the given planes intersects I and II in sections with the same area, then Volume (I) = Volume (II). *(Lesson 10–5, p. 490)*

Postulates of Logic:

Law of Detachment: If you have a statement or given information p and a justification of the form $p \Rightarrow q$, you may conclude q. *(Lesson 13–1, p. 630)*
Law of Transitivity: If $p \Rightarrow q$ and $q \Rightarrow r$, then $p \Rightarrow r$. *(Lesson 13–1, p. 631)*
Law of the Contrapositive: A statement $p \Rightarrow q$ and its contrapositive   not $q \Rightarrow$ not p are either both true or both false. *(Lesson 13–2, p. 636)*
Law of Ruling Out Possibilities: When p or q is true and q is not true, then p is true. *(Lesson 13–3, p. 640)*
Law of Indirect Reasoning: If Reasoning from a statement p leads to a false conclusion, then p is false. *(Lesson 13–4, p. 647)*

Postulates of Euclid:
1. Two points determine a line segment.
2. A line segment can be extended indefinitely along a line.
3. A circle can be drawn with any center and any radius.
4. All right angles are congruent.
5. If two lines are cut by a transversal, and the interior angles on the same side of the transversal have a total measure less than 180, then the lines will intersect on that side of the transversal. *(Lesson 13–6, p. 661)*

Theorems are statements that have been proved, or can be proved, from the postulates. They are given here in order of appearance.

Theorem: Two different lines intersect in at most one point. *(Lesson 1-7, p. 36)*

Betweenness Theorem: If *B* is between *A* and *C*, then *AB* + *BC* = *AC*. *(Lesson 1-8, p. 41)*

Theorem: If *A, B,* and *C* are distinct points and *AB* + *BC* = *AC*, then *B* is on $\overline{AC}$. *(Lesson 1-9, p. 48)*

Theorem: For any three points *A, B,* and *C, AB* + *BC* ≥ *AC*. *(Lesson 1-9, p. 48)*

Linear Pair Theorem: If two angles form a linear pair, then they are supplementary. *(Lesson 3-2, p. 115)*

Vertical Angle Theorem: If two angles are vertical angles, then they have equal measures. *(Lesson 3-2, p. 115)*

Parallel Lines and Slopes Theorem: Two nonvertical lines are parallel if and only if they have the same slope. *(Lesson 3-4, p. 128)*

Transitivity of Parallelism Theorem: In a plane, if *ℓ // m* and *m // n,* then *ℓ // n. (Lesson 3-4, p. 129)*

Two Perpendiculars Theorem: If two coplanar lines *ℓ* and *m* are each perpendicular to the same line, then they are parallel to each other. *(Lesson 3-5, p. 133)*

Perpendicular to Parallels Theorem: In a plane, if a line is perpendicular to one of two parallel lines, then it is perpendicular to the other. *(Lesson 3-5, p. 133)*

Perpendicular Lines and Slopes Theorem: Two nonvertical lines are perpendicular if and only if the product of their slopes is −1. *(Lesson 3-5, p. 134)*

Figure Reflection Theorem: If a figure is determined by certain points, then its reflection image is the corresponding figure determined by the reflection images of those points. *(Lesson 4-2, p. 165)*

Theorem: The triangle constructed in Euclid's *Elements* is an equilateral triangle. *(Lesson 4-4, p. 177)*

Perpendicular Bisector Theorem: If a point is on the perpendicular bisector of a segment, then it is equidistant from the endpoints of the segment. *(Lesson 4-5, p. 183)*

Flip-Flop Theorem: If *F* and *F'* are points or figures and r(*F*) = *F'*, then r(*F'*) = *F*. *(Lesson 4-6, p. 188)*

Segment Symmetry Theorem: A segment has exactly two symmetry lines: **1.** its perpendicular bisector, and **2.** the line containing the segment. *(Lesson 4-7, p. 193)*

Side-Switching Theorem: If one side of an angle is reflected over the line containing the angle bisector, its image is the other side of the angle. *(Lesson 4-7, p. 194)*

Angle Symmetry Theorem: The line containing the bisector of an angle is a symmetry line of the angle. *(Lesson 4-7, p. 194)*

Isosceles Triangle Symmetry Theorem: The line containing the bisector of the vertex angle of an isosceles triangle is a symmetry line for the triangle. *(Lesson 5-1, p. 207)*

Theorem: In an isosceles triangle, the bisector of the vertex angle, the perpendicular bisector of the base, and the median to the base determine the same line. *(Lesson 5-1, p. 208)*

Isosceles Triangle Theorem: If a triangle has two equal sides, then the angles opposite them are equal. *(Lesson 5-1, p. 208)*

Kite Symmetry Theorem: The line containing the ends of a kite is a symmetry line for the kite. *(Lesson 5-4, p. 223)*

Kite Diagonal Theorem: The symmetry diagonal of a kite is the perpendicular bisector of the other diagonal and bisects the two angles at the ends of the kite. *(Lesson 5-4, p. 224)*

Rhombus Symmetry Theorem: Every rhombus has two symmetry lines, the bisectors of its diagonals. *(Lesson 5-4, p. 225)*

Trapezoid Angle Theorem: In a trapezoid, consecutive angles between a pair of parallel sides are supplementary. *(Lesson 5-5, p. 228)*

Theorem: In an isosceles trapezoid, both pairs of base angles are equal in measure. *(Lesson 5-5, p. 229)*

Isosceles Trapezoid Symmetry Theorem: The perpendicular bisector of one base of an isosceles trapezoid is the perpendicular bisector of the other base and a symmetry line for the trapezoid. *(Lesson 5-5, p. 230)*

Isosceles Trapezoid Theorem: In an isosceles trapezoid, the non-base sides are equal in measure. *(Lesson 5-5, p. 230)*

Rectangle Symmetry Theorem: Every rectangle has two symmetry lines, the perpendicular bisectors of its bases. *(Lesson 5-5, p. 231)*

// Lines $\Rightarrow$ AIA = Theorem: If two parallel lines are cut by a transversal, then alternate interior angles are equal in measure. *(Lesson 5-6, p. 234)*

AIA = $\Rightarrow$ // Lines Theorem: If two lines are cut by a transversal and form equal alternate interior angles, then the lines are parallel. *(Lesson 5-6, p. 235)*

Theorem: If a quadrilateral is a rhombus, then it is a parallelogram. *(Lesson 5-6, p. 236)*

Quadrilateral Hierarchy Theorem: If a figure is of any type on the hierarchy, it is also of all types connected above it. *(Lesson 5-6, p. 236)*

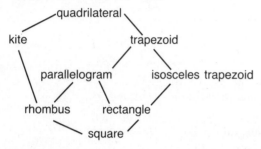

Triangle-Sum Theorem: The sum of the measures of the angles of a triangle is 180°. *(Lesson 5-7, p. 240)*

Quadrilateral-Sum Theorem: The sum of the measures of the angles of a convex quadrilateral is 360°. *(Lesson 5-7, p. 242)*

Polygon-Sum Theorem: The sum of the measures of the angles of a convex polygon of n sides is $(n - 2) \cdot 180°$. *(Lesson 5-7, p. 243)*

Two Reflection Theorem for Translations: If $m \;//\; \ell$, the translation $r_m \circ r_\ell$ slides figures two times the distance between ℓ and m, in the direction from ℓ to m perpendicular to those lines. *(Lesson 6-2, p. 261)*

Two Reflection Theorem for Rotations: The rotation $r_m \circ r_\ell$ where m intersects ℓ, "turns" figures twice the non-obtuse angle between ℓ, and m, measured from ℓ to m, about the point of intersection of the lines. *(Lesson 6-3, p. 267)*

Equivalence of Properties of $\cong$ Theorem: For any figures F, G, and H:
    Reflexive Property of Congruence: F $\cong$ F.
    Symmetry Property of Congruence: if F $\cong$ G, then G $\cong$ F.
    Transitive Property of Congruence: If F $\cong$ G and G $\cong$ H, then F $\cong$ H. *(Lesson 6-5, p. 280)*

A-B-C-D Theorem: Every isometry preserves Angle measure, Betweenness, Collinearity (lines), and Distance (lengths of segments). *(Lesson 6-5, p. 281)*

Segment Congruence Theorem: Two segments are congruent if and only if they have the same length. *(Lesson 6-5, p. 281)*

Angle Congruence Theorem: Two angles are congruent if and only if they have the same meausre. *(Lesson 6-5, p. 282)*

Glide Reflection Theorem: Let G $=$ T $\circ r_m$ be a glide reflection, and let G(P) $=$ P'. Then the midpoint of $\overline{PP'}$ is on m. *(Lesson 6-6, p. 287)*

Corresponding Parts in Congruent Figures (CPCF) Theorem: If two figures are congruent, then any pair of corresponding parts is congruent. *(Lesson 6-7, p. 292)*

Theorem: If two triangles have two pairs of angles congruent, then their third pair of angles is congruent. *(Lesson 7-1, p. 306)*

SSS Congruence Theorem: If, in two triangles, three sides of one are congruent to three sides of the other, then the triangles are congruent. *(Lesson 7-2, p. 310)*

SAS Congruence Theorem: If, two triangles, two sides and the included angle of one are congruent to two sides and the included angle of the other, then the triangles are congruent. *(Lesson 7-2, p. 311)*

ASA Congruence Theorem: If in two triangles two angles and the included ~~side~~ _angles_ of one are congruent to two ~~sides~~ _side_ and the included ~~angle~~ _side_ of the other, then the triangles are congruent. *(Lesson 7–2, p. 312)*

AAS Congruence Theorem: If, in two triangles, two angles and a non-included side of one are congruent respectively to two angles and the corresponding non-included side of the other, then the triangles are congruent. *(Lesson 7–2, p. 312)*

Theorem: If two angles of a triangle are congruent, then the sides opposite them are congruent. *(Lesson 7–3, p. 319)*

HL Congruence Theorem: If, in two right triangles, the hypotenuse and a leg of one are congruent to the hypotenuse and a leg of the other, then the two triangles are congruent. *(Lesson 7–5, p. 328)*

SsA Congruence Theorem: If, in two triangles, two sides and the angle opposite the longer of the two sides in one are congruent respectively to two sides and the angle opposite the corresponding side in the other, then the triangles are congruent. *(Lesson 7–5, p. 330)*

Properties of a Parallelogram Theorem: In any parallelogram: **a.** each diagonal forms two congruent triangles; **b.** opposite sides are congruent; **c.** the diagonals intersect at their midpoints. *(Lesson 7–6, p. 334)*

Theorem: The distance between parallel lines is constant. *(Lesson 7–6, p. 334)*

Center of a Regular Polygon Theorem: In any regular polygon there is a point (its center) which is equidistant from all its vertices. *(Lesson 7–6, p. 335)*

Sufficient Conditions for a Parallelogram Theorem: If, in a quadrilateral: (a) both pairs of opposite sides are congruent, or (b) both pairs of opposite angles are congruent, or (c) the diagonals bisect each other, or (d) one pair of sides is parallel and congruent, then the quadrilateral is a parallelogram. *(Lesson 7–7, p. 341)*

SAS Inequality Theorem: If two sides of a triangle are congruent to two sides of a second triangle, and the measure of the included angle of the first triangle is less than the measure of the included angle of the second, then the third side of the first triangle is shorter than the third side of the second. *(Lesson 7–8, p. 344)*

Equilateral Polygon Perimeter Formula: In an equilateral polygon with n sides of length s, the perimeter $p = ns$. *(Lesson 8–1, p. 358)*

Right Triangle Area Formula: The area of a right triangle is half the product of the lengths of its legs. *(Lesson 8–5, p. 378)*

Triangle Area Formula: The area of a triangle is half the product of a side and the altitude to that side. *(Lesson 8–5, p. 379)*

Trapezoid Area Formula: The area of a trapezoid equals half the product of its altitude and the sum of the lengths of its bases. *(Lesson 8–6, p. 385)*

Parallelogram Area Formula: The area of a parallelogram is the product of one of its bases and the altitude for that base. *(Lesson 8–6, p. 386)*

Pythagorean Theorem: In any right triangle with legs a and b and hypotenuse c, $a^2 + b^2 = c^2$ *(Lesson 8–7, p. 391)*

Pythagorean Converse Theorem: If a triangle has sides of lengths a, b, and c, and $a^2 + b^2 = c^2$, then the triangle is a right triangle. *(Lesson 8–7, p. 393)*

Circle Circumference Formula: If a circle has circumference C and diameter d, then $C = \pi d$. *(Lesson 8–8, p. 398)*

Circle Area Formula: The area A of a circle radius r is $A = \pi r^2$. *(Lesson 8–9, p. 402)*

The Four-Color Theorem: Suppose regions which share a border of some length must have different colors. Then any map of regions on a plane or a sphere can be colored in such a way that only four colors are needed. *(Lesson 9–8, p. 456)*

Right Prism-Cylinder Lateral Area Formula: The lateral area L.A. of a right prism (or cylinder) is the product of its height h and the perimeter (circumference) p of its base. L.A. $= ph$ *(Lesson 10–1, p. 469)*

Prism-Cylinder Surface Area Formula: The total surface area S.A. of any prism or cylinder is the sum of its lateral area L.A. and twice the area B of a base. S.A. $=$ L.A. $+ 2B$ *(Lesson 10–1, p. 470)*

Regular Pyramid-Right Cone Lateral Area Formula: The lateral area L.A. of a regular pyramid (or right cone) is half the product of the slant height and the perimeter p (circumference) of its base.   L.A. $= \frac{1}{2} \ell p$ *(Lesson 10-2, p. 475)*

Pyramid-Cone Surface Area Formula: The total surface area S.A. of any pyramid or cone is the sum of its lateral area L.A. and the area B of its base.   S.A. $=$ L.A. $+ B$ *(Lesson 10-2, p. 475)*

Cube Volume Formula: The volume of a cube with edge s is s^3. *(Lesson 10-3, p. 480)*

Prism-Cylinder Volume Formula: The volume V of any prism or cylinder is the product of its height h and the area B of its base. $V = Bh$ *(Lesson 10-5, p. 490)*

Pyramid-Cone Volume Formula: The volume V of any pyramid or cone equals $\frac{1}{3}$ the product of its height h and its base area B. $V = \frac{1}{3}BH$ *(Lesson 10-7, p. 501)*

Sphere Volume Formula: The volume V of any sphere is $\frac{4}{3}\pi$ times the cube of its radius. $V = \frac{4}{3}\pi r^3$ *(Lesson 10-8, p. 506)*

Sphere Surface Area Formula: The surface area S.A. of a sphere with radius r is $4\pi r^2$.   S.A. $= 4\pi r^2$ *(Lesson 10-9, p. 511)*

Distance Formula: The distance between two points (x_1, y_1) and (x_2, y_2) in the coordinate plane is $\sqrt{(x_2 - x_1)^2 + (y_2 - y_1)^2}$. *(Lesson 11-2, p. 528)*

Theorem (Equation for a Circle): The circle with center (h, k) and radius r is the set of points (x, y) satisfying $(x - h)^2 + (y - k)^2 = r^2$. *(Lesson 11-3, p. 533)*

Midpoint Formula: If a segment has endpoints (a, b) and (c, d), its midpoint is $\left(\dfrac{a + c}{2}, \dfrac{b + d}{2}\right)$ *(Lesson 11-4, p. 538)*

Midpoint Connector Theorem: The segment connecting the midpoints of two sides of a triangle is parallel to and half the length of the third side. *(Lesson 11-5, p. 545)*

Distance Formula in Three Dimensions: The distance between two points (x_1, y_1, z_1) and (x_2, y_2, z_2) is $\sqrt{(x_2 - x_1)^2 + (y_2 - y_1)^2 + (z_2 - z_1)^2}$. *(Lesson 11-6, p. 551)*

Diagonal of a Box Formula: In a box with dimensions a, b, and c, the length of the diagonal is $\sqrt{a^2 + b^2 + c^2}$ *(Lesson 11-6, p. 552)*

Theorem (Equation for a Sphere): The sphere with center (h, k, j) and radius r is the set of points (x, y, z) satisfying $(x - h)^2 + (y - k)^2 + (z - j)^2 = r^2$. *(Lesson 11-6, p. 553)*

Midpoint Formula in Three Dimensions: If a segment has endpoints (a, b, c) and (d, e, f), then its midpoint is $\left(\dfrac{a + d}{2}, \dfrac{b + e}{2}, \dfrac{c + f}{2}\right)$ *(Lesson 11-6, p. 553)*

Theorem: Let S_k be the transformation mapping (x, y) onto (kx, ky), $k > 0$. Let $P' = S_k(P)$ and $Q' = S_k(Q)$. Then
(1) $\overrightarrow{P'Q'} \parallel \overrightarrow{PQ}$,
(2) $P'Q' = k \cdot PQ$. *(Lesson 12-1, p. 565)*

Theorem: The transformation S_k, where $S_k(x, y) = (kx, ky)$ is the size change with center $(0, 0)$ and magnitude k. *(Lesson 12-2, p. 571)*

Size Change Distance Theorem: Under a size change with magnitude $k > 0$, the distance between any two image points is k times the distance between their preimages. *(Lesson 12-3, p. 575)*

Theorem: Size transformations preserve betweenness and collinearity. *(Lesson 12-3, p. 576)*

Theorem: A line and its image under a size transformation are parallel. *(Lesson 12-3, p. 576)*

Size Change Theorem: Under a size transformation:
(a) angles and their measures are preserved;
(b) betweenness is preserved;
(c) collinearity is preserved; and
(d) lines and their images are parallel. *(Lesson 12-3, p. 577)*

Figure Size Change Theorem: If a figure is determined by certain points, then its size change image is the corresponding figure determined by the size change images of those points. *(Lesson 12-3, p. 578)*

Theorem (Means-Extremes Property): If $\frac{a}{b} = \frac{c}{d}$, then $ad = bc$. *(Lesson 12–4, p. 582)*

Theorem (Means Exchange Property): If $\frac{a}{b} = \frac{c}{d}$, then $\frac{a}{c} = \frac{b}{d}$.

(Reciprocals Property): If $\frac{a}{b} = \frac{c}{d}$, then $\frac{b}{a} = \frac{d}{c}$. *(Lesson 12–4, p. 583)*

Similar Figures Theorem: If two figures are similar, then: (a) corresponding angles are congruent; (b) corresponding lengths are proportional. *(Lesson 12–5, p. 587)*

Fundamental Theorem of Similarity: If $G \sim G'$ and k is the ratio of similtude, then

(a) Perimeter $(G') = k \cdot$ Perimeter(G) or $\frac{\text{Perimeter}(G')}{\text{Perimeter}(G)} = k$

(b) Area$(G') = k^2 \cdot$ Area(G) or $\frac{\text{Area}(G')}{\text{Area}(G)} = k^2$

(c) Volume $(G') = k^3 \cdot$ Volume(G) or $\frac{\text{Volume}(G')}{\text{Volume}(G)} = k^3$. *(Lesson 12–6, p. 594)*

SSS Similarity Theorem: If the three sides of one triangle are proportional to the three sides of a second triangle, then the triangles are similar. *(Lesson 12–8, p. 605)*

AA Similarity Theorem: If two triangles have two angles of one congruent to two angles of the other, then the triangles are similar. *(Lesson 12–9, p. 610)*

SAS Similarity Theorem: If, in two triangles, the ratios of two pairs of corresponding sides are equal and the included angles are congruent, then the triangles are similar. *(Lesson 12–9, p. 611)*

Side-Splitting Theorem: If a line is parallel to a side of a triangle and intersects the other two sides in distinct points, it "splits" these sides into proportional segments. *(Lesson 12–10, p. 615)*

Side-Splitting Converse: If a line intersects $\overrightarrow{OP}$ and $\overrightarrow{OQ}$ in distinct points X and Y so that $\frac{OX}{XP} = \frac{OY}{YQ}$, then $\overleftrightarrow{XY} \parallel \overline{PQ}$. *(Lesson 12–10, p. 616)*

Theorem: If a line is perpendicular to a radius of a circle at the radius's endpoint on the circle, then it is tangent to the circle. *(Lesson 13–5, p. 652)*

Theorem: If a line is tangent to a circle, then it is perpendicular to the radius drawn to the point of tangency. *(Lesson 13–5, p. 652)*

Radius-Tangent Theorem: A line is tangent to a circle if and only if it is perpendicular to a radius at the radius's endpoint on the circle. *(Lesson 13–5, p. 653)*

Uniqueness of Parallels Theorem (Playfair's Parallel Postulate): Through a point not on a line, there is exactly one parallel to the given line. *(Lesson 13–6, p. 660)*

Theorem: In a glide reflection, the midpoint of the segment connecting a point to its image lies on the glide-reflection line. *(Lesson 13–6, p. 661)*

Exterior Angle Theorem: In a triangle, the measure of an exterior angle is equal to the sum of the measures of the two nonadjacent interior angles. *(Lesson 13–7, p. 665)*

Exterior Angle Inequality: In a triangle, the measure of an exterior angle is greater than the measure of either nonadjacent interior angle. *(Lesson 13–7, p. 666)*

Unequal Sides Theorem: If two sides of a triangle are not congruent, then the angles opposite them are not congruent, and the larger angle is opposite the longer side. *(Lesson 13–7, p. 667)*

Unequal Angles Theorem: If two angles of a triangle are not congruent, then the sides opposite them are not congruent, and the longer side is opposite the larger angle. *(Lesson 13–7, p. 667)*

Exterior Angles of a Polygon Sum Theorem: In any convex polygon, the sum of the measures of the exterior angles, one at each vertex, is 360. *(Lesson 13–8, p. 671)*

Isosceles Right Triangle Theorem: In an isosceles right triangle, if a leg is x then the hypotenuse is $x\sqrt{2}$. *(Lesson 14–1, p. 684)*

30-60-90 Triangle Theorem: In a 30-60-90 right triangle, if the short leg is x then the longer leg is $x\sqrt{3}$ and the hypotenuse is $2x$. *(Lesson 14–1, p. 685)*

Geometric Mean Theorem: The geometric mean of the positive numbers a and b is $\sqrt{ab}$. *(Lesson 14–2, p. 691)*

Right Triangle Altitude Theorem: In a right triangle, **a.** the altitude to the hypotenuse is the geometric mean of the segments into which it divides the hypotenuse; and **b.** each leg is the geometric mean of the hypotenuse and the segment of the hypotenuse adjacent to the leg. *(Lesson 14–2, p. 692)*

Theorem: Two vectors are equal if and only if their initial and terminal points are preimages and images under the same translation. *(Lesson 14–5, p. 709)*

Vector Addition Theorem: The sum of the vectors (a, b) and (c, d) is the vector $(a + c, b + d)$. *(Lesson 14–6, p. 714)*

Properties of Vector Addition Theorem: (1) Vector addition is commutative. (2) Vector addition is associative. (3) (0, 0) is an identity for vector addition. (4) Every vector (a, b) has an additive inverse $(-a, -b)$. *(Lesson 14–6, p. 715)*

Chord-Center Theorem: a. The line containing the center of a circle perpendicular to a chord bisects the chord. **b.** The line containing the center of a circle and the midpoint of a chord bisects the central angle determined by the chord. **c.** The bisector of the central angle of a chord is perpendicular to the chord and bisects the chord. **d.** The perpendicular bisector of a chord of a circle contains the center of the circle. *(Lesson 15–1, p. 735)*

Arc-Chord Congruence Theorem: In a circle or in congruent circles: **a.** If two arcs have the same measure, they are congruent and their chords are congruent. **b.** If two chords have the same length, their minor arcs have the same measure. *(Lesson 15–1, p. 736)*

Inscribed Angle Theorem: In a circle the measure of an inscribed angle is one-half the measure of its intercepted arc. *(Lesson 15–3, p. 746)*

Theorem: An angle inscribed in a semicircle is a right angle. *(Lesson 15–3, p. 748)*

Angle-Chord Theorem: The measure of an angle formed by two intersecting chords is one-half the sum of the measures of the arcs intercepted by it and its vertical angle. *(Lesson 15–5, p. 758)*

Angle-Secant Theorem: The measure of an angle formed by two secants intersecting outside a circle is half the difference of the arcs intercepted by it. *(Lesson 15–5, p. 759)*

Tangent-Chord Theorem: The measure of an angle formed by a tangent and a chord is half the measure of the intercepted arc. *(Lesson 15–6, p. 764)*

Tangent-Secant Theorem: The measure of an angle between two tangents, or between a tangent and a secant, is half the difference of the intercepted arcs. *(Lesson 15–6, p. 764)*

Secant Length Theorem: Suppose one secant intersects a circle at A and B, and a second secant intersects the circle at C and D. If the secants intersect at P, then $AP \cdot BP = CP \cdot DP$. *(Lesson 15–7, p. 769)*

Tangent Square Theorem: The power of point P for $\odot$ O is square of the length of a segment tangent to $\odot$ O. *(Lesson 15–7, p. 771)*

Isoperimetric Theorem: Of all plane figures with the same perimeter, the circle has the most area. *(Lesson 15–8, p. 776)*

Isoperimetric Inequality: If a plane figure has area A and perimeter p, then $A \le \dfrac{p^2}{4\pi}$. *(Lesson 15–8, p. 776)*

Isoperimetric Theorem: Of all plane figures with the same area, the circle has the least perimeter. *(Lesson 15–8, p. 777)*

Isoperimetric Theorem (space version): Of all solids with the same surface area, the sphere has the most volume. *(Lesson 15–8, p. 780)*

Isoperimetric Theorem (space version): Of all solids with the same volume, the sphere has the least surface area. *(Lesson 15–9, p. 781)*

Angle Formulas

n = number of sides, θ = measure of angle

Triangles:	Sum = $180°$	*(Lesson 5-7)*
Convex n-gons:	Sum = $(n - 2)\cdot 180°$	*(Lesson 5-7)*
Regular polygons:	$\theta = \dfrac{(n - 2)\cdot 180°}{n}$	*(Lesson 7-6)*

Perimeter Formulas

p = perimeter, w = width, s = side, n = number of sides, ℓ = length, a, b, c = sides of triangles or kites, C = circumference, r = radius, d = diameter

Triangles:	$p = a + b + c$	*(Lesson 8-1)*
Right triangles:	$c^2 = a^2 + b^2$	*(Lesson 8-7)*
Kites:	$p = 2a + 2b$	*(Lesson 8-1)*
Parallelograms:	$p = 2\ell + 2w$	*(Lesson 8-1)*
Regular polygons:	$p = ns$	*(Lesson 8-1)*
Circles:	$C = \pi d = 2\pi r$	*(Lesson 8-8)*

Area Formulas

A = area, b = base, ℓ = length, s = side, h = height, b_1, b_2 = base, w = width, r = radius

Rectangles:	$A = \ell w$	*(Lesson 8-3)*
Squares:	$A = s^2$	*(Lesson 8-3)*
Triangles:	$A = \frac{1}{2}hb$	*(Lesson 8-5)*
Trapezoids:	$A = \frac{1}{2}h(b_1 + b_2)$	*(Lesson 8-6)*
Parallelograms:	$A = hb$	*(Lesson 8-6)*
Circles:	$A = \pi r^2$	*(Lesson 8-9)*

Hero's Formula:

$$\text{Area}(\triangle ABC) = \sqrt{s(s - a)(s - b)(s - c)}$$

where a, b, and c are sides of $\triangle ABC$ and s is half the perimeter *(Lesson 10-6)*

Lateral Area and Surface Area Formulas

L.A. = lateral area, S.A. = surface area, B = area of base, h = height, ℓ = slant height or length of box, p = perimeter, r = radius, s = edge, w = width

Right prisms:	L.A. = ph	*(Lesson 10-1)*
Prisms:	S.A. = L.A. + $2B$	*(Lesson 10-1)*
Right cylinders:	L.A. = $ph = 2\pi rh$	*(Lesson 10-1)*
Cylinders:	S.A. = L.A. + $2B$	*(Lesson 10-1)*
Pyramids:	L.A. = $\frac{1}{2}\ell p$	*(Lesson 10-2)*
	S.A. = L.A. + B	*(Lesson 10-2)*
Right cones:	L.A. = $\frac{1}{2}\ell p = \pi r\ell$	*(Lesson 10-2)*
Cones:	S.A. = L.A. + B	*(Lesson 10-2)*
Boxes:	S.A. = $2\ell h + 2wh + 2\ell w$	*(Lesson 10-6)*
Cubes:	S.A. = $6s^2$	*(Lesson 10-1)*
Spheres:	S.A. = L.A. = $4\pi r^2$	*(Lesson 10-9)*

Volume Formulas

V = volume, B = area of base, h = height, ℓ = length, r = radius, s = edge, w = width

Boxes:	$V = \ell wh$	*(Lesson 10-3)*
Cubes:	$V = s^3$	*(Lesson 10-3)*
Prisms:	$V = Bh$	*(Lesson 10-5)*
Cylinders:	$V = Bh = \pi r^2 h$	*(Lesson 10-5)*
Pyramids:	$V = \frac{1}{3}Bh$	*(Lesson 10-7)*
Cones:	$V = \frac{1}{3}Bh = \frac{1}{3}\pi r^2 h$	*(Lesson 10-7)*
Spheres:	$V = \frac{4}{3}\pi r^3$	*(Lesson 10-8)*

CONVERSION FORMULAS

	Customary	**Metric**

Length

ft = foot, in. = inch, yd = yard, mi = mile

cm = centimeter, mm = millimeter, m = meter, km = kilometer

$$1 \text{ ft} = 12 \text{ in.}$$
$$1 \text{ yd} = 3 \text{ ft}$$
$$1 \text{ mi} = 5280 \text{ ft}$$

$$1 \text{ cm} = 10 \text{ mm}$$
$$1 \text{ m} = 100 \text{ cm}$$
$$1 \text{ km} = 1000 \text{ m}$$

$$1 \text{ inch} = 2.54 \text{ centimeters}$$

Area

$$1 \text{ sq ft} = 144 \text{ sq in.}$$
$$1 \text{ sq yd} = 9 \text{ sq ft}$$

$$1 \text{ sq cm} = 100 \text{ sq mm}$$
$$1 \text{ sq m} = 10,000 \text{ sq cm}$$

Land area

$$1 \text{ sq mi} = 640 \text{ acres}$$

$$1 \text{ hectare} = 10,000 \text{ sq m}$$

Volume

$$1 \text{ ft}^3 = 1728 \text{ in.}^3$$
$$1 \text{ yd}^3 = 27 \text{ ft}^3$$

$$1 \text{ cm}^3 = 1000 \text{ mm}^3$$
$$1 \text{ m}^3 = 1,000,000 \text{ cm}^3$$

Liquid volume

pt = pint, qt = quart, gal = gallon

$$1 \text{ pt} = 28.875 \text{ in.}^3$$
$$1 \text{ qt} = 57.75 \text{ in.}^3$$
$$1 \text{ gal} = 231 \text{ in.}^3$$

mL = milliliter, L = liter

$$1 \text{ mL} = 1000 \text{ mm}^3$$
$$1 \text{ L} = 1000 \text{ cm}^3$$

$$1.06 \text{ quarts} \approx 1 \text{ liter}$$

Weight (Mass)

lb = pound, oz = ounce

$$1 \text{ lb} = 16 \text{ oz}$$
$$1 \text{ ton} = 2000 \text{ lb}$$

g = gram, kg = kilogram, mg = milligram

$$1 \text{ g} = 1000 \text{ mg}$$
$$1 \text{ kg} = 1000 \text{g}$$
$$1 \text{ metric ton} = 1000 \text{ kg}$$

$$2.2 \text{ pounds} \approx 1 \text{ kilogram}$$

LESSON 1-1 (pp. 3–7)
11. Sample: **See below. 13.** The one with 200 rows and 300 columns **15. a.** black squares (black ink on white paper). **b.** by clustering the squares **17.** Sample: **See below. 19.** 7.5 **21. a.** 23 **b.** 15 **c.** 8.3 **d.** 12

11.

17.

LESSON 1-2 (pp. 8–13)
7. 353 **9.** $|x - y|$ or $|y - x|$ **13.** Sample: The makers of the almanac may have chosen different points of reference within New York and Los Angeles from which to compute the road mileage or may have used different routes. **15.** 67 miles **17. a.** $AB = 150$, $BC = 225$, $AC = 375$ **b.** True **19.** 72,960 **21.** a line made up of points with space between their centers

23. $(3, -\frac{2}{3})$, $(-2, -\frac{7}{3})$, $(5,0)$

LESSON 1-3 (pp. 14–18)
3. oblique **5.** vertical **9. See below. 11. See below.**
13. $y = -5$ **15. a. b: See below. c.** $(3, -2)$ **17.** The Hitachi resolution is greater than the IBM PC (about 660 pixels/square in.) but less than the Macintosh (about 110 pixels/square in.)
19. about 1.8 cm **21. a.** 94 miles **b.** about 1.7 hours

9.

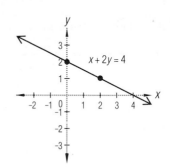

11.

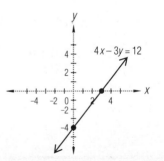

15.

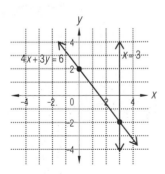

LESSON 1-4 (pp. 19–24)
11. T to R to S to T to U to R **13. a.** Sample: from A to C to B to D to A to E to B **b.** either A or B **15. a.** 0 even, 4 odd **b.** No **17. See below. 19. See below. 21. See below. 23.** 20 **25.** 5

17. a. sample:

b. sample: ●——————●

19.

Dots	Ordered Pairs	Locations	Nodes
S	A	A	N
A	A	A	N
S	A	A	S

21.

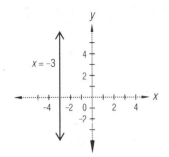

7. See below. 9. **a.** I, IV **b.** See below. 11. See below. 13. not traversable; more than 2 odd nodes 15. **a.** See below. **b.** No 17. **a.** See below. **b.** Answers may vary; the actual point of intersection is $(\frac{9}{7}, \frac{13}{7})$. 19. 56 cm

7. **a.** sample: **b.** sample:

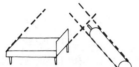

9. **b.**

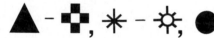

11.

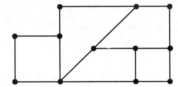

15. **a.**

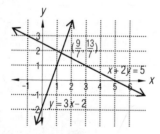

17. **a.**

LESSON 1·6 (pp. 30–34)
9. Sample: 3; concord, harmony, agreement, concord. 11. Sample: 2; satire, irony, satire. 13. Sample: quanity. 15. See below. 17. See below. 19. 5.3 21. **a.** 1 **b.** 2 **c.** 0 **d.** 3 23. See below.

15. **a.** **b.**

17.

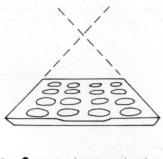

23.

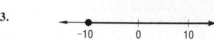

3. No 5. Yes 7. True 9. $\overline{XA}$ or $\overleftrightarrow{AX}$ 11. a set of books of postulates and theorems by Euclid 13. Transitive Property of Equality 15. Addition Property of Equality 17. Equation to Inequality Property 19. Distributive Property 21. Addition Property of Equality 23. Sample: 3; proboscis, snout, nose, snout. 25. **a.** See below. **b.** No 27. **a.** horizontal **b.** oblique

25.

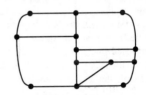

1. C is between A and B since $-2 < \sqrt{2} < 2$. 5. M, N 7. (d) 9. $AB = |3 - 14| = 11$, $BC = |14 - 82| = 68$, $AC = |3 - 82| = 79$. Since $11 + 68 = 79$, $AB + BC = AC$. 11. **a.** See below. **b.** a segment 13. 38 15. 16 or -26 17. $4x$ 19. Multiplication Property of Equality 21. **a.** True **b.** True **c.** False 23. See below. 25. parts (a), (c), (d)

11. **a.**

23.

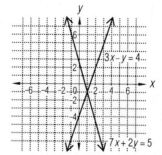

Point of intersection is (1, -1).

LESSON 1-9 (pp. 46–51)
3. a. Yes **b.** Yes **c.** No **d.** No **5. a.** No **b.** Yes **c.** Yes **7.**
$BC = BA + AC$ **11.** True **13. a.** Yes **b.** No **15.** $x - y$,
$x + y$ **17.** 15 **19.** Commutative Property of Addition **21.**
a. See below. b. Yes **23.** 28

21. a. sample:

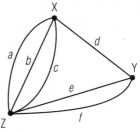

CHAPTER 1 PROGRESS SELF-TEST (p. 53)

1. $AB = |-8 - -4| = |-4| = 4$ units **2. See below. 3. See
below. 4.** The Triangle Inequality states that the sum of two
sides of a triangle must be longer than the third side. Since
$4.8 + 3.7 = 8.5 < 9.2$, the three lengths cannot be the sides
of a triangle. **5. See below. 6.** "A line contains infinitely
many points" is always true for dots, locations, and ordered
pairs (because the lines have no ends) and is never true for
nodes (an arc has only two nodes). **7.** "A point has size" is
always true for points as dots, and never true for locations,
ordered pairs, and nodes. **8.** Space has three dimensions:
length, width, and depth. **9.** Ignoring thickness, a sheet of
paper is "flat," like a plane, so it has two dimensions. **10.** If,
in defining a word, you return to that original word, circularity
has occurred. **11. a.b.** The screen that is 180×310 pixels has
55,800 pixels; the screen that is 215×350 pixels has 75,250
pixels. The screen with more pixels per unit of area, which is
the 215×350 screen, has better resolution. **12. See below.
13.** The distances are different because the air distance may be
measured along a straight path, perhaps between airports, and
the road distance may be measured along a path that follows
highways, perhaps between two downtown locations. **14. See
Below. 15.** Two points on $x = \frac{3}{2}$ are $(\frac{3}{2}, 0)$ and $(\frac{3}{2}, 10)$; the
line determined by these points is vertical. **16.** Two points on
$11x + y = 3$ are $(0, 3)$ and $(\frac{3}{11}, 0)$; the line determined by
those points is oblique. **17. a.** The network has no more than
two odd vertices, so it is traversable. **b.** Sample: V to Z to T
to V to W to Z to X to W **18. a. See below. b.** The network
has more than two odd vertices, so it is not traversable. **19.
See below. 20.** If $3x > 11$, the Addition Property of
Inequality lets you conclude that $3x + 6 > 17$. **21.** If $AB +
BC = 10$ and $AB = 7$, then Substitution lets you conclude that
$7 + BC = 10$. **22. See below. 23. See below. 24.** EF is a
number; that is choice (a). $\overrightarrow{EF}$, $\overline{EF}$, and $\overleftrightarrow{EF}$ are sets of points.

2. a. sample:

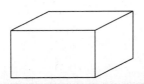

b. sample:

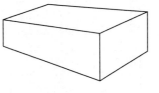

3.

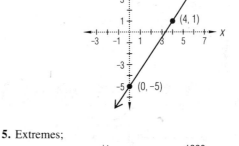

5. Extremes;

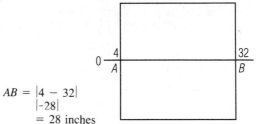

The distance d from Manilla to Shanghai is less than or
equal to $1115 + 1229$ and greater than or equal to
$1229 - 1115$, or $114 \le d \le 2344$.

12.

$AB = |4 - 32|$
$|-28|$
$= 28$ inches

14.

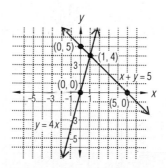

18. a.

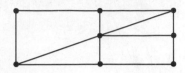

19. Extremes:

The time t needed to get from H to C is less than or equal to $8 + 6$ and more than or equal to $8 - 6$, so $2 \le t \le 14$.

22.

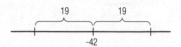

The coordinate of a point 19 units from -42 is either
$-42 - 19 = -61$ or $-42 + 19 = -23$.

23.

The set of points is a ray.

The chart below keys the **Progress Self-Test** questions to the objectives in the **Chapter 1 Review** on pages 54–57. This will enable you to locate those **Chapter Review** questions that correspond to questions you missed on the **Progress Self-Test**. The lesson where the material is covered is also indicated in the chart.

Question	1	2	3	4	5	6–7	8–9	10
Objective	J	B	K	G	I	D	C	E
Lesson	1-2	1-5	1-3	1-9	1-9	1-1, 1-2, 1-3, 1-4	1-2	1-6

Question	11	12–13	14–16	17–18	19	20–21	22–23	24
Objective	C	H	K	A	I	E	F	J
Lesson	1-2	1-2	1-3	1-4	1-9	1-7	1-8	1-2

CHAPTER 1 REVIEW (pp. 54–57)

1. a. 5 **b.** 2 **3. a.** No **b.** It has more than two odd nodes.
5. See below. 7. a. not in perspective. **9.** 2 **11.** 0 **13.** 1
15–19. See below. 21. point, line, plane **23.** to determine what descriptions of points, lines, and planes will be used
25. Distributive Property **27.** Addition Property of Equality
29. Addition Property of Inequality **31.** Transitive Property of Equality **33.** Multiplication Property of Equality **35. a. See below. b.** ray **37.** 78.5 **39.** -6 or 28 **41.** 16 **43.** No
45. Yes **47.** Yes **49. a.** Yes **b.** longer than 9" and shorter than 11" **51.** 8° **53.** 96 miles **55.** at least 10 minutes and no more than 40 minutes **57.** at least 1.8 light years and no more than 10.4 light years **59.** 2.5 **61.** 42 **63.** 78 **65.** $|x - y|$ or $|y - x|$ **67. See below. 69.** oblique **71.** oblique **73.** $y = 1$

5. sample: **a.**   **b.**

	Dot	Location	Ordered Pair	Node
15.	N	A	A	A
17.	S	A	A	N
19.	S	N	N	S

35. a.

67.

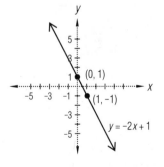

LESSON 2-1 (pp. 58–64)

5. 9 (not including the pictures at the beginning of the lesson or in the questions) **7.** No **9.** Yes **11. See below. 19.** -6 **21.** $x = 101.5$ **23.** $15z = m$

11. Sample:

LESSON 2-2 (pp. 65–69)

1. If a parallelogram has a right angle, then it is a rectangle. **3.** If a figure is a square, then it is a polygon. **9.** 1 **11.** If a figure is a square, then it is a quadrilateral. **13.** $40 = 37 + 3$ or $40 = 29 + 11$ or $40 = 23 + 17$ **15.** No **17. a.** Sample: the line $y = x + 1$ **b.** the line $x = 2$ or the line $y = 3$ **19. a.** nonconvex **b.** nonconvex **c.** convex **21.** longer than $9x$ but shorter than $17x$ **23.** $-32 < z < 58$

LESSON 2-3 (pp. 70–75)

5. See below. 7. The statement says nothing about polygons with 4 or fewer sides. **9.** True **11. a.** No **b.** It is changed to "yes." **13. a.** The formula gives an approximation of the area of a circle of radius R. **b.** when $R \leq 0$ **15.** If a figure is a cube with side s, then its volume is s^3. **17. a.** $|x| = 10$ **b.** $x = -10$ **19.** A counterexample is a traversable network with no odd nodes. **(See art below.) 21. See below.**
23. $161 > q > 71$

5. COMPUTE NUMBER OF DIAGONALS IN POLYGON
  ENTER THE NUMBER OF SIDES
  ? 100
  THE NUMBER OF DIAGONALS IS 4850

19.

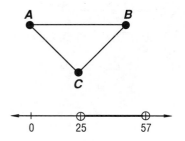

21.

LESSON 2-4 (pp. 76–80)

3. a. If you are at least 13 years old, then you are a teenager. **b.** False **5. a.** A counterexample is a 10×3 rectangle. **b.** A counterexample is a 21×2 rectangle. **7. a.** $p \Rightarrow q$: If $2x + 31 = 4 - x$, then $x = -9$. $q \Rightarrow p$: If $x = -9$, then $2x + 31 = 4 - x$. **b.** $p \Rightarrow q$ and $q \Rightarrow p$ are both true **9. a.** $p \Rightarrow q$: If $AB + BC = AC$, then B is between A and C. $q \Rightarrow p$: If B is between A and C, then $AB + BC = AC$. **b.** $p \Rightarrow q$ and $q \Rightarrow p$ are both true. **11. a.** $p \Rightarrow q$: If B is between A and C, then A is between C and B. $q \Rightarrow p$: If A is between C and B, then B is between A and C. **b.** Both $p \Rightarrow q$ and $q \Rightarrow p$ are false. **13.** No **15. a. See below. b.** Same two first lines, then: ? 1 [The program merely ends if n<3.] **17.** If a person was born in New York City, then that person is a U.S. citizen. **19.** a segment **(See art below.) 21.** Beta

15. a. COMPUTE SUM OF ANGLE MEASURES IN POLYGON
    ENTER THE NUMBER OF SIDES
    ? 6
    THE SUM OF THE ANGLE MEASURES (IN DEGREES) IS 720

19.

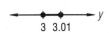

LESSON 2-5 (pp. 81–86)

9. a. 7 **b.** 7 **c.** $\frac{1}{2}$ **d.** $\frac{1}{2}$ **11.** Choice (d) contains all the points inside the circle as well as the circle itself, so it violates the definition. **13.** sufficient condition **15.** meaning **17.** A set is convex if and only if all segments connecting points of the set lie entirely in the set. **19.** Sample: A bisector of a segment is a line, ray, or segment that intersects the segment at its midpoint and at no other point. **21. a.** If $x^2 = \frac{4}{9}$, then $x = -\frac{2}{3}$.
b. No **23. a.** If A is between B and C, then $\overrightarrow{AB}$ and $\overrightarrow{AC}$ are opposite rays. **b.** Yes **25. See below.**

25.

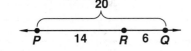

LESSON 2-6 (pp. 87–91)

3. $A \cup B = \{-3, 0, 2, 5, 8\}$; $A \cap B = \{-3, 2\}$ **7.** the points A and B **11.** $G \cup H =$ all residents of Indonesia; $G \cap H =$ all residents of Jakarta. **13.** $G \cup H =$ students in all geometry classes; $G \cap H = \emptyset$. **15.** $\overline{GH}, \overline{HI}, \overline{IJ}, \overline{GJ}, \overline{GI}$ **17. a.** violates property II **b.** violates property III **c.** violates property I **19.** sufficient condition half **21. See below. 23.** Antecedent: You work more than 40 hours a week. Consequent: You will receive time-and-a-half for overtime. **25. See below.**

21. Sample:

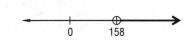

25.

LESSON 2-7 (pp. 92–97)

9. convex **11.** convex **13.** (a) **15.** figure, two-dimensional figure, polygon, triangle, isosceles triangle, equilateral triangle **17. See below. 19.** *AEYD, ABXE, EXCY, ABCD* **21.** If a figure is a union of three or more segments in the same plane such that each segment intersects exactly two others, one at each of its endpoints, then it is a polygon. **23. See below. 25.** Sides are not segments in this definition. **27. See below. 29. a.** 605.5 miles **b.** 1243.5 miles

17. sample:

23. sample:

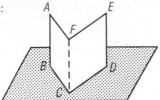

27. sample:

CHAPTER 2 PROGRESS SELF-TEST (pp. 99-100)

1. The "definition" contains too much information (not needed is "$\frac{1}{2} AB = AM$, and $\frac{1}{2} AB = MB$"). That is a violation of the third listed property. **2. See below. 3.** The antecedent is the "if clause" and the consequent is the "then clause": <u>Two angles have equal measure</u> if <u>they are vertical angles.</u> **4.** In if-then form: If a figure is a trapezoid, then it is a quadrilateral. **5. See below. 6. See below. 7.** $p \Leftrightarrow q$: There are over 10 books on that shelf if and only if the shelf falls. In simpler language: The shelf will not hold more than 10 books. **8. a.** Every triangle is a polygon, so the statement "If a figure is a triangle, then it is a polygon" is true. **b.** Converse: If a figure is a polygon, then it is a triangle. **c.** A counterexample to the converse is any quadrilateral, pentagon, or other polygon with more than three sides. **9.** The statement is "If you do your homework every night, you will be guaranteed passing grade." If you only know that the consequent is satisfied (Liane received a passing grade), it is impossible to tell if the antecedent (she did her homework every night) is true. **10.** If 6 is entered for V, then the antecedent in line 20 is satisfied, so the computer prints 36 (which is V^2). The antecedent in line 30 is not satisfied, so the computer ignores line 30. **11.** If 5 is entered for V, then the computer ignores line 20 because the antecedent is not satisfied. In line 30, the antecedent *is* satisfied, and the computer prints TOO SMALL (then the program ends). **12.** In the statement, the defined term (convex set) is in the antecedent, so the statement is the sufficient condition half. **13. See below. 14. a.** Hexagons have six sides; that is figure (iii). **b.** Quadrilaterals have four sides; that is figure (i). **c.** Octagons have eight sides; that is figure (iv). **15.** A figure is an isosceles triangle if and only if it is a triangle with two (or more) sides of equal length. **16. See below. 17. See below. 18.** The figure outlined has 18 sides, so it is an 18-gon.

2. sample:

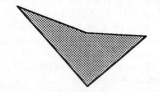

5.

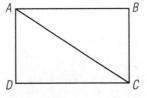

$r \cup t = ABCD \cup \triangle ADC$
$= \{\overline{AB}, \overline{BC}, \overline{CD}, \overline{DA}\} \cup \{\overline{AD}, \overline{DC}, \overline{AC}\}$
$= \{\overline{AB}, \overline{BC}, \overline{CD}, \overline{DA}, \overline{AC}\}$

So $r \cup t$ is the rectangle and its diagonal $\overline{AC}$.

6.

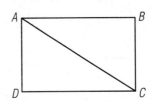

$r \cap t = \{\overline{AB}, \overline{BC}, \overline{CD}, \overline{DA}\} \cap \{\overline{AD}, \overline{DC}, \overline{AC}\}$
$= \{\overline{AD}, \overline{DC}\}$

So $r \cap t$ consists of segments $\overline{AD}$ and $\overline{DC}$.

13.

$AN = 20 + 10 = 30$

16. sample:

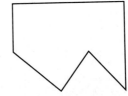

17.

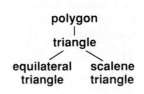

The chart below keys the **Progress Self-Test** questions to the objectives in the **Chapter 2 Review** on pages 101–103. This will enable you to locate those **Chapter Review** questions that correspond to questions you missed on the **Progress Self-Test.** The lesson where the material is covered is also indicated in the chart.

Question	1	2	3–4	5–6	7	8	9	10–11
Objective	D	A	E	F	G	C	H	J
Lesson	2-1	2-7	2-2	2-6	2-4	2-4	2-4	2-3

Question	12	13	14–15	16	17	18
Objective	D	D	B	A	K	I
Lesson	2-5	2-5	2-7	2-7	2-7	2-7

CHAPTER 2 REVIEW QUESTIONS (pp. 101–103)
1. nonconvex **3.** convex **5. See below. 7. See below. 9. See below. 11. a.** If M is the midpoint of $\overline{AB}$, then $AM = MB$. **b.** True **13.** so people can agree on what things mean **15.** It is inaccurate. **17.** circle, line, interesects, two, point **19.** If a figure is a radius, then it is a segment **21.** If $AB = 7$, then $BA = 7$. **23.** If p, then q. **25. See below. 27. a.** $-15 \le n \le 15$ **b.** the set of all real numbers **29. a.** If $\triangle ABC$ has three 60° angles, then $\triangle ABC$ is equilateral. **b.** $\triangle ABC$ is equilateral if and only if $\triangle ABC$ has three 60° angles. **31.** true, false **33.** True **35.** pentagon **37. See below. 39.** 0.8 **41. See below.**

5. sample:

7. sample:

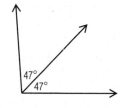

9.

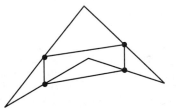

25. sample:

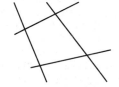

37. COMPUTE NUMBER OF DIAGONALS IN POLYGON
?20
THE NUMBER OF DIAGONALS IS 170

41.

figure
|
triangle
⟋   ⟍
isosceles   scalene
triangle   triangle

LESSON 3-1 (pp. 104–112)
3. a. P **b.** $\overrightarrow{PR}$ or $\overrightarrow{PT}$ and $\overrightarrow{PS}$ or $\overrightarrow{PM}$ or $\overrightarrow{PN}$ **c.** Sample: $\angle 1$, $\angle RPM$, $\angle TPS$, $\angle NPT$, $\angle P$. **7. a.** ≈22 **b.** ≈100 **9. a.** 120 **b.** Angle Addition Property **11. a.** $\angle CAB$, $\angle BAD$, and $\angle DAC$ **b.** 120 **13. a. See below. b.** part (b) of the postulate **15. a.** sample: 175 **b.** sample: 30 **17. a.** Answers may vary. **b.** 35° **19. a. See below. b.** 14 **21.** 19 **23. a.** If a line, ray, or segment is a bisector of $\overline{AB}$, then it contains the midpoint of $\overline{AB}$. **b.** If a line, ray, or segment contains the midpoint of $\overline{AB}$, then it is a bisector of $\overline{AB}$.

13. a.

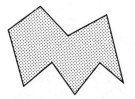

19. a.

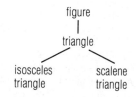

LESSON 3-2 (pp. 113–119)
3. obtuse **5.** vertical **7. a.** $180 - x$ **b.** x **c.** $180 - x$ **9. See below. 11. See below. 13. a.** If two angles are supplementary, then they form a linear pair. **b. See below. c.** The converse is not true. **15. a.** right **b.** acute **c.** obtuse **17.** 95 **19.** ≈19° **21. a.** 8 **b.** 6 **c.** 5 **d.** 3 **e.** 4 **f.** 7 **g.** 9 **h.** 10 **i.** 35 **j.** n **23. a.** 7 **b.** 1

9. sample:

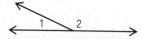

11.

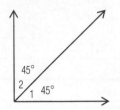

13. b.

LESSON 3-3 (pp. 120–125)

5. Vertical Angle Theorem **9.** Sample: **a.** $y = 8$ **b.** Multiplication Property of Equality **11.** (a) **13.** definition of supplementary angles (meaning) **15.** definition of angle bisector (sufficient condition) **17.** The segment with endpoints A and B is the set consisting of the distinct points A and B and all points between A and B. **19.** m∠T = 15 **21.** 38.5 **23.** 45 **25.** 59 **27.** If X and Y are two angles, then they cannot be both acute and supplementary.

LESSON 3-4 (pp. 126–131)

1. ∠3 **3.** Lines m and n should be drawn parallel. **5.** True

7. $-\frac{2}{3}$ **11.** 4 **15. a.** ∠1, ∠4, ∠7 **b.** ∠2, ∠3, ∠5, ∠8

17. ∠FCD **19.** True **21.** corr. ∠s = ⇒ ∥ lines **23. See below. 25.** -35

23. sample:

LESSON 3-5 (pp. 132–139)

5. Two Perpendiculars Theorem **7.** $-\frac{3}{2}$ **11. a.** 90 **b.** 50 **13. a.** ∥ lines ⇒ corr. ∠s = **b.** $\ell \perp m$ and $m \parallel n \Rightarrow \ell \perp n$ **c.** ∥ lines ⇒ corr. ∠s = **d.** $\ell \perp m \Rightarrow$ 90° angle **15.** $\frac{9}{2}$ **17.** m∠2 = 70, m∠3 = 110, m∠4 = 70, m∠5 = 110, m∠6 = 110, m∠7 = 70, m∠8 = 110 **19.** corr. ∠s = ⇒ ∥ lines **21.** m∠6 ≈ 100 **23.** {D, H}

25.

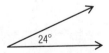

LESSON 3-6 (pp. 140–145)

7. See below. 9. See below. 11. See below. 13. See below. 15. See below. 17. Meaning: If two lines are perpendicular, then they form a 90° angle at the point of intersection. Sufficient condition: If two lines form a 90° angle at their point of intersection, then the lines are perpendicular. **19.** m∠1 = 84

7. sample:

9.

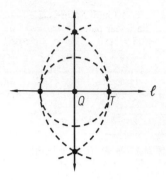

11.

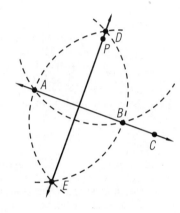

13.

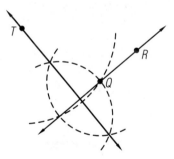

15. △ABC is an equilateral triangle.

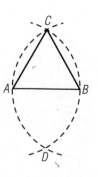

CHAPTER 3 PROGRESS SELF-TEST (pp 147–148)
1. See below. 2. m∠3 = m∠4 because of the Vertical Angle Theorum. So if m∠3 = 77, then m∠4 = 77 by the Transitive Property of Equity. **3.** ∠3 and ∠4 are called Vertical Angles. **4.** ∠3 and ∠5 form a linear pair, so m∠3 + m∠5 = 180. If m∠3 = 2x, then m∠5 = 180 − 2x by the Addition Property of Equality. **5.** From eye level (horizontal) to straight up (vertical) is 90°. So from 15° to 90° is (90−15)° = 75°. **6.** If ∠1 and ∠2 are complementary, then m∠1 + m∠2 = 90 (definition of complementary (meaning)). Substituting m∠1 = 5x − 7 and m∠2 = 4x + 16, then (5x − 7) + (4x + 16) = 90, or 9x + 9 = 90, so 9x = 81 and x = 9. Finally, m∠1 = 5x − 7 = 5(9) − 7 = 45 − 7 = 38. **7. See below. 8. See below. 9. See below. 10.** For two adjacent angles, the statement that the sum of the measures of the two smaller angles equals the measure of the large angle is the Angle Addition Property; that is choice (d). **11. See below. 12.** $\overrightarrow{BC}$ bisects ∠ABD, so m∠ABC = m∠CBD or 14y − 3 = 37 − y. So 15y = 40, and y = $\frac{40}{15}$ = $\frac{8}{3}$. **13. See below. 14. See below. 15.** The slope of $\overline{AB}$ is $\frac{y_2 - y_1}{x_2 - x_1}$ = $\frac{1 - 0}{4 - 0}$ = $\frac{1}{4}$. **16.** The slope of any line, segment, or ray perpendicular to $\overline{AB}$ is -4, because $(\frac{1}{4})$(-4) = -1. **17.** Two points on 2x − y = 6 are (0, -6) and (3, 0). The slope of the line through those points is $\frac{y_2 - y_1}{x_2 - x_1}$ = $\frac{0 - -6}{3 - 0}$ = $\frac{6}{3}$ = 2. **18.** The slope of any line perpendicular to 2x − y = 6 is -$\frac{1}{2}$, because (2)(-$\frac{1}{2}$) = -1. **19.** m∠4 = m∠3 because // lines ⇒ AIA =. ∠3 is supplementary to a 40° angle, so m∠4 = 140 by the Transitive Property of Equality. **20.** m∠5 = 40 because // lines ⇒ AIA =. **21.** The shortest path from point H to the street is the length of the ⊥ segment from H to the street, or segment x ; that is choice (b). **22. See below. 23.** If Q is the midpoint of $\overline{OP}$, then OQ = OP; that is the definition of midpoint (meaning).

1. sample:

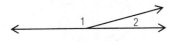

7.

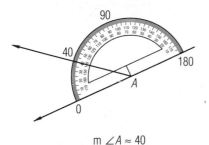

m ∠A ≈ 40

8.

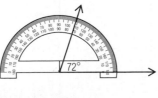

m∠A ≈ 40

9.

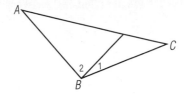

m∠ABC = 110, so m∠1 + m∠2 = 110.
m∠2 = 4 · m∠1, so m∠1 + 4m∠1 = 110.
5m∠1 = 110
m∠1 = 22

11. ∠1 is acute, so 0 < 21 + x < 90.
−21 < x < 69

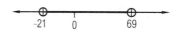

13. Two lines (ℓ and m) perpendicular to the same line (n) are parallel to each other.

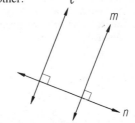

14. Two lines (ℓ and m) parallel to the same line (n) are parallel to each other.

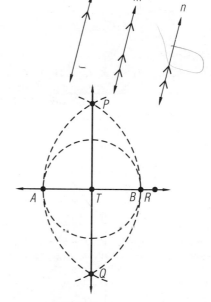

22.

Step 1: ⊙T, intersecting $\overleftrightarrow{TR}$ at A and B.   (Compass rule)
Step 2: ⊙A containing B, ⊙B containing A; they intersect at P and Q.   (Compass rule)
Step 3: $\overleftrightarrow{PQ}$ (Straightedge rule)

The chart below keys the **Progress Self-Test** questions to the objectives in the **Chapter 3 Review** on pages 149–153. This will enable you to locate those **Chapter 3 Review** questions that correspond to questions you missed on the **Progress Self-Test**. The lesson where the material is covered is also indicated in the chart.

Question	1–4	5	6	7–8	9	10	11–12	13	14
Objective	A	G	C	B	C	F	C	F	F
Lesson	3-2	3-2	3-2	3-1	3-1	3-3	3-2	3-5	3-4

Question	15	16	17	18	19–20	21	22	23
Objective	I	J	I	J	D	H	E	F
Lesson	3-4	3-5	3-4	3-5	3-4	3-6	3-6	3-3

CHAPTER 3 REVIEW (pp. 149–153)

1. a. ∠LPO or ∠NPM **b.** sample: ∠LPL **c.** sample: ∠LPM and ∠MPO **d.** ∠MPL, ∠LPM **3. See below. 5. a.** 102 **b.** 102 **c.** 78 **7.** m∠R ≈ 52 **9. See below. 11. See below.**

13. $x = -168$ **15.** m∠1 = 144, m∠2 = 36 **17.** $x = \frac{47}{17}$

19. 16 **21.** 69 **23.** $w = \frac{17}{2}z$ **25.** 135 **27. See below. 29. See below. 31. a. See below. b.** the center of the circle containing X, Y, and Z **c.** Step 1: Straightedge rule; Step 3, Straightedge rule; Step 5: Point rule **33.** (a) **35.** (a) **37.** Linear Pair Theorem **39.** Angle Addition Property **41. See below. 43.** 135 **45. See below. 47.** -1 **49.** $\frac{5}{3}$ **51.** $y = 3x$ **53.** $-\frac{2}{3}, \frac{3}{2}$ **55.** (c)

3. sample:

9.

11.

27.

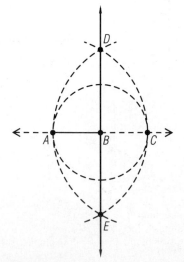

29.

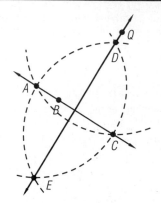

31. a.

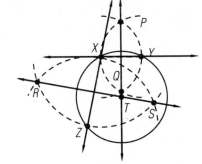

41.

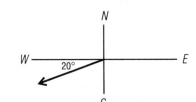

45.

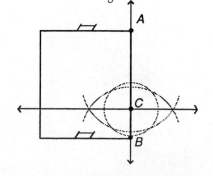

LESSON 4-1 (pp. 154–162)
5. See below. **9.** See below. **11. a.** (3, -5) **b.** (-3, 5) **13.**
a. (*c*, -*d*) **b.** (-*c*, *d*) **15.** See below.

17. a. HELP! I'M TRAPPED INSIDE THIS PAGE. **b.** N
19. See below. **21.** (b) **23.** 25

5. a.

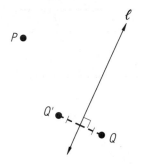

b.

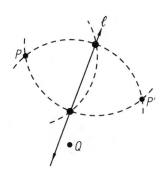

9.

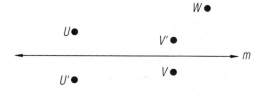

15.

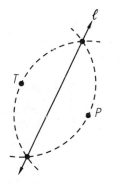

19.

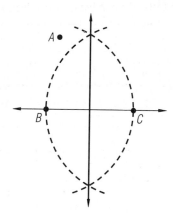

LESSON 4-2 (pp. 163–169)
3. *V'* will be between *A'* and *Z'*. **5. a.** No **b.** Reflections
preserve angle measure, and these angles have different
measures. **7.** $\overline{ZS}$ **9. a.** $\overline{D'E'}$ and $\overline{D'F'}$ **b.** at *G* and *H* **11.** See
below. **13.** 3 **15.** None are needed. **17.** (d) **19.** (e) **21.** See
below. **23.** See below. **25.** See below. **27.** -3, $\frac{1}{3}$ **29.** If *a* = *b*
and *b* = *c*, then *a* = *c*.

11.

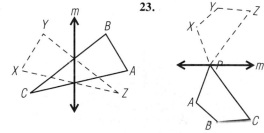

21.

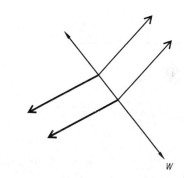

23.

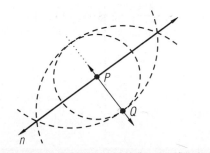

25.

LESSON 4-3 (pp. 170–175)
3. a. $AB = AD \approx 21$ mm; $BC = DC \approx 16$ mm **b.**
Reflections preserve distance. **5. a.** They are equal. **b.**
Reflections preserve distance. **7. a.** They have the same
measure. **b.** Reflections preserve angle measure. **9. a.**
Answers may vary. **b.** $\angle 1$ and $\angle 3$, $\angle 2$ and $\angle 4$, $\angle 8$ and $\angle 6$,
$\angle 7$ and $\angle 5$ **c.** $\parallel$ lines $\Rightarrow$ corr. $\angle$s = (Parallel Lines Postulate)
11. a-c. See below. d. $BC = DC = FE = EB$ because
reflections preserve distance. **e.** Samples: m$\angle DAC =$
m$\angle CAB =$ m$\angle BAE =$ m$\angle FAE$; m$\angle ADC =$ m$\angle ABC =$
m$\angle ABE =$ m$\angle AFE$; m$\angle DCA =$ m$\angle BCA =$ m$\angle BEA =$
m$\angle FEA$. **13. See below. 15.** $P' = (2, 0)$, $Q' = (4, 3)$, $R' =$
$(-2, 7)$ **19.** $\angle ABC$, $\angle CBA$, $\angle B$, $\angle 1$ **21.** A $\cap$ B = {I,N,S}

11. a-c. Answers may vary. Sample:

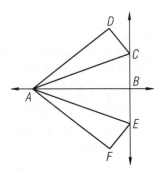

13.

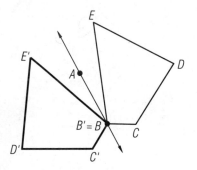

LESSON 4-4 (pp. 176–182)
3. definition of $\odot$ (meaning) **5. a.** $\parallel$ lines $\Rightarrow$ corr. $\angle$s =
(Parallel Lines Postulate) **b.** Vertical Angle Theorem **c.**
Transitive Property of Equality (steps a and b) **7.** No **9.** No
11. No **13.** $m \parallel n$ and $\angle 5$ and $\angle 7$ are vertical angles. **15. See
below. 17. a. See below. b.** Reflections preserve distance.
19. 35 **21.** Addition Property of Equality **23.** All angles of
$\triangle ABC$ and $\triangle ABD$ have measure 60. All sides of $\triangle ABC$
and $\triangle ABD$ have equal lengths (which for the sample shown is
$\frac{1}{2}$ inch). **(See art below.)**

15. Conclusions	Justifications
1. m$\angle ABE =$ m$\angle CBD$	Vertical Angle Theorem
2. m$\angle ABE =$ m$\angle D$	Transitive Property of Equality (given and step 1)

17. a.

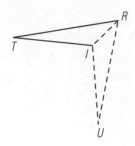

23.

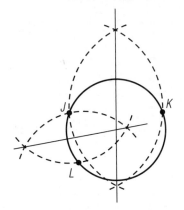

LESSON 4-5 (pp. 183–186)
1. a. The reflection image over a line of a point on the line is
the point itself. **b.** definition of reflection (sufficient condition)
c. Reflections preserve distance. **5.** Construct the $\perp$ bisector
of $\overline{JK}$ and $\overline{JL}$ to find the center O. Construct $\odot O$ through J.
(See art below.) 7. See below. 9. See below. 11. K, N **13.**
m$\angle 1 =$ m$\angle 3 =$ m$\angle 8 =$ m$\angle 6$, m$\angle 4 =$ m$\angle 2 =$ m$\angle 5 =$ m$\angle 7$

5.

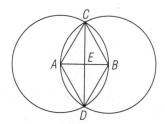

7. Conclusions	Justifications
1. r$_{\overleftrightarrow{QR}}(Q) = Q$	The reflection over a line of a point on the line is the point itself.
2. $CQ = DQ$	Reflections preserve distance.

9. Conclusions	Justifications
1. $BC = AC$	Def. of equilateral triangle (meaning)
2. $AC = CD$	Def. of midpoint (meaning)
3. $BC = CD$	Transitive Property of Equality

LESSON 4-6 (pp. 187–191)
1. See below. 3. See below. 5. a. clockwise **b.** clockwise
c. counterclockwise **7.** True **9. a.** *I* **b.** ∠*XSI* **c.** $\overleftrightarrow{IS}$ **d.** $\overline{XS}$
11. counterclockwise **13. See below. 15. a.** (iii) **b.** (iii)
c. (i) **d.** (ii) **17. a.** definition of reflection (meaning) **b.**
definition of reflection (meaning) **c.** Two Perpendiculars
Theorem **19. a.** $\frac{-3}{2}$ **b.** $\frac{2}{3}$ **21.** Let *x* be 45.

1.

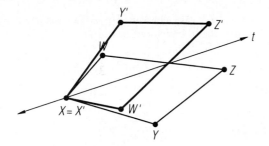

3. Sample:

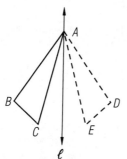

13. Sample:

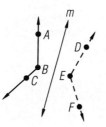

LESSON 4-7 (pp. 192–197)
3. See below. 5. See below. 7. See below. 9. a. $\overrightarrow{FG}$ **b.** $\overrightarrow{FJ}$
c. ∠*GFJ* **11. See below. 13. See below. 15. a. See below.**
b. True **17. See below. 19.** (d) **21. a.** m∠*AOB* = m∠*BOC*
b. definition of angle bisector (meaning) **c.** m∠*AOB* =
m∠*COD* **23.** 2 **25. See below.**

3.

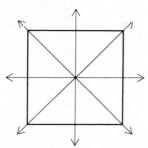

5.

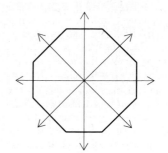

7.

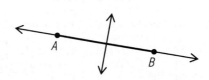

11.

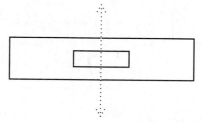

13.   **15. a.**

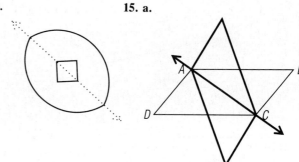

17.

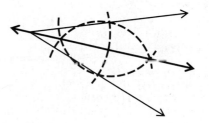

CHAPTER 4 PROGRESS SELF-TEST (p. 199)

1. Point *B* is the reflection image of *A*, and point *D* is the reflection of *C*. So $\overline{BD}$ is the reflection image of $\overline{AC}$, and *AC* = *BD* because reflections preserve distance. **2.** Point *B* is the reflection image of *A* over line *m*, so $m \perp \overline{AB}$ by the definition of reflection (meaning). **3.** The image of *X* is *D*, so $r_m(X) = D$. **4.** The images of points *A*, *B*, and *C* are *W*, *Z*, and *Y*, respectively, so $r_m(\angle ABC) = \angle WZY$. **5.** The orientation of *WXYZ* is clockwise, so the orientation of the image of *WXYZ* is counterclockwise. **6.** Polygon *ABCD* is symmetric across line *n*, so *A* and *B* are images of each other, and so are *D* and *C*. So $r_n(ABCD) = BADC$. **7.** $r_n(\angle BDA) = \angle ACB$, so if m∠*BDA* = *x*, then m∠*ACB* = *x*, because reflections preserve angle measure. **8. See below. 9.** In general, a reflection over the *x*-axis of (*x*, *y*) is (*x*, -*y*). So if *M* = (2, 0), then *M′* = (2, -0) = (2, 0); if *N* = (5, -1), then *N′* = (5, −(-1)) = (5, 1); if *P* = (-3, 4), then *P′* = (-3, -4). **10–15. See below.**

8.

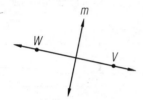

m is the ⊥ bisector of $\overline{WV}$.

10.

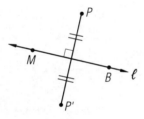

$\overleftrightarrow{MB}$ is the ⊥ bisector of $\overline{PP'}$.

11.

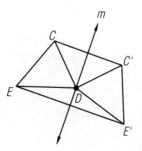

m is the ⊥ bisector of $\overline{CC'}$, $\overline{EE'}$.

12.

△*FGH* is isosceles, with vertex ∠*H*. There is one line of symmetry, the ⊥ bisector of base $\overline{FG}$.

13.

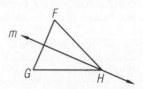

The figure appears to be a regular pentagon. That figure has 5 lines of symmetry, the ⊥ bisectors of the sides.

14.

Conclusions	Justifications
1. m∠1 = m∠2	Given
2. m∠1 = m∠3	Vertical Angle Theorem
3. m∠3 = m∠2	Transitive Property of Equality (steps 1, 2)

15.

Conclusions	Justifications
1. $\ell \perp \overline{YZ}$	definition of reflection (meaning)
2. $\ell \perp \overline{WX}$	definition of reflection (meaning)
3. $\overline{WX} \parallel \overline{YZ}$	Two perpendiculars Theorem

The chart below keys the **Progress Self-Test** questions to the objectives in the **Chapter 4 Review** on pages 200−203. This will enable you to locate those **Chapter Review** questions that correspond to questions you missed on the **Progress Self-Test**. The lesson where the material is covered is also indicated in the chart.

Question	1	2	3–5	6	7	8	9	10
Objective	E	E	E	F	D	A	I	A
Lesson	4-2	4-1	4-6	4-7	4-6	4-1	4-2	4-1

Questions	11	12	13	14	15
Objective	B	C	H	G	G
Lesson	4-2, 4-3	4-7	4-7	4-4	4-5

CHAPTER 4 REVIEW (pp. 200–203)

1. See below. **3.** See below. **5.** See below. **7.** See below. **9.** See below. **11.** See below. **13.** $180 - x$ **15.** ℓ is the $\perp$ bisector of $\overline{AB}$. **17.** Figure Reflection Theorem **19.** Reflections preserve distance. **21.** clockwise **23.** $\angle Y$ and $\angle W$, $\angle YXZ$ and $\angle WXZ$, $\angle YZX$ and $\angle WZX$ **25.** True **27.** True **29.** Conclusion 1: Flip-Flop Theorem Conclusion 2: Reflections preserve distance. **31.** See below. **33.** See below. **35.** See below. **37.** (3, -7) **39.** (-a, b)

1.

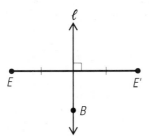

3.

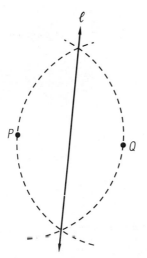

5.

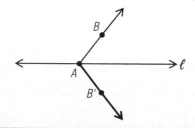

7.

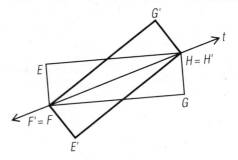

9.

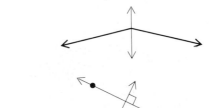

11.

31.

Conclusions	Justifications
1. $m\angle 1 = m\angle 4$	// lines $\Rightarrow$ corr. $\angle$s =
2. $m\angle 4 = m\angle 6$	Vertical Angle Theorem
3. $m\angle 1 = m\angle 6$	Transitive Property of Equality (steps 1 and 2)

33.

35.

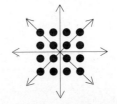

LESSON 5-1 (pp. 204–212)

1. a. $\overline{WN}$ **b.** $\angle I$ **c.** $\angle W$ and $\angle N$ **d.** $\angle W$ and $\angle N$ **3.** (d) **5.** See below. **7. a.** (iii) **b.** (i) **c.** (iv) **9.** $\angle P$ and $\angle H$, $\angle HOE$ and $\angle POE$, $\angle HEO$ and $\angle PEO$ **11.** See below. **13.** (d) **15.** F **17.** See below. **19.** equilateral triangle, rectangle, pentagon, 7-gon, octagon, nonagon

5.

Conclusions	Justifications
1. $m\angle 1 = m\angle XYZ$	Vertical Angle Theorem
2. $m\angle XYZ = m\angle 2$	Isosceles Triangle Theorem
3. $m\angle 1 = m\angle 2$	Transitive Property of Equality (steps 1 and 2)

11.

Conclusions	Justifications
1. $m\angle B = m\angle ACB$	Isosceles Triangle Theorem
2. $m\angle ACB = m\angle ECD$	Vertical Angle Theorem
3. $m\angle ECD = m\angle CED$	Isosceles Triangle Theorem
4. $m\angle B = m\angle CED$	Transitive Property of Equality (steps 1, 2, and 3)

17. sample:

LESSON 5-2 (pp. 213–217)

17. $\overline{WZ} \perp \overline{WX}$; $\overline{WX} \perp \overline{XY}$; $\overline{XY} \perp \overline{ZY}$; $\overline{ZY} \perp \overline{WZ}$; rectangle **19.** $\overline{FG} \perp \overline{GH}$; $\overline{GH} \perp \overline{HE}$; $\overline{HE} \perp \overline{EF}$; $\overline{EF} \perp \overline{FG}$; $FG = GH = EH = EF$; square **21. a.** definition of circle (meaning) **b.** definition of circle (meaning) **c.** definition of kite (sufficient condition) **25. a.** 10 **b.** 33 **27.** See below.

27. sample:

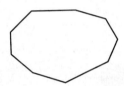

LESSON 5-3 (pp. 218–222)

3. counter example **5. a.** $ABCD$ **b.** $PQRS$ **7.** The diagonals of a rectangle have equal length. **9.** See below. **11.** See below. **13.** See below. **15.** Opinions will vary. **17.** Opinions will vary. **19.** A quadrilateral is a parallelogram if and only if both pairs of its opposite sides are parallel. **21.** A triangle is isosceles if and only if it has two (or more) sides of equal length. **23.** polygon, quadrilateral, kite, rhombus, square **25. a.** E **b.** $FEHG$ **c.** $\angle FHG$

9. Sample conjecture: A diagonal of a rhombus forms 4 equal angles with the sides of the rhombus.

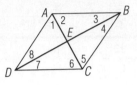
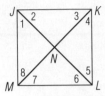
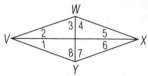

	ABCD		JKLM		VWXY
	angle measure		angle measure		angle measure
1	60	1	45	1	20
2	60	2	45	2	20
3	30	3	45	3	70
4	30	4	45	4	70
5	60	5	45	5	20
6	60	6	45	6	20
7	30	7	45	7	70
8	30	8	45	8	70

11. sample:

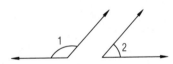

13. sample:

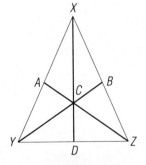

LESSON 5-4 (pp. 223–227)

5. a. I and E **b.** $\overline{EI}$ **c.** $\angle ITE$ **7.** $ED = 15$; $BD = 30$; $m\angle BAC = 50$; $m\angle DCA = 30$; $m\angle BEA = m\angle AED = m\angle DEC = m\angle BEC = 90$; $m\angle BAD = 100$; $m\angle BCD = 60$ **9. a.** Kite Symmetry Theorem **b.** Kite Diagonal Theorem **c.** definition of reflection (suff. cond.) **d.** definition of reflection (suff. cond.) **e.** Figure Reflection Theorem **f.** Reflections preserve angle measure. **11. a.** See below. **b.** Yes **c.** Yes **13.** See below. **15.** A quadrilateral is a trapezoid if and only if it has one pair of parallel sides. **17.** isosceles trapezoids, rectangles, squares **19.** See below. **21.** 15

11. a. sample:

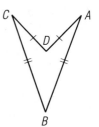

13. sample:

19.

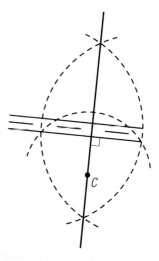

LESSON 5-5 (pp. 228–233)
5. m∠*I* = 125; m∠*Z* = m∠*D* = 55; *DI* = 12 cm **9. a.**
definition of trapezoid (sufficient condition) **b.** Isosceles
Triangle Theorem **c.** definition of isosceles trapezoid
(sufficient condition) **11. See below. 13. a.** True **b.** True
c. True **15.** *RT* = 3; *IT* = 4; *KE* = 8; *KT* = 6; m∠*KIE* =
49; m∠*KIT* = 98; m∠*KEI* = m∠*TEI* = 22; m∠*TRE* =
m∠*TRI* = m∠*KRE* = m∠*KRI* = 90 **17. a.** *B* and *D*
b. Yes, $\overleftrightarrow{BD}$ **c.** Yes **19. a.** angle measure, betweenness,
collinearity, distance **b.** orientation **21. a.** 16 **b.** 134

CHAPTER 5 PROGRESS SELF-TEST (p. 248)
1. Squares are below rectangles in the Quadrilateral Hierarchy,
so it is true that every square is a rectangle. **2. See below.**
3. a. The sum of the three angle measures is 180, so (5*x*) +
(90 − *x*) + (*x*) = 180, or 5*x* + 90 = 180, so 5*x* = 90 and *x*
= 18. **b.** m∠*A* = *x* = 18; m∠*B* = (90 − *x*) = 90 − 18 =
72; m∠*C* = 5*x* = 5(18) = 90. (To check: m∠*A* + m∠*B* +
m∠*C* = 18 + 72 + 90 = 180.) **4. See below. 5. See below.**
6. a. △*MNP* is equilateral, so it is also equilangular; m∠*M* =
60. **b.** The two acute angles at point *N*, ∠*MNP* and ∠*PNO*,
are parts of equilateral triangles. So each angle has measure

---

11.

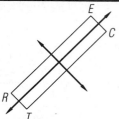

LESSON 5-6 (pp. 234–239)
1. a. ∠7, ∠2, ∠3, ∠6 **b.** ∠7 and ∠6, ∠2 and ∠3 **3.** ∠5,
∠6, ∠7, ∠8 **9.** *ABCD* is a parallelogram, from the
Quadrilateral Hierarchy Theorem. Therefore, $\overline{AD}$ ∥ $\overline{BC}$ by the
definition of parallelogram (meaning). **11. a.** Vertical Angle
Theorem **b.** Transitive Property of Equality **c.** Corresponding
∠s = ⇒ ∥ lines **13.** m∠4 = 135; m∠7 = 140; m∠2 = 95;
m∠3 = 40; m∠1 = 45 **15.** m∠*DEG* = m∠*BEC* = m∠*FGE*
= 123; m∠*EHI* = m∠*AED* = m∠*BEH* = 137; m∠*BEG* =
m∠*CED* = 57; m∠*GEH* = m∠*AEC* = 80; m∠*DEH* =
m∠*AEB* = 43; m∠*AEG* = m∠*CEH* = 100 **17. a.** Yes
b. No **19.** isosceles right triangle **21.** 97 **23.** 0°, 180°

25. sample:

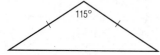

LESSON 5-7 (pp. 240–245)
1. a. ∥ Lines ⇒ AIA = Theorem **b.** ∥ Lines ⇒ AIA =
Theorem **c.** substitution **3.** 20, 60, 100 **7. a.** Sample: a
triangle formed by two north-south lines and the equator. **b.**
non-Euclidean geometries **9. a.** 180 **b.** Triangle-Sum
Theorem **11. a.** 3240 **b.** Polygon-Sum Theorem **13.** 82°26′
15. a. 60 **b.** The sum of the measure of the interior angles is
180, and they are all of the same measure, so any one angle
measures $\frac{180}{3}$ = 60. **17.** 39 and 102 or 70.5 and 70.5 **19. See
below. 21.** A quadrilateral is a trapezoid if and only if it has
at least one pair of parallel sides. **23.** *R:* 15°E of S; *Q:* 30°S
of W

19.	Conclusions	Justifications
	1. m∠*CBE* = m∠*E*	∥ Lines ⇒ AIA = Theorem
a.	2. m∠*D* = m∠*E*	Transitive Property of Equality (step 1 and given)
	3. *ABED* is a trapezoid	def. of trapezoid (suff. cond.)
	4. *ABED* is an isosceles trapezoid.	def. of isosceles trapezoid (suff. cond.)
b.	5. ∠*A* and ∠*D* are supplementary.	Trapezoid Angle Theorem

60, and m∠*MNO* = 120. **7.** △*MNO* is equilateral, so *MN* =
MP = *NP*, and △*NOP* is equilateral so *NO* = *PO* = *NP*. By
the Transitive Property of Equality, *MN* = *NO* = *OP* = *MP*,
So *MNOP* is a rhombus (*True*) by the definition of rhombus
(sufficient condition). **8. See below. 9. a.** *ABCD* is a
parallelogram, so it is also a trapezoid. So m∠*A* + m∠*B* =
180 by the Trapezoid Angle Theorem. **b.** *ADCB* is a
parallelogram, so $\overleftrightarrow{AD}$ ∥ $\overleftrightarrow{BC}$. So m∠*D* = m∠*DCE* because ∥
lines ⇒ AIA =. **10. See below. 11. a.** ∠5 and ∠6 form a
linear pair, so m∠5 + m∠6 = 180. Since *ℓ* ∥ *m*, ∠6 = ∠3 by
∥ lines ⇒ AIA =. So m∠5 + m∠3 = 180 or (9*z* − 52) +

$(2z + 45) = 180$. Then $11z - 7 = 180$ or $11z = 187$, so $z = 17$. **b.** m$\angle 3 = 2z + 45 = 2(17) + 45 = 34 + 45 = 79$.
12. See below. 13. See below. 14. a. For most briefcases, the top has the shape of a rectangle. **b.** Opinions may vary. One explanation is that the rectangular outline of the briefcase is convenient for carrying books and papers. **15. See below.**
2.

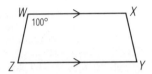

False; a kite has only one line of symmetry.

4. a. Sample:

b. m$\angle X = 100$ by the Isosceles Trapezoid Theorem. The sum of m$\angle W$ + m$\angle X$ + m$\angle Y$ + m$\angle Z = 360$ because of the Quadrilateral Sum Theorem, so m$\angle Y$ + m$\angle Z = 160$ by the Addition Property of Equality. By the Isosceles Trapezoid Theorem, m$\angle Y$ = m$\angle Z$, so m$\angle Y$ = m$\angle Z = 80$.

5.

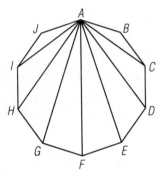

ABCDEFGHIJ, a convex decagon, can be triangulated into 8 triangles. The sum of the measures of the 8 triangles is $8(180) = 1440$.

8. a-b.

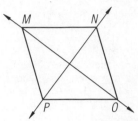

MNOP has two symmetry lines, $\overleftrightarrow{MO}$ and $\overleftrightarrow{NP}$.

10.

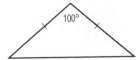

Conclusions	Justifications
1. $AB = BC$	Given
2. m$\angle A$ = m$\angle ACB$	Isosceles Triangle Theorem
3. m$\angle ACB$ = m$\angle ECD$	Vertical Angle Theorem
4. m$\angle A$ = m$\angle ECD$	Transitive Property of Equality (Steps 2 and 3)

12. sample:

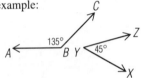

13. a-b. Counterexample:

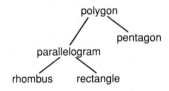

The counterexample shows that the conjecture is false. $\angle 1$ and $\angle 2$ are supplementary, but they do not form a linear pair.

15.

polygon
pentagon
parallelogram
rhombus   rectangle

The chart below keys the **Progress Self-Test** questions to the objectives in the **Chapter 5 Review** on pages 249–251. This will enable you to locate those **Chapter Review** questions that correspond to questions you missed on the **Progress Self-Test**. The lesson where the material is covered is also indicated in the chart.

Question	1	2	3	4a	4b	5	6	7	8
Objective	D	E	C	A	B	C	C	D	E
Lesson	5-2	5-4	5-7	5-5	5-5	5-7	5-1	5-2	5-4
Question	**9a**	**9b**	**10**	**11**	**12**	**13**	**14**	**15**	
Objective	B	B	G	B	A	F	H	I	
Lesson	5-5	5-6	5-1	5-6	5-1	5-3	5-2	5-2	

CHAPTER 5 REVIEW (pp. 249–251)
1. See below. 3. See below. 5. m∠T = 120; m∠R = 60
7. a. 53 **b.** 127 **9.** 57 **11.** 27 **13.** 42 **15.** 46 **17. a.** 58 **b.**
m∠D = 59, m∠E = 60, and m∠F = 61 **19.** 1080 **21.**
polygon, quadrilateral, parallelogram, rhombus, square **23.**
isosceles trapezoid **25.** True **27.** Yes **29.** (c) **31.** False
33. True **35.** Answers may vary. **37.** Answers may vary.
39. a. False **b. See below. 41. See below. 43. See below.**
45. See below. 47. a. square **b.** Answers may vary. On a
major league field, the dimensions are 90 feet on a side. **c.**
Answers may vary. **49. See below.**

1. sample:

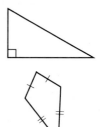

3. sample:

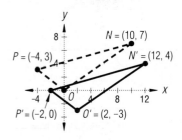

39. b. counterexample:

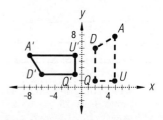

41.

Conclusions	Justifications
1. $\overline{EF} \parallel \overline{GH}$	AIA = ⇒ ∥ Lines Theorem
2. EFHG is a trapezoid.	definition of trapezoid (sufficient condition)

43.

Conclusions	Justifications
1. AB = AC	definition of isosceles triangle (meaning)
2. AC = CD	definition of isosceles triangle (meaning)
3. AB = CD	Transitive Property of Equality

45.

Conclusions	Justifications
1. OQ = OR	definition of circle (meaning)
2. PQ = PR	definition of circle (meaning)
3. OQPR is a kite.	definition of kite (sufficient condition)

49.

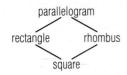

LESSON 6-1 (pp. 252–258)
9. a. (7,0) **b.** Yes **11. a. See below. b.** slide **13.** Two of the
outside vertices do not move, while the others do. This
makes, for example, ∠O different from ∠O′. **15. a.,b. See
Below. c.** turn
17. (b) **19. a.** Yes **b.** The right angle has measure 90; the
other two have measure 45. **21. See below. 23.** 16

11. a.

15. a.,b.

21. sample:

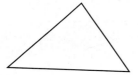

LESSON 6-2 (pp. 259–265)
5. a. D **b.** E **9. a.** 2 cm **b.** vertically up **11.** $\overline{AB}$ **13.** Slide
each preimage point 6 inches to the left, or reflect it across
each of two parallel, vertical lines where the second reflecting
line is 3 inches to the left of the first. **15.** about 8′8″ **17.**
a. (6, -1) **b.** (x + 4, y - 6) **19.** (-12, 15) **21. a.** True
b. False **23.** A circle is the set of points in a plane at a certain
distance (its radius) from a certain point (its center).

LESSON 6-3 (pp. 266–272)
5. a. Reflections preserve distance. **b.** Reflections preserve
distance. **c.** Transitive Property of Equality **7.** 80 **9. See
below. 11. See art below. a.** (-4, -2) **b.** 180°(or -180°) with
center at the origin **13. See below. 15. a.** -172° **b.** 172°
c. 86 **17.** (d) **19.** (13, -212) **21.** 135.75° **23. a.** 24° **b.** 2°

9.

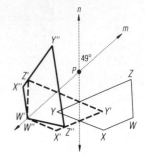

11.

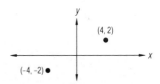

13.

Conclusions	Justifications
1. $\overline{MN} = \overline{PQ}$; $\overline{PQ} = \overline{ST}$	Reflections preserve distance.
2. $\overline{MN} = \overline{ST}$	Transitive Property of Equality

LESSON 6-4 (pp. 273–278)

3. See below. **5.** See below. **7.** See below. **9.** See below.
11. See below. **13.** m∠1 = m∠2 =45 **15.** See below.
17. center: (6, 2); magnitude: 180° **19. a.** 80 **b.** acute

3.

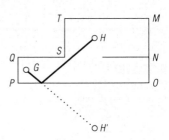

5.

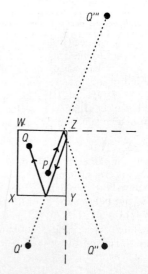

7.

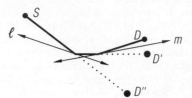

9.

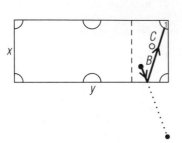

11.

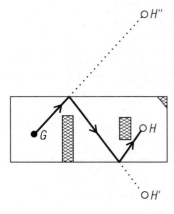

15.

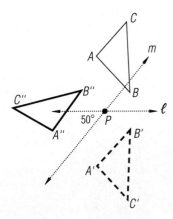

LESSON 6-5 (pp. 279–284)

3. a. $\overline{GH}$ **b.** ∠HFG **c.** △GHE **5.** Symmetric Property of
Congruence **7. a.** $r_n \circ r_p$ **b.** $r_p \circ r_n$ **13.** m∠C = m∠T **15.** An

isosceles triangle has two congruent sides. **17. See below.**
19. Yes **21.** maps it onto itself **23. a.** $\overline{AC}$ and $\overline{AD}$ **b.** ∠ACB
25. See below. 27. a. 60° **b.** -120° **29. a.** Yes **b.** 30

17. samples:

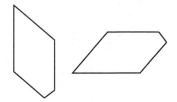

25.

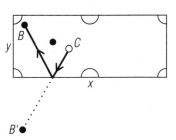

LESSON 6-6 (pp 285–291)

7. See below. 9. See below. 11. reflection, rotation, translation, glide reflection **13. a.** angle measure, betweenness, collinearity, distance **b.** orientation **15. a. See below. b.** No **17.** Segment Congruence Theorem **19.** The bisector of an angle splits it into two congruent angles. **21. a.** C and I **b.** $\overline{CI}$ **c.** $\triangle CIH$ **d.** $\triangle CIH$ **23. a.** $89 < m\angle T \le 180$ **b.** Yes

7.

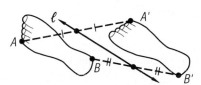

Figure I   Figure II

9. sample:

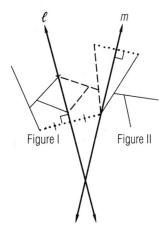

Figure I   Figure II

15. a.

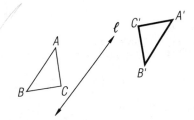

LESSON 6-7 (pp. 292–295)

5. a. $\angle C$ **b.** $\angle IMC$ **c.** $\overline{VT}$ **7.** $\overline{FA}$ **9.** $\angle ETG$ **11. a.** $\triangle ABD \cong \triangle CBD$ **b.** $\overline{AB} \cong \overline{CB}$, $\overline{BD} \cong \overline{BD}$, $\overline{AD} \cong \overline{CD}$; $\angle A \cong \angle C$, $\angle ABD \cong \angle CBD$, $\angle ADB \cong \angle CDB$ **13. a.** $\triangle MNO \cong \triangle PON$ **b.** $\overline{MN} \cong \overline{PO}$, $\overline{MO} \cong \overline{PN}$, $\overline{ON} \cong \overline{NO}$, $\angle M \cong \angle P$, $\angle PNO \cong \angle MON$, $\angle PON \cong \angle MNO$ **15. See below. 17.** translation, rotation, reflection, glide reflection **19. a.** $-\frac{1}{3}$ **b.** 3

21. translation **23.** If a triangle has two congruent sides, then the angles opposite them are congruent. **25.** $(2x, 3y)$

15. samples:

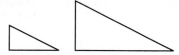

CHAPTER 6 PROGRESS SELF-TEST (pp. 297–298)

1. See below. 2. The composition of two reflections is a rotation, so $r_\ell \circ r_m(\triangle ABC)$ is a rotation; that is choice (b). **3. See below. 4. See below. 5.** The image of $\angle C$ is $\angle H$, and the image of $\angle H$ is $\angle L$. Because reflections preserve angle measure, the angle in $\triangle JKL$ with the same measure as $\angle C$ is $\angle L$. **6.** $\overline{FG}$ is the image of $\overline{AB}$, and the image of $\overline{FG}$ is $\overline{KJ}$. Because reflections preserve length, the segments with the same length as FG are $\overline{AB}$ and $\overline{KJ}$. **7.** $r_m(\triangle ABC) = \triangle FED$, and $r_\ell(\triangle FED) = \triangle HGI$. So $\triangle ABC \cong \triangle FED \cong \triangle HGI$. **8.** According to the CPCF (Corresponding Parts of Congruent Figures) Theorem, if $\triangle ABC \cong \triangle DEF$, then all six pairs of corresponding parts are congruent: $\angle A \cong \angle D$, $\angle B \cong \angle E$, $\angle C \cong \angle F$, $\overline{AB} \cong \overline{DE}$, $\overline{AC} \cong \overline{DF}$, and $\overline{BC} \cong \overline{EF}$. **9.** Five properties preserved by translations are angle measure, betweenness of points, collinearity of points, distances between points, and orientation. **10.** Four kinds of isometries are slides, rotations, reflections, and glide reflections.

11. True. Since reflections are isometries, and isometries preserve congruence, then a series of reflections results in congruent figures. **12. See below. 13.** A hexagon has six sides and six vertices, so V(hexagon) = 6. **14–17. See below.**

1. a.

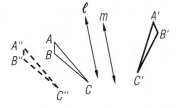

$r_\ell \circ r_m(\triangle ABC) = r_\ell(\triangle A'B'C')$
$= \triangle A''B''C''$

b. The transformation is a translation, in the direction $\perp$ to ℓ and m, in the direction from m to ℓ, with a distance twice that between ℓ and m.

3.

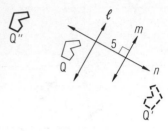

$$r_\ell \circ r_m(Q) = r_\ell(Q')$$
$$= Q''$$

The transformation is a translation, in the direction n, from m to ℓ, with a distance 10, which is twice the distance from m to ℓ.

4.

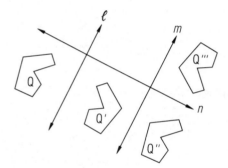

$$r_n \circ r_m \circ r_\ell(Q) = r_n \circ r_m(Q')$$
$$= r_n(Q'')$$
$$= Q'''$$

The transformation is a glide reflection, over the reflecting line n, at a distance twice that from ℓ to m, in the direction from ℓ to m.

12. a.

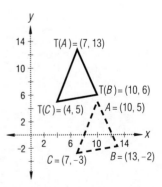

b. The transformation is a translation of 3 units to the left and 8 units up.

14.

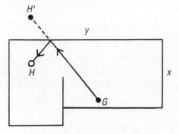

15.

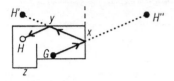

16.

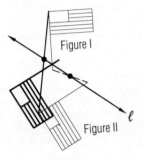

This isometry is a glide reflection: reflection over ℓ followed by a translation parallel to ℓ.

17.

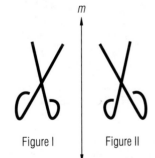

The isometry is a reflection across line m.

The chart below keys the **Progress Self-Test** questions to the objectives in the **Chapter 6 Review** on pages 299–301. This will enable you to locate those **Chapter 6 Review** questions that correspond to questions you missed on the **Progress Self-Test**. The lesson where the material is covered is also indicated in the chart.

Question	1	2	3,4	5	6	7	8	9	10	11
Objective	A	C	B	D	D	B	D	D	C	C
Lesson	6-2	6-3	6-3	6-5	6-7	6-2	6-6	6-5	6-2	6-6

Question	12a	12b	13	14,15	16,17
Objective	G	G	G	F	E
Lesson	6-1	6-2	6-1	6-4	6-6

CHAPTER 6 REVIEW (pp. 299–301)

1. See below. **3. a.** See below. **b.** a translation ⊥ to *m* and *n*, in the direction from *m* to *n*, with a magnitude twice the distance from *m* to *n*. **5.** See below. **7.** (a) **9.** ∠*B* **11.** a rotation with center *Q*, magnitude 180° **13.** 15°, *C* **15.** ∠*F*, ∠*H* **17.** True **19.** translation, rotation, reflection, glide reflection **21.** *CDAB, KLIJ* **23.** definition of congruence (sufficient condition) **25.** Reflexive Property of Congruence **27.** glide reflection **29.** translation **31.** glide reflection **33.** See below. **35.** See below. **37. a., b.** See below. **c.** The transformation stretches the figure by a factor of 2 in the horizontal direction only and then reflects it about the line *y* = *x*. **39.** 4 **41.** (a)

1. a rotation with center *Z* and magnitude ≈98°, in the positive direction

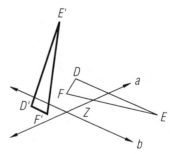

3. a.

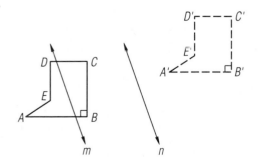

5. sample (two images are possible):

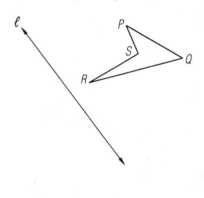

33.

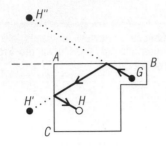

35.

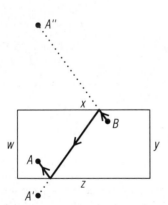

37. a., b.

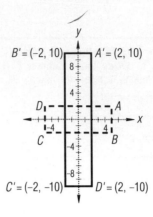

LESSON 7-1 (pp. 302–309)

7–19. See below. 21. translation **23.** The line containing the ends of a kite is a symmetry line for the kite. **25.** greater than 53 cm but less than 129 cm

7. sample:

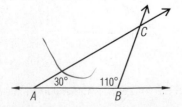

9.

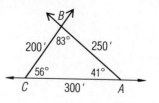

11. a. samples:

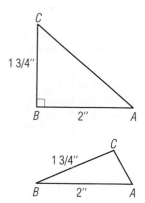

b. No

13. a. samples:

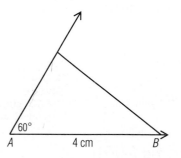

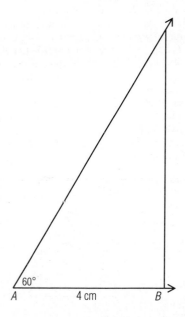

b. No

15. a. samples:

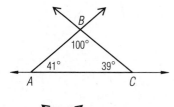

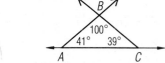

b. No

17. a.

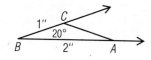

b. Yes

19. a.

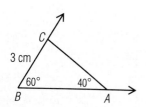

b. Yes

LESSON 7-2 (pp. 310–316)
9. a. Side-Switching Theorem **b.** Side-Switching Theorem
c. △*GFH* **11.** not necessarily congruent **13.** by the ASA
Congruence Theorem, △*OYN* ≅ △*YOX* **15.** by the ASA
Congruence Theorem, △*CGO* ≅ △*IPN* **17. See below. 19.
See below. 21.** because of the ASA Congruence Theorem
23. figure, quadrilateral, kite, rhombus, square

17. a.

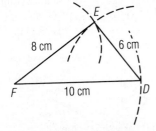

b. Yes, because of the SSS Congruence Theorem

19. a.

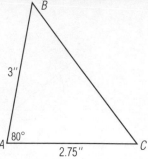

b. Yes, because of the SAS Congruence Theorem

LESSON 7-3 (pp. 317–322)

3. See below. **5. a.** Reflexive Property of Congruence **b.** CPCF Theorem **7.** See below. **9.** See below. **11.a.** True **b.** False **13.** See below. **15.** This is not possible since it violates the Triangle Inequality. **17.** $\frac{x}{4}$ **19.** See below.

3.

Conclusions	Justifications
1. $\overline{AC} \cong \overline{AC}$	Reflexive Property of Congruence
2. $\triangle ABC \cong \triangle CDA$	SSS Congruence Theorem (step 1 and given)
3. $\angle 2 \cong \angle 4$	CPCF Theorem
4. $\overline{BC} \parallel \overline{AD}$	AIA $= \Rightarrow \parallel$ Lines Theorem

7.

Conclusions	Justifications
1. $AB = CD$; $BC = AD$	Given
2. $AC = AC$	Reflexive Property of Congruence
3. $\triangle ABC \cong \triangle CDA$	SSS Congruence Theorem (steps 1 and 2)

9.

Conclusions	Justifications
1. $BA = BC$	definition of isosceles triangle (meaning)
2. $AD = DC$	definition of midpoint (meaning)
3. $\overline{BD} \cong \overline{BD}$	Reflexive Property of Congruence
4. $\triangle ABD \cong \triangle CBD$	SSS Congruence Theorem (steps 1, 2, and 3)

13.

Conclusions	Justifications
1. $BC = CD$	definition of midpoint (meaning)
2. $\triangle ABC \cong \triangle EDC$	SAS Congruence Theorem (step 1 and given)

19. a. sample:

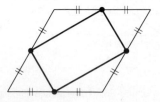

b. Opinions may vary, but diagrams like the one above show a counterexample to the conjecture. (A true conjecture is that the resulting figure is a rectangle.)

LESSON 7-4 (pp. 323–326)

1. a. 8 **b.** $\triangle DAU$ **c.** $\triangle QUD$, $\triangle DAQ$ **3–7.** See below. **9. a.** Vertical Angle Theorem **b.** SAS Congruence Theorem (step 1 and given) **c.** CPCF Theorem **d.** Vertical Angle Theorem **e.** Transitive Property of Equality **11.** $\triangle PCA \cong \triangle PCB$ by the SAS Congruence Theorem. So $PA = PB$ by the CPCF Theorem. **13.** True **15.** acute

3.

Conclusions	Justifications
1. $\angle H \cong \angle K$, $\angle GJI \cong \angle GIJ$	Isosceles Triangle Theorem
2. $\triangle GHJ \cong \triangle GKI$	AAS Congruence Theorem (step 1 and given)
3. $\angle HGJ \cong \angle KGI$	CPCF Theorem

5.

Conclusions	Justifications
1. $\angle A \cong \angle A$	Reflexive Property of Congruence
2. $\triangle AEB \cong \triangle ADC$	ASA Congruence Theorem (given and step 1)
3. $EB = CD$	CPCF Theorem

7.

Conclusions	Justifications
1. $RS = RS$	Reflexive Property of Equality
2. $\triangle PRS \cong \triangle QSR$	SSS Congruence Theorem (given and step 1)
3. $m\angle P = m\angle Q$	CPCF Theorem

LESSON 7-5 (pp. 327–332)

1. See below. **3.** (c) **5. a.** HL Congruence Theorem **b.** $\triangle ABC \cong \triangle FED$ **7. a.** HL Congruence Theorem **b.** $\triangle ABD \cong \triangle CBD$ **9.** See below. **11. a.** definition of a circle (meaning) **b.** definition of a circle (meaning) **c.** SsA Congruence Theorem (steps 1, 2, 3, and given) **13.** Let T be the top of the maypole, M the point on the maypole that is the same height as June's and April's hands, J the position of June's hands, and A the position of April's hands. $\overline{JA}$ is parallel to the ground, since J and A are equal in height (given). So $\overline{JA} \perp \overline{TM}$ by the Perpendicular to Two Parallels Theorem. Since $\overline{TM} \cong \overline{TM}$ (by the Reflexive Property) and $\overline{TJ} \cong \overline{TA}$ (given), $\triangle TJM \cong \triangle TAM$ by the HL Congruence Theorem. So $\overline{JM} = \overline{AM}$ by the CPCF Theorem.

1. samples:

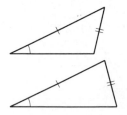

9.

Conclusions	Justifications
1. △WXZ ≅ △VXY	HL Congruence Theorem (given)
2. ∠W ≅ ∠V	CPCF Theorem

15. a.

Conclusions	Justifications
1. AB = AC	given
2. m∠B = m∠C	Isosceles Triangle Theorem
3. △ABD ≅ △ACE	SAS Congruence Theorem (Step 2 and given)
4. $\overline{AD} \cong \overline{AE}$	CPCF Theorem
5. ∠ADE ≅ ∠AED	Isosceles Triangle Theorem

b. 6. △ADE is isosceles. | definition of isosceles triangle (sufficient condition)

17. a.

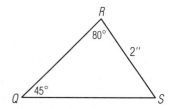

b. The drawings will be congruent because of the AAS Congruence Theorem.

LESSON 7-6 (pp. 333–338)
1. a. definition of parallelogram (meaning) **b.** ∥ Lines ⇒ AIA = Theorem **c.** Reflexive Property of Congruence **d.** ASA Congruence Theorem (steps 2, 4, and 5) **3. a.** $\overline{AB}, \overline{AC}, \overline{CD}, \overline{BD}$ (all are ≅) **b.** ∠A ≅ ∠D, ∠B ≅ ∠C **c.** $\overline{AD}, \overline{BC}$ **7. See below. 9.** $OS = SQ = RS = SP = \frac{x}{2}$ **11–17. See below.**

19. ∠B ≅ ∠X for ASA; $\overline{AC} \cong \overline{YZ}$ for SAS; ∠C ≅ ∠Z for AAS

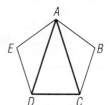

7.

Conclusions	Justifications
1. $\overline{AB} \cong \overline{AE}$	definition of regular pentagon (meaning)
2. $\overline{BC} \cong \overline{ED}$	definition of regular pentagon (meaning)
3. ∠B ≅ ∠E	definition of regular pentagon (meaning)
4. △ABC ≅ △AED	SAS Congruence Theorem (steps 1,2,3)
5. $\overline{AC} \cong \overline{AD}$	CPCF Theorem

11. a. sample:

b. 1440° **c.** 144°

13.

Conclusions	Justifications
1. △AEF ≅ △BDC	HL Congruence Theorem (step 1 and given)
2. ∠F ≅ ∠C	CPCF Theorem

15.

Conclusions	Justifications
1. $\overline{MX} = \overline{NX}$	definition of midpoint (meaning)
2. ∠M ≅ ∠N; ∠MXZ ≅ ∠NXY	Given
3. △MXZ ≅ △NXY	ASA Congruence Theorem (steps 1 and 2)
4. ∠Y ≅ ∠Z	CPCF Theorem

17. a.

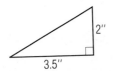

b. Yes, by the SAS Congruence Theorem

LESSON 7-7 (pp. 339–343)
5. Step 6: CPCF Theorem   Step 7: AIA = ⇒ ∥ Lines Theorem **7. See below. 9.** kite, parallelogram **11.** Since the vertical sides of V, W, X, and Y are congruent and parallel, the vertical sides of Z are both congruent and parallel by the transitivity of congruence and parallelism. **13.** If both pairs of opposite sides are congruent, then the figure is a parallelogram, by the Sufficient Conditions for a Parallelogram Theorem. Then both pairs of opposite angles are congruent by the Properties of a Parallelogram Theorem. **15–19. See below.**

7.   Justifications
1. Point-Line-Plane Postulate
2. Reflexive Property of Equality
3. ∥ lines ⇒ AIA = Theorem
4. SAS Congruence Theorem (steps 2,3, and given)
5. CPCF Theorem
6. AIA = ⇒ ∥ Lines Theorem
7. definition of parallelogram (sufficient condition)

15. Use rectangle *ABCD*.

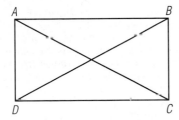

Conclusions	Justifications
1. *ABCD* is a parallelogram.	Quadrilateral Hierarchy Theorem
2. $\overline{AD} \cong \overline{BC}$	Properties of a Parallelogram Theorem
3. $\angle ADC \cong \angle BCD$	Both are right angles (def. of rect.).
4. $\overline{DC} \cong \overline{DC}$	Reflexive Property of Congruence
5. $\triangle ADC \cong \triangle BCD$	SAS Congruence Theorem (parts 2, 3, and 4)
6. $\overline{AC} \cong \overline{BD}$	CPCF Theorem

17. a.

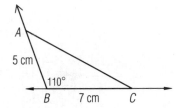

b. Yes **c.** SAS Congruence Theorem

19. a. sample:

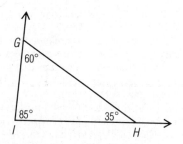

b. No **c.** Triangles with longer or smaller sides could still have these same angle measures.

LESSON 7-8 (pp. 344–347)
3. (c) **5. a.** Yes **b.** trigonometry **7.** $QT = TS$ and $RT = RT$, but m$\angle QTR = 75$ while m$\angle STR = 105$. So, applying the SAS Inequality Theorem in $\triangle QTR$ and $\triangle STR$, $RS > QR$.
9. 5 cm **11.** See below. **13.** can't conclude congruence **15.** See below. **17.** rotation

CHAPTER 7 PROGRESS SELF-TEST (p. 349)
1.a. Since $\angle 1 \cong \angle 3$ and $\angle 2 \cong \angle 4$ (given) and $\overline{AC} \cong \overline{AC}$ (Reflexive Property of Congruence), $\triangle ABC \cong \triangle CDA$. **b.** The justification for the congruence is the ASA Congruence Theorem. **2.a.** Since it is given that *M* is the midpoint of $\overline{AC}$, then $AM = MC$ by the definition of midpoint (meaning). **b.** $\angle AMB \cong \angle CMD$ because of the Vertical Angle Theorem. **c.** Since it is given that $\overrightarrow{AB} \parallel \overrightarrow{CD}$, then $\angle MBA \cong \angle MDC$ because $\parallel$ lines $\Rightarrow$ AIA =. **d.** $\triangle MBA \cong \triangle MDC$ by the AAS Congruence Theorem (from parts **a, b, c**). **3.** See below. **4.** See below. **5.** Each of the following conditions is sufficient for a quadrilateral to be a parallelogram: both pairs of opposite sides are parallel; both pairs of opposite angles are congruent; both pairs of opposite sides are congruent; one pair of opposite sides are parallel and congruent; two pairs of consecutive

11. Use quadrilateral *ABCD*:

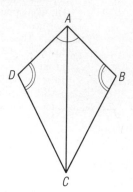

Conclusions	Justifications
1. $\overline{AC} \cong \overline{AC}$	Reflexive Property of Congruence
2. $\angle D \cong \angle B$	Given
3. $\angle DAC \cong \angle BAC$	Definition of bisector
4. $\triangle DAC \cong \triangle BAC$	AAS Congruence Theorem (parts 1, 2, 3)
5. $\overline{AD} \cong \overline{AB}$; $\overline{DC} \cong \overline{BC}$	CPCF Theorem
6. *ABCD* is a kite.	Definition of kite (sufficient condition)

15. a.

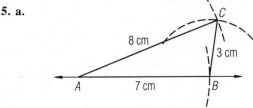

b.

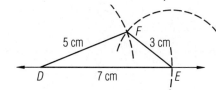

c. m$\angle A$ = m$\angle D \approx 22$; m$\angle C \approx 30$, m$\angle F \approx 150$, so $\angle C$ and $\angle F$ are supplementary.

angles are supplementary. **6.** If, in two triangles, two pairs of sides are congruent, then for the angles contained by those sides, the side opposite the greater angle has the greater length. (Exact wordings may differ.) **7–10.** See below. **11.** In $\triangle ADB$ and $\triangle ADC$, $\overline{AD} \cong \overline{AD}$ (by the Reflexive Property of Equality), $\overline{BD} \cong \overline{CD}$ (given), and $\angle ADB \cong \angle ADC$ (they are both right angles). So $\triangle ADB \cong \triangle ADC$ by the SAS Congruence Theorem, and $AB = AC$ by the CPCF Theorem.

3. a.

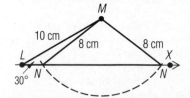

b-c. There are two possible triangles, so it is not necessarily so that everyone else's triangle will be congruent to yours.

4. a.

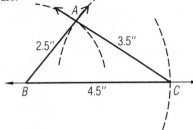

2.5"   3.5"
B   4.5"   C

b-c. Given the lengths of 3 sides (and after checking that those three lengths can be the lengths of sides of a triangle), every triangle having sides with those lengths must be congruent, because of the SSS Congruence Theorem.

7.

	Conclusions	Justifications
a. 1.	$\overline{QP} = \overline{QP}$	Reflexive Property of Congruence
2.	$\triangle QPS \cong \triangle QPT$	HL Congruence Theorem (step 1 and given)
3.	$QS = QT$	CPCF Theorem
b. 4.	$\angle SQP \cong \angle TQP$	CPCF Theorem
5.	$\overline{QP}$ bisects $\angle SQT$.	Definition of angle bisector (sufficient condition)

8. If $\overline{AB}$ and $\overline{CD}$ are both parallel and congruent, then $ABDC$ is a parallelogram by the Sufficient Conditions for a Parallelogram Theorem, part d.

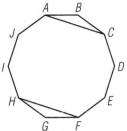

9.

	Conclusions	Justifications
1.	$\overline{AB} \cong \overline{FG},$ $\overline{BC} \cong \overline{GH},$ $\angle B \cong \angle G$	Definition of regular polygon (meaning)
2.	$\triangle ABC \cong \triangle FGH$	SAS Congruence Theorem (step 1)
3.	$AC = FH$	CPCF Theorem

10.

	Conclusions	Justifications
1.	$\angle W \cong \angle W$	Reflexive Property of Congruence
2.	$\triangle WYU \cong \triangle WXV$	AAS Congruence Theorem
3.	$\overline{WU} \cong \overline{WV}$	CPCP Theorem
4.	$\triangle WUV$ is isosceles.	Definition of isosceles triangle (sufficient condition)

The chart below keys the **Progress Self-Test** questions to the objectives in the **Chapter 7 Review** on pages 350–353. This will enable you to locate those **Chapter 7 Review** questions that correspond to questions you missed on the **Progress Self-Test**. The lesson where the material is covered is also indicated in the chart.

Question	1	2	3a	3bc	4a	4bc	5	6
Objective	B	C	A	A	A	A	E	Voc
Lesson	7-2	7-3	7-1	7-2	7-1	7-2	7-7	7-8

Question	7	8	9	10	11			
Objective	D	E	D	D	F			
Lesson	7-5	7-7	7-3	7-4	7-2			

CHAPTER 7 REVIEW (pp. 350–353)
1. a. See below. **b.** Yes **c.** SSS Congruence Theorem **3. a.** See below. **b.** Yes **c.** ASA Congruence Theorem **5. a.** See below. **b.** Yes **c.** HL Congruence Theorem **7. a.** See below. **b.** No **c.** There are two noncongruent triangles that fit the given information **9. a.** See below. **b.** Yes **c.** SsA Congruence Theorem **11. a.** AAS Congruence Theorem **b.** $\triangle MOP \cong \triangle PNM$ **13. a.** SAS Congruence Theorem **b.** $\triangle GFE \cong \triangle GIH$ **15. a.** ASA Congruence Theorem **b.** $\triangle NOP \cong \triangle ORQ$ **17.** See below. **19.** See below. **21. a.** Reflexive Property of Congruence **b.** SSS Congruence Theorem (given and step 1) **c.** CPCF Theorem **23.** See below. **25.** See below. **27.** congruent **29.** bisect each other **31.** See below. **33.** $\triangle XBD \cong \triangle XBA \cong \triangle XBC$ by use of the AAS Congruence Theorem, so $DB = AB = CB$. **35.** SAS Inequality Theorem **37.** parallelogram

1. a.

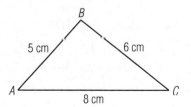

B
5 cm   6 cm
A   8 cm   C

3. a.

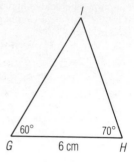

5. a.

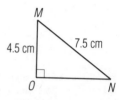

7. a.

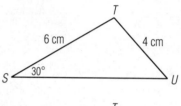

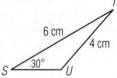

9. a.

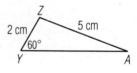

17.

Conclusions	Justifications
1. $\overline{AC} \cong \overline{AC}$	Reflexive Property of Congruence
2. $\triangle ADC \cong \triangle ABC$	HL Congruence Theorem (step 1 and given)

19.

Conclusions	Justifications
1. $\angle YUX \cong \angle WUV$	definition of angle bisector (meaning)
2. $\triangle UVW \cong \triangle UXY$	AAS Congruence Theorem (step 1 and given)

23.

Conclusions	Justifications
1. $\angle KJM \cong KJL$	definition of angle bisector (meaning)
2. $\overline{JK} \cong \overline{JK}$	Reflexive Property of Congruence
3. $\triangle KJM \cong \triangle KJL$	SAS Congruence (steps 1, 2, and given)
4. $\angle M \cong \angle L$	CPCF Theorem

25.

Conclusions	Justifications
1. $\overline{BC} \cong \overline{BC}$	Reflexive Property of Congruence
2. $\triangle ABC \cong \triangle DCB$	AAS Congruence Theorem (step 1 and given)
3. $\overline{AC} \cong \overline{DB}$	CPCF Theorem

31.

Conclusions	Justifications
1. $BD = BD$	Reflexive Property of Equality
2. $m\angle ABD = m\angle CDB$	// Lines $\Rightarrow$ AIA = Theorem
3. $\triangle ABD \cong \triangle CDB$	AAS Congruence Theorem (steps 1,2, and given)
4. $AB = DC$	CPCF Theorem
5. $ABCD$ is a parallelogram.	Sufficient Conditions for a Parallelogram Theorem

---

LESSON 8-1 (pp. 354–361)

3. a. 1199 miles **b.** 23 hours, 1 minute **5.** 8 miles **7.** $4t$ **9.** $7(x + 1)$ or $7x + 7$ **11.** 0.9 meters **13.** 1.25 ft **15. a.** $8s + 18m + 2\ell$ **b.** 1300 meters **c.** 1200 meters **17. See below.**

19. (d) **21.** Yes **23. a.** $\frac{2}{2.54} \approx .79$ inch **25.** 1.5 **27.** Sample counterexample: If $x = -1$, then $(x + 1)(2x - 3) = 0$, but $2x^2 - 3 = -1$. **29. a.** ≈ 60 mph **b.** ≈ 51 mph **c.** Sample: the route from Dallas to Atoka has more stops or slower speed limits.

17.

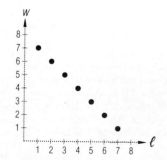

LESSON 8-2 (pp. 362–366)
11. the roughly triangular region determined by connecting the noses of the fish **(See below for art.) 13.** (c) **15.** 2.6 **17.** 108
19. See below. 21. $\sqrt{27} \approx 5.2$. $-\sqrt{27} \approx -5.2$

11.

19.

Conclusions	Justifications
1. $\overline{BD} \cong \overline{BD}$	Reflexive Property of Congruence
2. $\triangle BAD \cong \triangle DCB$	ASA Congruence Theorem (Step 1 and given)
3. $AB = CD$	CPCF Theorem

LESSON 8-3 (pp. 367–372)
1. a. 27 units^2 **b.** 75 units^2 **3. a.** 9200 miles **b.** 4,800,000 sq miles **7. See below. 9. a.** 100 units^2 **b.** k^2 units^2 **11.** $\frac{1}{2}$ yard
13. a. 288 sq in. **b.** 2 sq ft **c.** 144 **15.** 3w^2 units^2 **17. See below. 19.** 4, -4 **21.** (b) **23.** 10, 15, 20 units

7. $45 \times 43 = 1935$
   $1320 + 120 + 345 + 150 = 1935$

17.

25.

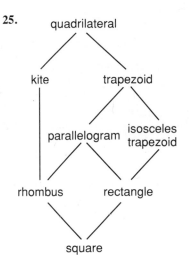

quadrilateral

kite   trapezoid

parallelogram   isosceles trapezoid

rhombus   rectangle

square

LESSON 8-4 (pp. 373–377)
7. $\approx$ 4,245 dots/in.^{2} **9.** $\approx$14.25 km^2 **11.** about $\frac{1}{3}$ or about .34 mi^2 **13.** farm in U.S. **15.** $(x - y)(x + y)$ **17.** 56 linear units **19. See below. 21.** x = -4 or 4 **23.** (a)

19.

Conclusions	Justifications
1. $\triangle PQA \cong \triangle DRA$	AAS Congruence Theorem (given)
2. $\overline{PA} \cong \overline{DA}$	CPCF Theorem
3. $\triangle PAD$ is isosceles.	definition of isosceles triangle (suff. cond.)

LESSON 8-5 (pp. 378–383)
7. a. 24 units^2 **b.** 60 units^2 **c.** 84 units^2 **9.** 12 units^2 **11.**
a. 9 units^2 **b.** 15 units^2 **c.** 24 units^2 **13. See below. 15.** $\frac{48}{7} \approx$
6.86 units **17.** 23 units^2 **19. a.** 288,000 sq miles, answers may vary $\pm$ 25,000 sq miles **b.** 266,400 sq miles, answers may vary $\pm$ 10,000 sq miles **21.** 124 units^2 **23.** $3\sqrt{5}$

13. a. Shown below is the construction of the altitude from Z.

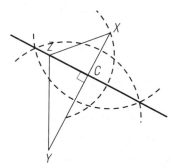

b. $XY \approx$ 8.1 cm; $CZ \approx$ 2.3 cm; area $\approx$ 9.3 cm^2 (Measurements are based on Students' Edition text.)

LESSON 8-6 (pp. 384–389)
3. a. bases: $\overline{EF}$ and $\overline{GH}$; altitude: $\overline{IF}$ **b.** 6720 units^2 **9.** 57 units^2 **13.** 16,800 units^2 **15.** $\frac{1}{2}bc$ units^2 **17.** (d) **19.** Place a grid over the fabric. Add the number of squares entirely inside the figure to half the number of squares partially covering the figure, and multiply the result by the area of each square.
21. 12x **23.** $ac + ad + bc + bd$

LESSON 8-7 (pp. 390–395)
3. a. $\frac{1}{2} ab$ **b.** $(a + b)^2$ or $a^2 + 2ab + b^2$ **c.** $a^2 + b^2$
d. $\sqrt{a^2 + b^2}$ **5.** (c) **7.** $\sqrt{18} = 3\sqrt{2} \approx$ 4.24 units **9.** 12 units **11.** 24″ **13.** Yes **15.** No **17.** Yes **19.** Yes **21.** 54″ **23.** 74 meters **25.** $\frac{1400}{90} \approx$ 15.56 minutes **27.** 16,320 sq ft **29.** 4.5 units^2 **31.** 1 unit and 12 units

LESSON 8-8 (pp. 396–401)
1. $\overline{RS}, \overline{SP}, \overline{PQ}, \overline{QR}, \overline{QS}$ **3. a.** 180° **b.** 180° **c.** 150° **5.** central **13. a.** 8π units **b.** 25.1 units **15. a.** $\frac{15\pi}{6}$ units **b.** 2.62 units **17. a.** 8640° **b.** $960\pi \approx$ 3016 ft **19.** 20 units **21.** $A = \frac{1}{2} h(b_1 + b_2)$ **23.** $p = 4s$ **25.** $\frac{(n - 2) \cdot 180}{n}$ **27.** (b) **29.** $\approx$20 mph

LESSON 8-9 (pp. 402–406)
1. a. 10 units **b.** $10\pi \approx$ 31.42 units **c.** $100\pi \approx$ 314.2 units^2 **3.** 4900π sq in. **5.** 15,394 in.^{2} **7. a.** $3600\pi \approx$ 11,300 sq meters **b.** 377 meters **9. a.** $64 - 8\pi \approx$ 38.87 units^2 **b.** $24 + 4\pi \approx$ 36.57 units **11. a.** $\frac{1}{16}$ **b.** $\frac{15}{16}$ **13. a.** 72° **b.** $6\pi \approx$ 18.8 units **15.** $90\pi \approx$ 282.74 units **17. a.** $18x^2$ units^2
b. $(13 + \sqrt{97})x \approx$ 22.8x units **19. a.** 24,200 sq miles, answers may vary $\pm$ 3500 sq miles **b.** 22,300 sq miles, answers may vary $\pm$ 900 sq miles **21.** m$\angle E$ = 130, m$\angle D$ = m$\angle F$ = 50 **23. a.** .01 **b.** 36 **c.** 1760

CHAPTER 8 PROGRESS SELF-TEST (pp. 408-409)
1. See below. 2. Using formula $A = \ell \times w$, Area = 200m^2 and length = 25m; $200 = 25 \times w$, then $w = 8$m. **3.** In a regular polygon, all sides have the same length. So if a regular hexagon has perimeter q, then each of its 6 sides has length one-sixth of the perimeter, or $\frac{q}{6}$. **4.** Using the formula $A = \frac{1}{2}bh$ with $b = 210$ units and $h = 80$ units, $A = \frac{1}{2}(210)(80)$ $= (105)(80) = 8400$ units^2. **5.** Using the formula $A = bh$ with $b = 40$ units and $h = 11$ units, $A = (40)(11) = 440$ units^2. **6.** Using the formula $A = \frac{1}{2}h(b_1 + b_2)$ with height h and bases a and c, $A = \frac{1}{2}h(a + c)$. **7. See below. 8. See below. 9.** The perimeter of the square is $p = 4s = 4(10) = 40$ units. The circumference of the circle is $C = 2\pi r = 2\pi(5)$ $= 10\pi$. The difference is $p - C = 40 - 10\pi \approx 8.6$ units. **10.** The area of the circle is $A = \pi r^2 = \pi(5)^2 = 25\pi$. The area of the square is $A = s^2 = 10^2 = 100$. The probability that a point inside the square is also inside the circle is $\frac{25\pi}{100} =$ $\frac{\pi}{4} \approx .785$. **11.** The entire circumference is $C = 2\pi r = 2\pi 20$ $= 40\pi$. $\overarc{CD}$ represents 45° or $\frac{1}{8}$ of the circle, so the length of $\overarc{CD}$ is $\frac{40\pi}{8} = 5\pi \approx 15.7$ units. **12.** m$\overarc{CBD} = 360° - m\overarc{CD}$. Since $\overarc{CD}$ is $\frac{1}{8}$ of the circle, or 45°, then m$\overarc{CBD} = 360° - 45°$ $= 315°$. **13.** There seem to be 29 unit squares inside the island and 36 unit squares on the island's boundary, and each unit square represents $10^2 = 100$ miles^2. Adding half the number of boundary squares to the number of squares inside the island, and multiplying by 100, the area of Hawaii can be approximated as 4700 square miles. (Answers may vary.) **14. See below. 15.** Using the formula $A = \pi r^2$ with $r = 80$ miles, $A = \pi(80)^2 = 6400\pi \approx 20,100$ miles^2. **16.** In yards, 9 ft by 15 ft is 3 yds by 5 yds; that product is 15 yds.^{2} **17.** If the perimeter of a square is 2640 ft, then each side has length $\frac{2640}{4} = 660$ ft. The area of a square with side 660 ft is $660^2 =$ 435,600 ft^2. **18. See below. 19.a.** $11^2 + 60^2 = 121 + 3600$ $= 3721 = 61^2$. Since $a^2 + b^2 = c^2$, the three lengths (11, 60, 61) can be the lengths of sides of a right triangle. **b.** The statement, if $a^2 + b^2 = c^2$, then a, b, and c can be the lengths of sides of a right triangle, is the Pythagorean Converse Theorem. **20. See below. 21. See below.**

1. sample:

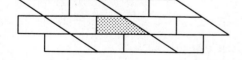

7.

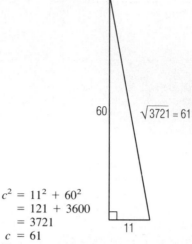

$c^2 = 11^2 + 60^2$
$= 121 + 3600$
$= 3721$
$c = 61$

The perimeter of the triangle is $60 + 11 + 61 = 132$ units.

8.

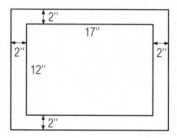

The outside dimensions are $12 + 4$ and $17 + 4$, or 16″ and 21″. The outside perimeter is $2(16 + 21) = 2(37) = 74″$.

14.

$x^2 + 1.8^2 = 5^2$
$x^2 = 25 - 3.24$
$= 21.76$
$x \approx 4.66476$
≈ 4.7 meters

18.

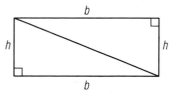

The area of a rectangle with height h and base b is $A = bh$. Two right triangles, each with base b and height h, make up that rectangle, so a formula for the area of either right triangle is $A = \frac{1}{2}bh$.

20.

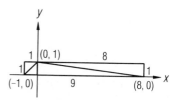

The horizontal base has length 9, and the height is 1, so the area of the triangle is $A = \frac{1}{2}bh = \frac{1}{2}(9)(1) = 4.5$ units^2

21.

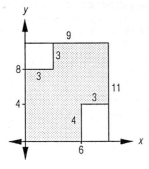

The area of the shaded octagon is the area of the large rectangle ($\ell = 9$, $w = 11$, $A = \ell \times w = 99$), less the area of the small rectangle at the upper left ($\ell = 3$, $w = 3$, $A = \ell \times w = 9$), then less the area of the small rectangle at the lower right ($\ell = 3$, $w = 4$, $A = \ell \times w = 12$). So the area of the octagon is $99 - 9 - 12 = 78$ units^2.

The chart below keys the **Progress Self-Test** questions to the objectives in the **Chapter 8 Review** on pages 410–413. This will enable you to locate those **Chapter 8 Review** questions that correspond to questions you missed on the **Progress Self-Test**. The lesson where the material is covered is also indicated in the chart.

Question	1	2	3	4	5–6	7	8	9	10	11–12
Objective	A	E	C	D	D	G	J	F	M	F
Lesson	8-2	8-3	8-1	8-5	8-6	8-7	8-1	8-8	8-9	8-8

Question	13	14	15	16–17	18	19	20	21
Objective	B	K	M	L	I	H	N	N
Lesson	8-4	8-7	8-9	8-3	8-5	8-7	8-5	8-3

CHAPTER 8 REVIEW (pp. 410–413)

1. See below. **3.** See below. **5.** $230,000 \pm 2500$ sq ft **7.** 32 units **9.** 235 meters **11.** 10 cm **13.** 12.5 units and 25 units **15.** 625 sq ft **17.** $288x^2$ units^2 **19.** 84 units^2 **21.** 20 mm **23.** $3.5s$ units **25. a.** $C = 20\pi$ units, $A = 100\pi$ units^2 **b.** $C \approx 62.83$ units, $A \approx 314.16$ units^2 **27.** 24 units **29. a.** $20°$ **b.** $160°$ **c.** $200°$ **31.** $\sqrt{5} \approx 2.24$ units **33.** $13x + x\sqrt{85} \approx 22.2x$ units **35.** 75 cm **37.** Yes **39.** No **41.** Area of trapezoid: $A = \frac{1}{2}h(b_1 + b_2)$, but in a parallelogram $b_1 = b_2 = b$, so $A = \frac{1}{2}h(b + b) = \frac{1}{2}h \cdot 2b = hb$. **43.** (b) **45.** $8s^2$ units^2 **47.** 80 cm **49.** 37 feet **51.** ≈ 8.7 ft **53.** 44,100 m^2 **55.** 780,000 sq ft **57.** $\frac{1}{9}$ or $11.\overline{1}\%$ **59.** 1885 feet **61.** $\frac{100}{\pi} \cong 32$ ft **63.** 2025 units^2 **65.** 32 units^2

1. sample:

3. sample:

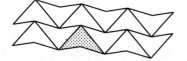

LESSON 9-1 (pp. 414–420)

11. a. always (unless the center of gravity is not above the triangular region determined by the legs) **b.** when the ends of the legs are coplanar **c.** Through three noncollinear points, there is exactly one plane. (part f) **13.** by measuring the length of a segment perpendicular to both walls with one endpoint on each wall **15.** sample: the floor and a wall **17.** sample: the ceiling and intersecting line of the south and west walls **19. See below. 21. a.** 90° **b.** 30° **23.** A polygon is the union of three or more segments in the same plane such that each segment intersects exactly two others, one at each of its endpoints. **25.** A figure is a rectangle if and only if it is a quadrilateral with four right angles. **27.** $x = 67.5$, $y = 112.5$

19. sample:

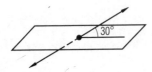

LESSON 9-2 (pp. 421–426)

3. a. edge **b.** six **c.** *ABCD* and *GHEF*, or *ABHG* and *DCEF*, or *ADFG* and *BCEH* **d.** 12. **e.** samples: $\overline{AD}$ and $\overline{HE}$, $\overline{AG}$ and $\overline{CE}$ **5–7. See below. 9.** box **11.** solid right prism (often hexagonal) **13. See below. 15. a.** 15 units **b.** $36\pi \approx 113.1$ square units **17. See below. 19.** intersecting planes **21.** an infinite number of planes **23. See below. 25.** $2w(l + h)$ **27.** $\pi r(r + 2h)$

5. sample:

7. sample:

13. sample:

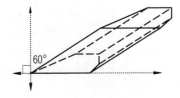

17.

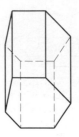

23. sample:

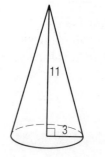

LESSON 9-3 (pp. 427–431)

1. a. *ABDE* **b.** *C* **c.** $\overline{BC}$ or $\overline{AC}$ or $\overline{DC}$ or $\overline{EC}$ **d.** $\triangle BCD$ or $\triangle ACB$ or $\triangle ACE$ or $\triangle DCE$ **3. a.** right cone **b.** $\overrightarrow{MO}$ **c.** $\overline{MN}$ or $\overline{ML}$ **d.** *M* **e.** $\odot O$ **f.** *MO* **g.** *ML* or *MN* **5.** hexagonal pyramid **7. See below. 9. a.** 10 units **b.** $\sqrt{116} \approx 10.77$ units **11. See below. 13. See below. 15. a.** above the vertex **b.** left of front in the plane of the base **c.** in front of a corner in the plane of the base **17.** In a right cylinder, the direction of the translation is perpendicular to the base; in an oblique cylinder it is not. **19. a.** Triangle-Sum Theorem **b.** definition of perpendicular (sufficient condition) **c.** definition of right triangle (sufficient condition) **d.** Pythagorean Theorem **21.** Larger has six times the area of smaller. **23.** $h(l + w)$

7. sample:

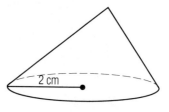

11. a.

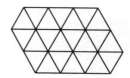

b. $\sqrt{130} \approx 11.4$ cm **c.** $9\pi \approx 28.3$ cm²

13. sample:

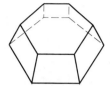

LESSON 9-4 (pp. 433–438)
5. the intersection of a sphere and a plane not containing the center of the sphere **7. See below. 9.** the plane sections of two congruent right conical surfaces, with the same axis, joined at their vertices: circle, ellipse, parabola, and hyperbola **13–21. See below. 23. a.** 10 **b.** 10 **c.** $\sqrt{200} \approx$ 14.14 units **25. a.** the point Q such that ℓ is the perpendicular bisector of $\overline{PQ}$ **b.** A plane figure F is a reflection-symmetric figure if and only if there is a line m such that $r_m(F) = F$.

7. a. sample:

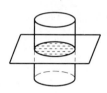

b. They are congruent.

13. a. sample:

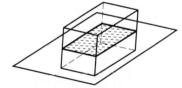

b. sample:

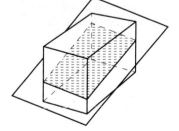

c. rectangles

15. a. sample:

b. sample:

c. circle and ellipse

17.

21. sample:

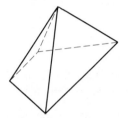

LESSON 9-5 (pp. 439–443)
1. a. Yes **b.** infinitely many **3. a.** Yes **b.** infinitely many
5. a. Yes **b.** infinitely many **11.** 9 **13. See below. 15. See below. 17.** solid right cylinder **19. a.** a square pyramid **b.** *FOUR* **c.** Z **d.** $\overline{ZF}$, $\overline{ZO}$, $\overline{ZU}$, $\overline{ZR}$ **e.** $\triangle ZRF$, $\triangle ZRU$, $\triangle ZUO$, $\triangle ZOF$, *FOUR* **21. See below. 23.** $x(xy - 4)$

13.

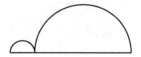

15. a. sample:

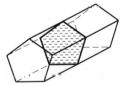

b. sample:

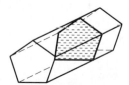

c. Part (a) is a pentagon congruent to the bases. Part (b) is a pentagon.

21. a.

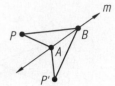

b. kite

LESSON 9-6 (pp. 444–448)

3–9. See below. 11. ≈ 28 ft **13.** 9 **15.** 6 units **17.** regular heptagonal prism **19. a.** $\sqrt{11} \approx 3.32$ units **b.** $\sqrt{22} \approx 4.69$ units **21. See below. 23.** $\pi(r^2 + 2rh - h)$

3.

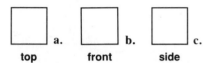

a. top **b.** front **c.** side

5.

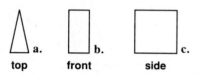

a. top **b.** front **c.** side

7. a.

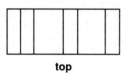

top

b.

front

c.

side

9. sample:

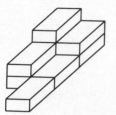

21.

Conclusions	Justifications
1. $\overline{AB} \cong \overline{CD}$	Properties of a Parallelogram Theorem
2. $\overline{AB} \parallel \overline{CD}$	definition of parallelogram (meaning)
3. $\angle ABQ \cong \angle CDQ$, $\angle QAB \cong \angle QCD$	$\parallel$ Lines $\Rightarrow$ AIA = Theorem
4. $\triangle AQB \cong \triangle CQD$	ASA Congruence Theorem (steps 1 and 3)

LESSON 9-7 (pp. 449–455)

5. a. back **b.** up **c.** left **7. See below. 9. a.** cone without a base **b.** Answers may vary slightly. **11. See below. 13. a.** 9 **b.** 16 **c.** 9 **15. See below. 17. a.** 3 **b.** 3 **c.** middle, left section **19. a.** Yes **b.** one **21. a.** 4 units **b.** 3 units **c.** 12 units² **23.** definition of a rhombus (sufficient condition)

7.

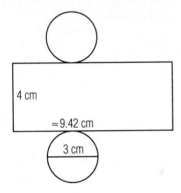

11. sample:

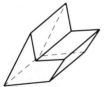

15. sample:

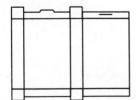

846

LESSON 9-8 (pp. 455–459)

3. 124 **5. See below. 9. See below. 11. See below. 13.** surface, polyhedron, prism, right prism, box **15. See below.** **17. See below. 19. a.** $\sqrt{136} \approx 11.7$ units **b.** $\sqrt{1800} \approx 42.4$ square units **21.** 23

5. sample:

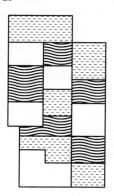

9. sample:

11. sample:

15. sample:

17. sample:

The chart below keys the **Progress Self-Test** questions to the objectives in the **Chapter 9 Review** on pages 462–465. This will enable you to locate those **Chapter 9 Review** questions that correspond to questions you missed on the **Progress Self-Test**. The lesson where the material is covered is also indicated in the chart.

Question	1–5	6	7–8	9	10	11–12	13	14	15
Objective	G	A	A	B	J	G	D	C	B
Lesson	9-2	9-1	9-2	9-4	9-5	9-3	9-7	9-6	9-4

Question	16	17	18	19	20	21		22	23
Objective	D	E	E	H	I	K		F	L
Lesson	9-7	9-3	9-2	9-7	9-2	(prev. course)		9-6	9-8

CHAPTER 9 PROGRESS SELF-TEST (p. 461)

1. The figure is a prism, since it has parallel bases. Moreover, the bases are triangles, and are ⊥ to the planes of the sides. So the figure is a right triangular prism. **2.** The edges are $\overline{AD}$, $\overline{BE}$, $\overline{CF}$, $\overline{AB}$, $\overline{BC}$, $\overline{AC}$, $\overline{DE}$, $\overline{EF}$, and $\overline{DF}$; there are 9 edges. **3.** The faces are *ABC, DEF, ABED, BCFE,* and *ACFD;* there are 5 faces. **4.** The vertices are *A, B, C, D, E,* and *F;* there are 6 vertices. **5.** A solid is the union of a surface and all the points in the interior of the surface. **6–10. See below.** **11. a.** There are four lateral edges; $\overline{GI}$, $\overline{GJ}$, $\overline{GK}$, and $\overline{GH}$. **b.** The vertex is point *G.* **12–16. See below.** **17.a.** The height of the cone is represented by segment $\overline{AD}$. **b.** The base of the cone is a circle with radius *OB* = 10 cm. The area of the base is $A = \pi r^2 = \pi(10)^2 = 100\pi \approx 314.16$ cm². **18.a.** *FIHG* is a rectangle with height 22″. The length is the leg of a right triangle with hypotenuse 9″ and leg 4″, or $\sqrt{9^2 - 4^2} = \sqrt{81 - 16} = \sqrt{65}$ inches. So Area(*FIHG*) = $22\sqrt{65} \approx 177.4$ inches². **b.** The area of right triangle *EFG* is one-half the product of the legs, or $\frac{1}{2}(4)(\sqrt{65}) = 2\sqrt{65} \approx 16.12$ inches². **19.** A box is a hexahedron, which is a prism, which is a polyhedron. A box is not a pyramid; that is choice (b). **20. See below.** **21.** $\pi r^2 + 2\pi rh = \pi r(r + 2h)$ **22–23. See below.**

6. sample:

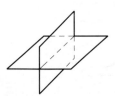

7. sample:

8. sample:

9. sample:

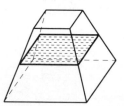

10. view from above:

There are 4 symmetry planes. Each is ⊥ to the bases of the pyramid. Two planes bisect opposite pairs of angles of the bases, and two planes bisect opposite pairs of sides of the bases.

12.

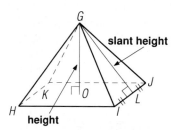

GO is the height of the pyramid and *GL* is the slant height.

13.

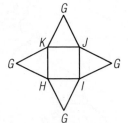

14.

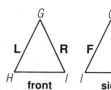
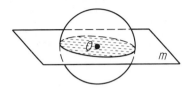

15.

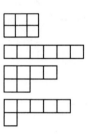

The intersection of sphere O and plane m containing O is called a great circle of sphere O.

16. samples:

20.

The figure is a solid, right, square prism.

22. sample:

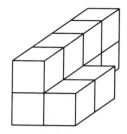

a. The building is two stories tall.
b. It is 4 sections from front to back.
c. The tallest parts are all the sections on the left side.

23. sample:

CHAPTER 9 REVIEW (pp. 462–465)
1-13. See below. **15.** (c) and (d) only **17.** See below.
19. a. ≈ 62.4 square units **b.** 8 units **21. a.** $9\pi \approx 28.3$ square
cm **b.** $\sqrt{32} \approx 5.66$ cm **23.** See below. **25. a.** 2 **b.** 3
c. back section **27. a.** box, rectangular parallelipiped, or
hexahedron **b.** twelve **c.** sample: $\overline{BC}$ and $\overline{HE}$ **29. a.** 7
b. 13 **c.** 2 **d.** octahedron **31.** Yes; any face could be the base.
33. solid pentagonal prism **35.** sphere **37.** rectangular solid
39. a. Yes **b.** infinitely many **41.** See below. **43.** $\ell w(h + 2)$
45. $\pi r^2(4 + r)$ **47.** in a plane or on a sphere **49.** See below.

1. sample:

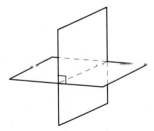

3. sample:

5.

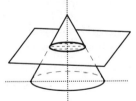

7. a. sample:

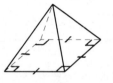

b. sample:

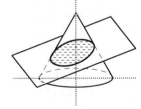

c. Part a is a circle; part b is an ellipse.

9. a. sample:

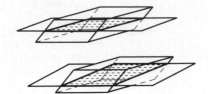

b. sample:

c. part a is a parallelogram; part b is a parallelogram.

11. a.   **b.**   **c.**

top   front   right

13. a.   **b.**   **c.**

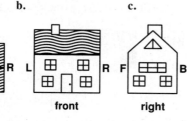

top   front   right

17. sample:

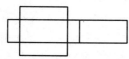

23. a.

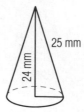

25 mm
24 mm

b. $49\pi \approx 153.9$ square mm

41.

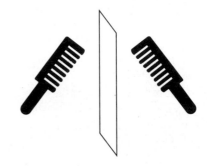

49. sample:

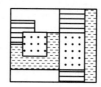

LESSON 10-1 (pp. 466–472)
3. 1040 cm² **5. a.** cube **b.** 100 square units **c.** 150 square units **7. a.** right cylinder **b.** $15\pi \approx 47$ square units **c.** $19.5\pi \approx 61$ square units **9. a.** $B = \pi r^2$ **b.** L.A. $= 2\pi rh$ **c.** S.A. $= 2\pi rh + 2\pi r^2$, or $2\pi r(h + r)$ **11.** L.A. ≈ 154 in.²; S.A. ≈ 174 in.² **13.** surface area **15.** surface area **17.** 598 cm² **19.** $6s^2$ **21.** Exactly: $2 \cdot \frac{4375\pi}{45} \approx 611$ gallons; about 610–620 gallons are needed. **23.** the point in the interior of the polygon that is equidistant from all of its vertices **25.** $\frac{8}{27}$

LESSON 10-2 (pp. 473–477)
1. See below. **7.** sides of the base **9.** the center of the base **11. a.** ≈ 587.4 ft **b.** $\approx 887,000$ ft² **13.** (a) **15.** See below. **17.** See below. **19. a.** ≈ 47.5 cm² **b.** ≈ 164 cm² **21.** See below. **23.** See below.

1. sample:

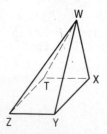

W
T   X
Z   Y

15. a.

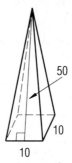

50
10
10

b. 1000 units² **c.** 1100 units²

17. a.

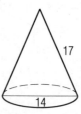

17
14

b. $119\pi \approx 374$ units²
c. $168\pi \approx 528$ units²

23. a.

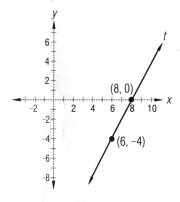

b. 2 **c.** $-\frac{1}{2}$

LESSON 10-3 (pp. 478–482)

1. 176,400 cm³ **3.** No **7.** $\sqrt[3]{50}$ **9. a.** adds 84 in.² **b.** no change **11.** 12 inches **13.** 7.57 **15. a.** 3 **b.** 9 **c.** 27 **17. See below. 19. a.** $156\pi \approx 490$ in.² **b.** 4 square feet **21. a.** polyhedron **b.** radius **c.** vertex

17. a.

b. $48\pi \approx 150.8$ units²

LESSON 10-4 (pp. 483–487)

7. $2x^2 + 21x + 27$ **9.** $a^3 + 6a^2 + 11a + 6$ **11.** multiplied by 3 **13.** The volume is increased by 6 times the product of the width and the height. **15. a.** Bag X holds about twice as much as bag Y. **b.** Bag X should cost about twice as much as bag Y. **17.** $y^2 - x^2$ **19.** $a^2 + b^2 + c^2 + 2ab + 2ac + 2bc$ **21.** 1.46 **23.** about 1.8 cm³ **25.** $\pm\sqrt{\frac{10}{\pi}} \approx \pm 1.8$

LESSON 10-5 (pp. 488–493)

3. (d) **7.** $225\pi \approx 707$ cubic units **9.** 500 m³ **11.** 210 ft³ **13. See below. 15.** 189 m³ **17.** The plane sections parallel to but not including the base will not be of the same area. **19.** doubles the volume **21.** $4x^2 + 3xy + 28x - 10y^2 - 35y$ **23.** 20 cm³ **25.** 108 square units **27. See below.**

13. Answers may vary; samples are shown here. The volume of each is 252π cubic units.

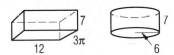

27.

Conclusions	Justifications
1. $\overline{CE} \cong \overline{CE}$	Reflexive Property of Congruence
2. $\angle FEC \cong \angle DCE$	// Lines $\Rightarrow$ AIA = Theorem
3. $\triangle FEC \cong \triangle DCE$	SAS Congruence Theorem (steps 1,2,and given)
4. $\angle FCE \cong \angle DEC$	CPCF Theorem

LESSON 10-6 (pp. 494–498)

7. L.A. = $2\pi rh$ **11. a.** L.A. = $\frac{1}{2}\ell(2\pi r) = \pi r\ell$ **b.** S.A. = $\pi r\ell + \pi r^2 = \pi r(\ell + r)$ **13. a.** $\sqrt{(18)(9)(6)(3)} = 54$ units² **b.** The triangle is a right triangle, so Area = $\frac{1}{2}hb = \frac{1}{2}(9)(12)$ = 54 units². **15.** $\sqrt{600 \cdot 200 \cdot 200 \cdot 200} \approx 69,282$ units² **17.** $39,366\pi \approx 123,672$ cubic units **19.** The volume is decreased by $8a^2$ cubic units. **21. See below. 23.** $-\frac{b}{a}$

21. a.

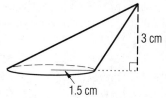

3 cm

1.5 cm

b. $16 + 2.25\pi \approx 23$ cm²

LESSON 10-7 (pp. 499–504)

3. 114 units³ **5.** $\frac{32\pi}{3} \approx 33.5$ ft³ **7.** 56 units³ **9.** $\sqrt{\frac{24}{\pi}} \approx 2.8$ cm **11.** $\approx 116,000,000$ ft³ **13.** The volume is multiplied by 49. **15. a.** 6 units **b.** $128\pi \approx 402$ units³ **17.** L.A. = $4(\frac{1}{2}\ell s) = 2\ell s$ **19.** $(x + z)(y + 8) = xy + 8x + zy + 8z$ **21.** 15

LESSON 10-8 (pp. 505–509)

1. a. $20\pi \approx 62.8$ units² **b.** $20\pi \approx 62.8$ units² **7.** 4 m **9. a.** 10.7, or almost 11 days **b.** 4.3, or just over 4 days **11.** $\frac{500\pi}{3} \approx 524$ units³ **13.** Additive Property **15.** boxes, cylinders, prisms **17. a.** True **b.** False **19. a.** It is multiplied by 9. **b.** It is multiplied by 27. **21. a.** 64 units² **b.** 16 **c.** 8 **d.** none **e.** none **23.** x

LESSON 10-9 (pp. 510–513)

5. a. 10,000 π sq in. **b.** 31,416 sq in. **7.** $\approx 1.84\%$ **9.** $\approx 75\%$ of the surface area of the sphere yields a cost of about $9200. **11. a.** The moon has about $\frac{1}{16}$ the surface area of the earth. **b.** The moon has about $\frac{1}{64}$ the volume of the earth. **13.** They are the same; both are $4\pi r^2$. **15. a. See below. b.** $\frac{62.5\pi}{3} \approx$ 65.45 cubic cm **17.** The wider, shorter jar holds twice as much jam. **19.** 22.2 units **21. See below.**

21. $A' = (6, 3)$; $B' = (-3, -3)$; $C' = (0, -9)$

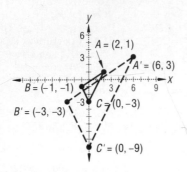

15. a.

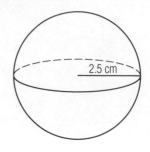

2.5 cm

b. $\frac{62.5\pi}{3} \approx 65.45$ cubic cm

CHAPTER 10 PROGRESS SELF-TEST (p. 515)

1–2. See below. 3. Using $V = \frac{4}{3}\pi r^3$ with $r = \frac{1}{2}(620) = 310$ mi, $V = \frac{4}{3}\pi(310)^3 = \frac{119,164,000\pi}{3} \approx 124,788,249 \approx 1.25 \times 10^8$ mi³. **4. See below. 5.** The figure is a right cylinder with radius 3″ and height 20″. Using $V = Bh$, $V = \pi(3^2)(20) = 180\pi \approx 565.5$ in.³ **6.** Using $V = \frac{1}{3}Bh = \frac{1}{3}\pi r^2 h$ with $r = 8$ and $h = 15$, $V = \frac{1}{3}\pi(8)^2(15) = 320\pi \approx 1005.3$ units³. **7–10. See below. 11.** Using S.A. $= 4\pi r^2$ with S.A. $= 100\pi$, $100\pi = 4\pi r^2$ so $25 = r^2$ and $r = 5$ units. **12.** $\sqrt[3]{400} = 400$ $\boxed{y^x}$ 3 $\boxed{1/x}$ $\boxed{=}$ 7.368063 $\approx$ 7. **13.** Cavalieri's Principle: Let I and II be two solids included between parallel planes. If every plane P parallel to the given planes intersects I and II in sections with the same area, then Volume (I) = Volume (II). **14. See below. 15.** The ratio of surface areas is the square of the ratio of similitude, so Jupiter's surface area is 11^2 or 121 times as large as the earth's. **16.** S.A. $=$ L.A. $+ B$ is the formula for a figure with one base, so it is the formula for pyramids and cones. **17.** L.A. $= ph$ is the formula for right cylindric solids, so it is the formula for prisms (including boxes and cubes) and right cylinders. **18.** The volume can be expressed as a product of its three dimensions or as a sum of the volumes of the eight small boxes. So $V = (x + 1)(y + 2)(z + 6) = xyz + yz + 2z + 2xz + 6xy + 6y + 12 + 12x$.

1. a. sample

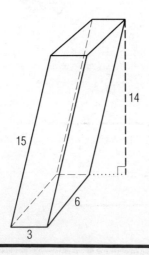

14

15

6

3

The formula for the volume of a prism is $V = Bh$.
b. Using $V = Bh$ with $B = (6)(3) = 18$ and $h = 14$, $V = (18)(14) = 252$ cm³.

2. a.

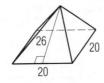

26   20

20

The formula for the lateral area of a regular prism is L.A. $= \frac{1}{2}p\ell$.
b. Using L.A. $= \frac{1}{2}p\ell$ with $p = 4(20) = 80$ and $\ell = 26$, L.A. $= \frac{1}{2}(80)(26) = 1040$ units².

4.

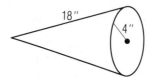

18″   4″

Using L.A. $= \frac{1}{2}C\ell$, with $C = 2\pi r = 8\pi$ and $\ell = 18$, L.A. $= \frac{1}{2}(8\pi)(18) = 72\pi \approx 226$ in².

7. Using L.A. $= ph$ with $p = 32$ and $h = 30$, L.A. $= (32)(30) = 960$ units².

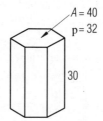

$A = 40$
$p = 32$

30

8. Using $V = Bh$ with $B = 40$ and $h = 30$, $V = (40)(30) = 1200$ units³.

9.

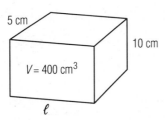

Using $V = \ell wh$, $400 = \ell(5)(10)$ so $400 = 50\ell$ and $\ell = 8$ cm.

10. Using the figure from Question 9,
S.A. $= 2B + ph$
$= 2(5 \times 8) + 2(5 + 8)(10)$
$= 80 + 260$
$= 340$ cm^2

14.

By the Pyramid-Cone Volume Formula, the volume of the pyramid is one-third the volume of the prism.

The chart below keys the **Progress Self-Test** questions to the objectives in the **Chapter 10 Review** on pages 516–519. This will enable you to locate those **Chapter 10 Review** questions that correspond to questions you missed on the **Progress Self-Test**. The lesson where the material is covered is also indicated in the chart.

Question	1a	1b	2a	2b	3	4	5	6	7	8
Objective	A	B	A	C	J	I	J	C	B	B
Lesson	10-1	10-5	10-2	10-2	10-8	10-2	10-5	10-7	10-1	10-5

Question	9	10	11	12	13	14	15	16-17	18
Objective	B	B	D	E	H	H	G	F	K
Lesson	10-5	10-1	10-9	10-3	10-5	10-7	10-4	10-6	10-4

CHAPTER 10 REVIEW (pp. 516–519)
1. See below. **3.** See below. **5. a.** $72\pi \approx 226$ units^2 **b.** $104\pi \approx 327$ units^2 **c.** $144\pi \approx 452$ units^3 **7.** 720 units^3 **9.** 150 units^2 **11.** S.A. $= \pi(3.5)\sqrt{112.25} + \pi(3.5)^2 \approx 155$ units^2; Volume $= 10 \cdot (3.5)^2 \cdot \frac{\pi}{3} \approx 128.3$ units^3 **13. a.** 50 units **b.** 8000 units^2 **c.** 14,400 units^2 **15.** 200 units^2 **17.** S.A. $= 20{,}736\pi \approx 65{,}144$ units^2; Volume $= 497{,}644\pi \approx 1{,}563{,}458$ units^3 **19.** 6 units **21.** 30 **23.** 5.04 **25.** $s^2 + 2s\ell$ **27. a.** It is multiplied by 9. **b.** It is multiplied by 27. **29.** The new volume is 4 times as large. **31.** Plane sections at any level other than at the bases will not have the same area.
33. a. True **b.** False **35.** 8 ft^2 **37.** $200\sqrt{5000} \approx 14{,}142$ cubits^2 **39.** $300\pi \approx 942.5$ cm^3 **41.** $\frac{500{,}000}{3} \approx 167{,}000$ cubits^3
43. See below. **45.** $(2x + 7)(x + 12) = 2x^2 + 7x + 24x + 84 = 2x^2 + 31x + 84$
1.

3.

43. $20xy + 15x + 8y + 6$

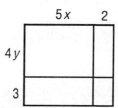

LESSON 11-1 (pp. 520–526)

7–13. See below. 15. (5, -2) **17. a.** $200\pi \approx 628.3$ sq ft
b. ≈ 1257 bushels **19.** Pythagorean Theorem **21. a.** 450 **b.** 450

7. Conclusions

1. slope of $\overline{XY} = -\frac{1}{2}$
   slope of $\overline{XZ} = 2$
2. The product of their slopes is -1, so $\overline{XY} \perp \overline{XZ}$.
3. $\triangle XYZ$ is a right triangle.

Justification

definition of slope (meaning)

Perpendicular Lines and Slopes Theorem

definition of right triangle (sufficient condition)

9. Conclusions

1. slope of $\overline{EF} = 1$
   slope of $\overline{FG} = -1$
   slope of $\overline{GH} = 1$
   slope of $\overline{EH} = -1$
2. The product of their slopes is -1, so $\overline{EF} \perp \overline{FG}$, $\overline{FG} \perp \overline{GH}$, $\overline{GH} \perp \overline{EH}$, and $\overline{EH} \perp \overline{EF}$.
3. $EFGH$ is a rectangle.

Justifications

definition of slope (meaning)

Perpendicular Lines and Slopes Theorem

definition of a rectangle (sufficient condition)

11. Conclusions

1. slope of $\overline{WX} = 0$
   slope of $\overline{XY} = \frac{c}{b}$
   slope of $\overline{YZ} = 0$
   slope of $\overline{ZW} = \frac{c}{b}$
2. $\overline{WX} \parallel \overline{YZ}, \overline{XY} \parallel \overline{ZW}$
3. $WXYZ$ is a parallelogram.

Justifications

definition of slope (meaning)

Parallel Lines and Slopes Theorem

definition of parallelogram (sufficient condition)

13. a.

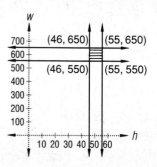

b. The graph is the rectangular region with vertices (46, 550), (55, 550), (55, 650), and (46, 650).

LESSON 11-2 (pp. 527–531)

1. 11 **3.** $\sqrt{146} \approx 12.08$ **5.** $\sqrt{52} \approx 7.21$ **7.** $\sqrt{65} \approx 8.06$ miles **9. See below. 11. a.** False; sample counterexample: Let $x_1 = 4$; $x_2 = 1$. Then $|x_2 - x_1| = 3$, but $x_2 - x_1 = -3$.
b. True **c.** True **d.** True **13.** $BC = \sqrt{145}$ and $BA = \sqrt{145}$.

Thus, by the definition of circle (sufficient condition), C and A are on the same circle with center B. **15. See below. 17.** (12.25, 13) **19.** The area of the triangle is one-half the area of the parallelogram. **21.** 90

9. Conclusions

1. $AB = \sqrt{20}$
   $BC = \sqrt{20}$
   $CD = \sqrt{212}$
   $AD = \sqrt{212}$
2. $AB = BC$, $CD = AD$
3. $ABCD$ is a kite.

Justifications

Distance Formula

Transitive Property of Equality

definition of kite (sufficient condition)

15. Conclusion

1. slope of $\overline{PQ} = -\frac{1}{2}$
   slope of $\overline{QR} = 2$
2. $\overline{PQ} \perp \overline{QR}$
3. $\triangle PQR$ is a right triangle.

Justifications

definition of slope (meaning)

Perpendicular Lines and Slopes Theorem

definition of right triangle (sufficient condition)

LESSON 11-3 (pp. 532–536)

1. a. Yes. **b.** Yes. **c.** No. **d.** Yes. **3. See below. 9. a.** (-6, -2) **b.** 1 **c.** sample: (-6, -3) **11–13. See below. 15.** $41x$ **17. See below. 19.** They are collinear. **21. See below.**

3. a. $\sqrt{(x - 7)^2 + (y - 1)^2}$ **b.** $(x - 7)^2 + (y - 1)^2 = 25$

c.

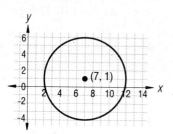

d. samples: (2, 1), (12, 1), (7, 6), (7, -4)

11. (0, 5), (3, 4), (4, 3) (5, 0), (4, -3), (3, -4), (0, -5), (-3, -4), (-4, -3), (-5, 0) (-4, 3), (-3, 4)

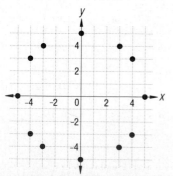

13.

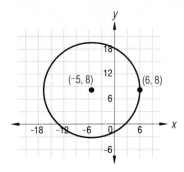

17.

Conclusions	Justifications
1. slope of $\overline{TQ} = \frac{9b}{5a}$	definition of slope (meaning)
slope of $\overline{SR} = \frac{9b}{5a}$	
2. $\overline{TQ} \parallel \overline{SR}$	Parallel Lines and Slopes Theorem
3. $QRST$ is a trapezoid.	definition of trapezoid (sufficient condition)

21. sample:

LESSON 11-4 (pp. 537–543)

1. $\frac{350}{3} = 116\frac{2}{3}$ **3.** 1634 **5.** (5.5, 5) **7. a.** (5, -6) **b.** The distance from (12, -4) to (5, -6) = $\sqrt{53}$. The distance from (-2, -8) to (5, -6) = $\sqrt{53}$. The slope between (12, -4) and (5, -6) = $\frac{-2}{-7} = \frac{2}{7}$. The slope between (-2, -8) and (5, -6) = $\frac{2}{7}$. **9. See below. 11.** $\frac{a + c - 2a}{2}$ or $\frac{c - a}{2}$ **13.** $\frac{2d - (b + d)}{2c - (a + c)}$ or $\frac{d - b}{c - a}$ **15.** $-\frac{23}{5} = -4.6$ **17.** 46 or 54, depending on which piece was cut from each end. **19. a.** (0, 0) **b.** $\sqrt{75} \approx 8.66$ units **c.** sample: $(\sqrt{75}, 0)$ **d.** 75π **21.** (3, -5) **23. a.** 2560 cm³ **b.** ≈ 1249.6 cm² **25. a.** x **b.** $2x$ **c.** $x\sqrt{5}$

9. a. $L = (6.5, 0)$, $M = (8, 6)$, $N = (1.5, 6)$

b.

Conclusions	Justifications
1. slope of $\overrightarrow{LM} = 4$	definition of slope (meaning)
slope of $\overline{DE} = 4$	
2. $\overline{LM} \parallel \overline{DE}$	Parallel Lines and Slopes Theorem

c.

Conclusions	Justifications
1. slope of $\overline{MN} = 0$	definition of slope (meaning)
slope of $\overline{EF} = 0$	
2. $\overline{MN} \parallel \overline{EF}$	Parallel Lines and Slopes Theorem

d.

Conclusions	Justifications
1. $MN = 6.5$	Distance Formula
$EF = 13$	
2. Since $6.5 = \frac{1}{2}(13)$, $MN = \frac{1}{2}EF$.	Substitution

LESSON 11-5 (pp. 544–549)

1. $AL = AN = BC = 6$ **5. See below 7. See below 9.** $(a^2 + b^2)$, 4, $a^2 + b^2$ **11. See below 13.** 30 units **15.** $DC = 20$, $EC = RT = 40$, $YD = 29$, $EY = RY = 21$, $ER = TC = 42$ **17.** (3.2, 3) **19. a.** 13 **b.** $-\frac{12}{5} = -2.4$ **c.** (8.5, 27) **21.** $(x + 2)^2 + y^2 = 25$

5. sample:

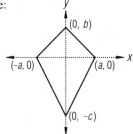

7. sample:

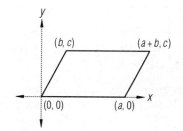

11. samples:

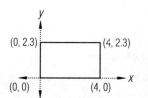

LESSON 11-6 (pp. 550–556)

3. See below. 5. $\sqrt{227} \approx 15.07$ units **7.** (4, -2, -1) **9. See below. 11.** $\sqrt{149} + \sqrt{338} + \sqrt{275} \approx 47.17$ **13.** $\sqrt{2025} = 45$ inches **15.** (0, 0), (12, 0) and (0, 16) or (0, 0), (0, 12) and (16, 0) **17. See below. 19. a.** (14, 5) **b.** $\sqrt{109} \approx 10.44$ units **c.** True **21.** (5.4, 6)

3.

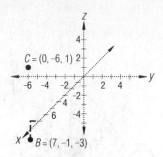

$C = (0, -6, 1)$

$B = (7, -1, -3)$

9. a.

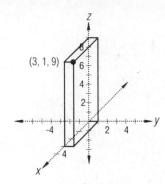

$(3, 1, 9)$

b. 27 units^3

17.

Conclusions	Justifications
1. $\overline{PL} \parallel \overline{MN}$	Midpoint Connector Theorem
2. $\angle QLP \cong \angle QNM$	$\parallel$ lines $\Rightarrow$ corr. $\angle$s $=$

CHAPTER 11 PROGRESS SELF-TEST (p. 558)

1. $\overline{FD}$ connects the midpoints of $\overline{BC}$ and $\overline{AC}$, so $\overline{FD} \parallel \overline{AB}$ and $FD = \frac{1}{2}AB$ by the Midpoint Connector Theorem. $EB = \frac{1}{2}AB$ by the definition of midpoint (meaning), so $FD = EB$ by the Transitive Property of Equality. Then $EBDF$ is a parallelogram by the Sufficient Conditions for a Parallelogram Theorem, part d. **2.** If $AB = 11$ and $BC = 22.3$, then $AE = EB = 5.5$ and $BD = DC = 11.15$ by the definition of midpoint (meaning), and $FD = 5.5$ and $ED = 11.15$ by the Midpoint Connector Theorem (while the lengths $AF = FC = ED$ and $AC = 2AF$ are not known, a restriction is that $11.15 - 5.5 = 5.65 < AC < 11.15 + 5.5 = 16.65$.) **3. See below. 4.** The coordinates of the center of gravity are the means of the x- and y-coordinates: $(\frac{-5 + 6 + 9 + 6 + -8}{5}, \frac{4 + 4 + 0 + -4 + -4}{5}) = (\frac{8}{5}, \frac{0}{5}) = (1.6, 0)$. **5. a. b.** Comparing $(x + 1)^2 + (y - 9)^2 = 25$ with the general equation $(x - h)^2 + (y - k)^2 = r^2$, where (h, k) is the center and r is the radius, the center is $(-1, 9)$ and the radius is 5. **c.** Four points on the circle can be found by moving 5 units from the center; those four points are $(-6, 9)$, $(4, 9)$, $(-1, 14)$, and $(-1, 4)$. **6–7. See below. 8.** E is the midpoint of $\overline{HR}$; its coordinates are $(\frac{6 + 16}{2}, \frac{8 + 8}{2}) = (\frac{22}{2}, \frac{16}{2}) = (11, 8)$. I is the midpoint of $\overline{RB}$; its coordinates are $(\frac{10 + 16}{2}, \frac{0 + 8}{2}) = (\frac{26}{2}, \frac{8}{2}) = (13, 4)$. O is the midpoint of $\overline{MB}$; its coordinates are $(\frac{0 + 10}{2}, \frac{0 + 0}{2}) = (5, 0)$. U is the midpoint of $\overline{MH}$; its coordinates are $(\frac{0 + 6}{2}, \frac{0 + 8}{2}) = (3, 4)$. **9.** Here is one proof (of many possible) that $EIOU$ is a rectangle: First, $EI = UO$ and $UE = OI$ (by drawing $\overline{HB}$ and $\overline{MR}$, and using the Midpoint Connector Theorem). So $EIOU$ is a parallelogram by the Sufficient Conditions for a Parallelogram Theorem. The slope of $\overline{UO}$ is $\frac{y_2 - y_1}{x_2 - x_1} = \frac{0 - 4}{5 - 3} = \frac{-4}{2} = -2$ and the slope of $\overline{OI}$ is $\frac{y_2 - y_1}{x_2 - x_1} = \frac{4 - 0}{13 - 5} = \frac{4}{8} = \frac{1}{2}$. Then $\overline{UO} \perp \overline{OI}$ by the Perpendicular Lines and Slopes Theorem, so $EIOU$ is a rectangle by the definition of rectangle (sufficient condition).

10. See below. 11. For $P = (3, -1, 8)$ and $Q = (-4, 9, 0)$,
$\overline{PQ} = \sqrt{(x_2 - x_1)^2 + (y_2 - y_1)^2 + (z_2 - z_1)^2} = \sqrt{(-4 - 3)^2 + (9 - -1)^2 + (0 - 8)^2} = \sqrt{(-7)^2 + (10)^2 + (-8)^2} = \sqrt{49 + 100 + 64} = \sqrt{213} \approx 14.59$ units. **12.** Using the formula $(x - h)^2 + (y - k)^2 + (z - j)^2 = r^2$ with $(h, k, j) = (0, -19, 4)$ and $r = 6$, the equation is $(x - 0)^2 + (y - -19)^2 + (z - 4)^2 = 6^2$ or $x^2 + (y + 19)^2 + (z - 4)^2 = 36$. **13. See below. 14.** The midpoint of $\overline{WY}$ is $(\frac{0 + (2a + 2b)}{2}, \frac{0 + (2c)}{2}) = (a + b, c)$, and the midpoint of $\overline{XZ}$ is $(\frac{2b + 2a}{2}, \frac{2c + 0}{2}) = (a + b, c)$. So $\overline{WY}$ and $\overline{XZ}$ have the same midpoint.

3.

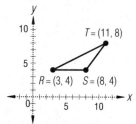

$T = (11, 8)$

$R = (3, 4)$ $S = (8, 4)$

$RS = |3 - 8| = |-5| = 5$

$ST = \sqrt{(x_2 - x_1)^2 + (y_2 - y_1)^2}$
$\qquad = \sqrt{(11 - 8)^2 + (8 - 4)^2}$
$\qquad = \sqrt{3^2 + 4^2}$
$\qquad = 5$

$RT = \sqrt{(x_2 - x_1)^2 + (y_2 - y_1)^2}$
$\qquad = \sqrt{(11 - 3)^2 + (8 - 4)^2}$
$\qquad = \sqrt{8^2 + 4^2}$
$\qquad = \sqrt{64 + 16}$
$\qquad = \sqrt{80}$

The perimeter is $5 + 5 + \sqrt{80} = 10 + \sqrt{80} \approx 18.94$ units.

6.

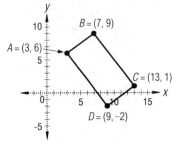

The slope of $\overline{AB} = \frac{y_2 - y_1}{x_2 - x_1} = \frac{9 - 6}{7 - 3} = \frac{3}{4}$.

The slope of $\overline{BC} = \frac{y_2 - y_1}{x_2 - x_1} = \frac{1 - 9}{13 - 7} = \frac{-8}{6}$.
$$= \frac{4}{-3}.$$

The slope of $\overline{CD} = \frac{y_2 - y_1}{x_2 - x_1} = \frac{-2 - 1}{9 - 13} = \frac{-3}{-4}$.

The slope of $\overline{DA} = \frac{y_2 - y_1}{x_2 - x_1} = \frac{6 - -2}{3 - 9} = \frac{8}{-6}$.
$$= \frac{4}{-3}.$$

Since opposite sides are parallel (by the Parallel Lines and Slope Theorem), $ABCD$ is a parallelogram. Since adjacent sides are $\perp$ (by the Perpendicular Lines and Slopes Theorem), $ABCD$ is a rectangle. The answer is choice (a).

7. Place Selkirk at $(0, 0)$. Then $G = (-12, 60)$ and $C = (39, -36)$.

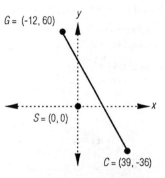

The distance GC $= \sqrt{(x_2 - x_1)^2 + (y_2 - y_1)^2} =$
$\sqrt{(39 - -12)^2 + (-36 - 60)^2} = \sqrt{51^2 + (-96)^2} =$
$\sqrt{2601 + 9216} = \sqrt{11817} \approx 108.7$ miles.

8.

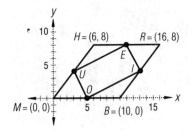

10.

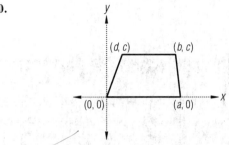

13. $2x - 3y = -8$.
$4x - 5y = 20$
Multiply the first equation by -2 to eliminate the x-variable:
$$-4x + 6y = -16$$
$$\underline{4x - 5y = 20}$$
$$y = 4$$
$$2x - 3(4) = 8$$
$$2x - 12 = 8$$
$$2x = 20$$
$$x = 10$$
The solution is $(10, 4)$.

The chart below keys the **Progress Self-Test** questions to the objectives in the **Chapter 11 Review** on pages 559-561. This will enable you to locate those **Chapter 11 Review** questions that correspond to questions you missed on the **Progress Self-Test** The lesson where the material is covered is also indicated in the chart.

Question	1, 2	3	4	5	6	7
Objective	C	F	D	G	A	E
Lesson	11-5	11-2	11-4	11-3	11-2	11-2
Question	8	9	10	11, 12	13	14
Objective	H	A	I	J	K	B
Lesson	11-4	11-1	11-5	11-6	11-1	11-4

CHAPTER 11 REVIEW (pp. 559-561)

1. $AB = \sqrt{145}$; $AC = \sqrt{145}$. Since $AB = AC$, $\triangle ABC$ is isosceles by the definition of an isosceles triangle (sufficient condition). 3. trapezoid 5. Let the midpoint of $\overline{PQ}$ be $K = (0, 2b)$; of $\overline{QR}$ be $L = (2a, 0)$; of $\overline{RS}$ be $M = (0, -2b)$; of $\overline{PS}$ be $N = (-2a, 0)$. Then $KL = \sqrt{4a^2 + 4b^2}$; $LM = \sqrt{4a^2 + 4b^2}$; $MN = \sqrt{4a^2 + 4b^2}$; and $NK = \sqrt{4a^2 + 4b^2}$. So $KL = LM = MN = NK$. 7. slope of $\overline{WY} = \frac{s - 0}{s - 0} = \frac{s}{s} = 1$; slope of $\overline{XZ} = \frac{s - 0}{0 - s} = \frac{s}{s} = -1$. Since $1 \cdot -1 = -1$, $\overline{WY} \perp \overline{XZ}$ by the Perpendicular Lines and Slopes Theorem. 9. $WX = 41$, $VX = 82$, $VZ = 80$ 11. Applying the Midpoint Connector Theorem to $\triangle BCD$, $\overline{EF} \parallel \overline{BD}$. Thus $BDEF$ is a trapezoid by the definition of trapezoid (sufficient condition). 13. $(0, -1.2)$ 15. at its midpoint 17. $\sqrt{146} \approx 12.1$ miles 19. 28 inches 21. $\sqrt{136} \approx 11.66$ units 23. $10 + \sqrt{90} \approx 19.49$ units 25. $(x - 8)^2 + (y + 1)^2 = 225$ 27. a. $(6, -3)$ b. 13 c. sample: $(19, -3)$ 29. See below. 31. $(4.5, 0)$ 33. $\frac{30}{55} = \frac{6}{11}$ 35. (a, b), $(a, -b)$, $(-a, -b)$, $(-a, b)$ 37. $(25, 5)$ 39. See below. 41. $(x - 4)^2 + (y + 3)^2 + z^2 = 100$ 43. $(4, -3)$ 45. $(7, 29)$

29.

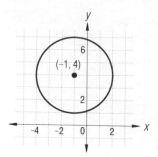

39. a.

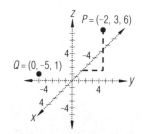

b. $(-1, -1, 3.5)$
c. $\sqrt{93} \approx 9.64$ units

LESSON 12-1 (pp. 562–568)

3. $BC = \sqrt{(-15 - 0)^2 + (-6 - 3)^2} = 3\sqrt{34}$; $B'C' = \sqrt{(-10 - 0)^2 + (-4 - 2)^2} = 2\sqrt{34} = \frac{2}{3}BC$. 5. See below. 7. $OA = \sqrt{(-9 - 0)^2 + (15 - 0)^2} = \sqrt{306} = 3\sqrt{34}$; $OA' = \sqrt{(-6 - 0)^2 + (10 - 0)^2} = \sqrt{136} = 2\sqrt{34}$; $AA' = \sqrt{(-9 - -6)^2 + (15 - 10)^2} = \sqrt{34}$. Since $OA' + AA' = OA$, then A' is between O and A. 9. a. (x, y) b. S_1 is the identity size change transformation. 11. a. $P' = (-15, 60, 20)$ b. $Q' = (10, -40, 0)$ c. $QP = \sqrt{(2 - -3)^2 + (-8 - 12)^2 + (0 - 4)^2} = \sqrt{441} = 21$; $Q'P' = \sqrt{(10 - -15)^2 + (-40 - 60)^2 + (0 - 20)^2} = \sqrt{11025} = 105 = 5QP$. 13. If a figure is determined by certain points, then its reflection image is the corresponding figure determined by the reflection images of those points. 15. $x = 13.5$ 17. $AB = 36$

5. a.

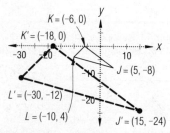

K = (-6, 0); K' = (-18, 0); J = (5, -8); L' = (-30, -12); L = (-10, 4); J' = (15, -24)

b. The sides of $\triangle J'K'L'$ are parallel to and 3 times the length of the corresponding sides of $\triangle JKL$. Each preimage-image pair is collinear with the origin.

LESSON 12-2 (pp. 569–574)

3. See below. 5. 6 11. $\frac{3}{5}$ 13. $\frac{3}{4}$ 15–19. See below. 21. 1200′ 23. a. 63,360 b. 1,000,000

3.

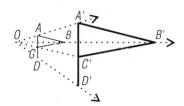

15. $k \approx \frac{3}{4}$

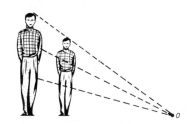

17.

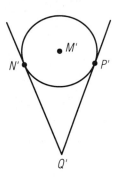

19. $A' = (0, -12)$, $B' = (-39, 1)$, $C' = (21, 33)$

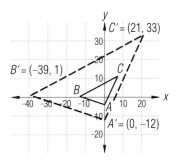

LESSON 12-3 (pp. 575-580)

1. Divide the length of the image segment by the length of the preimage segment. **3.** False **7.** They are parallel. **9.** $TXJ = 73$ **11. a.** 2.5 **b.** 15 **c.** 12 **13–15. See below. 17.** $AC = \frac{24}{7} \approx 3.43$; $OD \approx 7.117$; $CD = 1.017$; $OB = 7$ **19.** $.00001 = 10^{-5}$ **21.** $\sqrt{306} \approx 17.5$ ft **23.** $k = \frac{900}{7} \approx 128.57$ **25.** $t = -11$

13. $k = \frac{5}{6}$

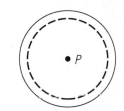

15. $k = 4$.

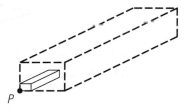

LESSON 12-4 (pp. 581–585)

5. a. $ru = st$ **b.** $\frac{r}{t} = \frac{s}{u}$ **c.** $\frac{s}{r} = \frac{u}{t}$ **7.** $\frac{2}{4} \neq \frac{6}{8}$, $\frac{2}{6} \neq \frac{4}{8}$, $\frac{2}{8} \neq \frac{4}{6}$ **9.** 12.5 **11.** Samples: $\frac{u}{v} = \frac{w}{x}$, $\frac{w}{x} = \frac{y}{z}$, $\frac{u}{v} = \frac{y}{z}$, $\frac{u}{w} = \frac{v}{x}$, $\frac{x}{v} = \frac{w}{u}$, $\frac{v}{u} = \frac{x}{w}$ **13.**

a. True **b.** True **c.** False **15.** $\approx$ \$1.83 **17.** Any three of the following: $\frac{w}{y} = \frac{z}{x}$, $\frac{w}{z} = \frac{y}{x}$, $\frac{y}{w} = \frac{x}{z}$, or $\frac{z}{w} = \frac{x}{y}$ **19.** $S(A) = (8, -3)$, $S(B) = (5, 4)$, $AB = \sqrt{6^2 + 14^2} = \sqrt{232} = 2\sqrt{58}$ $S(A)S(B) = \sqrt{3^2 + 7^2} = \sqrt{58}$; $\sqrt{58} = \frac{1}{2} \cdot 2\sqrt{58}$

21. 10 in. **23. a.** Since $GHJKL$ is regular, $\overline{GL} \cong \overline{HJ}$. Since triangles FGL and HIJ are regular, $\overline{FG} \cong \overline{GL} \cong \overline{FL}$; $\overline{HI} \cong \overline{JI} \cong \overline{HJ}$. Thus, by the Transitive Property of Congruence, all six of these segments are congruent. So by the SSS Congruence Theorem, $\triangle FGL \cong \triangle HIJ$. **b.** 168

LESSON 12-5 (pp. 586–592)

1. a similarity transformation **3.** congruent, similar **7.** Yes **9.** No **11.** Yes **13.** Yes **15.** False **17.** $\frac{4x}{7}$ **19. See below. 21.** $w = \sqrt{32} \approx 5.66$ cm **23.** 6 **25.** $\approx$ \$3.34 **27. a.** True **b.** True **c.** 15 **29. a.** No **b.** The triangles could be similar with a ratio of similitude not equal to 1.

19. a.

b. It is the image under an expansion with scale factor 3.

LESSON 12-6 (pp. 593–598)

1. a. $\frac{5}{7}$ (or $\frac{7}{5}$) **b.** $\frac{25}{49}$ (or $\frac{49}{25}$) **c.** $\frac{125}{343}$ (or $\frac{343}{125}$) **5.** 2176 units^3 **7.** $\frac{5}{13}$ (or $\frac{13}{5}$) **9. a.** $20 + \sqrt{40} \approx 26.32$ units **b.** $100 + 5\sqrt{40} \approx 131.62$ units **11. a.** 337.5 in.^{3} **b.** ≈ 29.63 in.^{3} **13. a.** 18 cm^2 **b.** 1000 cm^3 **15.** (b) **17.** $DE = 7.5$; $EF = 12.5$; m$\angle E = 135$ **19.** $\frac{x}{11} = \frac{10}{y}$; $\frac{10}{x} = \frac{y}{11}$; $\frac{11}{x} = \frac{y}{10}$ **21.** $33\frac{1}{3}$ percent

LESSON 12-7 (pp. 599–603)

3. 144; $144^3 = 2,985,984$ **5.** The giantess would weigh about 125 times the weight of the woman. **7.** The giantess's standing area would be about 25 times the area of the woman's. **9.** False **11.** The weight of the animal increases as the cube of their heights; thus, to support this greater weight, the cross-section of the skeleton of the larger animal, which signals the strength of the skeleton, must be correspondingly larger. **13.** 15.625 kg **15. a.** No **b.** The taller box has twice

b. The taller box has twice the volume of the shorter. **c.** The taller box has more surface area than the shorter, but you cannot express the ratio of their surface areas as a simple fraction. **17. a.** $\sqrt{13} \approx 3.6$ **b.** $(\sqrt{13})^3 \approx 46.9$ **19.** m$\angle R = 42$; m$\angle T = 42$; m$\angle S = 43$; $MT = 12.24$; $RQ \approx 29.8$

21.

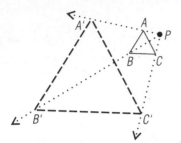

LESSON 12-8 (pp. 604–608)

1. a. $\triangle DEF \sim \triangle UVW$ **b.** $\frac{10}{33}$ or $\frac{33}{10}$ **c.** $UV = 7.\overline{57}$; $VW = 9.\overline{69}$
3. $\frac{ST}{VW}$, $\frac{TR}{WU}$ **7.** False **9. a.** $\triangle PQR \sim \triangle TVU$ **b.** Sample: apply S_3 to $\triangle PQR$ with center Q. Take the image and reflect over the $\perp$ bisector of $\overline{P'T}$. Then rotate with magnitude m$\angle Q''TV$ with center T. **11. See below. 13.** 43.94 lb **15.** 972π units³
17. a. volume of a pyramid or cone with height h and base of area B **b.** surface area of a rectangular solid with sides l, w, h **c.** perimeter of a triangle with sides a, b, c **d.** volume of a cylinder of height h and base of radius r **e.** lateral area of a cone with base of radius r and slant height l

11. Consider these two triangles:

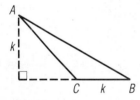

LESSON 12-9 (pp. 609–614)

1. a. $\triangle ABC \sim \triangle YXZ$ **b.** $\frac{1}{2}$ or 2 **c.** m$\angle Y = 60$ **9. a.** Yes
b. SSS Similarity Theorem **11–13. See below. 15. a.** No
b. $\frac{12}{8} \neq \frac{16}{12} \neq \frac{20}{16}$

11.

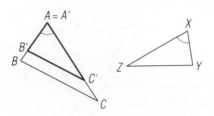

Let $k = \frac{XY}{AB}$, and then find $\triangle A'B'C' \sim \triangle ABC$ with ratio of similitude k.
Then $A'B' = k \cdot AB$ $\qquad A'C' = k \cdot AC$
$\qquad\quad = \frac{XY}{AB} \cdot AB$ $\qquad\qquad = \frac{XY}{AB} \cdot AC$
$\qquad\quad = XY$ $\qquad\qquad\quad = \frac{XZ}{AC} \cdot AC$
$\qquad\qquad\qquad\qquad\qquad = XY$
So $\triangle A'B'C' \cong \triangle XYZ$ by the SAS Congruence Theorem. Thus $\triangle ABC$ can be mapped onto $\triangle XYZ$ by a composite of size changes and reflections, so $\triangle ABC \sim \triangle XYZ$.

13.

Conclusions	Justifications
1. m$\angle WYZ = $ m$\angle ZVY$	Vertical Angle Theorem
2. $\frac{WY}{XY} = \frac{3 \cdot VY}{3 \cdot YZ} = \frac{VY}{YZ}$	Mult. Prop. of Equality
3. $\triangle WXY \sim \triangle VZY$	SAS Similarity Theorem

17.

LESSON 12-10 (pp. 615–620)

1. a. $\frac{AB}{AY} = \frac{CB}{XY}$ **b.** $\frac{AC}{CX}$ **3.** 24 **5.** $\frac{7}{6}$ **7.** (c) **9.** $AC = 24$, $CE = 36$
11. $\frac{y}{x} = \frac{w}{z}$; $\frac{x}{z} = \frac{y}{w}$; $\frac{z}{x} = \frac{w}{y}$; $\frac{x}{x+y} = \frac{z}{z+w}$; $\frac{x+y}{x} = \frac{z+w}{z}$ **13.** $x = 125$ m; $y = 100$ m **15.** No **17.** Yes, $\triangle STO \sim \triangle XYZ$ by the SSS Similarity Theorem **19.** 93.75 miles

---

CHAPTER 12 PROGRESS SELF-TEST (pp. 622–623)

1. See below. 2. See below. 3. A size change is a similarity transformation. It does not necessarily preserve distance, area, and volume, but it does preserve angle measure (also betweenness, collinearity, and orientation). The answer is choice (a) **4.** Under a size change of magnitude $\frac{3}{4}$, the area of the image changes by the square of the ratio of similitude, so Area($\triangle A'B'C'$) = $(\frac{3}{4})^2$ Area($\triangle ABC$) = $\frac{9}{16}$ Area($\triangle ABC$).

5. Two figures are similar if and only if there is a similarity transformation (that is, a composite of size changes and reflections) mapping one onto the other. **6.** $\overleftrightarrow{WX} \parallel \overleftrightarrow{YZ}$, so $\overleftrightarrow{WX}$ divides $\overline{YV}$ and $\overline{ZV}$ proportionally. So $\frac{VW}{WY} = \frac{VX}{XZ}$. **7.** Using $\frac{VW}{VY} = \frac{VX}{VZ}$ with $VW = 11$, $VY = VW + WY = 11 + 13 = 24$, and $VZ = 30$, then $\frac{11}{24} = \frac{VX}{30}$, so $330 = 24VX$, and $VX = 13.75$ units.

8. Using $\frac{VW}{VY} = \frac{WX}{YZ}$ with $WX = 8$, $YZ = 20$, and $WV = 10$, then $\frac{10}{VY} = \frac{8}{20}$ so $8VY = 200$ and $VY = 25$ units. **9.** If $\frac{a}{b} = \frac{c}{d}$, then some other true proportions are $\frac{a}{c} = \frac{b}{d}$, $\frac{d}{b} = \frac{c}{a}$, $\frac{b}{a} = \frac{d}{c}$, $\frac{c}{a} = \frac{d}{b}$. (To check, the means-extremes product should be $ad = bc$.) **10.** $\triangle ACB \sim \triangle ECD$ ($\angle BAC \cong \angle DEC$ by ∥ lines $\Rightarrow$ AIA =; $\angle ACB \cong \angle ECD$ by the Vertical Angle Theorem), so $\frac{AC}{EC} = \frac{BC}{DC}$. Using $AC = 32$, $CE = 24$, and $DC = 20$, then $\frac{32}{24} = \frac{BC}{20}$ so $640 = 24BC$ and $BC = 26.\overline{6} = 26\frac{2}{3}$ units. **11.** $\angle AUQ$ corresponds to $\angle O$, so m$\angle AUQ =$ m$\angle O = 37$. The ratio of similitude can be found using $\frac{DQ}{RF} = \frac{6}{8} = \frac{3}{4}$. So $DA = \frac{3}{4}RU = \frac{3}{4}(27) = \frac{81}{4} = 20.25$ units, and $AU = \frac{3}{4}UO$ or $24 = \frac{3}{4}UO$, $UO = \frac{4}{3}(24) = 4(8) = 32$ units. **12.** The ratio of volumes is the cube of the ratio of sides, so the ratio of volumes is $5^3 : 1^3 = 125 : 1$. **13.** Using the proportion $\frac{w_1}{w_2} = \left(\frac{h_1}{h_2}\right)^3$, where w represents weight and h represents height, $\frac{5}{w_2} = \left(\frac{4}{12}\right)^3 = \frac{64}{1728}$. So $64w_2 = 8640$ and $w_2 = 135$ lb. **14.** The ratios of side lengths can be written as $\frac{8}{12} = \frac{2}{3}$, $\frac{12}{18} = \frac{2}{3}$, and $\frac{18}{27} = \frac{2}{3}$. Since all 3 ratios are equal, the two triangles are similar by the SSS Similarity Theorem. **15.** $\angle A \cong \angle E$ and $\angle B \cong \angle D$ because ∥ lines $\Rightarrow$ AIA = (also, $\angle BCA \cong \angle DCE$ by the Vertical Angle Theorem). So the triangles are similar by the AA Similarity Theorem. **16.** The parallel streets, Washington, Adams, and Jefferson, divide Martha Lane and Abigail Avenue proportionally. So $\frac{200}{150} = \frac{x}{165}$ and $150x = 33,000$, so $x = 220$ m. **17.** The slides are similar figures, so $\frac{5}{3} = \frac{x}{25}$ (note that both shorter sides, 3 cm and 25 cm, appear in corresponding positions in the fractions). Then $3x = 125$ and $x = 41.\overline{6} = 41\frac{2}{3}$ cm. **18.** The ratio of the lengths of feet equals the ratio of heights, because each is a linear measurement. So $\frac{2}{30} = \frac{0.4}{x}$ (note that both numerators are in meters, while both denominators are in centimeters). Then $2x = 12$ and $x = 6$ cm. **19.** The ratio of weights is the cube of the ratio of heights, and the ratio of (foot) areas is the square of the ratio of heights. So the weight would be $6^3 = 216$ times as much and corresponding areas would differ by a factor of $6^2 = 36$. **20. See below.**

1.

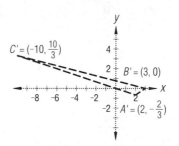

Draw $\overline{OA}$, $\overline{OB}$, and $\overline{OC}$. Then find A', B', and C' so that $OA' = \frac{3}{4}OA$, $OB' = \frac{3}{4}OB$, and $OC' = \frac{3}{4}OC$.

2.

Draw $\overrightarrow{FD}$ and $\overrightarrow{FE}$. Then find D' and E' so that $FD' = 2.8FD$ and $FE' = 2.8FE$.

20.

Under a size change of magnitude $\frac{2}{3}$, centered on the origin,
$A = (6, -2)$ so $A' = (2, -\frac{2}{3})$;
$B = (9, 0)$ so $B' = (3, 0)$;
$C = (-30, 10)$ so $C' = (-10, 3\frac{1}{3})$.

The chart below keys the **Progress Self-Test** questions to the objectives in the **Chapter 12 Review** on pages 624–627. This will enable you to locate those **Chapter 12 Review** questions that correspond to questions you missed on the **Progress Self-Text**. The lesson where the material is covered is also indicated in the chart.

Questions	1,2	3	4	5	6–8	9	10,11		
Objective	A	D	D	D	B	E	C		
Lesson	12-2	12-3	12-6	12-5	12-10	12-4	12-5		
Question	12	13		14	15	16	17,18	19	20
Objective	D	H		F	F	G	G	H	I
Lesson	12-6	12-7		12-8	12-9	12-10	12-5	12-7	12-1

1. See below. 3. See below. 5. It is *DEFG* itself. **7.** 100
9. 8 **11.** 12 **13.** m∠*H* = 100, *PE* = 4.1$\overline{6}$, *OU* = 7.92
15. 90, 57, 33 **17.** 625 units² **19. a.** *J* **b.** 1.5 **c.** True **21.** If
the ratio of similitude is *k*, the ratio of the volumes is k^3.

23. 2:1 **25.** $\frac{a}{m} = \frac{e}{t}$, $\frac{m}{t} = \frac{a}{e}$, $\frac{t}{m} = \frac{e}{a}$ **27.** $\frac{8}{12} = \frac{16}{24}$, $\frac{8}{16} = \frac{12}{24}$,
$\frac{16}{8} = \frac{24}{12}$, $\frac{12}{8} = \frac{24}{16}$ **29. a.** Yes **b.** by the SSS Similarity

Theorem **31.** Yes, by the SAS Similarity Theorem **33. See
below. 35.** 6.25″ **37.** 15 meters **39.** 20.$\overline{2}$″ **41.** ≈ \$15.08
43. ≈ 3.4 lb **45.** True **47. See below. 49. a.** *P′* = (-20,
-32, 44) **b.** *OP* = $\sqrt{25 + 64 + 121}$ = $\sqrt{210}$; *OP′* =
$\sqrt{400 + 1024 + 1936}$ = $\sqrt{3360}$ = $\sqrt{16 \cdot 210}$ = 4$\sqrt{210}$ =
4 · *OP*.

1.

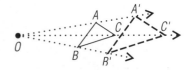

3.

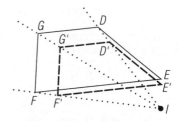

33.

Conclusions	Justifications
1. ∠*ACB* and ∠*ACD* are right angles.	definition of perpendicular (meaning)
2. m∠*ACB* = 90 m∠*ACD* = 90	definition of right angle (meaning)
3. m∠*ACB* = m∠*ACD*	Transitive Property of Equality
4. $\frac{BC}{AC} = \frac{x}{2x} = \frac{1}{2}$ $\frac{AC}{DC} = \frac{2x}{4x} = \frac{1}{2}$	Multiplication Property of Equality
5. $\frac{BC}{AC} = \frac{AC}{DC}$	Transitive Property of Equality
6. △*ABC* ~ △*DAC*	SAS Similarity Theorem

47.

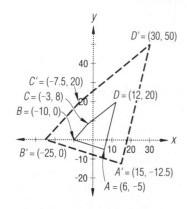

7. If you use Toothdazzle, the more popular you will be with
the opposite sex. **9.** If 7(*x* − 12) < 70, then *x* − 12 < 10. If
x − 12 < 10, then *x* < 22. Using the Law of Transitivity, we
conclude: If 7(*x* − 12) < 70, then *x* < 22. **11.** Boris Becker
is world class. **13.** No conclusion can be made. **15.** Joe is 16
or older. **17.** Nothing can be concluded. **19. See below. 21.**
a. 10 **b.** $\sqrt{116}$ **c.** $\sqrt{216}$ **d.** (iv) **23.** It is multiplied by 18.
25. 540 **27. See below. 29. a.** $x^2 − 2xy + y^2$ **b.** $4a^2$

19. sample:
   a. *p*: ∠*ABE* and ∠*ABC* are a linear pair.
      p ⇒ *q*: If two angles form a linear pair, then they are
      supplementary.
      Conclusion *q*: ∠*ABE* and ∠*ABC* are supplementary.
   b. Sample: *x* + m∠*ABC* = m∠*EBD* + m∠*DBC*.

27. sample:

1. The perimeter of an *n*-gon with side *s* is not *ns*. **3.** You
were late for school today. **9. a.** If you can get \$10 for that
old tape recorder, then you will bring it in Saturday. **b.** If you
cannot get \$10 for that old tape recorder, you will not bring it
in Saturday. **c.** If you do not bring that old tape recorder in

Saturday, you cannot get \$10 for it. **11.** (a) **13.** If the
Pythagorean Theorem holds for △*ABC*, then △*ABC* is a right
triangle. **15. a.** *x* ≠ 3 **b.** Detachment and Contrapositive
17. Yes **19.** None of these apples was grown in the shade.
21. From a statement or given information *p* and a
justification of the form *p* ⇒ *q*, you may conclude *q*. **23. See
below. 25.** -2 **27.** 5, -5

23.

Conclusions	Justifications
1. *ABCD* is a parallelogram.	definition of parallelogram (sufficient cond.)
2. $\overline{AB} \cong \overline{CD}$	Properties of a Parallelogram Theorem

3. *s* and *t* have exactly one point in common. **5.** Sample: The
teller is male, either Farmer or Guinness; Shirley is Ms Edwards.
7. Carol plays the clarinet, Sue plays the trombone,
Jill plays the flute, Dave plays the tuba, Jim plays the cornet.
9. Sample: $\overline{BC}$ is not parallel to $\overline{AD}$. **11.** Mike—chemist,
Darlene—dentist, Gary—teacher, Wanda—car dealer,
Ken—farmer, Brad—doctor, Joyce—lawyer **13. a.** If I eat
my hat, then Jackie is a good cook. **b.** If Jackie is not a good
cook, I will not eat my hat. **c.** If I don't eat my hat, then
Jackie is not a good cook. **15.** Diagonals in a square are
perpendicular.

17.

Conclusions	Justifications
1. $AC = BC$, $DC = EC$	definition of isosceles triangles (meaning)
2. $\angle ACD \cong \angle BCE$	Vertical Angle Theorem
3. $\triangle ACD \cong \triangle BCE$	SAS Congruence Theorem (steps 1 and 2)

LESSON 13-4 (pp. 645–650)

5. (a) **7.** Either $\sqrt{9800} = 99$ or $\sqrt{9800} \neq 99$. Assume $\sqrt{9800} = 99$. Then squaring both sides: $9800 = 99^2$. But, by the definition of power, $99 \cdot 99 = 9801$. These last two equations are contradictory, so by the Law of Indirect Reasoning, the assumption $\sqrt{9800} = 99$ is false, so $\sqrt{9800} \neq 99$. **9.** $\triangle ABC$ is scalene. **11.** contradictory **13.** not contradictory **15. a.** $x < -21$ **b.** direct reasoning **17.** Isobel—5′11″—brunette; Mary—5′10″—black; Ruth—5′8″—auburn; Marcia—5′7″—blond; Grace—5′6″—red **19. a.** If $\angle A$ is not congruent to $\angle D$, then $\triangle ABC$ is not similar to $\triangle DEF$. **b.** If $\angle A \cong \angle D$, then $\triangle ABC \sim \triangle DEF$. **c.** If $\triangle ABC$ is not similar to $\triangle DEF$, then $\angle A$ is not congruent to $\angle D$. **d.** The contrapositive is true. **21.** 12

LESSON 13-5 (pp. 651–657)

7. 9 **9.** sample: a ball on a floor **11.** $\sqrt{136} \approx 11.7$

13. a. Yes **b.** infinitely many **15.** See below. **17.** (b) **19. a.** Julie walks to school. **b.** Law of Ruling Out Possibilities **21. a.** If the diagonals of a figure are not congruent, then it is not a rectangle. **b.** Yes

15.

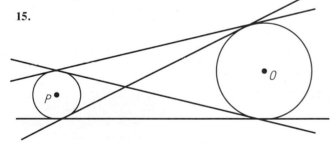

LESSON 13-6 (pp. 658–664)

3. not uniquely determined **5.** See below. **13–19.** See below. **21.** Compass Rule **23.** 12 units **25.** In 1960, Richard Nixon did not win the majority of electoral votes. **27.** rectangles

5.

13.,15.,17.

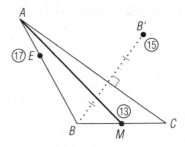

(17) is the only figure not uniquely determined.

19. sample:

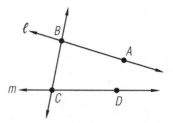

If $m\angle ABC + m\angle DCB < 180$, then ℓ and m intersect on the same side of $\overleftrightarrow{BC}$ as A and D are.

LESSON 13-7 (pp. 665–670)

1. a. 40 **b.** 140 **c.** 40 **3.** $\angle 2$ and $\angle 1$ **5.** $\angle 2$ and $\angle 3$ **7.** $\angle B$ **9.** $\overline{FE}$ **11.** True **13.** $\overline{GJ}$ **15.** $m\angle Q = 90$ (given). So, $m\angle 2 < 90$, since $m\angle 2 + m\angle SPQ = 90$. Therefore, $m\angle 2 < m\angle Q$, by substitution. So $PQ < PS$, by Unequal Angles Theorem. **17. a.** x **b.** $x + y$ **c.** $180 - 2x - y$ **19.** Through a point not on a line, there is exactly one parallel to the given line. **21.** 5 **23.** 32 cm

LESSON 13-8 (pp. 671–674)

5. See below. **7.** a regular 30-gon with sides of length 4 **9.** Assume a given figure is a convex decagon with 4 right interior angles. The corresponding exterior angles would also be right angles, and so the sum of their measures would be 360°. So the sum of the measures of all 10 exterior angles would exceed 360°, which contradicts the Exterior Angles of a Polygon Sum Theorem. Therefore, the assumption is false. So no convex decagon can have 4 right interior angles. **11.** $\angle 3$ is an exterior angle of $\triangle XYV$, so $m\angle 3 > m\angle 2$ (from Exterior Angles Inequality Theorem). Similarly, $\angle 2$ is an exterior angle of $\triangle WXV$, so $m\angle 2 > m\angle 1$. Transitivity gives $m\angle 3 > m\angle 2 > m\angle 1$. So $\angle 1$ is the smallest. **13.** See below. **15.** the square **17.** $\angle ACD$, $\angle CBP$

5. TO OCT
   REPEAT 8 [FORWARD 12 RIGHT 45]
   END

13. not uniquely determined; sample:

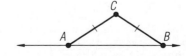

1.a. A hexagon is a specific kind of polygon, so the statement is true. **b.** Inverse: If a figure is not a hexagon, then it is not a polygon. **c. See below. 2.** If two angles do not form a linear pair, then they are not adjacent angles. **b. See below. 3.a.** An angle may be acute, right, or obtuse. If it is neither acute nor obtuse, then it must be a right angle. **b.** The conclusion in part **a** is based on the Law of Ruling Out Possibilities. **4.** If all three angles of a triangle are less than 50°, then the sum of the measures of the angles of the triangle must be under 150. This is a contradiction, since the sum of the measures of the three angles in a triangle must be 180. Therefore the original assumption, that the measures of the three angles in a triangle can all be under 50°, must be false.

5. Suppose $\sqrt{80} = 40$. Then $80 = (\sqrt{80})^2 = 40^2 = 1600$. But $80 \neq 1600$. So the original assumption, that $\sqrt{80} = 40$, is false, and $\sqrt{80} \neq 40$. **6-9. See below. 10.a.** $\angle ABD$ and $\angle CBD$ form a linear pair, so they are supplementary. So if m$\angle ABD = 120$, then m$\angle CBD = 60$. **b-c.** In $\triangle BCD$, $\angle ABD$ is an exterior angle and $\angle C$ and $\angle D$ are the nonadjacent interior angles. So m$\angle C < 120$ and m$\angle D < 120$ by the Exterior Angle Inequality. **11.** Until the discovery of non-Euclidean geometries, postulates were thought to be *definitely* true. Now it is realized that they are only *assumed* true. **12-13. See below. 14.** $\overline{PT}$ and $\overline{PU}$ are tangents to $\odot O$, so $\overline{PT} \perp \overline{QT}$ and $\overline{PU} \perp \overline{OU}$. $\angle P$ is given to be a right angle, and $\angle O$ is a right angle because the sum of the four angles in quadrilateral $OUPT$ is 360°. So $OUPT$ is a rectangle by the definition of rectangle (sufficient condition). Moreover, $PT = PU$ because two tangents to a circle from an external point have the same length. So $OUPT$ is a square by the definition of square (sufficient condition). **15.** Drawing $\overline{AE}$ and $\overline{DB}$, each is $\perp$ to the common tangent $\overleftrightarrow{CE}$. So $\triangle CBD \sim \triangle CAE$ by the AA Similarity Theorem (each triangle contains $\angle C$, and $\angle CDB$ and $\angle CEA$ are right angles). Then $\frac{CD}{CE} = \frac{DB}{EA}$. Using $BD = 9$, $CD = 20$, and $CE = 50$, $\frac{20}{50} = \frac{9}{EA}$ or $20EA = 450$ and $EA = 22.5$. So the radius of $\odot A$ is 22.5 units. **16. See below.**

1.c. counterexamples:

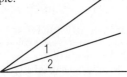

Any n-gon, where $n \neq 6$, is not a hexagon (so the antecedent of the inverse is satisfied), but it is a polygon (so the consequent is not satisfied).

2.b. counterexample:

Angles 1 and 2 do not form a linear pair (so the antecedent of the contrapositive is satisfied), but they are adjacent (so the consequent is not satisfied).

6.

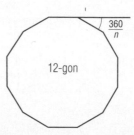

12-gon

The measure of the exterior angle of a regular duodecagon (12-gon) is $\frac{360}{12} = 30$.

7. Sample:
```
TO REGOCT
   REPEAT 8 [FORWARD 6 RIGHT 45]
END
```
This program draws a side of length 6, then moves through an exterior angle of 45° (because $\frac{360}{8} = 45$). The program does this 8 times.

8. Assign letters to statements:
$b \Rightarrow h$ (All babies are happy.)
$t \Rightarrow b$ (If someone is teething, that person is a baby.)
$n \Rightarrow \textit{not-h}$ (Nate is sad.)
Then starting with n, the fourth statement lets you conclude *not-h*. From the contrapositive of the first conditional, you can conclude *not-b*. From the contrapositive of the second conditional, you can conclude *not-t*. Thus you can state $n \Rightarrow$ *not-t*, or "Nate is not teething."

9.

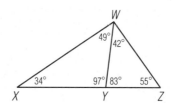

Fill in the measures of the angles: m$\angle XWY = 180 - (34 + 97) = 49$, m$\angle WYZ = 180 - 97 = 83$; m$\angle YWZ = 180 - (83 + 55) = 42$. Then, in $\triangle XYW$, $\overline{WY}$ is opposite the smallest angle, so it is the shortest of the three segments. Then, in $\triangle WYZ$, $\overline{YZ}$ is shorter than $\overline{WY}$ because $\overline{YZ}$ is opposite the smaller angle. So $\overline{YZ}$ is the shortest segment; that is choice (f).

12.

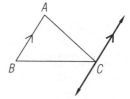

There is a unique line through C parallel to $\overleftrightarrow{AB}$; that is the Uniqueness of Parallels Theorem.

13.

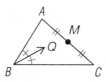

The bisector $\overrightarrow{BQ}$ of $\angle B$ does not necessarily contain the midpoint M of $\overline{AC}$. ($\overrightarrow{BQ}$ does contain M if $AB = BC$.)

16.

	20th	19th	18th	17th
Jack	X_2	X_2	O	X_3
Queen	X_1	O		
King	O			X_1
Ace	X_3			O

From clue 1, the Queen is not from the 20th century and the King is not from the 17th century. From clue 2, the Jack is not from the 20th century and is not from the 19th century. From clue 3, the Jack is not from the 17th century, and the Ace is not from the 20th century. That means that the Jack must be from the 18th century, which makes the Queen from the 19th century, the King from the 20th century, and the Ace from the 17th century.

The chart below keys the **Progress Self-Test** questions to the objectives in the **Chapter 13 Review** on pages 678–681. This will enable you to locate those **Chapter 13 Review** questions that correspond to questions you missed on the **Progress Self-Test**. The lesson where the material is covered is also indicated in the chart.

Question	1–2	3	4–5	6	7	8
Objective	C	D	E	B	A	J
Lesson	13-2	13-3	13-4	13-8	13-8	13-2

Question	9	10	11	12–13	14–15	16
Objective	H	I	K	G	F	J
Lesson	13-7	13-7	13-6	13-6	13-5	13-3

CHAPTER 13 REVIEW (pp. 678–681)
1. See below. **3. a.** 46 **b.** 92 **5. a.** If $x^2 = 9$, then $x = 3$.
b. If $x \neq 3$, then $x^2 \neq 9$. **c.** If $x^2 \neq 9$, then $x \neq 3$. **d.** original, contrapositive **7. a.** All people in the U.S. live in New York. **b.** If a person is not a New Yorker, then that person does not live in the U.S. **c.** If a person does not live in the U.S., then that person is not a New Yorker. **d.** original, contrapositive. **9. a.** *LOVE* is a trapezoid. **b.** Law of Detachment **11. a.** $x \neq 11$ **b.** Law of Contrapositive and Law of Detachment **13. a.** ℓ is not perpendicular to m. **b.** Law of Contrapositive and Law of Detachment **15. a.** All names on this list are melodious. **b.** Laws of Transitivity, Detachment, Contrapositive, and Ruling Out Possibilities **17. a.** The teacher is incorrect. **b.** Law of Indirect Reasoning **19.** Assume that in quadrilateral $ABCD$, $\angle A$, $\angle B$, $\angle C$, and $\angle D$ are acute. Thus m$\angle A < 90$, m$\angle B < 90$, m$\angle C < 90$, and m$\angle D < 90$. So m$\angle A +$ m$\angle B +$ m$\angle C +$ m$\angle D < 360$, which contradicts the Quadrilateral-Sum Theorem. So by the Law of Indirect Reasoning, the assumption is false; a

quadrilateral cannot have four acute angles. **21.** Either $\sqrt{2} = \frac{239}{169}$ or $\sqrt{2} \neq \frac{239}{169}$. Assume $\sqrt{2} = \frac{239}{169}$. Then $2 = (\frac{239}{169})^2 = \frac{57,121}{28,561}$. Then $2 \cdot 28,561 = 57,121$; so $57,122 = 57,121$. This is a false conclusion, so by the Law of Indirect Reasoning, the assumption is false. So $\sqrt{2} \neq \frac{239}{169}$. **23.** $18\pi \approx 56.5$ units **25.** $3025\pi \approx 9503.3$ mm^2 **27.** Uniqueness of Parallels Theorem **29.** cannot be justified **31.** $\angle C$ **33.** $\overline{HI}$ **35.** $\angle 3$ is larger than $\angle 4$, because it is an exterior angle $\triangle TYZ$. Similarly, $\angle 2$ is larger than $\angle 3$, and $\angle 1$ is larger than $\angle 2$. So $\angle 1$ is the largest. **37.** Mary is too old for camp. **39. a.** Law of Ruling Out Possibilities **b.** He may not have included all possibilities. **41.** Through a point not on a line, there is exactly one line parallel to the given line.

1. TO HEXAGON
    REPEAT 6 [FORWARD 10 RIGHT 60]
    END

LESSON 14-1 (pp. 682–689)
3. $\overline{DG}$, $\overline{EH}$, $\overline{IF}$, $\overline{DH}$, $\overline{EG}$; $\triangle DIJ$, $\triangle DJL$, $\triangle HIJ$, $\triangle HJL$, $\triangle EKL$, $\triangle EKF$, $\triangle GKL$, $\triangle GKF$ $\triangle EHG$, $\triangle DHG$, $\triangle HED$, and $\triangle GED$ **5.** 105 **7.** $10\sqrt{2} \approx 14.14$ cm **9.** 10.4 cm, 12.0 cm **11.** $\frac{E\sqrt{3}}{2}$ units **13.** $\frac{100}{\sqrt{2}} \approx 70.71$ ft **15.** $\triangle CBA$, $\triangle BPA$, $\triangle CPB$ (and also $\triangle ADC$) **17.** DE $= \pm\sqrt{150} \approx \pm12.25$ (But if DE is a length, it must be positive.) **19.** (a) **21.** square

LESSON 14-2 (pp. 690–695)
1. 10.00 **3.** True **5.** 4 **7. a.** 13 **b.** $\frac{25}{13} \approx 1.92$ **c.** $\frac{60}{13} \approx 4.62$ **9. a.** Yes **b.** True **11. a.** Right Triangle Altitude Theorem **b.** Geometric Mean Theorem **c.** Addition Property of Equality **d.** Distributive Property **e.** Substitution Property of Equality **13. a.** $\frac{5\sqrt{3}}{2} \approx 4.33$ units **b.** $\frac{25\sqrt{3}}{4} \approx 10.83$ units^2 **15.** The prism

≅ △MEC by the SSS Congruence Theorem, so ∠D ≅ ∠E by CPCT. Thus △ADE is isosceles, with AD = AE. By the Betweenness Property and subtraction, AB = AD − BD and AC = AE − CE. So AB = AC, by substitution, and ABMC is a kite because it has two distinct pairs of congruent consecutive sides. **19.** 2 or 1

LESSON 14-3 (pp. 696–701)

1. See below. 3. 3.271 **5.** $\frac{7}{24}$ ≈ .292 **7.** $\frac{1}{\sqrt{3}}$ or $\frac{\sqrt{3}}{3}$ **9. See below. 11. a.** ∠4 **b.** ∠1 **13. a.** $\frac{x}{h}$ **b.** $\frac{h}{y}$ **c.** $\frac{x}{h} = \frac{h}{y}$ **d.** part a **15.** △ACD, △CBD **17.** $\sqrt{89}$ ≈ 9.43″

1. sample: tan 40° ≈ $\frac{30}{36}$ = .8$\overline{3}$.

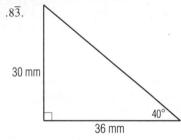

30 mm

36 mm

40°

9.

4

6

a. between 30° and 35° **b.** between 55° and 60°

LESSON 14-4 (pp. 702–707)

3. a. $\frac{2}{2\sqrt{5}} = \frac{1}{\sqrt{5}}$ ≈ .447 **b.** $\frac{4}{2\sqrt{5}} = \frac{2}{\sqrt{5}}$ ≈ .894 **c.** 2 **d.** $\frac{4}{2\sqrt{5}} = \frac{2}{\sqrt{5}}$ ≈ .894 **5. a.** $\frac{1}{\sqrt{2}}$ or $\frac{\sqrt{2}}{2}$ **b.** $\frac{1}{\sqrt{2}}$ or $\frac{\sqrt{2}}{2}$ **c.** 1 **7. a.** .228 **b.** .974 **9.** ≈12.7 ft **11. a.** Sample: sin B ≈ $\frac{25}{46}$ ≈ .543; sin B′ ≈ $\frac{17}{32}$ ≈ .531. **b.** They will probably not be equal due to measurement error, but very close. **13.** ≈ 20.1 ft **15.** ≈ 670 ft **17.** ≈86.60 **19. a.** Converse: If PM + MQ = PQ, then M is between P and Q. Inverse: If M is not between P and Q, then PM + MQ ≠ PQ. Contrapositive: If PM + MQ ≠ PQ, then M is not between P and Q. **b.** All are true. **21. a.** $50\sqrt{2}$ **b.** $58\sqrt{2}$

LESSON 14-5 (pp. 708–713)

1. a. Winds in the upper atmosphere affect the flying time. **b.** The trip east to west usually takes longer. **3.** initial point: O; terminal point: A; magnitude: 400; direction: 20° south of east **7.** -4 + -2 = -6 **13–17. See below.**

19. tan R = $\frac{35}{15}$ ≈ 2.33; sin R = $\frac{35}{38}$ ≈ 0.92; cos R = $\frac{15}{38}$ ≈ 0.39

21. ≈ 11.7 meters **23.** 576π ≈ 1810 units²

13.

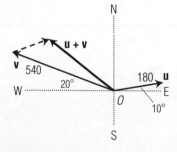

15.

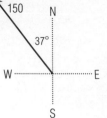

150

N

37°

W

E

S

17.

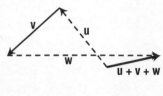

v

u

W

u + v + w

LESSON 14-6 (pp. 714–719)

5. $(\frac{1}{2} - \frac{\sqrt{3}}{2})$ **9–15. See below. 17.** ≈ -.032 (or .032, depending on the direction of the plane) **19.** horizontal: $\sqrt{3}$; vertical: 1 **21. See below. 23.** False **25.** 1

9. a.

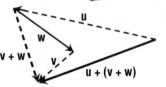

v

u

u + v

w

(u + v) + w

b.

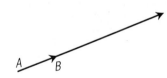

u

w

v + w

v

u + (v + w)

c. Vector additon is associative.

11.

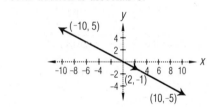

(-10, 5)

(2, -1)

(10, -5)

13.

A

B

15.

Conclusions	Justifications
(a, b) + (c, d) = (a + c, b + d)	Vector Addition Theorem
= (c + a, d + b)	Commutativity of Real Number Addition
= (c, d) + (a, b)	Vector Addition Theorem

21.

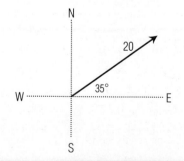

N

20

35°

W

E

S

LESSON 14-7 (pp. 720–724)

3. horizontal: $-10\cos 20° \approx -9.4$; vertical: $10\sin 20° \approx 3.42$ **5.** horizontal: 0; vertical: -3 **7.** magnitude = $2\sqrt{10} \approx$ 6.32; direction: $\approx 18.4°$ N of E (or 71.6° E of N) **9.** magnitude ≈ 183 lbs; direction: $\approx 17°$ S of E (or 73° E of S) **11.** about 93.6 feet away; $\approx 20°$ below horizontal **13–15. See below. 17.** $\frac{225\sqrt{3}}{4} \approx 97.4$ units^2 **19.** The $\frac{1}{8}$-size cello is $\frac{1}{2}$ the height of a full-size cello.

13.

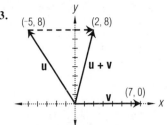

15.

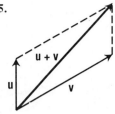

CHAPTER 14 PROGRESS SELF-TEST (pp. 726–727)

1. The three sides have lengths $XY \approx 5.5$ cm, $XZ \approx 1.6$ cm, and $YZ \approx 5.3$ cm. So $\cos Y = \frac{\text{side adjacent to } \angle Y}{\text{hypotenuse}} = \frac{YZ}{XY} \approx \frac{5.3}{5.5} \approx$ 0.96. **2.** The tangent ratio is $\frac{\text{opposite side}}{\text{adjacent side}}$. For the three numbered angles, the opposite side is constant, so the smallest tangent will be associated with the shortest adjacent side; $\angle 3$ will have the smallest tangent. **3.** $\sin B = \frac{\text{side opposite } \angle B}{\text{hypotenuse}} = \frac{AC}{AB}$ $= \frac{\text{side adjacent to } \angle A}{\text{hypotenuse}} = \cos A$. So if $\sin B = \frac{9}{11}$, then $\cos A = \frac{9}{11}$. **4–5.** To find WZ and WY, use the property that each leg is the mean proportional between the hypotenuse and its segment adjacent to the leg. For WZ, $\frac{YZ}{XZ} = \frac{XZ}{WZ}$ or $\frac{75}{45} = \frac{45}{WZ}$. So $75WZ = 2025$, or $WZ = 27$ units. For WY, $\frac{YZ}{XY} = \frac{XY}{WY}$ or $\frac{75}{60} = \frac{60}{WY}$. So $75WY = 3600$, or $WY = 48$ units. **6.** In right triangle CDB, $CD^2 = \sqrt{CB^2 - DB^2} = \sqrt{6^2 - 2^2} = \sqrt{36 - 4} = \sqrt{32}$. Then, since the altitude is the mean proportional to the segments of the hypotenuse, $\frac{AD}{CD} = \frac{CD}{DB}$ or $\frac{AD}{\sqrt{32}} = \frac{\sqrt{32}}{2}$. So $2AD = 32$ and $AD = 16$. Since $AB = AD + DB$, then $AB = 16 + 2 = 18$ units. **7.** CD, the altitude to the hypotenuse of a right triangle, is the mean proportional to the lengths of the segments of the hypotenuse, which are the distances AD and DB. **8.** $\triangle ABC$ is an isosceles triangle with legs $\overline{AB}$ and $\overline{BC}$. Since AB is given to be 7 units, then $BC = 7$ units. **9.** $\triangle ABC$ is a 45-45-90 triangle, so its hypotenuse is $\sqrt{2}$ times the length of a leg. So $AC = 7\sqrt{2} \approx 9.9$ units. **10.** $\triangle ACD$ is a 30-60-90 triangle so AD is twice the length of the side $\overline{AC}$ opposite the 30° angle. Since $AC = 7\sqrt{2}$ (from Question 9), then $AD = 2(7\sqrt{2}) = 14\sqrt{2} \approx 19.8$ units. **11.** $\tan D = \frac{\text{side opposite } \angle D}{\text{side adjacent to } \angle D} = \frac{EF}{DF} = \frac{48}{14} \approx 3.43$. **12.** $\cos E = \frac{\text{side adjacent to } \angle E}{\text{hypotenuse}} = \frac{EF}{DE} = \frac{48}{50} = .96$. **13–14. See below.** **15.** $\frac{18}{x} = \frac{x}{30}$ so $x^2 = (18)(30) = 540$ and $x = \sqrt{540} \approx 23.2379 \approx 23.24$. **16.** To find the height of the tree above eye level, use $\tan 35° = \frac{h}{40}$. Using a calculator (in degree mode), 35 [tan] [×] 40 [=] $28.0083 \approx 28$ feet. Adding the five feet for eye level, the height of the tree is about 33 feet. **17–21. See below. 22.** For the horizontal component, $\cos 35° = \frac{x}{50}$ so $x = 50 \cos 35 \approx 40.958 \approx 41$; since horizontal component is in the negative direction, it is ≈ -41. For the vertical component: $\sin 35° = \frac{y}{50}$ so $y = 50 \sin 35 \approx$

$28.6788 \approx 28.7$; it is in the negative direction, so it is about -28.7. **23–25. See below.**

13.

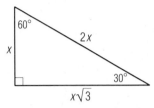

In a 30-60-90 triangle, the lengths of the sides are x, $x\sqrt{3}$, and $2x$. so $\sin 60° = \frac{x\sqrt{3}}{2x} = \frac{\sqrt{3}}{2}$.

14.

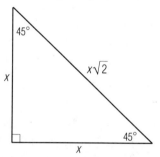

In a 45-45-90 triangle, the lengths of the sides are x, x, and $x\sqrt{2}$. So $\tan 45° = \frac{x}{x} = 1$.

17.

$\sin 80° = \frac{h}{15}$

$h = 15 \sin 80$
$= 80$ [sin] [×] 15 [=]
≈ 14.772116
≈ 14.77 ft

18. Use the parallelogram rule:

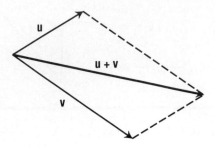

19. Use equal vectors such that the endpoint of one vector is the initial point of the next.

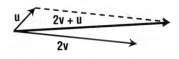

a. For the sum **2v + u,** its initial point is the initial point of the starting vector **v,** and its terminal point is the terminal point of vector **u.**

b.

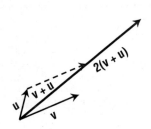

Find **v + u** using the parallelogram method. Then find 2(**v + u**) by starting another vector **v + u** at the terminal point of **v + u.**

20. The opposite of a vector has the same length but opposite direction. Below are vectors $\overline{AB}$ and several opposite vectors $\overline{CD}$ and $\overline{EF}$.

21.

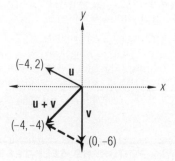

Find **u + v** either by the parallelogram rule or by adding the *x*- and *y*-coordinates: **u + v** = (-4 + 0, 2 + -6) = (-4, -4).

23.

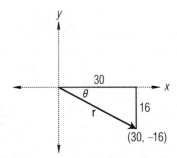

$\tan \theta = \frac{16}{30}$, so $\theta = 16 \boxed{\div} 30 \boxed{=} \boxed{\text{inv}} \boxed{\text{tan}} \approx 28°$.
$r = \sqrt{16^2 + 30^2} = \sqrt{256 + 900} = \sqrt{1156} = 34$.

The direction of the vector is about 28° south of east (or 62° east of south) and its magnitude is 34.

24.

The resultant speed is $700 - 150 = 550$ km/hr. In $3\frac{1}{2}$ hours, the plane could travel $(550)(3.5) = 1925$ km.

25.

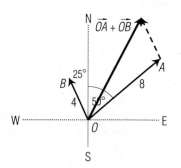

Using the Parallelogram Rule, the kayaker will be moving in a direction east of north.

Trigonometry can give a more exact answer.

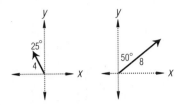

For the current vector, horizontal component is -4 sin 25°
≈ -1.69 and the vertical component is 4 cos 25° = 3.63,
so its terminal point is (-1.69, 3.63). For the
kayaker, the horizontal component is 8 sin 50 ≈ 6.13 and
the vertical component is 8 cos 50 ≈ 5.14, so its terminal
point is (6.13, 5.14). The components of the sum of the

vectors are (-1.69 + 6.13, 3.63 + 5.14) = (4.44, 8.77).

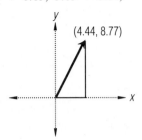

The direction of the resultant vector is 8.77 $\div$ 4.44
= inv tan ≈ 61.5° north of east, and its magnitude is
$\sqrt{4.44^2 + 8.77^2} = \sqrt{96.6265} \approx 9.83$ mph.

The chart below keys the **Progress Self-Test** questions to the objectives in the **Chapter 14 Review** on pages 728–731. This will
enable you to locate those **Chapter 14 Review** questions that correspond to questions you missed on the **Progress Self-Test**. The
lesson where the material is covered is also indicated in the chart.

Question	1	2	3	4–6	7	8–10	11	12–13	14	
Objective	B	B	F	D	G	A	C	C	C	
Lesson	14-4	14-3	14-4	14-2	14-2	14-1	14-3	14-4	14-3	
Question	15	16	17	18	19	20	21	22–23	24	25
Objective	Vocab.	I	I	E	E	H	K	L	J	J
Lesson	14-2	14-3	14-4	14-5	14-6	14-6	14-6	14-7	14-5	14-7

CHAPTER 14 REVIEW (pp. 728–731)

1. $AC = 4\sqrt{3} \approx 6.93$; $BC = 8$ **3.** $12\sqrt{2}$ **5. a.** $7\sqrt{2}$ **b.** 7
c. $7\sqrt{3}$ **d.** 14 **7.** $25\sqrt{3} \approx 43.30$ units **9.** Answers may vary.
Appoximate measures are m∠$E \approx 76$, sin $E \approx .97$, cos $E \approx$
.24, tan $E \approx 4.01$. **11.** ∠1 **13.** $\frac{24}{26} = \frac{12}{13}$ **15.** $\frac{10}{24} = \frac{5}{12}$ **17.** .843
19. 1.000 **21.** $\sqrt{3}$ **23.** $\frac{1}{\sqrt{2}}$ or $\frac{\sqrt{2}}{2}$ **25.** $\frac{49}{12} \approx 4.08$ **27.** $x = \frac{49}{25} =$
1.96; $z = \frac{576}{25} = 23.04$; $y = \frac{168}{25} = 6.72$ **29–35. See**
below. 37. $\frac{AC}{AB}$ **39.** $\frac{BC}{AC}$ **41.** sine **43.** x **45.** BD, DC **47.** DBA,
DAC **49. See below 51.** Yes **53.** ≈21.56 yards **55.** ≈ 66
feet **57.** 1750 km **59. See below. 61.** magnitude ≈ 6.2 mph;
direction: ≈ 32° E of S (or 58° S of E) **63-65. See below.**
67. ≈(-12.5, 21.65) **69.** magnitude = $\sqrt{1637} \approx 40.5$;
direction: ≈ 50° W of S (or ≈ 40° S of W)

29.

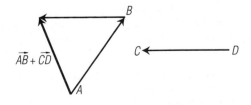

31.

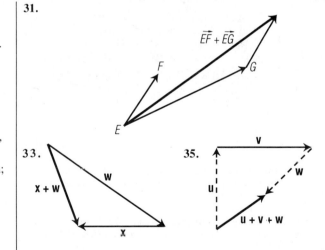

33.

35.

49. sample:

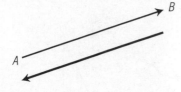

59. The boat will move in the direction $\overrightarrow{OM}$.

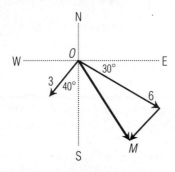

63.

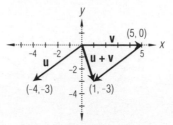

65.

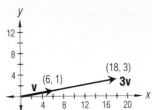

LESSON 15-1 (pp. 732–739)

3. 98° **5.** bisects **7. b.** median to the base, bisector of the vertex angle. **c.** bisector of the vertex angle, perpendicular bisector of the base **d.** perpendicular bisector of the base, altitude of the triangle **9.** False **11.** $25\sqrt{2} \approx 35.4$ m **13.** ≈ 22.3 m **15.** $\sqrt{2.75} \approx 1.66$ ft **17.** 12 units **19.** 360° **21.** $\frac{28}{15} \approx 1.87$ m³ **23. a.** $\frac{(n-2) \cdot 180}{n}$ **b.** 135

LESSON 15-2 (pp. 740–744)

1. 2 plays 7, 3 plays 5, 4 plays 6, 1 bye **3.** parallel **5.** 6–1, 5–2, 4–3, 7 bye **7. See below. 9.** True **11.** Two chords have the same length, so after 3 weeks, the pairings will be repeated. **13.** (c) and (d) **15.** $45\sqrt{3} \approx 77.9$ mm **17. See below. 19.** 1.8 miles **21. See below.**

7. Sample:

1st week	2nd	3rd	4th	5th	6th	7th
7–2	1–3	2–4	3–5	4–6	5–7	6–1
6–3	7–4	1–5	2–6	3–7	4–1	5–2
5–4	6–5	7–6	1–7	2–1	3–2	4–3
1–8	2–8	3–8	4–8	5–8	6–8	7–8

17.

Conclusions	Justifications
1. $\overline{\ell} \perp \overline{CE}$	Tangent to Circle Theorem
2. $\overline{AB} \perp \overline{CE}$	Chord-Center Theorem (parts b and c)
3. $\overline{AB} \parallel \ell$	Two Perpendiculars Theorem

21.

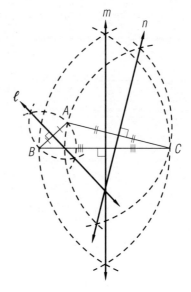

LESSON 15-3 (pp. 745–751)

3. 48.5 **7. a.** 25 **b.** 65 **c.** 90 **d.** right **9. a.** n **b.** $\frac{n}{2}$ **11. See below. 13.** m∠D = 90, m∠DCA = 60, m∠ACB = 45, m∠DCB = 105, m∠B = 90, m∠BAC = 45, m∠BAD = 75 **15. a.** Inscribed Angle Theorem **b.** Inscribed Angle Theorem **c.** Transitive Property of Equality (steps 1 and 2) **17. See below. 19. a.** 72° **b.** 500sin36° ≈ 294 units **21.** $\sqrt{700} \approx 26.46$ yards

11. Conclusions | Justifications
$\overline{\text{m}\angle ABC} = \text{m}\angle ABD - \text{m}\angle CBD$ | Angle Addition Postulate

$\quad = \frac{1}{2}\text{m}\widehat{AD} - \frac{1}{2}\text{m}\widehat{CD}$ | by Case I

$\quad = \frac{1}{2}(\text{m}\widehat{AD} - \text{m}\widehat{CD})$ | Distributive Property

$\quad = \frac{1}{2}\text{m}\widehat{AC}$ | Arc Addition

17. Sample: 2–11, 3–10, 4–9, 5–8, 6–7, 1–12. For the remaining weeks, rotate the chords of the diagram below:

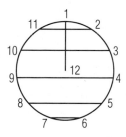

LESSON 15-4 (pp. 752–757)
1–7. See below. 11. a. m∠1 = 30, m∠2 = 30, m∠3 = 30, m∠4 = 30 **b.** True **13.** perpendicular bisector **15. a.** m∠A = m∠CDA = 30, m∠ACD = 120, m∠ADB = 90, m∠BCD = m∠BDC = m∠CBD = 60 **b.** *x* **c.** $7\sqrt{3} \approx 12.12$ **17.**
$625\pi \approx 1963.5$ square feet

1.

3. anywhere on $\widehat{ACB}$

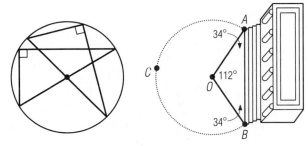

5. a. The photographer should stand at point *P*, which is about 25.9 m from the steps.

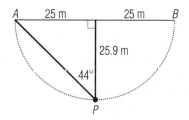

b. They can stand anywhere on $\widehat{APB}$.

7.

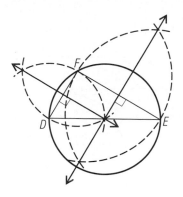

LESSON 15-5 (pp. 758–762)
1. a. 12.5 **b.** 48 **c.** 60.5 **d.** 119.5 **3.** 100 **5. a.** 65 **b.** 15 **7.** infinitely many **9. a.** 40 **b.** 70 **11. See below.**
13. m∠A = 122.5, m∠B = 85, m∠C = 95, m∠D = 102.5, m∠E = 135 **15.** $2\sqrt{107.25} \approx 20.71$ inches **17.** *x* = 8 or -8

11.

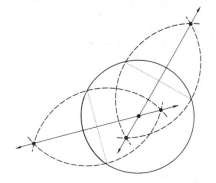

LESSON 15-6 (pp. 763–768)
1. a. 90 **b.** 55 **3.** 54 **5. a.** 142.5 **b.** 60 **c.** 97.5 **7.** m$\widehat{QTR}$ = 205°; m$\widehat{QSR}$ = 155° **9.** If the measure of the major arc $\widehat{BD}$ is *x*°, and the measure of the minor arc $\widehat{BD}$ is *y*°, then m∠C = $\frac{1}{2}(x - y)$, by Tangent-Secant Theorem. Rearranging this, *y* = *x* − 2m∠C. But *x* = 360 − *y*. So, substitution gives *y* = 360 − *y* − 2m∠C. This simplifies to 2*y* = 360 − 2m∠C, or *y* = 180 − m∠C. **11.** 110° **13. a.** 65 **b.** 92.5 **c.** 87.5 **d.** 22.5 **15. a.** Yes **b.** not necessarily **17.** 25π ≈ 78.5 in.² **19.** *BC* = 15; *JG* = 16; m∠G = 81 **21. a.** 2304π ≈ 7238.2 mm³ **b.** 576π ≈ 1809.6 mm²

LESSON 15-7 (pp. 769–774)
3. 8 **7.** 4 **9.** 6 **11.** True; *PA* · *PC* = *PB* · *PD*, so dividing by *PA* = *PD*, the result is *PC* = *PB*. **13.** Yes; since *D*, *C*, and *P* are collinear, and *B*, *A*, and *P* are collinear, then *D*, *C*, *P*, *B*, and *A* are coplanar. Points *D*, *C*, *A*, and *B* lie on the circle which is the intersection of that plane and the sphere. Apply the Secant Length Theorem to this circle. **15.** 135° **17. See below. 19. a.** 20 **b.** $\frac{20}{21} \approx .952$ **c.** $\frac{21}{29} \approx .724$ **d.** $\frac{21}{29} \approx .724$

17. You can stand anywhere on the part of the circle drawn below.

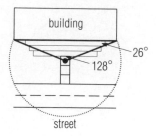

LESSON 15-8 (pp. 775–779)
1. a square with side 10 ft **3.** The minimum area is as close to zero as you like. **5. See below. 7.** $6\pi \approx 18.8$ cm **9.** Question 8 **11. a.** 540 ft^2 **b.** $\frac{2025}{\pi} \approx 645$ ft^2 **13. a.** 12.4 units **b.** 224 **15. a.** 130° **b.** 50° **17.** 64 **19. a.** If our class has done every lesson in the book, then we will have finished the next lesson. **b.** If we do not finish the next lesson, then our class will not have done every lesson in the book. **c.** If our class has not done every lesson in the book, then we will not have finished the next lesson.

5. sample:

LESSON 15-9 (pp. 780–784)
5. The minimum volume is as close to zero as you like. **9. a.** $36\pi \approx 113$ m^2 **b.** Sample: radius of 2 m, height of 9 m; surface area: $44\pi \approx 138$ m^2 **c.** Sample: radius of 6 m, height of 3 m; surface area; $36\pi + 18\pi\sqrt{5} \approx 240$ m^2 **d.** less
11. $\frac{\pi\sqrt{x^3}}{6}$ or $\frac{\pi x\sqrt{x}}{6}$ units^3 **13. a.** circle: $\frac{2304}{\pi} \approx 733$ in.^{2}; square: 576 in.^{2} **b.** square **15.** $AC \cdot CB = CD \cdot CE$ by the Secant Length Theorem, and $AC = CB$ by the Chord-Center Theorem, parts b and c. So, substitution gives $AC \cdot AC = CD \cdot CE$ or $\frac{CD}{AC} = \frac{AC}{CE}$. This means that AC is the geometric mean of CD and CE. **17.** $\overline{BC}$ **19.** It is between 21 and 893 miles.

CHAPTER 15 PROGRESS SELF-TEST(pp. 786–787)
1. See below. 2. See below. 3. Points O and M are equidistant from points X and Y, so $\overleftrightarrow{OM}$ is the $\perp$ bisector of $\overline{XY}$. Line ℓ is a tangent line, so $\ell \perp \overline{OQ}$. So $\ell \parallel \overline{XY}$ by the Two Parallels Theorem. **4.** Draw segments $\overline{JL}$ and $\overline{KM}$. In each of the four small right isosceles triangles, the side is 30 (the radius of the circle) so the hypotenuse is $30\sqrt{2}$. So the perimeter of $JKLM$ is $4(30\sqrt{2}) = 120\sqrt{2} \approx 169.7$ units. **5.** $\angle B$, an inscribed angle, is measured by half its intercepted arc. So m$\angle B = \frac{1}{2}(\overparen{DC}) = \frac{1}{2}(80) = 40$. **6.** To find m$\overparen{AB}$, use the property that $\angle DEC$ is measured by half the sum of the intercepted arcs. So m$\angle DEC = \frac{1}{2}(m\overparen{DC} + m\overparen{AB})$ or $110 = \frac{1}{2}(80 + m\overparen{AB})$. Then $220 = 80 + m\overparen{AB}$ and m$\overparen{AB} = 140°$,
7. To find m$\angle R$, first find m$\overparen{VT}$: m$\overparen{VT} = 360° - m\overparen{VUT} = 360° - (80° + 30° + 140°) = 360° - 250° = 110°$. Then m$\angle R = \frac{1}{2}(m\overparen{VT} - m\overparen{US}) = \frac{1}{2}(110 - 30) = \frac{1}{2}(80) = 40$. **8.** $\overline{PT}$ and $\overline{PU}$ are tangents to $\odot O$, so $\overline{PT} \perp \overline{OT}$ and $\overline{PU} \perp \overline{OU}$. Given that m$\overparen{UT} = 90$, then m$\angle O = 90$ and $\angle P$ is a right angle because the sum of the four angles in quadrilateral $OUPT$ is 360°. So $OUPT$ is a rectangle by the definition of rectangle (sufficient condition). Moreover, $PT = PU$ because two tangents to a circle from an external point have the same length. So $OUPT$ is a square by the definition of square (sufficient condition). **9.** For the two chords $\overline{BC}$ and $\overline{AD}$, $(AQ)(DQ) = (CQ)(BQ)$. Using $AQ = 19$, $BQ = 40$, and $CQ = 38$, then $(19)(DQ) = (38)(40)$ so $19(DQ) = 1520$ and $DQ = 80$ units. **10.** For the two secants $\overline{WY}$ and $\overline{WV}$, $(WX)(WY) = (WZ)(WV)$. Using $WX = 12$, $XY = 16$, and W2 = 10, then $(12)(12 + 16) = (10)(10 + ZV)$ so $(12)(28) = 100 + 10(ZV)$ or $336 = 100 + 10(ZY)$ and $236 = 10(XY)$ so $ZV = 23.6$ units. **11. a.** The figure with the greatest area for a fixed perimeter is a circle. **b.** Using $C = 2\pi r$ with $C = 30$ cm,

$30 = 2\pi r$ and $r = \frac{15}{\pi}$. Then using $A = \pi r^2$, $A = \pi (\frac{15}{\pi})^2 = \frac{225\pi}{\pi^2} = \frac{225}{\pi} \approx 71.6$ cm^2. **12.** For a given volume, a sphere has the smallest surface area. So if a cube and sphere have the same volume, the cube will have the larger surface area. **13–14. See below.**

1.

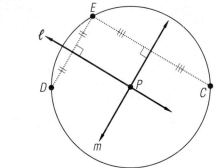

Construct the $\perp$ bisectors of $\overline{DE}$ and $\overline{EC}$. They meet at P, the center of the circle. Use point D, E, or C to draw the circle.

2. Start with 5 points equally spaced around a circle:

Draw chords connecting 5-2 and 4-3. This gives the first week's pairings:
Round 1: 2-5, 3-4, 1 bye
Rotate the chords around the circle for the next 4 rounds:
round 2: 1-3, 4-5, 2 bye
round 3: 2-4, 1-5, 3 bye
round 4: 3-5, 1-2, 4 bye
round 5: 1-4, 2-3, 5 bye.

13.

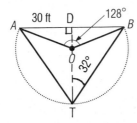

To find point T on the $\perp$ bisector of $\overline{AB}$: $\tan 32° = \frac{30}{TD}$, so TD = 30 ⌊ ÷ ⌋ 32 ⌊tan⌋ ⌊ = ⌋ ≈ 48. Find the circle through A, B, and T; then at any point on $\overset{\frown}{ATB}$ the entire stage will fit and fill the camera angle. **14.** From Question 13, you can stand 48 feet from the center of the stage.

The chart below keys the **Progress Self-Test** questions to the objectives in the **Chapter 15 Review** on pages 788–791. This will enable you to locate those **Chapter 15 Review** questions that correspond to questions you missed on the **Progress Self-Test**. The lesson where the material is covered is also indicated in the chart.

Question	1	2	3	4	5	
Objective	D	K	F	A	B	
Lesson	15-4	15-2	15-1	15-1	15-3	
Question	**6–7**	**8**	**9,10**	**11**	**12**	**13,14**
Objective	C	G	E	J	H	I
Lesson	15-5	15-6	15-7	15-8	15-9	15-4

CHAPTER 15 REVIEW (pp. 778–791)
1. 12 units **3.** 12 units **5.** $110\sin72° \approx 104.6$ mm **7.** 106°
9. 91 **11.** 52 **13.** $mDE = 65°$ **15.** 14 **17.** 78 **19–23.** See below. **25.** 21 units **27.** 12 units **29.** not necessarily true and so unjustifiable **31.** $m\angle ZWY = m\angle ZWX$, since both are right angles, by the Chord-Center Theorem, parts b and c. $YW = WX$, since W is the midpoint of $\overline{XY}$. $ZW = ZW$, so $\triangle ZWY$, $\cong \triangle ZWX$, by SAS Congruence. Therefore, $\overline{ZY} \cong \overline{ZX}$, from the CPCT Theorem, and so $\triangle ZYX$ is isosceles. **33.** $\frac{x}{2}$ **35. a.** a circle **b.** $\sqrt{\frac{800}{\pi}} \cdot 2\pi$, or about 100 feet **37. a.** square: 64 sq in.; circle: $\pi(\frac{32}{2\pi})^2 \approx 81.5$ sq in. **b.** the circle **39. a.** a cube **b.** $(\sqrt{8})^3 \approx 22.6$ in.^{3} **41. See below 43. a.** a sphere **b.** Sample answer: the container could easily roll off a shelf. **45–47. See below. 49.** Use the answer to Question 48. Replace the "bye" with the 12th team L.

19.

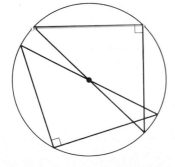

21.

23.

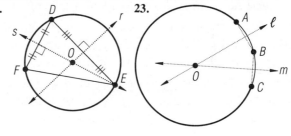

41. a. anywhere on $\overset{\frown}{APB}$ (or its reflection image over $\overleftrightarrow{AB}$)

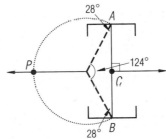

b. $\frac{60}{\tan31°} \approx 100$ yards

45. sample:

47. sample:

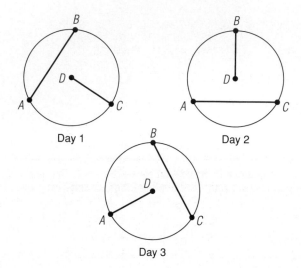

Day 1

Day 2

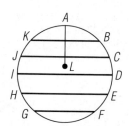

Day 3

Day 1: *A* vs. *B*, *C* vs. *D*
Day 2: *A* vs. *C*, *B* vs. *D*
Day 3: *A* vs. *D*, *B* vs. *C*

49.

compass, 141
Compass rule, 141, 142
complementary angles,
    complements, 114, 116
component vectors, 714, 721
composite, composition, 259, **260,**
    279
composite of reflections, 280
computer,
    automatic drawer, 170-173, 182
        (ex. 23-24), 186 (ex. 15), 212 (ex. 21),
        308 (ex. 11-19), 383 (ex. 25)
    programs, BASIC, 70, 71, 74
        (ex. 12-13), 75 (ex. 25), 80,
        (ex. 15), 99 (ex. 10-11), 103
        (ex. 36-40), 482 (ex. 16)
    programs, Logo, 672, 673 (ex. 7), 674
        (ex. 18), 676 (ex. 7), 678 (ex. 1-2)
    screens, 4, 17, 375
concave, 61
concentric circles, 331, 397
conclusion(s), 65, 121, 177
    justifying, 120-122
    the logic of making, 630-632
conditional statement, 65, 72, 76,
    121
    contrapositive of, 636-637
    converse of, **76,** 77-78, 127
    inverse of, 636
    negation of, 635
cone, 415, **428,** 429, 435, 451, 475,
    494, 499-501, 511
    lateral area, 475
    surface area, 475
congruence, congruent,
    arcs, 736
    circles, 736
    figures, **279, 439**
    reflexive, symmetric, transitive
        properties of, 280
    space figures, **439**
    transformation, 280
    triangles, 310-322
Congruence Property, of area, 368
    of volume, 479
conic
    section, 436
    solid, **428**
    surface, 428
conjecture, 210-220, 227 (ex. 14), 233
    (ex. 23), 248 (ex. 13), 250 (ex. 35-
    37), 251 (ex. 38-39), 322 (ex. 19),
    580 (ex. 27), 701 (ex. 19), 719 (ex.
    28), 757 (ex. 18), 784 (ex. 21)
    Four Color, 455
    unsolved, 222
consecutive,
    angles, 228
    sides, 93, 214
    vertices, 93

consequent, 65-67, 72, 76
    as a conclusion, 121
construction, 141-143
    altitude of a triangle, 182
    angle bisector, 196
    center of a circle, 184
    dividing a segment into n congruent
        parts, 620
    and drawing, 140
    duplicating the cube, 145
    impossible, 145
    perpendicular bisector of segment,
        142
    a perpendicular, 142-143
    squaring a circle, 145
    a triangle, given 3 sides, 305
    trisecting an angle, 145
contracting, 570
contradiction, contradictory, 645,
    646
contrapositive, 636, 667
converse, 76, 77-78, 127
conversion formulas, 810
convex, 94
    polyhedron, 452
    set, **61**
coordinate(s), 8, 522
    geometry, 521
    graphing, 14
    plane, 14
    and proofs, 522-523
    system, 3-dimensional, 550
    z-, 550
coordinatized line, 9
coplanar, 10
corollary, 230
correspondence, one-to-one, 35,
    164, 255, 416
corresponding angles,
    formed by a transversal, 126, 127
    in congruent triangles, 292
    in similar triangles, 606
    and nonincluded sides, 312
Corresponding Angles Postulate,
    127
corresponding parts, 292
Corresponding Parts in Congruent
    Figures (CPCF) Theorem, 292
cosine, 702, 703
counterclockwise, 188, 267
counterexample, 66, 67, 77, 120, 239
CPCF Theorem, 292
Crawford, Ralston, 25
cube, 10, 26, 449, 454, 781
cube root, 480
Cube Volume Formula, 480
cubic unit, 478
curve, simple closed, 222, 415
cycloid, (*i*)
cylinder, 415, 422, **423,** 424, 429, 435,

451, 488-490, 494, 495, 505, 511,
    780
    lateral area, 469
    surface area, 470
cylindric solid, 422, 423
cylindric surface, 422, 424

debugging, 71
decagon, 93
deduce, 521
definitions,
    good, 81-84
    meaning half and sufficient condition
        half, 83
    need for, 30-31, 60-61
degree,
    measure of an angle, **107**
    measure of a major arc, **396**
    measure of a minor arc, **396**
    measure of a semicircle, **396**
Dell Big Book of Crosswords and
    Pencil Puzzles, 139
dense, 10
depression, angle of, 706
Desargues, Gerard, 131
Desargues' Theorem, 131
Descartes, René, 14, 451, 521
determine, 35, 417, 658
diagonal,
    of a kite, 224
    of a polygon, 70, 71, 93
    of a quadrilateral, 72
Diagonal of a Box Formula, 522
diagram, assumptions from, 178
diameter,
    of a circle, 84
    of a sphere, 433
Dido of Carthage, 784
dilatation, dilation, 570
Dimension assumption, 35
dimensions, 15
    of a box, 421
    of a rectangle, 367
direct proof, 645
direct reasoning, 645
directed line segment, 708
direction,
    of a translation, 261
    of a vector, 708
discrete line(s), 5
    intersection of, 88
distance, 9, 15, 43, 82, 84, 163, 164,
    188, 261, 281, 587
    formula, 528
    formula in three dimensions, 551
    unique, assumption, 35
distinct, 192
Distributive Property, 37
dividing a segment into n
    congruent parts, 620

INDEX

perspective, 25
  drawing, 26, 29 (ex. 20)
  hidden lines, 27, 256. *See also*
    illustrations: 415, 418, 421, 422,
    427, 428, 433, 434, 436
pi, 397, 398
Pick's Theorem, 377
picture angle, 745
picture graph, 563
pixels, 4, 17
plane, 10, 31, 416-419, 421
  figure, 10
  geometry, 30
  postulates pertaining to, 35
  section, **434**
Playfair's Parallel Postulate, 660,
  662
Playfair, John, 662
point(s), 3, **5,** 6, **8,** 10, **14,** 15, 16, **20,**
  31, 40, 43, 82, 87, 88, 135, 164,
  416-418
  dots as, 5
  equidistant, 82
  lattice, 18
  locations as, 8
  in networks, 20
  as nodes, 20
  noncollinear, 417
  ordered pairs as, 14
  of tangency, 651, 653
  vanishing, 25
Point-Line-Plane Postulate, 35, 36,
  40, 416, 417, 658
Point rule, 141, 142
pointillism, 7
polygon, 60, 65, 70, 71, **92,** 93, 94,
  187, 188, 205, 243, 358, 378, 384,
  421, 671. *See also* kite;
  parallelogram; quadrilateral;
  rectangle; regular polygon;
  rhombus; square; trapezoid;
  triangle.
  equilateral, 358
  regular, 334
polygonal region, 94, 421
Polygon-Sum Theorem, 243
polyhedron, polyhedra, 449. *See
  also* prism; pyramid.
polynomial, 484
postulate(s), 35-37. *See* pp. 801-802
  for list.
  angle measure, 108
  area, 368
  from arithmetic and algebra, 37
  of Euclid, 661
  Point-Line-Plane, 35
  reflection, 164, 189
  volume, 479, 490
power of a point, 771
preimage, 156, 163-165, 254

preserved properties, 163, 164, 281,
  576, 577, 587
printer, dot-matrix, 4
prism, 415, **423,** 424, 429, 435,
  488-490, 494, 495, 500, 511
**Prism-Cylinder Surface Area
  Formula,** 470
**Prism-Cylinder Volume
  Formula,** 490
probability, 403
problem solving (Problem solving is
  found throughout this book.
  Below are selected
  appearances.)
  age, 633
  applications (*See* applications.)
  angle measures, 110-112, 118,
    131, 147, 152, 181, 186, 231,
    244-245, 271-272, 400,
    712-713, 727, 731, 751, 755,
    762, 767, 774, 791
  area, 291, 370-372, 376, 382-383,
    389, 395, 404-406, 408-409,
    410, 413, 420, 482, 579, 674,
    751, 779, 787, 791
  circumference, 400-401, 404-405,
    413, 438, 448, 580
  coins/money, 17
  compare quantities/distances, 17,
    50, 53, 56, 487, 508, 512-513,
    515, 518, 579, 602-603, 608,
    614, 623, 627, 724, 784, 787
  congruent figures, 309, 315-316,
    321-322, 332, 349, 352-353
  cost and value, 371, 584, 602, 627
  distance/mileage, 11-12, 18, 29,
    49, 50, 56, 96, 530, 536, 555,
    558, 619, 623, 694, 744, 784
  distance/rate/time, 18, 361, 395,
    400, 412-413, 585, 695, 712,
    718-719, 723, 727, 731, 784
  division, 12, 359, 372, 389,
    400-401, 404-406, 409
  lateral area, 477, 498, 513, 518,
    526
  latitude/longitude, 18, 45
  multiplication, 13, 370-372, 376,
    382, 389, 395, 400-401,
    404-405, 408-409, 413, 579
  networks, 23, 28, 33, 39, 51, 53,
    54, 91
  percent, 405, 508, 512-513, 598
  perimeter, 359-361, 370, 372, 382,
    409, 412, 579, 674, 779
  proportions, 584-585, 591, 598,
    602-503, 608, 614, 619,
    622-623, 626-627, 724
  Pythagorean Theorem, 688, 694,
    744
  rate, (*See* distance/rate/time.)

similar figures, 307, 585, 591-592,
  598, 602, 608, 614, 622-623,
  626-627
subtraction, 12, 18, 53, 56, 395,
  405, 457
surface area, 472, 477, 482,
  512-513, 515, 518, 787, 791
tangent ratio, 699-700
temperature, 56
tessellations, 365-366
too little information, 79, 102
trigonometry, 699-700, 706, 713,
  727, 731, 768
two-step, 18, 96, 359, 394, 512,
  531
vectors, 712-713, 717-718, 723,
  727, 731
volume, 487, 492-493, 503, 508,
  512-513, 515, 518-519, 526,
  592, 608, 787
with reflections, 275-278, 283-284,
  291, 298, 300-301, 674
with translations, 289, 300
problem-solving strategies
  (Problem-solving strategies are
  found throughout this book.
  Below are selected
  appearances.)
  list all possibilities, 743
  make a diagram, 23, 144, 152,
    276-278, 283-284, 291, 298,
    301, 307, 366, 394, 447-448,
    452-453, 458, 461, 462, 472,
    477, 492, 549, 556, 558, 567,
    579, 591, 657, 674, 712-713,
    718, 727, 731, 755, 774, 784,
    787
  make generalizations, 549
  rule out possibilities, 643-644, 649,
    681
  test a conjecture, 220-222
  test a special case, 472
  trial and error, 139, 372, 395, 472,
    477, 543
  use counterexamples, 68-69, 608
  use a diagram/picture, 23, 28-29,
    33, 44, 51, 53, 54, 80, 91, 100,
    102, 110, 118, 137, 148, 152,
    181, 186, 190, 244-245, 264,
    271, 275-277, 283-284, 289,
    291, 298, 300-301, 315, 322,
    326, 349, 352-353, 365-366,
    371, 376, 382-383, 394-395,
    400-401, 406, 408, 410,
    412-413, 420, 442, 446, 448,
    452-454, 458, 461, 462, 464,
    567, 591, 614, 623, 626-627,
    674, 688, 742, 744, 768, 774,
    787, 791
  use estimation, 376, 383, 389,
    395, 401, 406, 408, 410

ACKNOWLEDGMENTS

Illustrator's Acknowledgments

For permission to reproduce indicated information on the following pages, acknowledgement is made to:

Roger Boehm
344, 628

Paul Dolan
23, 25, 27, 49, 51, 73, 80, 91, 152, 245, 264, 372, 383, 508, 513, 529, 537, 562, 573, 614, 615, 698, 712, 718, 755, 787

Scott Donaldson
274, 277, 284, 298

David Ebinger
444

Chuck Gonzales
7, 137, 194, 260, 277, 332, 342, 354, 413, 448, 579, 604, 671, 699, 700, 704, 713, 727, 731, 767

Susan Hahn
567

Bryan Haynes
9, 10, 373

Min Jae Hong
79, 112, 227, 234, 276, 530, 598, 609, 694

Daniel Pelavin
591

Robert Pizzo
204

Sally Vitsky
33

Picture Acknowledgments

Unless otherwise acknowledged, all photographs are the property of Scott, Foresman and Company. The following abbreviations indicate position of photos on page: L (left), R (right), T (top), C (center), and B (bottom).

2-3 Georges Seurat, *Sunday Afternoon on the Island of La Grande Jatte*, 1884-1886, oil on canvas, 207.6 X 308.0 cm, Helen Birch Bartlett Memorial Collection, 1926.224. © The Art Institute of Chicago. All Rights Reserved. 3 Georges Seurat, *Sunday Afternoon on the Island of La Grande Jatte*. 1884-86, oil on canvas, 207.6 X 308.0 cm, Helen Birch Bartlett Memorial Collection, 1926.224: detail view #12. © The Art Institute of Chicago. All Rights Reserved. 4 David R. Frazier 5L Bob Daemmrich/The Image Works 5R David R. Frazier 8 Jon Feingersh/Stock Boston 12 Arthur Bilsten/Stock Imagery 13 R. Lebeck/The Image Bank 14 Groninger Museum, Groningen, The Netherlands 18 Courtesy Cadott Lions Club and the Cadott Chamber of Commerce from *The Cadott Sentinel* 22 Roger Ressmeyer/Starlight 23 Lionel Delevingne/Stock Boston 25T Tony Stone/Click/Chicago/Tony Stone 25B The Regis Collection, Minneapolis, MN 29 Michael Schuyt 30 AP/Wide World Photos 34 Arnold J. Kaplan/The Picture Cube 39 Philip A. Savoie/Bruce Coleman Inc. 40 Dominique Sarraute/The Image Bank 41 David Madison/Bruce Coleman Inc. 46 F. Hidalgo/The Image Bank 49 Lawrence Migdale 50 J. Clark/The Stock Market 54 John Kelly/The Image Bank 58-59 John S. Abbot 62 Terry Ashe/Uniphoto 64 Children's Television Workshop 68R Walter Chandoha 69 David R. Frazier 70 Lawrence Migdale 75 Don & Pat Valenti/DRK Photos 76 Robert Landau/West Light 81 Geoffrey Gove/The Image Bank 86D. Rowan/FPG 88 David R. Frazier 90T Billy E. Barnes/FPG 90B David R. Frazier 93 Courtesy Watertown Historical Society 97 Peter Eisenman, FAIA/Courtesy Eisenman Architects 99T Susan Van Etten, PhotoEdit 100 Courtesy Baha'i House of Worship, Wilmette, IL 102 Focus On Sports 104-105 Walter Hodges/Allstock 105B Wendell Metzen/Bruce Coleman Inc. 106 John Running/Stock Boston 110 Jeff Foott Productions 112B NASA 113 Elsilrac Enterprises 118 J. Ehlers/Bruce Coleman Inc. 126L David R. Frazier 126R Vince Streano/The Stock Market 139 Reprinted courtesy of Dell Magazines 1989, a division of Bantam Doubleday Dell Publishing Group, Inc. 140 Steve Niedorf/The Image Bank 143 Educational Directions/FPG 154-155 Tom Tracy/The Stock Market 155T Card IV Rorschach, *Psychodiagnostics*, Verlagttans Huber Bern, © 1921, renewed 1948 155C Courtesy Chrysler Corporation. Used with permission. 155B Charles Seaborn/Odyssey Productions 156T Rob Atkins/The Image Bank 156B Larry Reynolds 163 Eric Meola/The Image Bank 170 Hank Morgan/Rainbow 176 Scala/Art Resource 181 Ronnie Kaufman/The Stock Market 190 Bob Daemmrich, Stock Boston 191 Focus On Sports 192 Erwin & Peggy Bauer 194L The Cleveland Museum of Art, Purchase, Edward L. Whittemore Fund 199 Courtesy Chrysler Corporation. Used with permission. 206 David R. Frazier 211 Bohdan Hrynewych/Stock Boston 217TC David R. Frazier 217B Robert Frerck/Odyssey Productions 223 Jamie Tanaka/Bruce Coleman Inc. 231 Cliff Hollenbeck 240 Steve Monti/Bruce Coleman Inc. 244 Tony Freeman, Photo-Edit 252-253 © 1990 M.C. Escher/Heirs/Cordon Art—Baarn—Holland 259 Peter Angelo Simon/the Stock Market 265 Museum Boymans van Beuningen, Rotterdam, Herscovici/Art Resource 266 Manfred Kage/Peter Arnold Inc. 267 Ken & Miriam Rose/The Image Bank 271 Manfred Kage/Peter Arnold Inc. 273 © John Margolies/Esto 288, 289, 300 © 1990 M.C. Escher Heirs/Cordon Art—Baarn—Holland 302-303 Charles Osgood/Copyrighted Chicago Tribune Company. All rights reserved. Used with permission. 307 Peter F. Runyon, The Image Bank 309 Used by permission of Highlights for Children, Inc. Columbus, OH. Copyrighted 1986. 310 Robert Fried/Stock Boston 323 Gary Braasch 327 Ken Sherman/Bruce Coleman Inc. 331 Gabe Palmer/The Stock Market 345 Walter Chandoha 349 Ellis Herwig/Stock Boston 352 Peter Pearson/Click/Chicago/Tony Stone 356 Brent Jones 365 © 1990 M.C. Escher Heirs/Cordon Art—Baarn—Holland 368 Adam Woolfitt/Woodfin Camp & Associates, Inc. 378 John I. Koivula 389B Grant Heilman 391 The Bettmann Archive 392 David R. Frazier 396 Peter Menzel/Stock Boston 398 David Madison 400 Alan Magayne-Roshar/Third Coast Stock 401 Beringer/Dratch/the Image Works 402 Leslye Borden/PhotoEdit 405 Bill Robert/PhotoEdit 409 Chuck O'Rear/West Light 414-415 L.L.T. Rhodes/Click/Chicago/Tony Stone 416 California Institute of Technology 423 Charles Harbutt/Actuality Inc. 427T Roger Ressmeyer/Starlight 427C Larry Lee/West Light 432 Dallas & John Heaton/Click/Chicago/Tony Stone 439 Patti Murray/Animals Animals 440 Donald R. Specker/Animals Animals 444 David Ebinger 447 Milt & Joan Mann/Cameramann International Ltd. 472 David R. Frazeir 473T John Kinser/Bruce Coleman Inc. 473C Courtesy General Dynamics, Fort Worth Division 474 Carl Purcell 483 Cameron Davidson/Bruce Coleman Inc. 487 David Austen/Stock Boston 488 Martin Rogers/Stock Boston 497 The Bettmann Archive 498 John S. Flannery/Bruce Coleman Inc. 505 Kelly/Mooney Photography 512 Richard Pasley/Stock Boston 518 M. Timothy O'Keefe, Bruce Coleman Inc. 519 Harry Wilks/Stock Boston 520-521 T. Hoirata & T. Horiguchi/Siggraph 523 The Bettmann Archive 525 Len Rue Jr./Leonard Rue Enterprises 526 Reprinted with permission from: Medenbach, Olaf: *The Magic of Minerals*, 1988, © 1988 Springer-Verlager Berlin-Heidelberg. 527 David Lissy/Sportschrome, Inc. 532 Elisa Leonelli/Bruce Coleman Inc. 536 Tony Freeman, PhotoEdit 542 Bob Daemmrich 544 © 1986 Dale Seymour Publications 548 Mark Sherman/Bruce Coleman Inc. 550 Richard Pasley/Stock Boston 562-563 Jean Pragen/Click/Chicago/Tony Stone 575 Mary Kate Denny, Photo-Edit 581 Tony Freeman/PhotoEdit 585 Phil Degginger/Photo Kinetics 597 Ernest Hass/Magnum Photos 599 UPI/Bettmann Newsphotos 601 Donald R. Specker/Animals Animals 603 Leo Mason/*Sports Illustrated* 625 Runk/Schoenberger from Grant Heilman 630 Giraudon/Art Resource 632 Library of Congress 633 UPI/Bettmann Newsphotos 635 Robert Frerck/Odyssey Productions 637 Dr. E.R. Degginger/Color-Pic, Inc. 638 Richard Hutchings, InfoEdit 640 Erika Stone 641 Owen Franken/Stock Boston 643 Bob Daemmrich/The Image Works 645 Billy E. Barnes/Stock Boston 649 Bob Daemmrich/Stock Boston 651 NASA 657T Dr. E.R. Degginger/Color-Pic, Inc. 657B Dr. Brook Sandford and William H. Regan/Los Alamos Scientific Library 658 Superstock/Shostal Associates 664 UPI/Bettmann Newsphotos 674 Julian Baum/Bruce Coleman Inc. 676 Phil Degginger/Photo Kinetics* 677 Colonial Williamsburg 678 Michael George/Bruce Coleman Inc. 681 David R. Frazier 682-683 Dr. E.R. Degginger/Bruce Coleman Inc. 684 John Griffin/The Image Works 687 David R. Frazier 688 Jeff Foott Productions 690 Bill Gallery/Stock Boston 694 Steve Hansen/Stock Boston 695 Tim Carlson/Stock Boston 702 Miro Vintoniv/Stock Boston 708 David H. Wells/The Image Works 711 Bob Daemmrich/Stock Boston 714 Dr. Harold Edgerton (1990)/Courtesy Palm Press, Inc. 723 D. P. Hershkowitz/Bruce Coleman Inc. 724 Bob Daemmrich/The Image Works 727 D.H. Hessell/Stock Boston 732-733 Michael Ventura/Bruce Coleman Inc. 734 Norman Owen Tomalin/Bruce Coleman Inc. 740 David R. Frazier 744 Mitchell B. Reibe/Sportschrome, Inc. 745 Underwood & Underwood/The Bettmann Archive 751 Ellis Herwig/Stock Boston 755 Patsy Davidson/The Image Works 763 Gary Brettnacher/Click/Chicago/Tony Stone 775 David R. Frazier 780 John Eastcott & Yva Momatiuk/The Image Works.